Drug Discovery Targeting Metalloenzymes

Drug Discovery Targeting Metalloenzymes

Strategies and Applications

Edited by Guo-Bo Li

Volume 2

WILEY-VCH

Editor

Prof. Guo-Bo Li
Sichuan University
Chengdu, 610041
P.R. China

Cover Design: Wiley
Cover Image: Courtesy of Guo-Bo Li

Typesetting: Straive, Chennai, India
Printing and Binding: CPI Group (UK) Ltd, Croydon, CR0 4YY

Library of Congress Card No.: applied for

British Library Cataloguing-in-Publication Data A catalogue record for this book is available from the British Library.

Bibliographic information published by the Deutsche Nationalbibliothek
The Deutsche Nationalbibliothek lists this publication in the Deutsche Nationalbibliografie; detailed bibliographic data are available on the Internet at http://dnb.d-nb.de.

Print ISBN: 978-3-527-35640-9
ePDF ISBN: 978-3-527-84867-6
ePub ISBN: 978-3-527-84866-9
oBook ISBN: 978-3-52784-868-3

C9783527356409_170226

Contents

Preface

Metalloenzymes constitute an ubiquitous ensemble of enzymes that rely on metal ions for their bioactivity, structural integrity, signaling functions, and others. Remarkably, over one-third of all known enzymes are assigned as metalloenzymes. These enzymes have long been recognized for their significance across a wide range of research fields and societal applications. In synthetic biology, for example, functionally diverse artificial metalloenzymes have been developed, underscoring the potential to engineer novel biocatalytic transformations that are not found in nature. Given their critical roles in various biological processes and diseases, metalloenzymes have emerged as key targets for therapeutic intervention. Although several drugs and drug candidates targeting metalloenzymes have been identified, most disease associations and therapeutic potentials for metalloenzymes remain largely untapped, indicating a vast and largely unexplored frontier for drug discovery and development in this field.

Metalloenzymes are unique due to the presence of metal ion(s) with strong electron deficiencies, which makes drug design targeting metalloenzymes particularly challenging compared to other types of targets. This results in potentially more diverse mechanisms of drug action, while also presenting significant challenges in terms of drug selectivity. In recent years, a variety of approaches have emerged to enhance the efficiency of drug discovery targeting metalloenzymes, including chemo-/bio-informatics, bioinformatics, artificial intelligence technologies, proteomics, structural biology, and spectroscopy. Additionally, an increasing number of potential metalloenzyme drug targets have been identified, along with many successful drug discovery examples. To further advance the field of metalloenzyme drug discovery and attract more researchers to this area, I have leveraged my own research experience and knowledge to collaborate with experts in the field to compile this book, which aims to provide insights and drive progress in this exciting area of study.

This book is organized into three sectors: (i) computational and experimental strategies for metalloenzyme drug discovery (Chapters 1–5), (ii) approaches and cases for drug discovery targeting metalloenzyme families (Chapters 6–11), and (iii) approaches and cases for drug discovery targeting individual metalloenzymes (Chapters 12–18). The first sector begins with metalloenzyme informatics and state-of-the-art drug design techniques, which are important for advancing drug discovery targeting metalloenzymes. Given the critical role of metal ions in these enzymes, this section also includes metal-binding pharmacophores that interact with metal ions, particularly within metalloenzyme active sites, emphasizing the need for careful optimization to enhance both binding affinity and specificity. Quantum mechanical/molecular mechanical calculations have provided valuable insights into the complex catalytic mechanisms (reaction pathways) of metalloenzymes and play a critical role in the discovery of metalloenzyme inhibitors. Complementing this theoretical framework, the book also covers experimental strategies essential for studying metalloenzyme mechanisms, offering a well-rounded perspective that integrates both computational and laboratory approaches. Additionally, metallo-drugs, which primarily target metalloenzymes by interacting with or disrupting their metal ion centers through multifaceted interference, represent an emerging class of promising therapeutics. While challenges persist in developing selective metallo-drugs, recent successes highlight the potential of this approach in treating complex diseases, including cancer.

The second sector focuses on several key human metalloenzyme families that have emerged as important drug targets in recent years, including phosphodiesterases, histone deacetylases, and carbonic anhydrases. These families consist of multiple subtypes, each involved in distinct biological pathways and exhibiting varying tissue distributions, and are implicated in a wide range of diseases. As a result, drug discovery targeting these families spans a broad spectrum of therapeutic indications. While these families share common features that can guide cross-disciplinary approaches, there is also an urgent need for the development of subtype-specific drugs. Additionally, the sector explores bacterial metallo-β-lactamases and virus-associated metalloenzymes. Metallo-β-lactamases represent a large and expanding family of enzymes closely linked to antibiotic resistance, with drug development requiring careful consideration of bacterial membrane permeability. In contrast, several virus-related metal enzymes play crucial roles in virus replication, assembly, and host cell invasion, making them significant drug targets.

The third sector covers additional important metalloenzyme targets, which are involved in essential biological processes and often act as key regulators in disease progression, along with their drug discovery approaches and case studies. For example, autotaxin and ENPP1 play critical roles in regulating extracellular lipid signaling, and inhibiting these enzymes has shown promise for treating diseases such as cancer and fibrosis. In oxygen sensing, hypoxia-inducible factor prolyl hydroxylases are essential for the body's adaptive response to low oxygen levels, making them an attractive target for conditions like anemia and ischemia. Histone demethylases, such as KDM5B, regulate gene expression through epigenetic modifications, and inhibiting them could provide novel therapeutic strategies for cancer and other diseases driven by aberrant gene expression. LpxC, involved in bacterial outer membrane synthesis, holds promise for developing new antibiotics to combat antibiotic resistance in Gram-negative infections. Similarly, human glutaminyl cyclases, implicated in neurodegenerative diseases, and tryptophan/indoleamine 2,3-dioxygenase, which plays a key role in immune regulation, present exciting new opportunities for treating neurological disorders and immune-related diseases. These examples underscore the vast potential of targeting metalloenzymes in drug discovery, offering innovative therapeutic strategies across a wide range of diseases.

In addition to offering a comprehensive overview of current progress in strategies and cases, this book casts a forward-looking vision on the future of metalloenzyme drug discovery. The interplay between computational techniques and experimental strategies is set to fuel breakthroughs in drug discovery. There is also a need for new computational and experimental tools, including artificial intelligence models, with the ability to perform metalloenzyme profiling, to infer the relationships between metalloenzymes and diseases, and other issues in this field. The potential of targeting metalloenzymes for innovative drug discovery is vast, and this book offers a window into this rapidly evolving field.

Although my team and I have made some progress in the field of metalloenzyme drug discovery, the scope and depth of our work remain limited, and our understanding of key issues in this field still requires ongoing strengthening. I would like to express my sincere gratitude to the experts and teams whose invaluable contributions have shaped this book. Through their generous sharing of insights and experiences, this book has come to embody such rich and comprehensive content. A special thanks goes to my PhD supervisor, Professor Shengyong Yang, and my postdoctoral mentor, Professor Christopher J. Schofield; their guidance, inspiration, and mentorship have been instrumental in introducing me to the field of metalloenzyme drug discovery. I would also like to extend my thanks to Dr. Lifen Yang, Priyadarshini Natarajan, Sundhar Karuthudiyan, and the entire editorial team for their dedication and hard work in bringing this book to fruition. Finally, I am deeply grateful to my own team for their contributions to this work.

I hope that this book will serve as a valuable reference for researchers in the field. If there are any shortcomings or errors, we kindly ask you to point them out, and we will do our best to address them in future updates or incorporate them into our ongoing work. Additionally, I hope that this book will inspire a new generation of scientists to explore the untapped therapeutic potential of metalloenzymes. The path ahead is full of promise, and as our understanding of metalloenzyme mechanisms and their association with diseases deepens, so too will the opportunities to develop innovative and effective treatments for a wide range of diseases.

January, 2025 *Guo-Bo Li*

10

Drug Discovery Targeting Viral Metalloenzymes

Baohu Li[1,2], *Hui Xu*[1,#], *Jiahui Zhou*[1,#], *Kai Tang*[1,#], *Xinyong Liu*[1], *Jinfei Yang*[2], *and Peng Zhan*[1]

[1] *Shandong University, School of Pharmaceutical Sciences, Cheeloo College of Medicine, Department of Medicinal Chemistry, Key Laboratory of Chemical Biology (Ministry of Education), 44 West Culture Road, 250012, Jinan, Shandong, PR China*
[2] *University of Health and Rehabilitation Sciences, School of Health and Life Sciences, 369 Dengyun Road 266001, Qingdao, Shandong, PR China*

10.1 Current Status of HIV Prevalence and Treatment

Acquired immunodeficiency syndrome (AIDS), resulting from chronic infection by the human immunodeficiency virus (HIV), presents a grave disease situation. Despite the clinical approval of over 40 antiviral drugs for AIDS treatment, HIV prevalence and impact continue to pose a significant global health threat [1]. According to the latest statistics from the World Health Organization (WHO) in 2022, approximately 39 million individuals worldwide are infected with HIV-1, with 1.3 million new infections and 630,000 deaths attributed to AIDS-related diseases [2].

HIV replication heavily relies on its three key internally encoded enzymes: reverse transcriptase (RT), integrase (IN), and protease. Consequently, these three enzymes have become pivotal targets in HIV treatment strategies [3]. Highly active antiretroviral therapy (HAART), proposed by Chinese-American scientist Professor Dai-He in 1996, is one of the primary methods for treating AIDS [4]. HAART aims to minimize drug resistance while maximizing viral replication inhibition and partially or completely restoring impaired immune function through the combination of three or more classes of antiviral drugs. This approach not only helps delay disease progression and prolong patient life but also significantly improves quality of life. However, current challenges include drug accumulation toxicity, lack of patient compliance, and the emergence of multi-drug resistance, which urgently necessitate the development of anti-HIV drugs with novel targets, mechanisms, and structures [5–7].

[#] The contributions of these authors are equal

Drug Discovery Targeting Metalloenzymes: Strategies and Applications, First Edition. Edited by Guo-Bo Li.

10.1.1 Advances in Inhibitors Research Targeting HIV Integrase

10.1.1.1 Function in Biology and Disease

HIV IN plays a pivotal role as an essential enzyme in the process of HIV infection. Its primary function involves integrating viral cDNA into the genome of human host cells through two distinct steps: 3′-processing (3′-P) and strand transfer (ST) [8]. In retroviruses, the active site of HIV IN is highly conserved and comprises three essential acidic residues: Asp64, Asp116, and Glu152, which collectively form the aspartic acid-aspartic acid-glutamic acid (DDE) catalytic motif. The DDE motif serves as a metal ion-binding site capable of binding one or two catalytically active Mn^{2+} or Mg^{2+}. Alterations in the composition and conformation of the DDE domain can significantly impair its catalytic activity. Existing literature indicates that the representative drug resistance mutations observed in HIV IN include H51Y, T66I, E92Q, G118R, G140S/Q148H, Y143R, N155H, and R263K [9]. It should be noted that no mammalian enzyme homologous to HIV IN has been discovered; therefore, inhibitors targeting IN exhibit high specificity with minimal toxic side effects, offering new possibilities for HIV treatment. Currently, IN inhibitors are widely recognized as one of the most effective options for combination therapy in patients infected with HIV [10].

10.1.1.2 Inhibitors Development

The current study on anti-HIV drugs has identified five HIV IN chain transfer inhibitors (INSTIs) that have been approved by the US Food and Drug Administration (FDA) for the treatment of HIV infection(Figure 10.1): raltigravir (compound **1**), elvitegravir (compound **2**), dolutegravir (compound **3**), cabotegravir (compound **4**), and bictegravir (compound **5**) [11–14].

Compound **1** developed by Merck is the first INSTI to be clinically approved [14]. It has a significant inhibitory effect on IN-catalyzed chain transfer (IC_{50} = 10 nmol/l) and effectively prevents HIV replication in host cells (EC_{95} = 33 nmol/l) [15]. Importantly, it demonstrates remarkable efficacy against various drug-resistant clinical isolates belonging to different classes, such as nucleoside reverse transcriptase inhibitor (NRTI), Non-nucleoside Reverse Transcriptase Inhibitor (NNRTI), and Protease Inhibitor (PI). This provides a valuable therapeutic option for patients who have limited treatment alternatives following HAART failure at that time. Compound **1** is orally administered at a dosage of 400 mg twice daily [14]. Despite being regarded as a promising anti-AIDS medication, resistance to compound **1** arises due to mutations occurring within the catalytic domain of IN through three primary genetic pathways: Q148H/R/K, N155H, and the less frequently observed Y143C mutations [16]. These mutations significantly diminish the anti-HIV activity exerted by compound **1**, which has been confirmed by analyzing its cocrystalline structure with IN from PFV intasome [17] (Figure 10.2a). In this plane, two Mg^{2+} ions are coordinated by three heteroatoms at specific positions. The *p*-F-benzyl group replaces the 3′-terminal adenosine of the processed vDNA and forms a p-stacking interaction with the penultimate cytosine residue. The terminal oxadiazole ring forms a well-directed p-stacking interaction with Y212

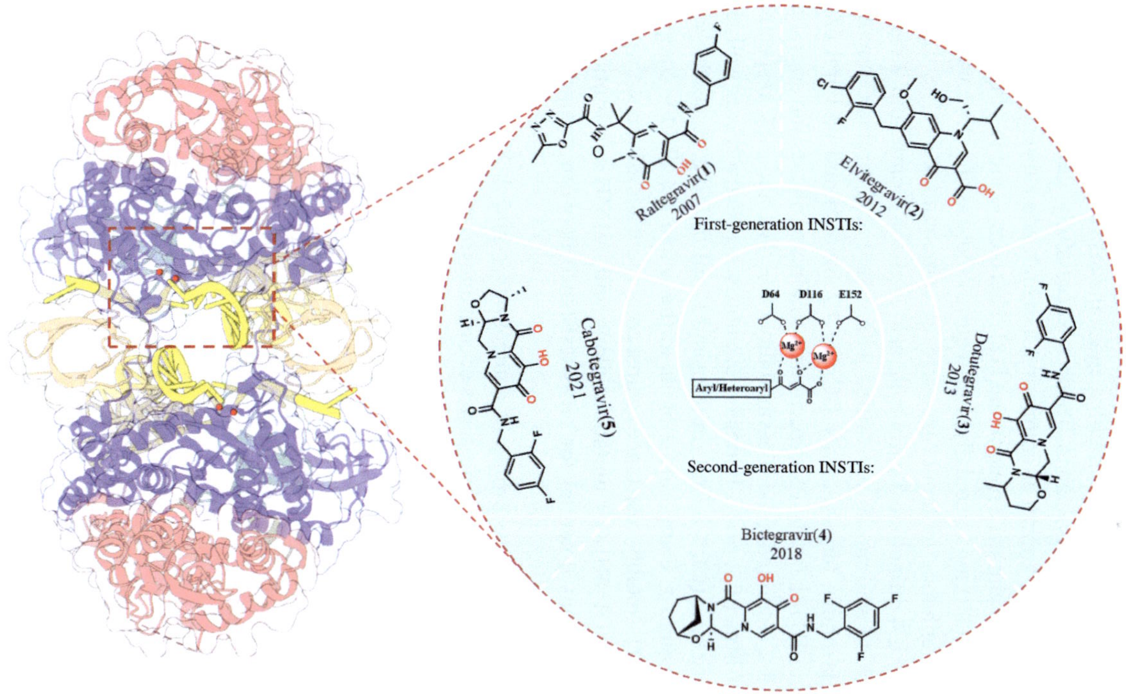

Figure 10.1 Approved HIV INSTIs.

(corresponding to Y143 in HIV-1 IN). This contact may play a crucial and unique role in compound **1**, potentially contributing to the impact on drug potency caused by the Y143 mutation. Although PFV IN residues Q217 and N224 (corresponding to Q148 and N155 in HIV-1 IN) do not directly interact with compound **1** in the crystal structure, mutations in these two residues could induce conformational changes within the catalytic pocket, leading to reduced binding efficiency.

With the progress of research on efflux mechanisms of diketo acid derivatives and other biological factors, Japan Tobacco successfully developed the novel generation IN inhibitor, known as compound **2**, which was subsequently licensed to Gilead Sciences for clinical development [18]. This compound is administered at a lower frequency (150 mg once daily) but requires the use of a pharmacokinetic (PK) booster to enhance systemic exposure to compound **2** [19]. Structurally characterized by a 4-quinolone-3-carboxylic acid skeleton, compound **2** can have coplanar monoketo acid motifs substituted with diketo acid motifs. Compound **2** demonstrated favorable target activity (IC_{50} = 7.2 nmol/l) and antiviral efficacy (EC_{50} = 0.9 nmol/l) [18]. *In vivo* PK experiments conducted on rats and dogs showed that compound **2** exhibited good bioavailability (F = 34% and 30%, respectively), acceptable half-lives ($T_{1/2}$ = 2.3 hoursand 5.2 hours, respectively), as well as low plasma clearance rates (CL = 8.3 mL/min/kg and 17 mL/min/kg, respectively) [11]. Similar to compound **1**, compound **2** binds to the active site of PFV comparably (Figure 10.2b) [17]. Notably, resistance against compound **2** is associated with T66I, E92Q, S147G, and Q148H/K/R mutations along with N155H substitution, which suggested a significant potential for cross-resistance between compound **2** and compound **1** [20].

To enhance the resistance profile of compounds **1** and **2**, Shionogi company performed optimization studies on a series of carbamoylpyridone analogues, which led to the discovery of compound **3** as a second-generation HIV-1 IN inhibitor [21]. This clinical candidate was approved for clinical use in 2013 and is administered once daily at an unboosted dose (50 mg). Compound **3** distinguished itself from the first-generation INSTI by featuring its chelating motif positioned on the tricyclic scaffold [22] (Figure 10.3a). Moreover, it possessed an elongated linker connecting the central chelating moiety with a halobenzyl group when compared with either compound **1** or compound **2**. Extensive studies have revealed that compound **3**

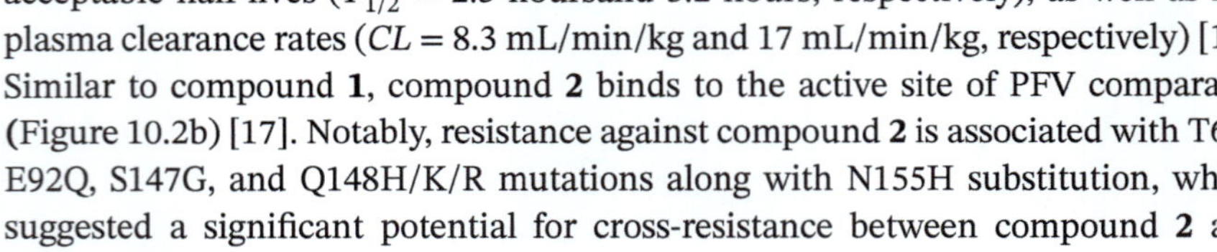

Figure 10.2 The cocrystal binding modes with PFV IN. (a) The X-ray crystal structure of **1** (PDB code: 3OYA) bound to PFV IN, Mg^{2+} are shown as green spheres. (b) The X-ray crystal structure of **2** (PDB code: 3L2U) bound to PFV IN, Mg^{2+} are shown as green spheres.

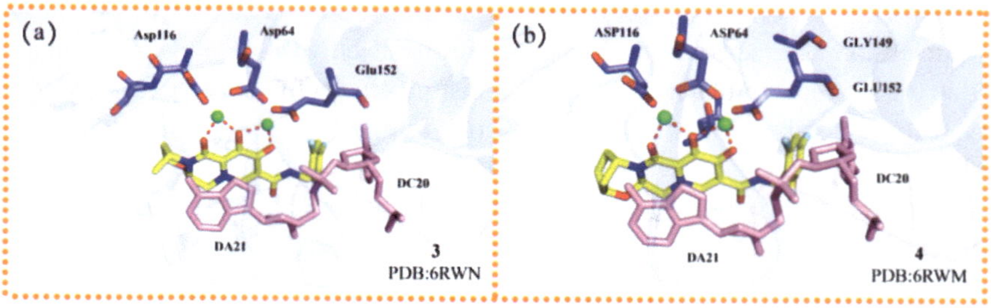

Figure 10.3 The cocrystal binding modes with SIVrcm IN. (a) The X-ray crystal structure of **3** (PDB code: 6RWN) bound to SIVrcm IN, Mg^{2+} are shown as green spheres. (b) The X-ray crystal structure of **4** (PDB code: 6RWN) bound to SIVrcm IN, Mg^{2+} are shown as green spheres.

exhibits a higher resistance barrier due to its stronger binding affinity with IN when compared to compounds **1** and **2** [23]. It demonstrates potent *in vitro* activities against wild-type (WT) or near-WT strains carrying a single primary resistance mutation observed *in vivo* at Q148, N155, and Y143 [24]. Furthermore, compound **3** displayed remarkable inhibitory activity (IC_{50} = 0.68 nmol/l) against the challenging Q148K mutant strain but reduced activity against E138K, G140S, or Q148H mutant strains.

Structure–activity relationship (SAR) studies of compound **3** revealed that modifying the *o*-nitrogen heterobridge and adding a fluorine atom within the 2,4-difluorophenyl ring significantly augments antiviral efficacy against G140S/Q148H. Consequently, compound **4** potently inhibited G140S/Q148H with an EC_{50} value of 3.1 nmol/l and displayed a statistically superior resistance profile compared to compound **1**, compound **2**, and compound **3** against a set panel of patient-derived INSTI-resistant viral isolates [25]. Despite the widespread clinical use of second-generation INSTIs, their specific mechanisms remain to be fully elucidated. In this context, Cherepanov et al. employed single-particle cryo-electron microscopy to unveil the binding mode of doravirine and bictegravir, two second-generation INSTIs, with the active site of simian immunodeficiency virus from red-capped mangabey integrase (SIVrcm) (Figure 10.3b) [22]. The research suggests that instances of clinical failure in INSTI therapy are frequently linked to mutations Q148H and G140S in IN, which disrupt the optimal coordination state of magnesium ions in the enzyme's active site. The unique elongated chemical structure of second-generation compounds provides additional binding force, thereby enhancing their inhibitory effect against Q148H and G140S mutant strains.

Compound **5** was initially developed by Gilead Sciences and exhibited a specific inhibition of the chain transfer reaction (IC_{50} = 7.5 nmol/l) while displaying comparatively weaker inhibition of HIV-1 IN 3′-processing (IC_{50} = 241 nmol/l). In MT-2 and MT-4 cells, it demonstrated EC_{50} values of 1.5 nmol/l and 2.4 nmol/l for inhibiting HIV-1 replication, respectively; however, its distinguishing characteristic lies in its extended half-life of nearly 40 days [26]. This compound can be formulated as a nanoparticle injection to allow for prolonged dosing intervals. The combination therapy comprising Compound **5** and rilpivirine, a non-nucleoside reverse-transcriptase inhibitor, received FDA approval in January 2021 as the first injectable agent with long-lasting effects for treating HIV-1 infections. Known as cabenuva, this dual long-acting injection regimen enables monthly administration and replaces the current daily pill-based treatment approach for managing HIV-1 infections, representing a significant paradigm shift from previous practices [4].

The success of HIV INSTIs has triggered a new wave of research into this category of drugs. Zhou et al. employed a virtual screening strategy based on molecular docking to develop a novel indole-2-carboxylic acid derivative, with the representative compound **6** (Figure 10.4) exhibiting an IC_{50} of 12.41 μmol/l against HIV IN [27]. Molecular docking analysis revealed that the indole core and C2 carboxyl group of compound **6** form crucial ligand bonds with the two magnesium ions in the IN active center. Through further structural optimization, a long-chain branch was introduced at the C3 position of the indole core to yield compound **7**, significantly enhancing its inhibitory activity against IN (IC_{50} = 0.13 μmol/l), suggesting promising potential for further development of the indole-2-carboxylic acid scaffold.

To gain a deeper understanding of the impact of structural diversity to tetrahydronalidipine on HIV IN inhibitory activity, Coleman et al. developed a five-membered ring system derived from the third ring based on compound **8** [28]. By increasing the polar surface area (PSA), compounds **9** with chiral hypo-alcohol groups and **10** with hydroxymethyl substituents were synthesized (Figure 10.5). Both compounds demonstrated remarkable potency against WT virus and maintained consistent efficacy against RAL-resistant mutants. However, their oral

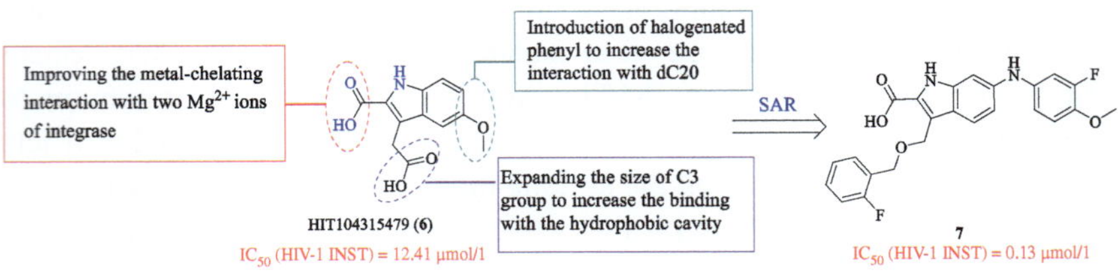

Figure 10.4 Pharmacophore analysis of the indole-2-carboxylic acid skeleton and the chemical structures of compounds **6** and **7**.

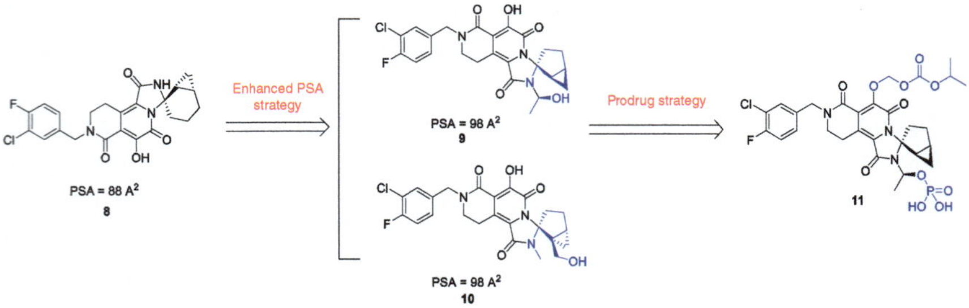

Figure 10.5 Chemical structures of compounds **8–11**.

exposure was suboptimal due to unfavorable physicochemical properties. To address this issue, Coleman et al. employed a prodrug strategy and successfully prepared acetylcarbonate/phosphate prodrug **11** (Figure 10.5), which significantly enhanced exposure levels.

Diketo acid derivatives containing α,γ-diketo acid functional groups have demonstrated selectivity as inhibitors of chain transfer reactions [29]. Representative compounds include 5-CITEP (**12**), L-708906 (**13**), L-731988 (**14**), L-870810 (**15**), L-870812 (**16**), and S-1360 (**17**) (Figure 10.6) [30, 31]. However, the application of diketo acids is limited due to issues related to absorption, membrane permeability, and toxicity. Therefore, their biological isoefflux is often utilized in drug development. In 2019, Deo et al. [32]synthesized a series of diketoquinoline analogues with representative compound **18** (Figure 10.6). The desired EC_{50} values against viral replication were 0.08 μmol/l.

Aknin et al. identified stilbene-disulfonic acid HIV IN inhibitors through high-throughput screening (HTS), including NSC76027 (**19**), NSC638352 (**20**), and NSC34931 (**21**, Figure 10.7). The inhibition rates of ST at a concentration of 10 μmol/l were found to be 77.8%, 62.8%, and 67.2%, respectively [33]. Further studies revealed that compound **21** exhibited inhibitory effects on both the enzyme activity of RT with an IC_{50} value of 0.32 μmol/l and the replication of HIV with an IC_{50} value of 0.18 μmol/l while demonstrating low cytotoxicity (CC_{50} = 59 μmol/l). Another derivative NSC34933 (**22,** Figure 10.7), a stilbene-disulfonic acid, inhibited RT activity with an IC_{50} value of 1.1 μmol/l and viral replication with an IC_{50} value of 0.5 μmol/l, respectively. Although it was slightly less potent than compound **21** *in vitro* IN inhibition, it showed antiviral activity against HIV with an EC_{50} value of 0.6 μmol/l and lower cytotoxicity compared to compound **21** (CC_{50} > 100 μmol/l).

Through virtual screening utilizing molecular docking techniques, Zhou et al. successfully synthesized compound **23** (Figure 10.8), an analogue derived from indole-2-carboxylic acid exhibiting potent inhibition against HIV IN chain transfer activity (IC_{50} = 12.41 μmol/l) [27]. Molecular docking analysis revealed that the indole ring and C2 carboxyl group of compound **23**′s indole core can chelate the two

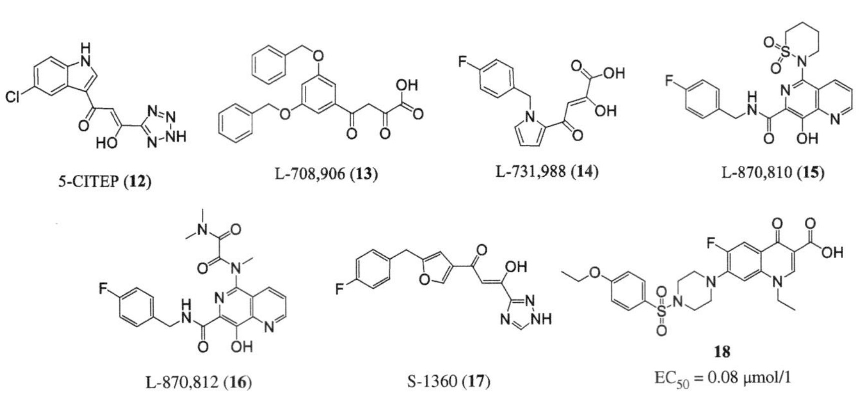

Figure 10.6 Chemical structures of compounds **12–18**.

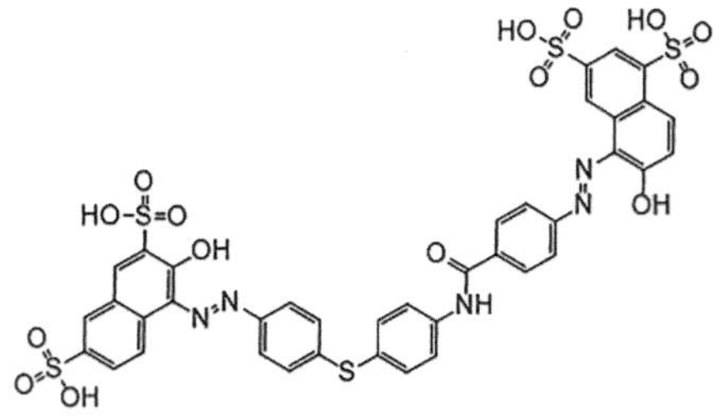

NSC76027 (**19**)
%ST inhibition in HIV-1 IN = 77.8% at 1 μmol/l

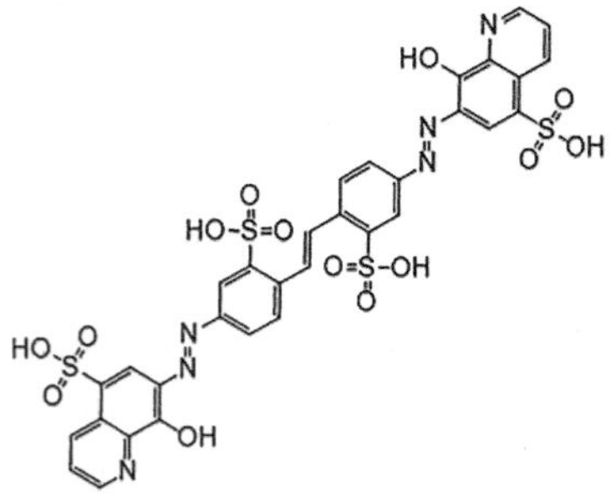

NSC638352 (**20**)
%ST inhibition in HIV-1 IN = 62.8% at 1 μmol/l

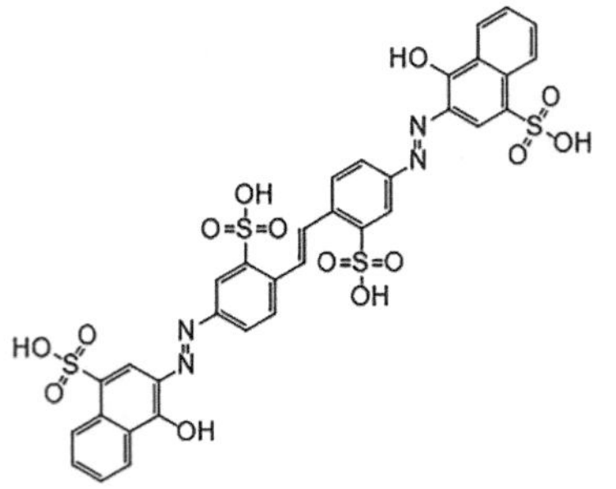

NSC34931 (**21**)

%ST inhibition in HIV-1 IN = 67.2% at 1 μmol/l
EC_{50} = 0.6 μmol/l
CC_{50} = 59 μmol/l

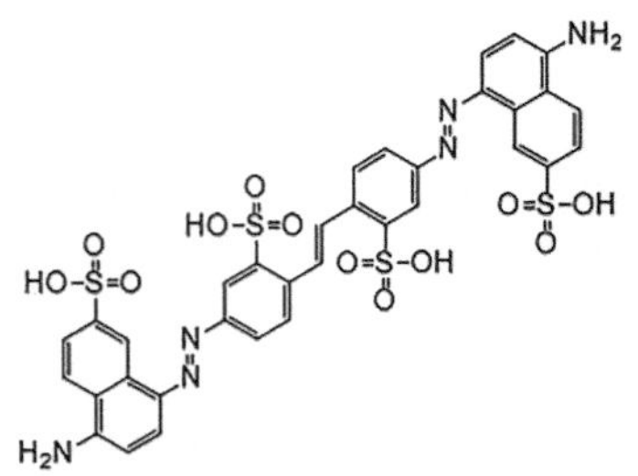

NSC34933 (**22**)

EC_{50} = 0.5 μmol/l
CC_{50} > 100 μmol/l

Figure 10.7 Chemical structures of compounds **19–22**.

magnesium ions in the active center of IN. By introducing a long branch to the indole core at the C3 position, the yielded compound **24** exhibited a significantly enhanced inhibitory effect on IN (IC_{50} = 0.13 μmol/l). These findings suggest that indole-2-carboxylic acid holds great promise as a scaffold for the development of IN inhibitors.

Walker et al. reported a series of bridging tricyclic pyrimidine ketone formamides, among which INSTIs, compound **25** (Figure 10.9), and compound **26** exhibited exceptional antiviral activity against the clinically relevant double mutant G140S/Q148H with EC_{50} values of 10 nmol/l and 3 nmol/l, respectively [34].

In the development of clinical drugs, INSTIs containing naphthyridine scaffold have shown better efficacy than existing drugs, with stronger antiviral activity against certain mutant strains [35–38]. For example, compounds **27** and **28** (Figure 10.10) have higher inhibitory activity against the G140S/Q148H mutant strain than clinical drug **3** [36]. Structural biology has revealed the interaction between these compounds and HIV IN [8, 37]. Recently, Lyumkis et al. discovered through structural biology that the nitrogen atom of the pyridine moiety in compound **28** can effectively coordinate with Mg^{2+} to form a more stable complex

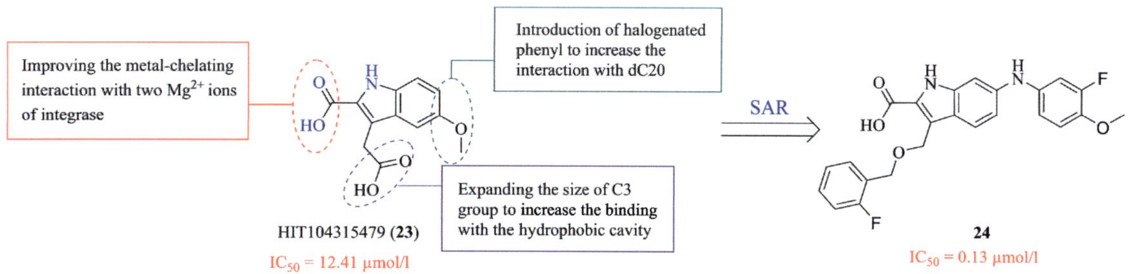

Figure 10.8 Chemical structures of compounds **23** and **24**.

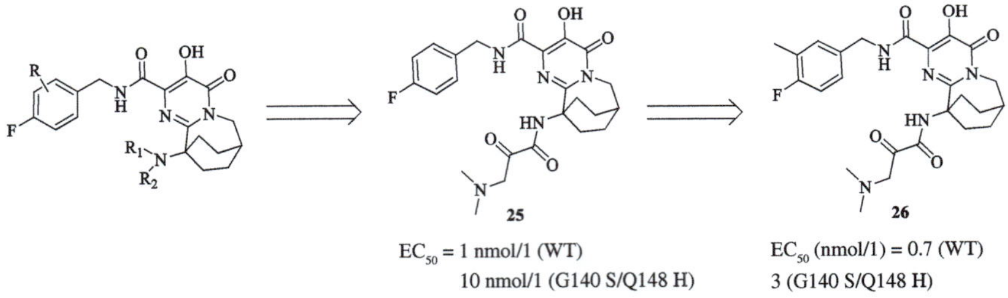

Figure 10.9 Chemical structures of compounds **25** and **26**.

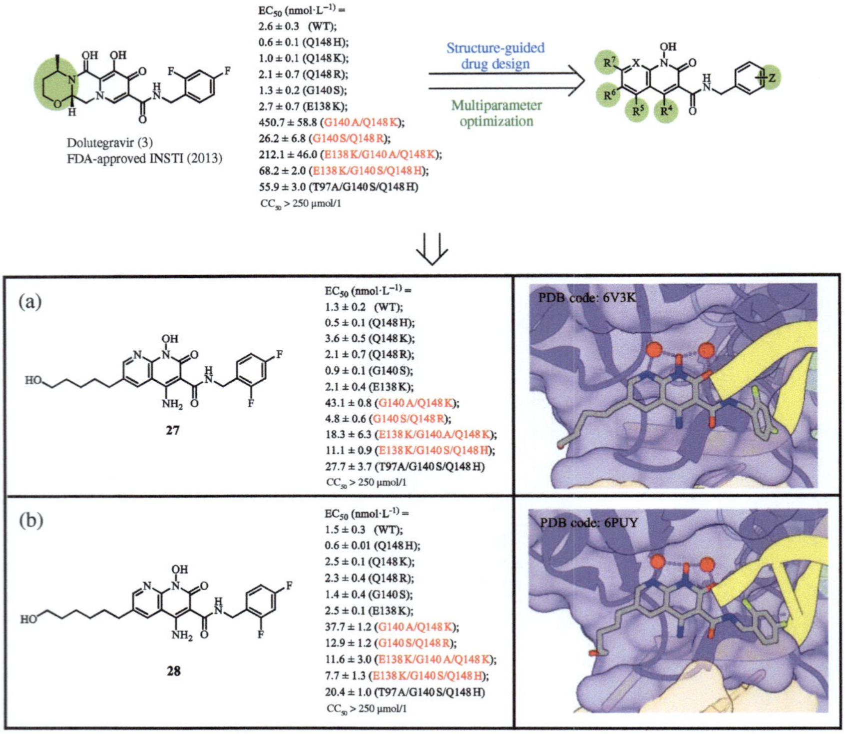

Figure 10.10 The cocrystal binding modes with HIV IN. (a) The X-ray crystal structure of **27** (PDB code: 6V3 K) bound to HIV IN. Mg^{2+} are shown as red spheres. (b) The X-ray crystal structure of **28** (PDB code: 6PUY) bound to HIV IN. Mg^{2+} are shown as red spheres.

with the HIV IN active site [39]. The conformational change of compound **28** when binding to the E138K/G140A/Q148K mutant IN is more favorable for binding, which is an advantage that compound **3** does not have. Free energy perturbation (FEP) calculations showed that in the presence of the E138K/Q148K double mutation, the G140A mutation is unfavorable for compound **3** to bind to the IN, while the effect of compound **28** is smaller, which is consistent with the experimental values (the EC_{50} of compound **3** for the E138K/G140A/Q148K mutant was 212.1 ± 46.0 nmol/l; the EC_{50} of compound **9** for the E138K/G140A/Q148K mutant was

18.3 ± 6.3 nmol/l). Furthermore, the amino group introduced at the 4th position of the pyridine framework in compound **28** can enhance its binding to the HIV IN and improve its inhibitory effect against drug-resistant mutations. At the same time, compound **28** can form π-π stacking interactions with the last adenine nucleotide of the vDNA, which helps stabilize its binding to the active site and enhance the inhibitory effect.

Burke Jr. et al. recently reported a series of *N*-substituted bicyclic carbamic acid pyridine derivatives. Among these, compound **29** (Figure 10.11) demonstrated significant inhibitory activity against WT HIV-1, with an EC_{50} value of 3.0 nmol/l [40]. In comparison to compound **5**, compound **29** exhibited more potent antiviral effects against the double mutant strains E138K/Q148K (EC_{50} = 62.5 nmol/l) and G140S/Q148R (EC_{50} = 11.3 nmol/l). This shows activities that were 12-fold and 36-fold higher than those of compound **5**, respectively. Additionally, compound **29** showed an EC_{50} value of 5.2 nmol/l against the IN^{R263K} mutant HIV strain.

In addition to the aforementioned structures, *N*-hydroxy derivatives [41–43], 3-hydroxy-pyran-4-keto-2-formamide derivatives [44], and polyphenol derivatives identified through HTS of natural products also exhibit inhibitory activity against HIV IN [45].

10.1.1.3 Current and Future Prospects

INSTIs plays a pivotal role as a clinical drug library for HIV treatment, however, due to the rapid evolution of viruses and their ability to develop resistance against therapy, INSTIs often fail to effectively suppress resistance mutations. In a broader context, drug resistance poses significant challenges in HIV treatment that extend beyond INSTI. Although second-generation INSTIs are less susceptible to resistance compared to other ARV drug classes, they still encounter the emergence of resistant mutations which can substantially diminish therapeutic efficacy. A multidisciplinary approach encompassing structural, biochemical, virological, and computational analyses is indispensable in dissecting the underlying principles governing the effectiveness or ineffectiveness of different compounds targeting HIV IN. Acquiring such an understanding will be a pivotal step toward designing novel and broadly effective INSTIs while also providing insights applicable to other drug targets. Addressing resistance necessitates elucidating the mechanisms through which it develops to facilitate the development of next-generation therapeutics specifically tailored to target resistant mutations.

10.1.2 Advances in Inhibitors Research Targeting HIV RNase H

10.1.2.1 Function in Biology and Disease

Reversal transcription is a pivotal process in the HIV-1 life cycle, requiring the presence of RT. RT possesses two enzymatic activities with distinct functions: RNA- and DNA-dependent DNA polymerase activity and ribonuclease H (RNase H) activity. These activities work synergistically to generate double-stranded DNA from viral genomic RNA [46].

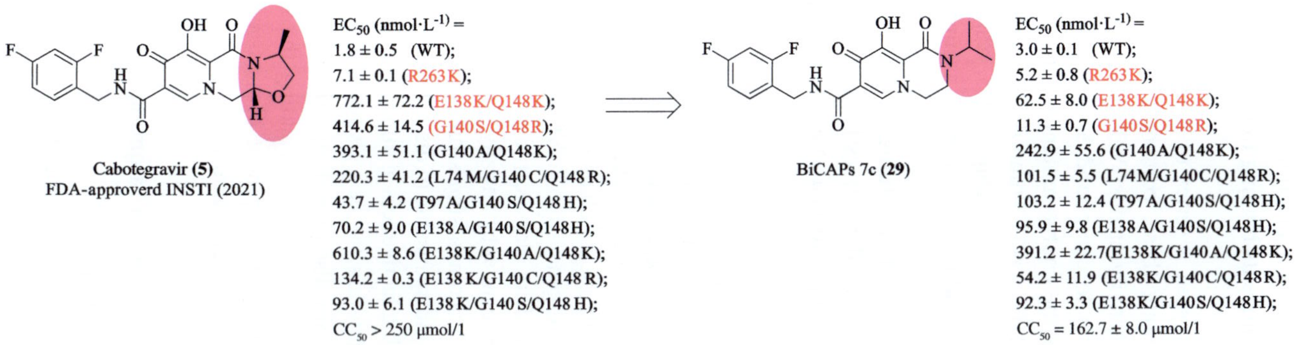

Figure 10.11 Chemical structures of compounds **29**.

10.1.2.2 Inhibitors Development

Hydroxytrophenone Inhibitors The natural product β-thujaplicinol (**30**, Figure 10.12) obtained through HTS, represents an early class of HIV RNase H inhibitors [47]. It is widely acknowledged that their mechanism of action involves effectively mimicking transition state intermediates to exert potent inhibitory activity [48].

Diketo Acid Inhibitors Diketo acids were initially employed as inhibitors for HIV IN [49]. Due to the structural similarity between the active sites of HIV IN and RNase H, many diketo acids have been reused for the development of RNase H inhibitors [50]. Among them, RDS1643 (**31**, Figure 10.12) stands out as the first RNase H inhibitor exhibiting both enzyme inhibitory activity (IC_{50} = 13 μmol/l) and anti-HIV-1 activity at the cellular level (EC_{50} = 7.3 μmol/l) [51]. By replacing the fluorine substitution at position 4 with a chlorine substitution at 2'position in the benzene ring of compound **30**, RDS1759 (**32**) was obtained with selective inhibition against RNase H activity with an IC_{50} value of 7.3 μmol/l [52]. Furthermore, it exhibits potent inhibition against HIV-1 replication at low micromolar concentrations (EC_{50} = 2.10 μmol/l), while showing no apparent cytotoxicity in MT4 cells (CC_{50} > 50 μmol/l).

Hydroxypyridone Carboxylic Acid Inhibitors In 2016, Wang et al. took hydroxypyridinone carboxylic acid (a metal ion chelating group common to the influenza virus (IFV) endonuclease inhibitor **33** (Figure 10.13a) and the approved HIV IN chain transfer inhibitor dolutegravir (**3**)), as the basic skeleton, and methylene as the linking group [53]. A series of novel RNase H inhibitors were designed and synthesized by introducing a benzene ring, naphthalene ring, and biphenyl structure with different substituents. Among them, compound **34** exhibited potent antiviral activity (EC_{50} = 10 μmol/l) and significant HIV-1 RNase H inhibitory activity (IC_{50} = 2.7 ± 0.6 μmol/l) at the cellular level. Compound **35** in this series displayed the most robust inhibitory activity (IC_{50} = 0.65 ± 0.05 μmol/l). The recently reported cocrystal structure of HIV-1 RNase H domain and compound **35** revealed that two Mg^{2+} ions can be chelated by carbonyl, hydroxyl, and carboxyl groups of pyridone in compound **35** while its hydroxyl and sulfonamide groups interacted with His539 and Lys540 respectively "thus establishing contact with RT's RNase H domain (Figure 10.13b) [53]". It is speculated that these additional interactions may contribute to the effective inhibition of RNase H by compound **35**.

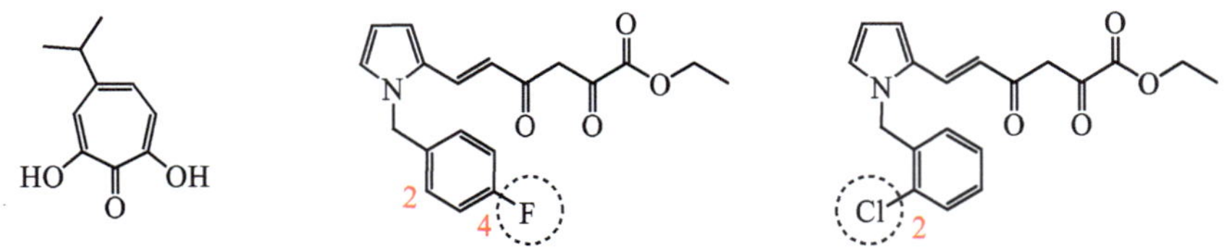

β-thujaplicinol (**29**)
IC_{50} = 0.2 μmol/l

RDS1643 (**30**)
IC_{50} = 13 μmol/l
EC_{50} = 7.3 μmol/l

RDS1759 (**31**)
EC_{50} = 2.1 μmol/l
CC_{50} > 50 μmol/l

Figure 10.12 Chemical structures of β-thujaplicinol and diketo acid derivatives.

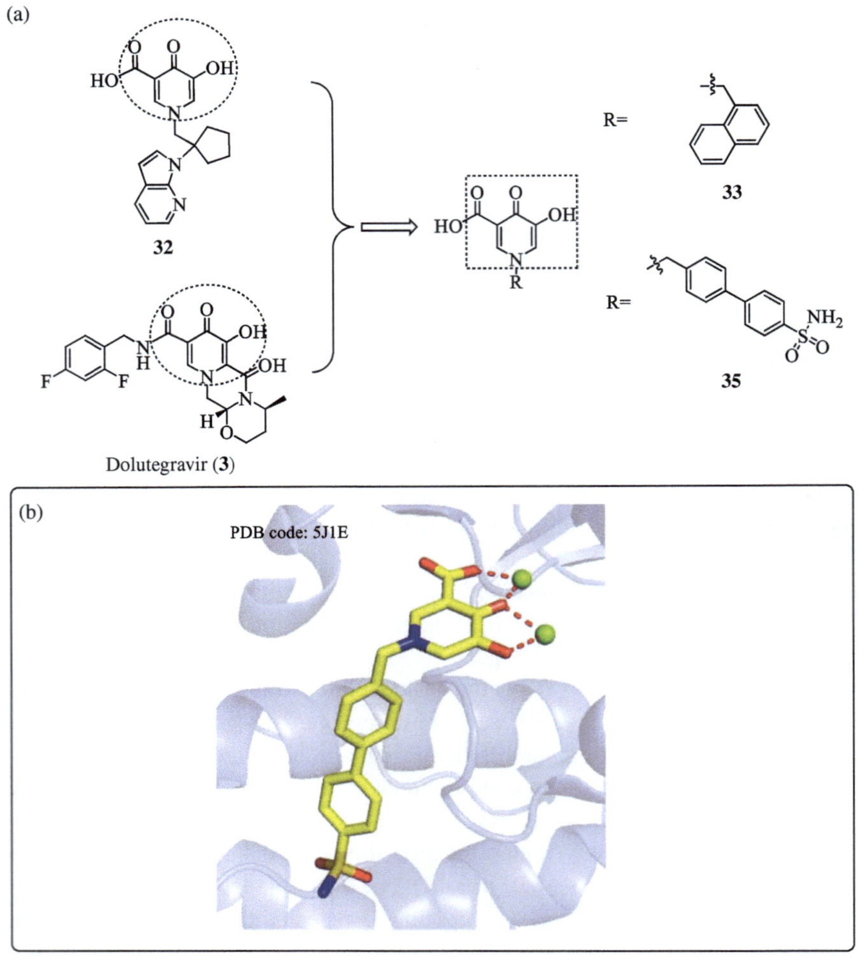

Figure 10.13 (a) Design and structures of hydroxypyridone carboxylic acids; (b) The crystal structure of compound **35** in complex with HIV-1 RT RNase H domain (PDB code: 5J1E).

Hydroxyisoquinolinedione Inhibitors As a prototypical Mg^{2+} chelator, 2-hydroxyisoquinolinedione(HID, **36**) was initially identified as one of the chemical scaffolds exhibiting inhibitory activity against RNase H [54]. Subsequent investigations revealed its potential as an inhibitor for IFV PA endonuclease [49] and hepatitis C virus NS5B [55]. In 2015, Wang et al. introduced compound **37** (Figure 10.14) into the biphenyl structure by using methylene as a connecting group at the sixth position of HID, which exhibited strong inhibitory activity against HIV-1 RNase H (IC_{50} = 0.8 μmol/l) [56]. However, compound **37** lacks selectivity since it also strongly inhibits DNA polymerase (IC_{50} = 1.6 μmol/l). In 2017, the team further explored the SAR around the HID structure and obtained two subtypes of compounds **38** and **39** by introducing benzyl groups at different positions on HID with amide bonds as a connecting group. Activity testing showed that both subtypes

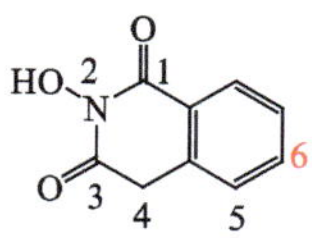

HID(36)

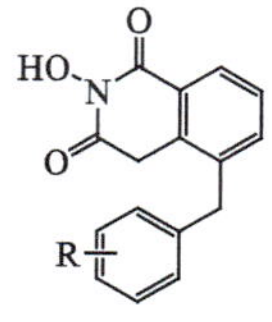

38

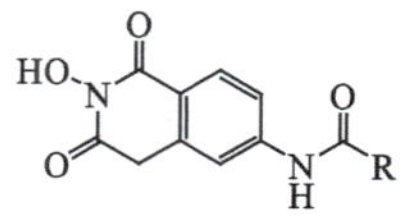

39

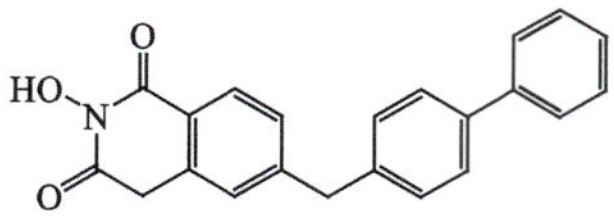

37

IC_{50} (RNase H) = 0.8 μmol/l
IC_{50} (RT pol) = 1.6 μmol/l
IC_{50} (INST) > 100 μmol/l
EC_{50} (HIV-1) = 3.0 μmol/l
CC_{50} = 50 μmol/l

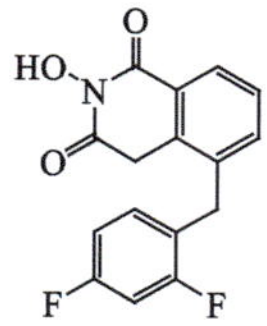

38a

IC_{50} (RNase H) = 0.8 μmol/l
IC_{50} (RT pol) = 9.3 μmol/l

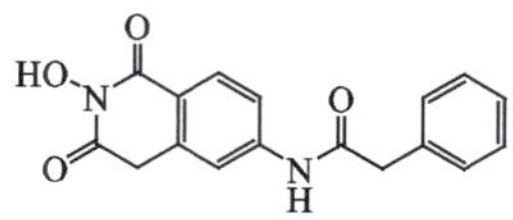

39a

IC_{50} (RNase H) = 0.2 μmol/l
IC_{50} (RT pol) = 1.4 μmol/l

Figure 10.14 Chemical structures of HID chemotypes.

inhibited HIV-1 RNase H in the nanomolar range with weak or better selectivity against DNA polymerase [57], with representative compounds being **38a** and **39a**.

3-hydroxypyrimidine-2,4-dione inhibitors The compound 3-hydroxypyrimidin-2,4-dione, meticulously engineered by the research team led by Wang et al. has been identified as a dual-target inhibitor of HIV-1 DNA polymerase and IN [58–60]. This compound incorporates a hydroxyl group on the third nitrogen atom of a non-nucleoside RT inhibitor **40** (Figure 10.15) [61]. In conjunction with the two carbonyl groups on both sides, it forms a Mg^{2+} chelating ternary complex to inhibit the IN activity. Compound **41** and its analogues exhibited inhibitory activity against RNase H at micromolar levels. Building upon the foundational work regarding the SAR of 3-hydroxypyrimidine-2,4-dione (HPD)-like compounds in 2016, the team has refined the HPD structure by strategically eliminating or reducing the size of

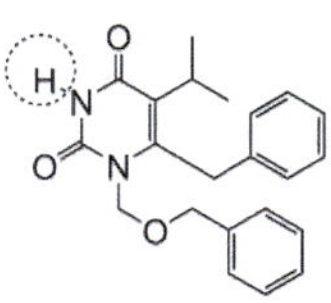

40

IC_{50} (RT pol) = 0.04 μmol/l
IC_{50} (INST) > 333 μmol/l
EC_{50} (HIV-1) = 0.013 μmol/l
CC_{50} > 20 μmol/l

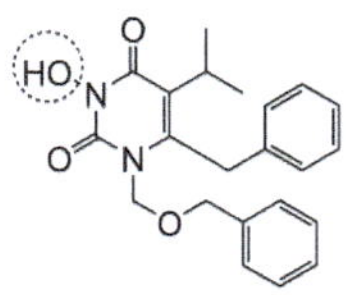

41

IC_{50} (RT pol) = 5.4 μmol/l
IC_{50} (INST) = 21 μmol/l
IC_{50} (RNase H) = 2.5 μmol/l
EC_{50} (HIV-1) = 0.008 μmol/l
CC_{50} > 20 μmol/l

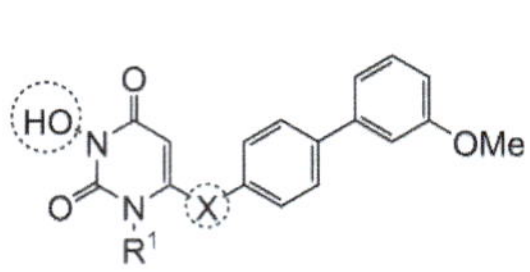

42:R^1 = Me,X = NH
IC_{50} (RNase H) = 0.80 μmol/l
43:R^1 = Me,X = O
IC_{50} (RNase H) = 2.0 μmol/l
44:R^1 = H,X = NH
IC_{50} (RNase H) = 0.15 μmol/l

Figure 10.15 Chemical structures of compounds **40–44**.

N-1 and *C*-5 substituent groups required for DNA polymerase inhibition [62, 63]. Simultaneously, they introduced a biphenyl group at position C-6 with either a nitrogen or oxygen atom as a linking group to achieve selective inhibition of RNase H. A series of HPD derivatives from **42** to **43** were designed and synthesized. The activity results demonstrated that compounds **42** and **43,** which have a methyl group substitution at the N-1 position, exhibited inhibitory activity against RNase H at low micromolar levels but did not show any inhibitory effect on DNA polymerase. In contrast, compound **44**, without substitution at the *N*-1 position, displayed significantly higher inhibition of RNase H (IC_{50} = 0.15 μmol/l) compared to RT DNA polymerase (IC_{50} = 7.3 μmol/l), indicating superior selectivity. The molecular model predicted a similar binding pattern between HIV-1RT and compound **44** as observed with other inhibitors targeting the active site of RNase H. The crucial interaction involves the HPD chelating group (2-C=O/3-OH/4-C=O) coordinating with two Mg^{2+} ions in the active site along with acidic residues Asp443, Glu478, Asp498, and Asp549 for mutual binding [63]. Additionally, the NH group at core position 1 of compound **44** can interact with the imidazole side chain of highly conserved His539 in RNase H. Other interactions may occur between the biaryl moiety and Lys540 side chain or enzyme residues/nucleic acids near the hydrophobic region of RNase H. Although cellular-level antiviral activity has not been demonstrated for these compounds yet, compound **44** has shown promising enzyme inhibitory properties and warrants further optimization as a lead compound.

To further enhance the activity of these compounds, Wang et al. introduced various connecting groups such as methylene [64], thioether [65], and non-flexible carbonyl [66] at the 6 positions of 3-hydroxypyrimidin-2,4-dione, resulting in the synthesis of compounds **45** to **48** (Figure 10.16). The aim was to discover HIV-1 RNase H inhibitors with both target activity and cellular activity [67]. All compounds **45** to **48** exhibited potent inhibitory effects on RNase H with IC_{50} values ranging from (0.005–0.027 μmol/l) and demonstrated significant antiviral activity at the cellular level in the low micromolar range without causing cytotoxicity. Compound **49** efficiently and selectively inhibited RNase H activity but lacked antiviral efficacy at the cellular level [63]. To address this issue, in 2017, Wang et al. 3-hydroxypyrimidine-2,4-diones as selective active site inhibitors of HIV RT-associated RNase H: design, synthesis, and biochemical evaluations designed and synthesized a series of novel dual-wing HPD compounds using a "two-wing" strategy by adding a wing to the *C*-5 position of HPD while considering the length and flexibility of both wings [68]. Among them, compound **50** displayed superior inhibitory activity against HIV-1 RNase H (IC_{50} = 0.004 μmol/l) along with significant antiviral potency at the cellular level (EC_{50} = 6.1 μmol/l).

1-Hydroxy-Pyrimidine Pyrimidine Ketone Inhibitors In 2014, Beilhartz et al. reported that GSK5750 (**51**, Figure 10.17), a derivative of 1-hydroxy-pyrimidine pyrimidine one, demonstrated novel inhibitory activity against the active site of HIV-1 RNase H [69]. Mechanistic experiments revealed that compound **51** bound to the active site of RNase H in a Mg^{2+}-dependent manner, resulting in significant inhibition of its function (IC_{50} = 0.33 ± 0.11 μmol/l).

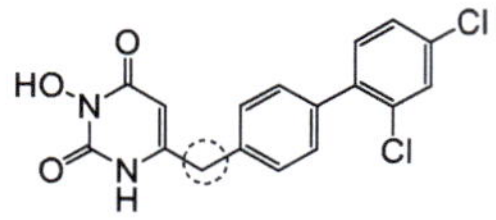

45

IC_{50} (RNase H) = 0.009 μmol/l
IC_{50} (RT pol) > 10 μmol/l
IC_{50} (INST) > 100 μmol/l
EC_{50} (HIV-1) = 13 μmol/l
CC_{50} > 100 μmol/l

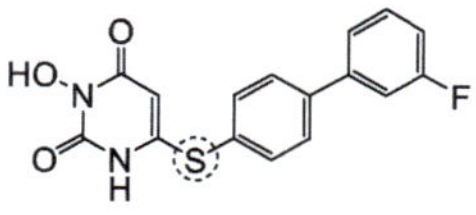

46

IC_{50} (RNase H) = 0.005 μmol/l
IC_{50} (RT pol) = 10 μmol/l
IC_{50} (INST) > 1.0 μmol/l
EC_{50} (HIV-1) = 7.2 μmol/l
CC_{50} > 100 μmol/l

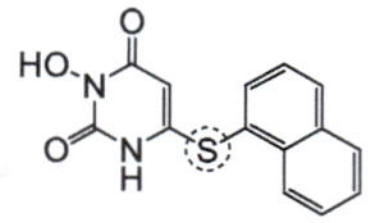

47

IC_{50} (RNase H) = 0.007 μmol/l
IC_{50} (INST) = 0.79 μmol/l
EC_{50} (HIV-1) = 6.3 μmol/l
CC_{50} > 100 μmol/l

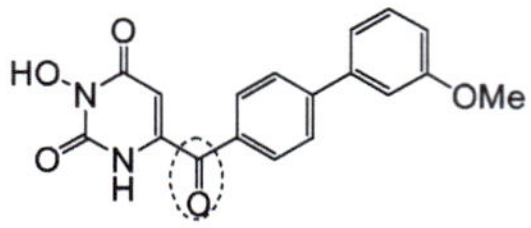

48

IC_{50} (RNase H) = 0.027 μmol/l
IC_{50} (RT pol) > 10 μmol/l
IC_{50} (INST) = 6.7 μmol/l
EC_{50} (HIV-1) = 9.0 μmol/l
CC_{50} > 100 μmol/l

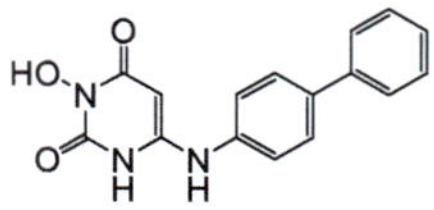

49

IC_{50} (RNase H) = 0.25 μmol/l
EC_{50} (HIV-1) > 25 μmol/l

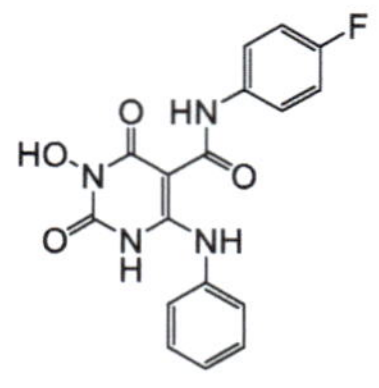

50

IC_{50} (RNase H) = 0.004 μmol/l
EC_{50} (HIV-1) = 6.1 μmol/l

Figure 10.16 Chemical structures of compounds **45–50**.

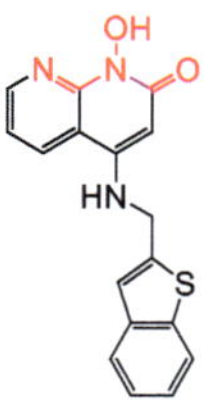

GSK5750 (**51**)

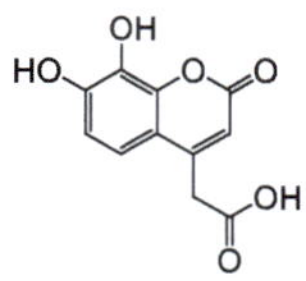

F3284-8495 (**52**)

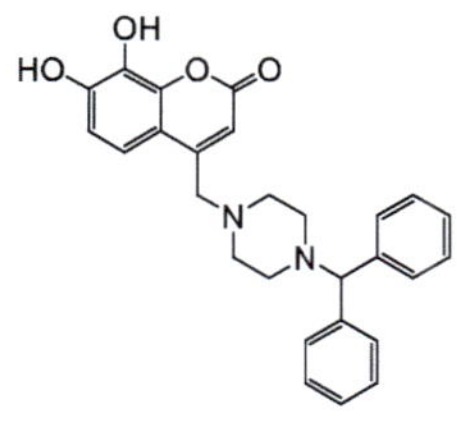

F3385-2581 (**53**)

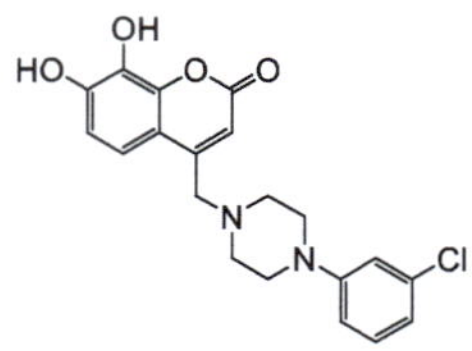

F3385-2590 (**54**)

Figure 10.17 Chemical structures of compounds **51–54**.

Dihydroxycoumarin Inhibitors In 2014, Himmel et al. discovered a dihydroxycoumarin-like compound F3284-8495 (**52**, Figure 10.17) through HTS that exhibited low micromolar inhibition of RNase H (IC_{50} = 4.8 μmol/l) and bound to the active site in the HIV-1 RNase H domain [70]. Based on cocrystal structure information between **52** and RNase H, Himmel et al. designed a series of analogues by replacing the acetic acid part of **52** with large substituents to introduce additional forces and improve antiviral activity [70]. Compounds F3385–2581 (**53**) and F3385–2590 (**54**) showed submicromolar inhibitory activity against p15-EC RNase H with IC_{50} values of 0.1 μmol/l and 0.2 μmol/l respectively; however, compound **54** was found to be the most effective analogue as it inhibited RT-RNase H under physiological conditions with an IC_{50} value of approximately sixfold greater than that of the lead compound at about 0.8 μmol/l. The enhanced inhibitory activity may be attributed to its piperazine ring forming hydrophobic interactions with ALa538 while its m-chlorobenzene ring connected to nitrogen at the distal end can contact residues such as Trp535, Pro537 and Lys540 near the active site of RNase H [70].

Other Classes of Inhibitors In 2021, Messore et al. employed the bioisosteric strategy to modify the quinolinedione compounds, resulting in a series of non-diketone quinolinedione derivatives [71]. Among them, compound **55** (Figure 10.18) exhibited a strong inhibitory effect on RNase H, with an IC_{50} of 1.51 μmol/l, and showed no inhibitory effect on HIV-1 IN.

In 2022, our research group [72] took the previously identified ellagic acid derivative II-25 (**56**, Figure 10.18) as the lead compound. To enhance the interaction with HIV-1 RNase H, structurally diverse hydrophobic groups were introduced at the C-2 and C-3 positions of the piperazine ring, resulting in a series of synthesized derivatives. Among them, the representative compound IA-6 (**57**) showed the best anti-HIV-1 RNase H activity, with an IC_{50} value of 0.067 ± 0.02 μmol/l. This is approximately 30 times higher than that of the lead compound. However, despite the low cytotoxicity at the tested concentrations (CC_{50} > 20 μmol/l), these derivatives did not exhibit significant antiviral activity.

In 2023, Ito et al. conducted a target-based virtual screening of 400 natural compounds and discovered anthraquinone RNase H inhibitors derived from lac, namely Laccaic acid A (**58,** Figure 10.18), Laccaic acid C (**59**), and Laccaic acid E (**60**) [73]. Among them, compound **59** exhibited the best inhibitory effect (IC_{50} = 8.1 μmol/l). The binding mode analysis revealed that the anthraquinone skeleton is co-planar with two Mn^{2+} ions and forms a chelation interaction with Mn^{2+} through a trioxygen structure.

10.1.2.3 Current and Future Prospects

The HIV-1 RNase H is an ideal target for drug development, necessitating the development of new therapies in the face of increasing multi-drug resistance

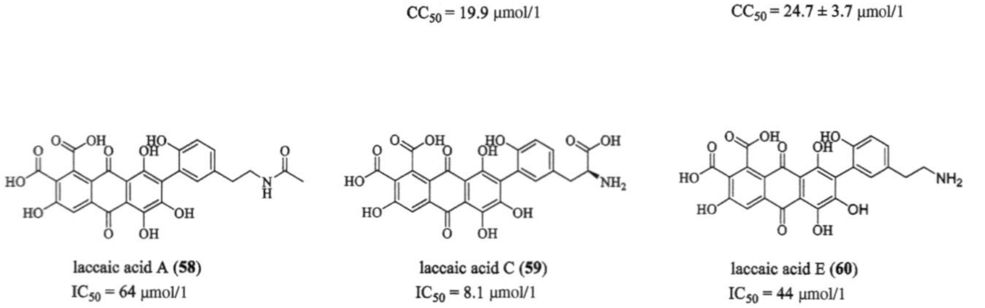

Figure 10.18 Chemical structures of compounds **55–60**.

and treatment-related toxicity. Despite the discovery of numerous compounds that inhibit the activity of RNase H over the past decade, few have demonstrated significant cellular activity. HTS and fragment-based drug design (FBDD), in conjunction with X-ray crystallography, have facilitated the design of lead compounds and the diversification of inhibitors. The dual-targeting strategy for RNase H and HIV IN shows promise due to the similarity of their metal-binding sites [74]. A systematic approach is required for the development of RNase H inhibitors, with early PK analysis to overcome the deficiency in cellular activity, especially for polar macrocyclic peptide (MBP) inhibitors. Despite the challenges, the research in this field holds promising prospects.

10.2 Current Status of HBV Prevalence and Treatment

Hepatitis B is a liver infection caused by HBV. WHO estimates in 2022, 254 million people will be living with chronic hepatitis B (CHB) infection, with 1.2 million new infections and around 1 million deaths each year. At present, new drugs for treating CHB can be roughly divided into two categories [75]. The first category mainly targets the lifecycle of HBV, including preventing HBV from entering cells, directly targeting covalently closed circular DNA (cccDNA), targeting HBV gene expression, inhibiting nucleocapsid assembly, and Hepatitis B surface antigen (HBsAg) release, etc. The second type mainly targets the host's immune system, including innate immunity and adaptive immunity. In recent years, significant progress has been made in many new drugs or strategies for antiviral treatment of CHB. According to incomplete statistics, there are a total of 146 new drugs for hepatitis B under development worldwide (with 50 of them being studied in China), of which approximately 66.4% (97/146) are still in clinical phase I or preclinical research, 31.5% (46/146) are in clinical phase II research, and only 2.1% (3/146) have entered clinical phase III.

10.2.1 Advances in Inhibitors Research Targeting HBV RNase H

10.2.1.1 Function in Biology and Disease

The biological function of the HBV RNase H is to eliminate the viral pregenomic RNA, which represents the RNA intermediate of the genome, after its conversion into DNA, thereby facilitating the synthesis of the second DNA strand. Inhibition of HBV RNase H exerts a profound impact on both sense and antisense DNA strand synthesis within the virus. RNase H inhibitors effectively hinder normal viral replication. Consequently, HBV RNase H emerges as a promising target for therapeutic intervention [76–79].

10.2.1.2 Inhibitors Development

Hu et al. reported that β-thujaplicinol (**30**, Figure 10.19) exhibited potent inhibition against RNase H from HBV genotype D and H in biochemical assays with IC_{50} values of 5.9 μmol/l and 2.3 μmol/l, respectively [80]. Moreover, It effectively suppressed

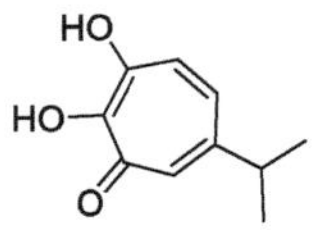

30

EC_{50} = 5 μmol/l
CC_{50} = 10.1 μmol/l

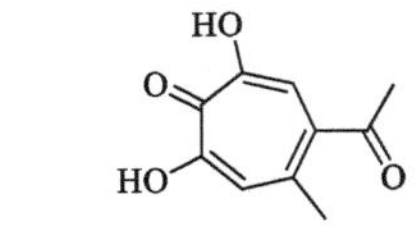

61

EC_{50} = 0.34 μmol/l

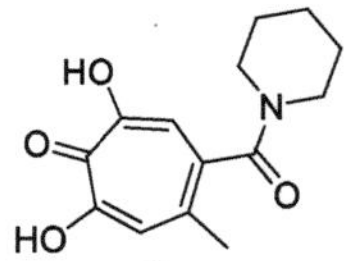

62

EC_{50} = 0.31 μmol/l
CC_{50} = 24.9 μmol/l

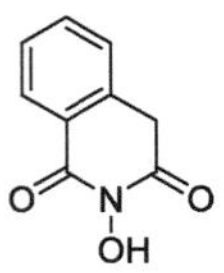

63

EC_{50} = 4.2 μmol/l
CC_{50} = 75 μmol/l

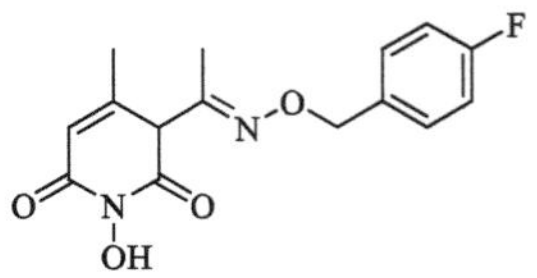

64

EC_{50} = 0.11 μmol/l
CC_{50} = 33 μmol/l

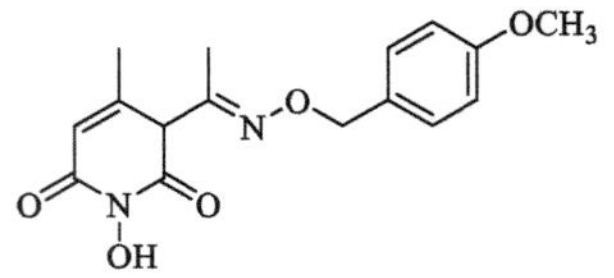

65

EC_{50} = 0.29 μmol/l
CC_{50} > 0.1 μmol/l

Figure 10.19 HBV RNase H inhibitors.

the replication of HBV genotypes A and D in cell culture by specifically targeting the RNase H (EC50 = 5 μmol/l, CC_{50} = 10.1 μmol/l).

Lu et al. identified a series of hydroxytocophenone derivatives through HTS technology. Among them, compound **61** (Figure 10.19) showed excellent anti-HBV activity at the cellular level (EC_{50} = 0.34 μmol/l). Its SAR revealed that the presence of α-hydroxyl ketones on the left wing is essential for inhibitory activity, while a short-chain substituent with carbonyl groups on the wing can effectively enhance the anti-HBV activity [81].

Li et al. synthesized and analyzed a library of 57 amide-containing α-hydroxytropolones (αHTs) as potential leads for the development of anti-HBV drugs [82]. The 50 % effective concentrations ranged from 0.31 to 54 μmol/l, with selectivity indexes in cell culture reaching up to 80, and further tests confirmed these compounds possess mild enzymatic inhibitory activities against HBV RNase H through semi-quantitative enzymatic assays. Overall, the compounds exhibited limited activity against human RNase H, with IC_{50} values of 5.1 to >1000 μmol/l. Compound **62** (Figure 10.19) displays the outstanding anti-HBV activity at the cellular level (EC_{50} = 0.31 μmol/l). These findings suggest that amide αHTs possess strong and specific inhibitory effects on HBV and warrant further development for use in combination therapies aimed at improving treatment outcomes for chronically infected patients.

Cai et al. established a low-throughput screening method to identify inhibitors of the HBV RNase H and viral replication. They screened a series of twenty-three nitrogen-based polyoxygenated heterocycles including sixteen 2-hydroxyisoquinoline-1,3(2*H*,4*H*)-dione derivatives for anti-HBV RNase H activity. Of the compounds tested, nine inhibited HBV RNase H with marginal activity observed in eight others, the optimal compound **63** (Figure 10.19) showed potential potency against HBV RNase H (IC_{50} = 28.1 μmol/l, EC_{50} = 4.2 μmol/l). It preferentially suppressed the accumulation of the viral plus-polarity DNA strand in replication inhibition assays by suppressing HBV RNase H activity. It had a CC_{50} value of 75 μmol/l and yielded a therapeutic index of 18 [83].

In 2017, according to Edwards et al., HPDs can significantly inhibit HBV replication in cells by targeting RNase H. Notably, compounds **64** and **65** (Figure 10.18) exhibited superior anti-HBV activity at the micro to submicro molar levels, thus possessing the potential for further research as lead compounds [84].

10.2.1.3 Current and Future Prospects

The existing HBV RNase H inhibitors currently contain a large number of hydroxyl groups, which have strong polarity, poor membrane permeability, poor water solubility, and weak antiviral activity. Accelerating the research on the structural biology of HBV RNase H and developing new HBV RNase H inhibitors with good drug properties and strong antiviral activity is an important research direction.

10.3 Current Status of SARS-CoV-2 Prevalence and Treatment

COVID-19 is the disease caused by the severe acute respiratory syndrome coronavirus 2 (SARS-CoV-2). According to the WHO, more than 760 million cases and 6.9 million deaths have been recorded globally as of August 2023, although the actual numbers are thought to be higher. At present, breakthrough progress has been made in the development of small molecule anti-SARS-CoV-2 drugs, mainly targeting important links in the virus lifecycle to terminate virus replication [85]. RNA-dependent RNA polymerase (RdRp), namely Nsp12, is an important enzyme that regulates viral RNA replication and transcription in the process of viral infection. It catalyzes the synthesis of viral RNA chains under the action of cofactors Nsp7 and Nsp8. The subcomplex formed by Nsp12, Nsp7, and Nsp8 is the smallest core component of viral RNA replication, and the function of RdRp is relatively conserved in RNA viruses. Studies have shown that the RdRp sequence of SARS-CoV-2 has 96% consistency with the sequence of SARS-CoV. Therefore, RdRp can serve as an important target for anti-SARS-CoV-2, which is beneficial for the design and development of new broad-spectrum antiviral drugs based on viral structure and the reuse of existing RdRp inhibitors

10.3.1 Advances in Inhibitors Research Targeting SARS-CoV-2 Helicase

10.3.1.1 Function in Biology and Disease

The SARS-CoV-2 non-structural protein 13 (NSP13), weighing 67 kDa, is a member of the helicase superfamily 1B. It utilizes the energy derived from nucleotide triphosphate hydrolysis to catalyze the unwinding of double-stranded DNA or RNA in a 5′ to 3′ direction [86]. The NSP13 has been identified as a promising target for antiviral therapy due to its high degree of sequence conservation and indispensable role in viral replication. NSP13 has demonstrated interaction with the viral RNA-dependent RNA polymerase NSP12, functioning synergistically with the replication-transcription complex (NSP7/NSP8/NSP12). The findings suggest that this interaction could potentially exert a substantial impact on the activity of NSP13 helicase through mechanical regulation.

10.3.1.2 Inhibitors Development

White et al. employed homology modeling to generate a structural model of NSP13 bound with ATP/RNA in the apo state [87]. The ATP binding site of NSP13 protein served as the primary docking site for conducting virtual HTS and molecular docking on 970,000 compounds to identify potential SARS-CoV-2 NSP13 inhibitors. Among them, the score for nilotinib (**66**, Figure 10.20) and rumacato (**67**) is relatively high. Compound **66** is a BCR-ABL tyrosine kinase inhibitor that has been reported to potentially inhibit the novel coronavirus activity mediated by the NSP12-NSP7-NSP8 complex [88, 89]. To validate the results obtained from high-throughput virtual screening, they further evaluated the inhibitory activity of 10 compounds with high scores on recombinant COVID-19 NSP13 protein's ATPase *in vitro*. These findings led to the discovery of compound **67** and cepharanthine (**68**) that inhibit the ATPase of NSP13 with IC_{50} values of 0.3 μmol/l and 0.4 μmol/l, respectively.

Ugurel et al. conducted a comprehensive analysis of the genome sequences of multiple COVID-19 isolates from various regions worldwide, revealing a higher mutation rate for C17747T and A17858G compared to other mutations. Notably, these mutations were found to occur on the NSP13 protein [90]. They employed homologous modeling and molecular dynamics simulations to assess the impact of missense mutations on protein structure and drug-protein interaction. The findings highlighted that an optimal drug could effectively interact with key amino acid residues near the ATP hydrolysis active site. To identify novel potent drug candidates, Ugurel et al. performed HTS of FDA-approved drug libraries targeting the ATP binding pocket in NSP13 [90]. Among them, cantalore (**69**, Figure 10.20), fludarabine (**70**), folic acid (**71**) and resveratrol glycoside (**72**) exhibited significant promise as they demonstrated inhibitory activity against both WT and mutant COVID-19 helicase.

In 2020, Yuan et al. found that ranitidine bismuth citrate (RBC, **73**, Figure 10.21), an anti-ulcer drug commonly employed in clinic practice and containing bismuth metal, exhibited the potential against COVID-19 through the innovative repurposing of existing drugs [91]. RBC demonstrated inhibitory effects on SARS-CoV-2 replication, significantly reduced the viral load associated with COVID-19, and alleviated virus-induced inflammation. By irreversibly replacing zinc ions within its structure with bismuth (III), **73** effectively hindered the activities of ATPase (IC_{50} = 0.69 μmol/l) and DNA helicase (IC_{50} = 0.70 μmol/l). This groundbreaking finding suggested that drugs containing bismuth (III) or other metals hold substantial implications for the treatment of SARS-CoV-2 infection.

Zeng et al. developed a high-throughput fluorescence resonance energy transfer-based method for in vitro determination of NSP13 helicase activity [92]. Using this method, they screened over 5000 known compounds and identified

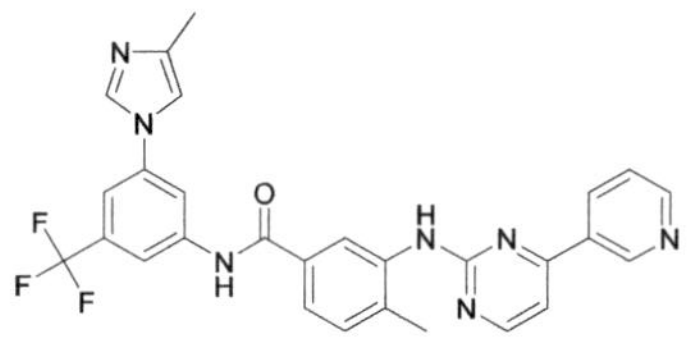

Nilotinib(**66**)

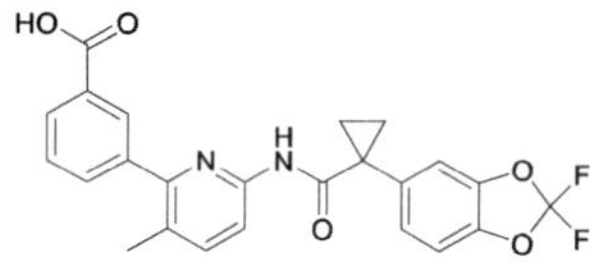

Lumacaftor(**67**)
IC_{50} = 0.3 μmol/l

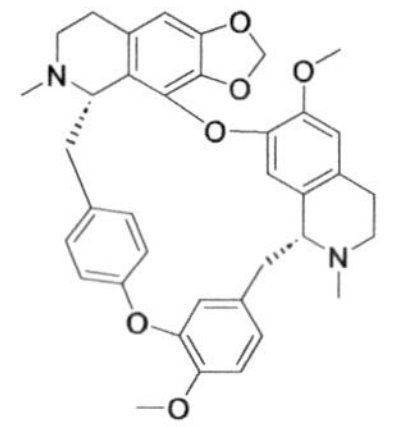

Cepharanthine(**68**)
IC_{50} = 0.4 μmol/l

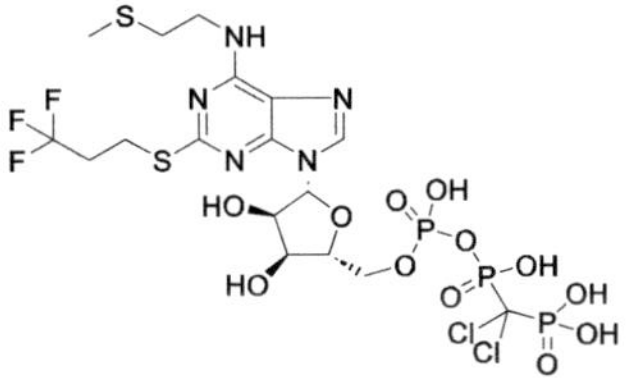

Cangrelor(**69**)

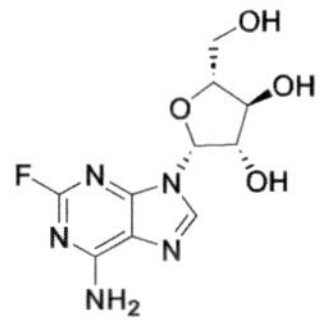

Fludarabine(**70**)

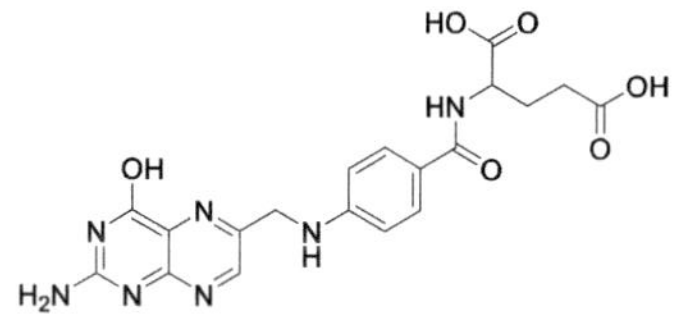

Folic acid(**71**)

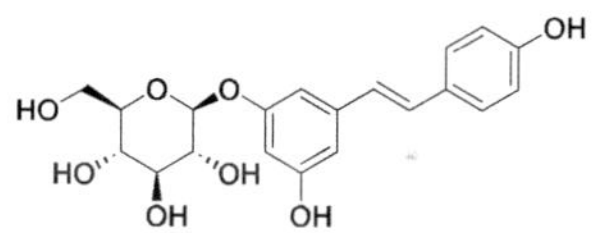

Polydatin(**72**)

Figure 10.20 SARS-CoV-2 helicase inhibitors.

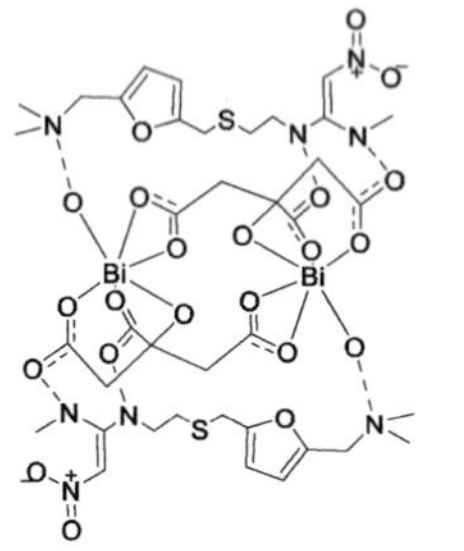

RBC(**73**)
IC_{50} = 70 μmol/l

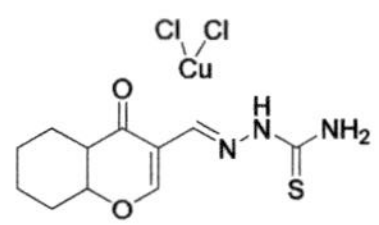

FPA-124(**74**)
EC_{50} = 10 μmol/l

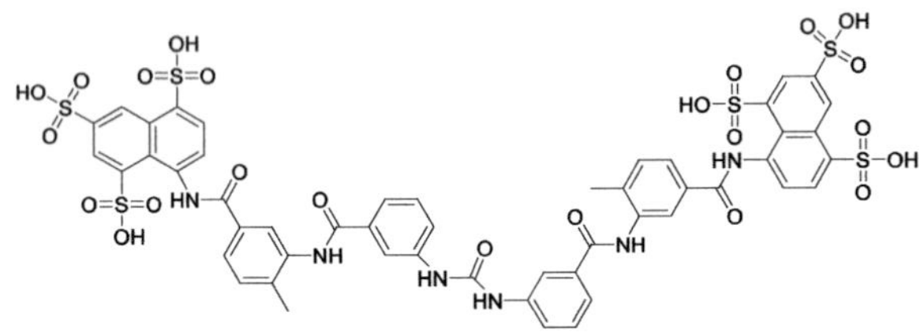

Suramin(**75**)

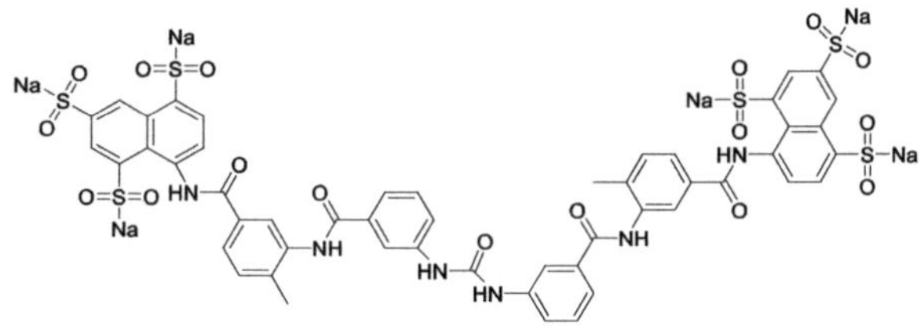

Suramin hexasodium(**76**)
IC_{50} = 5.42 μmol/l

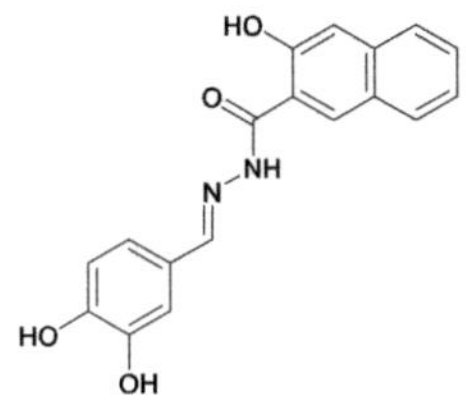

Dynasore(**77**)
IC_{50} = 6.22 μmol/l

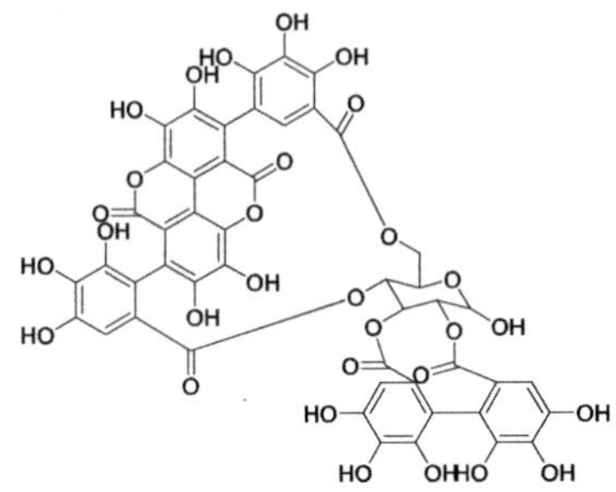

Punicalagin(**78**)
EC_{50} = 196 nmol/l
CC_{50} = 47 μmol/l

Figure 10.21 The representative SARS-CoV-2 helicase inhibitors.

FPA-124 (**74**) and Suramin (**75**) as the most promising candidates. **74** is an AKT inhibitor with good cell permeability that induces apoptosis in various cancer cell lines [93]. The compound **74** exhibits an IC_{50} value of approximately 9 μmol/l against NSP11. Furthermore, its structural analogue inhibits NSP13 in vitro with an IC_{50} value of approximately 1 μmol/l and shows an EC_{50} value of around 10 μmol/l at the cellular level for virus inhibition, indicating its broad-spectrum antiviral effect [94].

In 2022, Corona et al. established a biochemical detection method to assess the activity of SARS-CoV-2 NSP13-related enzymes. Through virtual screening of a small internal natural compound library, they identified myricetin, quercetin, kaempferol, and flavonoids as exhibiting inhibitory activity against SARS-CoV-2 NSP13, among these compounds, flavonoids demonstrated the most potent effect [95]. However, extensive research revealed that while flavonoids can interact with viral proteins and inhibit specific enzyme activities, their ability to impede viral replication is limited. Consequently, they are deemed unsuitable for use as therapeutic agents. Nevertheless, by further modifying and optimizing their chemical structures, novel derivatives can be synthesized that effectively target both enzyme activity and virus replication.

In 2024, Kuzikov et al. identified compounds that can inhibit SARS-CoV-2 NSP12 and NSP13 through drug reuse screening methods, to interfere with virus replication and transcription processes [96]. The researchers conducted further dose–response tests on the screened compounds to confirm their inhibitory activity and used nano differential scanning fluorescence to confirm the direct interaction between the inhibitor and the target protein. They successfully confirmed the activity of Suramine Hexasodium (**76**) on the SARS-CoV-2 RdRp complex (IC_{50} = 5.42 μmol/l), and it was determined that dynasore (**77**) is a new effective inhibitor (IC_{50} = 6.22 μmol/l provides a starting point for the development of new antiviral drugs.

Lu et al. identified punicalagin (PUG, **78**) as a novel NSP13 helicase inhibitor through HTS [97]. SPR-based analysis and molecular docking calculation revealed that PUG binds directly to the interface of domains 1A and 2A, with a *KD* value of 21.6 nmol/l. Further biochemical and structural analyses suggested that PUG inhibits NSP13 on ATP hydrolysis and prevents it from binding to DNA substrates. The antiviral studies showed that PUG can effectively suppress the SARS-CoV-2 replication in A549-ACE2 and Vero cells, with EC_{50} values of 347 nmol/l and 196 nmol/l, respectively.

10.3.1.3 Current and Future Prospects

The development prospect of the SARS CoV-2 Nsp13 inhibitor is promising. With an in-depth understanding of its unique functions and interactions with host proteins, and the newly developed high-throughput drug-screening platform, it is expected to find and optimize Nsp13 inhibitors with strong specificity, high potency, and low side effects in the future, providing new treatment options for anti-COVID-19, and may have broad-spectrum inhibitory effects on other coronaviruses, providing potential treatment strategies for future coronavirus outbreaks.

10.4 Current Status of IFV Prevalence and Treatment

Seasonal influenza (influenza) is an acute respiratory infection caused by IFV, resulting in 290,000–650,000 respiratory deaths each year. At present, small molecule antiviral drugs approved by the FDA for influenza treatment include neuraminidase inhibitors (NAI), M2 ion channel inhibitors, and viral RNA polymerase inhibitors (baloxavir) [98]. However, due to the widespread resistance of IFVs to M2 ion channel inhibitors, these drugs are no longer recommended for the clinical treatment of influenza. The representative drug of NAI, oseltamivir, is only effective when used within 48 hours after the onset of symptoms, and some viral mutations have also shown resistance to it. Therefore, there is an urgent need to seek more drugs for the treatment of IFV [99].

10.4.1 Advances in Inhibitors Research Targeting IFV PA

10.4.1.1 Function in Biology and Disease

The acidic protein (PA) in the RNA polymerase complex of the IFV is a binuclear metalloenzyme that plays an important role in the life cycle of the IFV and is highly conserved in various influenza strains, making it a popular target for developing new anti-influenza drugs [100].

10.4.1.2 Inhibitors Development

Baloxavir marboxil (**79,** Figure 10.22) is the first and currently the only FDA-approved PA inhibitor, used for the treatment of influenza A and B [101]. In addition, Baloxavir acid (BXA, **80**) is an active form of baloxavir, with a butterfly-like structure. One wing contains a polar oxazine pyridine triazine dione that can bind to two divalent cations in the active center of PA, thereby inhibiting the activity of PA and exerting antiviral effects. The other wing is the lipophilic difluoro dihydro dibenzothioheptane, which can come into contact with specific residues in the active center pocket through van der Waals forces. In 2016, Jones reported that the polycyclic inhibitor RO-7 (**81**) is an effective PA inhibitor with EC_{50} values of 5–15 nmol/l [102].

In 2020, Zhang et al. used a virtual screening technology to screen inhibitors from natural products that could effectively inhibit PA endonuclease and its mutant I38T [82, 103]. Bilobetin (**82**, Figure 10.22) can form strong interactions with the active pockets of PA_N and PA_N-I38T, and its IC_{50} values for PA_N and PA_N-I38T are 26.62 μmol/l and 38.84 μmol/l, respectively.

Yuan et al. conducted a screening approach that integrated the fluorescence resonance energy transfer-based endonuclease inhibitory assay with the DNA gel-based endonuclease inhibitory assay [104]. A small molecule compound ANA-0 (**83**, Figure 10.22) was identified as a potent inhibitor against the replication of multiple subtypes of influenza A virus, including H1N1, H3N2, H5N1, H7N7, H7N9, and H9N2, in cell cultures. ANA-0 shows potential to be developed as a novel anti-influenza agent.

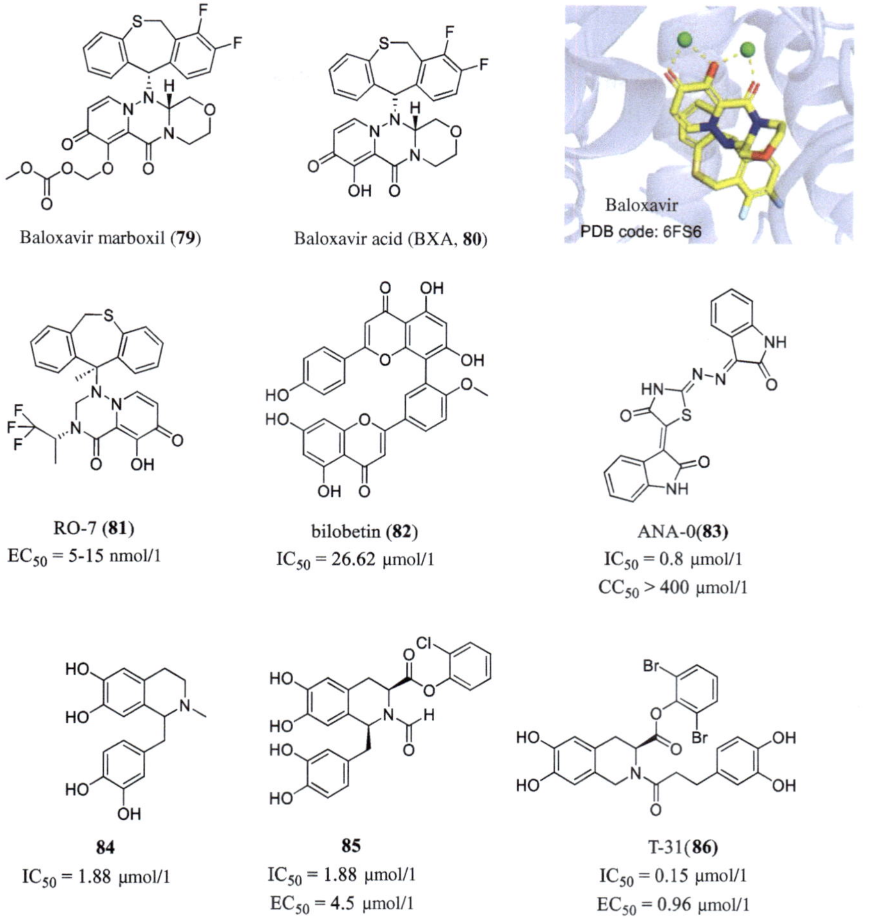

Figure 10.22 Chemical structures of compounds **79–86** and PA inhibitors binding modes of **80** in the active site of H1N1 endonuclease(PDB code: 6FS6).

In 2022, Liu's group found that the 6,7-dihydroxy-1,2,3,4-tetrahydroisoquinoline derivative **84** exhibited good inhibitory activity against PA_N, with an IC_{50} value of 1.88 μmol/l, but at a concentration of 20 μmol/l, **85** did not exhibit cellular level antiviral activity [105]. Therefore, to enhance their antiviral activity, they adopted a fragment growth strategy and conducted a systematic and in-depth SAR study on compound **84**, ultimately obtaining compound **85** (Figure 10.22) with greatly improved antiviral activity, with an EC_{50} value of 4.50 μmol/l. Further mechanistic studies have shown that **85** exerts antiviral effects by inhibiting the activity of PA_N, with an IC_{50} value of 1.88 μmol/l.

In 2024, Ruan et al. designed and synthesized the N, 3-disubstituted 1,2,3,4-tetrahydroisoquinoline derivative T-31 (**86**, Figure 10.22) through multi-site binding and conformational restriction strategies, exhibiting excellent performance as a PA_N endonuclease inhibitor and antiviral drug [106]. **86** exhibits effective and extensive anti-influenza activity *in vitro*, with an IC_{50} value of 0.15 μmol/l for inhibiting PA_N endonuclease activity, the EC_{50} value for anti-IFV is 0.96 μmol/l. Mechanism studies have shown that **86** not only tightly binds to the PA endonuclease of RNA-dependent RNA polymerase, but also blocks virus invasion into host cells and exhibits antiviral activity along with virus replication.

10.4.1.3 Current and Future Prospects

The research prospects for IFV endonuclease inhibitors are extensive. With a deeper understanding of the replication mechanism of the IFV, particularly focusing on strategies to inhibit key enzymes involved in virus RNA synthesis, it is anticipated that new efficient and low-toxicity anti-influenza drugs will be developed in the future. These inhibitors offer novel treatment options for inhibiting influenza by disrupting the virus's replication and transcription processes, especially in light of drug-resistant strains and outbreaks of novel IFVs, and hold significant potential for clinical application. Furthermore, research on inhibitors of IFV endonucleases may also facilitate the development of broad-spectrum antiviral drugs, offering new strategies for preventing and controlling influenza epidemics.

10.5 Current Status of HCMV Prevalence and Treatment

Human cytomegalovirus (HCMV), a prevalent viral infection affecting a substantial proportion of the global population, generally remains asymptomatic in immunocompetent adults [107]. However, congenital and perinatal HCMV infections are associated with profound congenital abnormalities, heightened morbidity, and mortality rates among pediatric populations [108–110]. Moreover, individuals with compromised immune systems including organ transplant recipients and those living with HIV/AIDS face an elevated susceptibility to HCMV infection and subsequent reactivation [111–113]. Currently, the primary therapeutic strategy for managing HCMV infection relies on direct antiviral agents that specifically target the virus's polymerase, such as ganciclovir (GCV, **87**, Figure 10.23) [114], cidofovir (CDV, **88**), and foscarnet (FOS, **89**). However, these drugs are hindered by their associated side effects and the emergence of drug-resistant strains [114–116]. In recent years, novel medications with a focus on HCMV have emerged, including letermovir (LTV, **90**), a terminase inhibitor, and maribavir (MBV, **91**), a kinase inhibitor [117, 118]. These innovative drugs have provided an extensive pharmacological arsenal for combating HCMV infections. Nevertheless, it is important to note that LTV has only been approved for prophylaxis use in stem-cell transplantation settings, while MBV is primarily employed for post-transplantation treatment purposes. Furthermore, both these drugs have demonstrated potential against drug-resistant mutations [119, 120]. Consequently, there exists an urgent necessity to develop new HCMV therapeutics with inventive mechanisms of action.

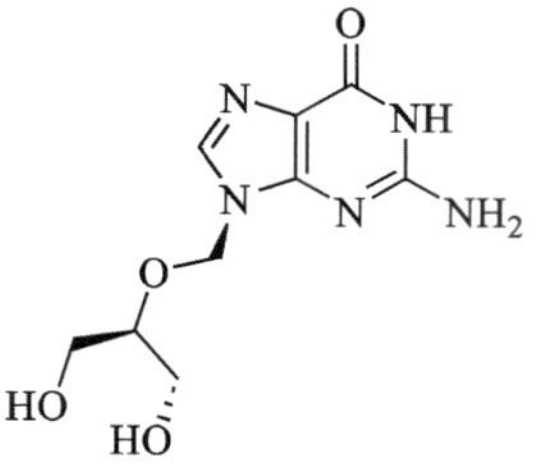

Ganciclovir (**87**)

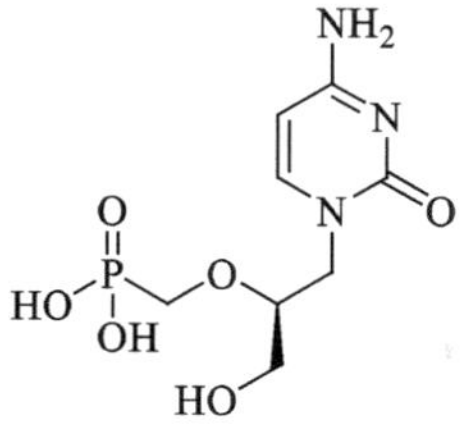

Cidofovir (**88**)

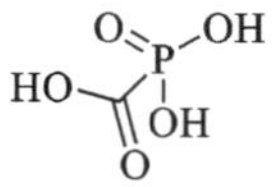

Foscarnet (**89**)

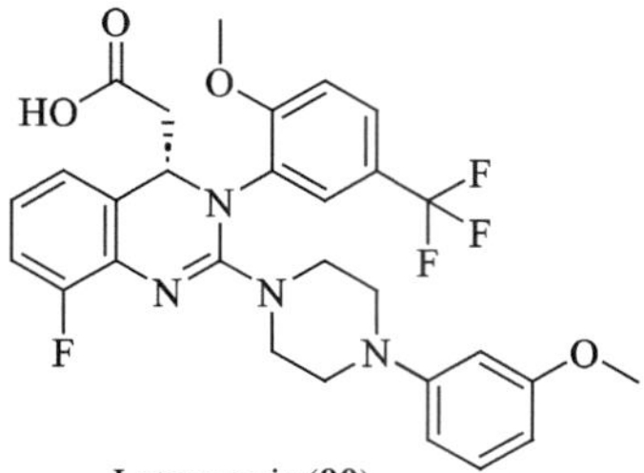

Letermovir (**90**)

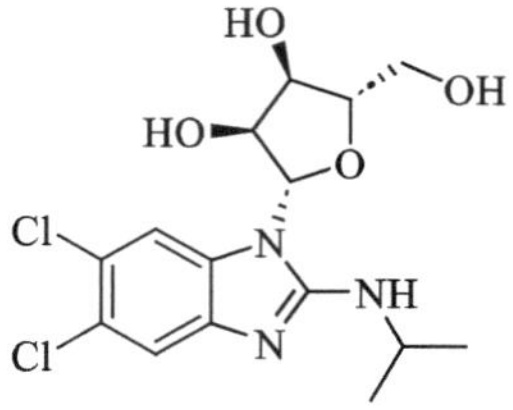

Maribavir (**91**)

Figure 10.23 Existing drugs for the treatment of HCMV.

10.5.1 Advances in Inhibitors Research Targeting HCMV pUL89-C Endonuclease

10.5.1.1 Function in Biology and Disease

Similar to other herpesviruses, HCMV undergoes replication of its genomic DNA into high molecular mass head-to-tail concatemers. These concatemers are subsequently enclosed within preformed capsids and precisely cleaved to release individual genome units inside the capsid. The process of cleavage and packaging is facilitated by a minimal complex comprising specific subunits of HCMV terminase, namely pUL56, pUL89, and pUL51. The past belief was that the pUL56 subunit recognizes a packaging motif present in genomic concatemers [121]. However, recent cryogenic electron microscopy (cryo-EM) imaging of recombinant herpes simplex virus (HSV) terminase complexes suggests that it may have a structural role without directly binding to DNA [122]. The pUL89 subunit possesses ATPase activity essential for providing the energy required for inserting DNA into the capsid and also exhibits endonuclease activity necessary for cutting packaged DNA from remaining chain-like DNA structures [123]. Additionally, the pUL51 subunit contributes to complex formation and localization within the nucleus [124]. Termination complexes are conserved across all herpesviruses, indicating a common mechanism for DNA packaging shared among double-stranded DNA viruses such as herpesviruses, adenoviruses, and certain bacteriophages [125–127]. Notably, resistance mutations against LTV, the first FDA-approved terminase inhibitor have been identified in the non-DNA-binding pUL56 subunit of the terminase complex; thus confirming its significance as an important target for developing new drugs against HCMV infection.

Conversely, reports have also emerged regarding small molecules that target the enzymatic pUL89 subunit; however, no inhibitors with resistance specifically targeting its endonuclease domain (pUL89-C) have been discovered yet [128, 129].

10.5.1.2 Inhibitors Development

Importantly, the HCMV endonuclease domain exhibited a structural similarity to HIV IN /RNase H-like domains with a metal-dependent catalytic mechanism [130]. Furthermore, the HIV-1 IN inhibitor raltegravir containing canonical metal-binding pharmacophores demonstrated limited inhibitory activity against pUL89-C. These findings, combined with the absence of a mammalian cell homologue during DNA processing, strongly support pUL89-C as an attractive target for antiviral intervention. Given that the active site necessitates two metal cofactors for catalysis, exploring metal-binding compounds to inhibit various ribonuclease H-like viral metalloenzymes has been extensively pursued in antiviral drug discovery [67].

Using raltegravir as the lead compound, Bongarzone et al. synthesized a series of α,γ-diketoacid (DKA) derivatives. Among these derivatives, compounds **92** and **93** (Figure 10.24a) could inhibit pUL89 at low micromolar concentrations (IC_{50} = 50 μmol/l and 4.5 μmol/l, respectively). The cocrystal analysis revealed that compound **92** specifically binds to the active site of pUL89-C (PDB code: 6EY7) [131]. Interestingly, in addition to chelating the acidic amino acids Asp463, Glu534, and Asp651 at the active site through the mediation of two Mg^{2+}ions like other α,γ-DKAs do, the 4-fluorophenyl ring of **92** also engages in supplementary interactions with the hydrophobic crevice formed by Asn536 and Met579 (Figure 10.24a).

Considering that the reported HIV RNase H inhibitors chelate two magnesium ions at the active site, repositioning the metal-chelating pharmacophore to chelate two manganese ions at the active site of HCMV pUL89-C is a time-saving and economical drug chemistry strategy [132]. Wang's team performed cell-based screening for anti-HCMV activity and pUL89-C activity of the previously reported HIV RNase H inhibitors, hydroxypyridonecarboxylic Acid (HPCA), 3-hydroxypyrimidine-2,4-dione (HPD), *N*-hydroxythienopyrimidine-2,4-dione (HtPD), and dihydroxypyrimidine (DHP). As a result, they obtained a series of compounds with improved activity, including compound **94** derived from the HPCA [133], compounds **95**, **96**, and **97** derived from the HPD, compounds **98** and **99** derived from the HtPD, and compounds **100**, **101**, and **102** derived from the DHP [134–137].

As a chelating chemotype, hydroxypyridinones possess structurally advantageous features in drug design due to their ability to form stable complexes with various metal ions including iron, aluminum, zinc, and others. Moreover, they exhibited remarkable antibacterial, anticancer, and antidiabetic properties [138]. The FDA-approved targeted HIV-1 INST antiviral drug dolutegravir contains a carboxylic acid-modified 3-hydroxy-4-pyridone MBP, while the IFV PA endonuclease inhibitor baloxavir [139] contains a 2-carboxylate [139, 140]. Additionally, a series of previously reported HPCA analogues were found to inhibit HIV RNase H through the mediation of two magnesium ions [53]. To identify new inhibitors for HCMV and pUL89 endonucleases, a lead compound **100** (IC_{50} = 6.0 μmol/l) was

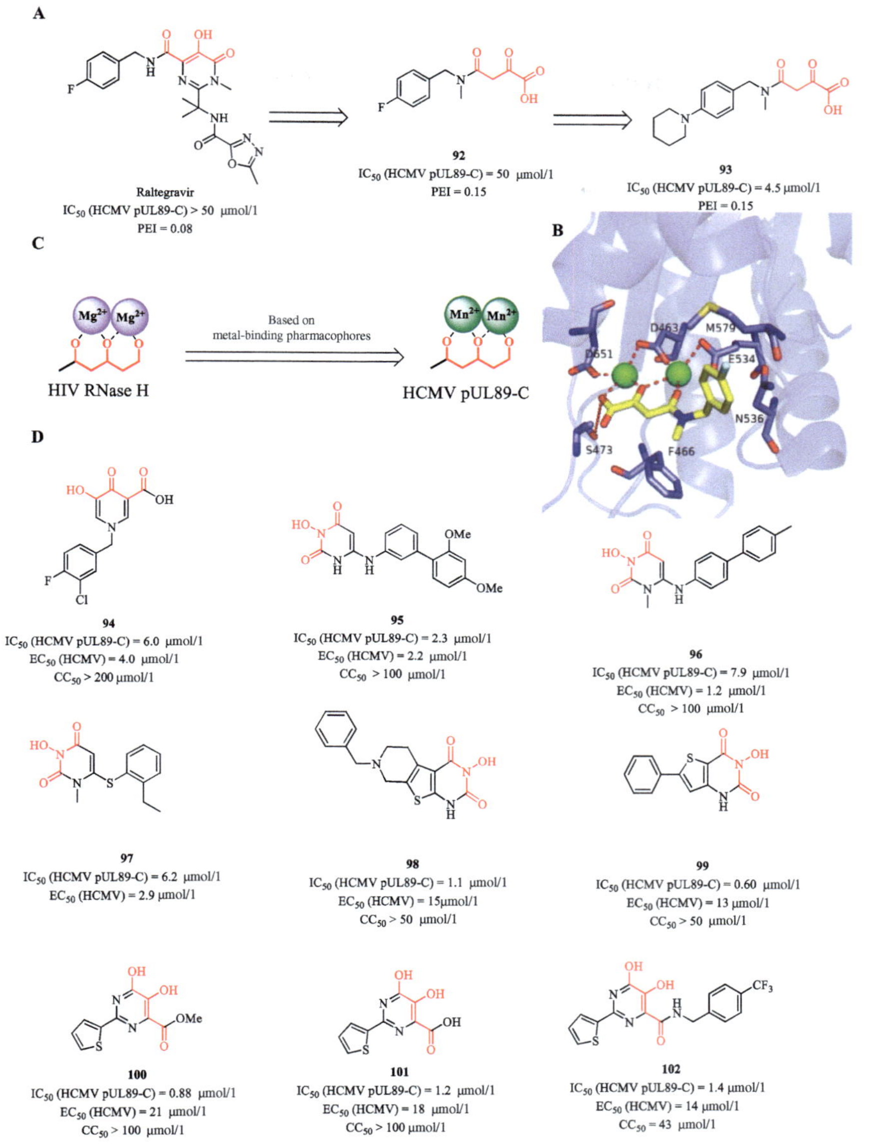

Figure 10.24 Research progress on HCMV pUL89-C inhibitors and the cocrystal binding modes with the enzyme. (a) α,γ-DKA analogues **92** and **93** were identified as inhibitors of pUL89-C, exhibiting a percentage efficiency index (PEI) of 0.15 μmol/l and 0.35 μmol/l, respectively, when calculated based on their concentration/molecular weight inhibition ratio. (b) The X-ray crystal structure of **92** (PDB code: 6EY7) bound to pUL89-C, Mn^{2+} are shown as green spheres. (c) Development of inhibitors for HCMV pUL89-C based on the repositioning of HIV RNase H inhibitors using metal-binding pharmacophores. (d) Inhibitors of HCMV pUL89-C belonging to the HPCA, HPD, HtPD, and DHP.

selected using ligand-based drug design and biochemical analysis methods to detect double-stranded DNA substrate cleavage. Molecular docking results also revealed hydrogen bonding with the active site amino acids Glu534 and Asp651. Sequential addition experiments confirmed that incubation conditions with Mn^{2+} played a crucial role in compound **3**'s inhibition of pUL89-C. Furthermore, cell-based antiviral assays demonstrated that compound **100** could act during late-stage viral replication to inhibit HCMV replication and prevent viral production without exhibiting cytotoxicity (EC_{50} = 4.0 μmol/l, CC_{50} > 200 μmol/l) [133]. Wang's team has also published a series of compounds **95–102** targeting HCMV pUL89-C, using the same medicinal strategy as the one employed in the discovery of compound **94**.

10.5.1.3 Current and Future Prospects

Although the FDA has approved a variety of drugs for the treatment of HCMV, there is still an urgent need to develop new small molecule drugs with new structures and mechanisms of action to effectively treat drug-resistant / refractory HCMV infection. pUL89-C plays an important role in HCMV replication. After analyzing the cocrystal structure of pUL89-C and small molecules, we found that its active site has a unique (aspartic acid-glutamic acid-aspartic acid-aspartic acid) DEDD catalytic motif, which depends on two divalent metal ions. This mechanism also exists in HIV / HBV RNase H and cap endonuclease of IFV. Therefore, this approach is expected to yield small molecule candidates for antiviral research by constructing a compound library containing different metal chelating groups and screening them against such metal enzyme targets. Using this strategy, several pUL89-C inhibitors were successfully discovered, showing good enzyme activity and cell activity. Further research and development mainly focus on further improving the druggability of such small molecules, especially *in vivo* PK properties.

10.6 Conclusions and Prospects

Antiviral drugs are facing increasing challenges in addressing drug resistance, toxic side effects, and clinical applications. To address these challenges, it has become particularly urgent to explore efficient and low-toxicity antiviral drugs with new targets and mechanisms. This article systematically reviews the significant progress of metalloenzymes in antiviral drug research in recent years and deeply analyzes the research progress of metalloenzyme-dependent inhibitors for important viruses such as HIV-1, HCMV, HBV, IFV, and SARS-CoV-2. The pharmacological activity, mechanism of action, and potential for clinical application of these inhibitors were discussed in detail.

Metalloenzymes play a crucial role in key processes such as virus replication, assembly, host cell invasion, and immune escape [30]. The in-depth study of the functional mechanisms of these proteins provides a new perspective and direction for the discovery of antiviral drugs. The challenges faced in designing virus metalloenzyme inhibitors include ensuring high selectivity and specificity, drug stability, bioavailability, ability to penetrate cells and viral membranes, and addressing drug resistance issues caused by high virus variability. In addition, controlling the toxic side effects, and PK properties, and developing multi-target mechanisms of action of drugs are also challenges that must be overcome in research. Effective strategies to address these challenges include structural-based drug design, HTS, fragment growth and multi-site binding strategies, applications of computational chemistry, natural product screening and drug reuse, multi-target drug design and combination therapy strategies, as well as prodrug strategies and in-depth evaluations of PKs and toxicology [74].

Metalloenzyme inhibitors have the following advantages due to their unique mechanism: they have functional groups that chelate metal ions, and the metal ion binding sites they target are extremely critical and highly conserved in the virus lifecycle, providing a solid foundation for the development of broad-spectrum and drug-resistant antiviral drugs. These characteristics and advantages demonstrate the enormous potential and bright prospects of metal ion-dependent protein inhibitors in antiviral drug research.

Glossary

AIDS acquired immunodeficiency syndrome
CHB chronic hepatitis B
cccDNA covalently closed circular DNA
CDV cidofovir
DDE aspartic acid-aspartic acid-glutamic acid
DEDD aspartic acid-aspartic acid-glutamic acid
DHP dihydroxypyrimidine
DKA α,γ-diketoacid
FBDD fragment-based drug design
FDA Food and Drug Administration
FEP free energy perturbation
FOS foscarnet
GCV ganciclovir
HAART highly active antiretroviral therapy
HBsAg hepatitis B surface antigen
HBV hepatitis B virus
HCMV human cytomegalovirus
HIV human immunodeficiency virus
HPCA hydroxypyridonecarboxylic acid
HPD 3-hydroxypyrimidine-2,4-dione
HSV herpes simplex virus
HtPD *N*-hydroxythienopyrimidine-2,4-dione
HTS high-throughput screening
IFV influenza virus
IN integrase
INSTIs integrase chain transfer inhibitors

LTV letermovir
MBP macrocyclic peptide
MBV maribavir
NRTI nucleoside reverse transcriptase inhibitor
NNRTI transcriptase inhibitor
NSP13 non-structural protein 13
PK pharmacokinetic
PI protease inhibitor
PSA polar surface area
PUG punicalagin
RBC ranitidine bismuth citrate
RdRp RNA-dependent RNA polymerase
RNase H ribonuclease H
RT reverse transcriptase
SARS-CoV-2 severe acute respiratory syndrome coronavirus 2
ST strand transfer
WHO World Health Organization
WT wild-type

References

1 Ma, Y., Frutos-Beltrán, E., Kang, D. et al. (2021). Medicinal chemistry strategies for discovering antivirals effective against drug-resistant viruses. *Chemical Society Reviews* 50: 4514–4540.
2 Mody, A., Sohn, A.H., Iwuji, C. et al. (2024). HIV epidemiology, prevention, treatment, and implementation strategies for public health. *Lancet* 403: 471–492.
3 Masenga, S.K., Mweene, B.C., Luwaya, E. et al. (2023). HIV-host cell interactions. *Cells* 12: 1351.
4 Lu, D.Y., Wu, H.Y., Yarla, N.S. et al. (2018). HAART in HIV/AIDS treatments: future trends. *Infectious Disorders Drug Targets* 18: 15–22.
5 Ndlovu, S.S., Ghazi, T., and Chuturgoon, A.A. (2022). The potential of moringa oleifera to ameliorate HAART-induced pathophysiological complications. *Cells* 11: 2981.
6 Bandera, A., Gori, A., Clerici, M., and Sironi, M. (2019). Phylogenies in ART: HIV reservoirs, HIV latency and drug resistance. *Current Opinion in Pharmacology* 48: 24–32.
7 Mccluskey, S.M., Siedner, M.J., and Marconi, V.C. (2019). Management of virologic failure and HIV drug resistance. *Infectious Disease Clinics of North America* 33: 707–742.
8 Passos, D.O., Li, M., Jóźwik, I.K. et al. (2020). Structural basis for strand-transfer inhibitor binding to HIV intasomes. *Science* 367: 810–814.

9 Du, S., Hu, X., Menéndez-Arias, L. et al. (2024). Target-based drug design strategies to overcome resistance to antiviral agents: opportunities and challenges. *Drug Resistance Updates* 73: 101053.

10 Smith, S.J., Zhao, X.Z., Passos, D.O. et al. (2021). Integrase strand transfer inhibitors are effective anti-HIV drugs. *Viruses* 13: 205.

11 Serrao, E., Odde, S., Ramkumar, K., and Neamati, N. (2009). Raltegravir, elvitegravir, and metoogravir: the birth of "me-too" HIV-1 integrase inhibitors. *Retrovirology* 6: 25.

12 Hare, S., Smith, S.J., Métifiot, M. et al. (2011). Structural and functional analyses of the second-generation integrase strand transfer inhibitor dolutegravir (S/GSK1349572). *Molecular Pharmacology* 80: 565–572.

13 Hassounah, S.A., Alikhani, A., Oliveira, M. et al. (2017). Antiviral activity of bictegravir and cabotegravir against integrase inhibitor-resistant SIVmac239 and HIV-1. *Antimicrobial Agents and Chemotherapy* 61: e01695-17.

14 Summa, V., Petrocchi, A., Bonelli, F. et al. (2008). Discovery of Raltegravir, a potent, selective orally bioavailable HIV-integrase inhibitor for the treatment of HIV-AIDS infection. *Journal of Medicinal Chemistry* 51: 5843–5855.

15 Croxtall, J.D., Lyseng-Williamson, K.A., and Perry, C.M. (2008). Raltegravir. *Drugs* 68: 131–138.

16 Souza Cavalcanti, J., Minhoto Lança, A., De Paula, F.J.L. et al. (2012). In-vivo selection of the mutation F121Y in a patient failing raltegravir containing salvage regimen. *Antiviral Research* 95: 9–11.

17 Hare, S., Gupta, S.S., Valkov, E. et al. (2010). Retroviral intasome assembly and inhibition of DNA strand transfer. *Nature* 464: 232–236.

18 Shimura, K. and Kodama, E.N. (2009). Elvitegravir: a new HIV integrase inhibitor. *Antiviral Chemistry and Chemotherapy* 20: 79–85.

19 Ramanathan, S., Mathias, A.A., German, P., and Kearney, B.P. (2011). Clinical pharmacokinetic and pharmacodynamic profile of the HIV integrase inhibitor elvitegravir. *Clinical Pharmacokinetics* 50: 229–244.

20 Shimura, K., Kodama, E., Sakagami, Y. et al. (2008). Broad antiretroviral activity and resistance profile of the novel human immunodeficiency virus integrase inhibitor elvitegravir (JTK-303/GS-9137). *Journal of Virology* 82: 764–774.

21 Kobayashi, M., Yoshinaga, T., Seki, T. et al. (2011). in vitro antiretroviral properties of S/GSK1349572, a next-generation HIV integrase inhibitor. *Antimicrobial Agents and Chemotherapy* 55: 813–821.

22 Cook, N.J., Li, W., Berta, D. et al. (2020). Structural basis of second-generation HIV integrase inhibitor action and viral resistance. *Science* 367: 806–810.

23 Hightower, K.E., Wang, R., Deanda, F. et al. (2011). Dolutegravir (S/GSK1349572) exhibits significantly slower dissociation than raltegravir and elvitegravir from wild-type and integrase inhibitor-resistant HIV-1 integrase-DNA complexes. *Antimicrobial Agents and Chemotherapy* 55: 4552–4559.

24 Llibre, J.M., Pulido, F., García, F. et al. (2015). Genetic barrier to resistance for dolutegravir. *AIDS Reviews* 17: 56–64.

25 Tsiang, M., Jones, G.S., Goldsmith, J. et al. (2016). Antiviral activity of bictegravir (GS-9883), a novel potent HIV-1 integrase strand transfer inhibitor with an improved resistance profile. *Antimicrobial Agents and Chemotherapy* 60: 7086–7097.

26 Hodge, D., Back, D.J., Gibbons, S. et al. (2021). Pharmacokinetics and drug-drug interactions of long-acting intramuscular cabotegravir and rilpivirine. *Clinical Pharmacokinetics* 60: 835–853.

27 Wang, Y.C., Zhang, W.L., Zhang, R.H. et al. (2023). The discovery of indole-2-carboxylic acid derivatives as novel HIV-1 integrase strand transfer inhibitors. *Molecules* 28: 8020.

28 Raheem, I.T., Walji, A.M., Klein, D. et al. (2015). Discovery of 2-pyridinone aminals: a prodrug strategy to advance a second generation of HIV-1 integrase strand transfer inhibitors. *Journal of Medicinal Chemistry* 58: 8154–8165.

29 Sari, O., Roy, V., Métifiot, M. et al. (2015). Synthesis of dihydropyrimidine α,γ-diketobutanoic acid derivatives targeting HIV integrase. *European Journal of Medicinal Chemistry* 104: 127–138.

30 Chen, A.Y., Adamek, R.N., Dick, B.L. et al. (2019). Targeting metalloenzymes for therapeutic intervention. *Chemistry Review* 119: 1323–1455.

31 Zhang, C., Xie, Q., Wan, C.C. et al. (2021). Recent advances in small-molecule HIV-1 integrase inhibitors. *Current Medical Chemistry* 28: 4910–4934.

32 Oliaie, S.S., Safakish, M., Roudsari, R.V. et al. (2023). Design, synthesis, docking studies, and biological evaluation of novel 2-hydroxyacetophenone derivatives as anti-HIV-1 agents. *Current HIV Research* 21: 290–300.

33 Aknin, C., Smith, E.A., Marchand, C. et al. (2019). Discovery of novel integrase inhibitors acting outside the active site through high-throughput screening. *Molecules* 24: 3675.

34 Patel, M., Naidu, B.N., Dicker, I. et al. (2020). Design, synthesis and SAR study of bridged tricyclic pyrimidinone carboxamides as HIV-1 integrase inhibitors. *Bioorganic and Medicinal Chemistry* 28: 115541.

35 Smith, S.J., Zhao, X.Z., Passos, D.O. et al. (2020). HIV-1 integrase inhibitors that are active against drug-resistant integrase mutants. *Antimicrobial Agents and Chemotherapy* 64: e00611-20.

36 Smith, S.J., Zhao, X.Z., Burke, T.R. Jr., and Hughes, S.H. (2018). HIV-1 integrase inhibitors That are broadly effective against drug-resistant mutants. *Antimicrobial Agents and Chemotherapy* 62: e01035-18.

37 Zhao, X.Z., Smith, S.J., Maskell, D.P. et al. (2016). HIV-1 integrase strand transfer inhibitors with reduced susceptibility to drug resistant mutant integrases. *ACS Chemical Biology* 11: 1074–1081.

38 Zhao, X.Z., Smith, S.J., Maskell, D.P. et al. (2017). Structure-guided optimization of HIV integrase strand transfer inhibitors. *Journal of Medicinal Chemistry* 60: 7315–7332.

39 Li, M., Oliveira Passos, D., Shan, Z. et al. (2023). Mechanisms of HIV-1 integrase resistance to dolutegravir and potent inhibition of drug-resistant variants. *Science Advances* 9: eadg5953.

40 Mahajan, P.S., Smith, S.J., Li, M. et al. (2024). *N*-substituted bicyclic carbamoyl pyridones: integrase strand transfer inhibitors that potently inhibit drug-resistant HIV-1 integrase mutants. *ACS Infectious Diseases* 10: 917–927.

41 Johnson, T.W., Tanis, S.P., Butler, S.L. et al. (2011). Design and synthesis of novel *N*-hydroxy-dihydronaphthyridinones as potent and orally bioavailable HIV-1 integrase inhibitors. *Journal of Medicinal Chemistry* 54: 3393–3417.

42 Billamboz, M., Suchaud, V., Bailly, F. et al. (2013). 4-substituted 2-hydroxyisoquinoline-1,3(2H,4H)-diones as a novel class of HIV-1 integrase inhibitors. *ACS Medicinal Chemistry Letters* 4: 606–611.

43 Zhao, X.Z., Smith, S.J., Métifiot, M. et al. (2014). Bicyclic 1-hydroxy-2-oxo-1,2-dihydropyridine-3-carboxamide-containing HIV-1 integrase inhibitors having high antiviral potency against cells harboring raltegravir-resistant integrase mutants. *Journal of Medicinal Chemistry* 57: 1573–1582.

44 Sirous, H., Chemi, G., Gemma, S. et al. (2019). Identification of novel 3-hydroxy-pyran-4-one derivatives as potent HIV-1 integrase inhibitors using in silico structure-based combinatorial library design approach. *Frontiers in Chemistry* 7: 574.

45 Righi, G., Pelagalli, R., Isoni, V. et al. (2018). Synthesis of potential HIV integrase inhibitors inspired by natural polyphenol structures. *Natural Product Research* 32: 1893–1901.

46 Sarafianos, S.G., Marchand, B., Das, K. et al. (2009). Structure and function of HIV-1 reverse transcriptase: molecular mechanisms of polymerization and inhibition. *Journal of Molecular Biology* 385: 693–713.

47 Budihas, S.R., Gorshkova, I., Gaidamakov, S. et al. (2005). Selective inhibition of HIV-1 reverse transcriptase-associated ribonuclease H activity by hydroxylated tropolones. *Nucleic Acids Research* 33: 1249–1256.

48 Himmel, D.M., Maegley, K.A., Pauly, T.A. et al. (2009). Structure of HIV-1 reverse transcriptase with the inhibitor beta-Thujaplicinol bound at the RNase H active site. *Structure* 17: 1625–1635.

49 Parkes, K.E., Ermert, P., Fässler, J. et al. (2003). Use of a pharmacophore model to discover a new class of influenza endonuclease inhibitors. *Journal of Medicinal Chemistry* 46: 1153–1164.

50 Tarrago-Litvak, L., Andreola, M.L., Fournier, M. et al. (2002). Inhibitors of HIV-1 reverse transcriptase and integrase: classical and emerging therapeutical approaches. *Current Pharmaceutical Design* 8: 595–614.

51 Tramontano, E., Esposito, F., Badas, R. et al. (2005). 6-[1-(4-Fluorophenyl) methyl-1H-pyrrol-2-yl]-2, 4-dioxo-5-hexenoic acid ethyl ester a novel diketo acid derivative which selectively inhibits the HIV-1 viral replication in cell culture and the ribonuclease H activity *in vitro*. *Antiviral Research* 65: 117–124.

52 Corona, A., Di Leva, F.S., Thierry, S. et al. (2014). Identification of highly conserved residues involved in inhibition of HIV-1 RNase H function by Diketo acid derivatives. *Antimicrobial Agents and Chemotherapy* 58: 6101–6110.

53 Kankanala, J., Kirby, K.A., Liu, F. et al. (2016). Design, synthesis, and biological evaluations of hydroxypyridonecarboxylic acids as inhibitors of HIV reverse transcriptase associated RNase H. *Journal of Medicinal Chemistry* 59: 5051–5062.

54 Klumpp, K., Hang, J.Q., Rajendran, S. et al. (2003). Two-metal ion mechanism of RNA cleavage by HIV RNase H and mechanism-based design of selective HIV RNase H inhibitors. *Nucleic Acids Research* 31: 6852–6859.

55 Chen, Y.L., Tang, J., Kesler, M.J. et al. (2012). The design, synthesis and biological evaluations of C-6 or C-7 substituted 2-hydroxyisoquinoline-1,3-diones as inhibitors of hepatitis C virus. *Bioorganic and Medicinal Chemistry* 20: 467–479.

56 Vernekar, S.K., Liu, Z., Nagy, E. et al. (2015). Design, synthesis, biochemical, and antiviral evaluations of C6 benzyl and C6 biarylmethyl substituted 2-hydroxylisoquinoline-1,3-diones: dual inhibition against HIV reverse transcriptase-associated RNase H and polymerase with antiviral activities. *Journal of Medicinal Chemistry* 58: 651–664.

57 Tang, J., Vernekar, S.K.V., Chen, Y.L. et al. (2017). Synthesis, biological evaluation and molecular modeling of 2-Hydroxyisoquinoline-1,3-dione analogues as inhibitors of HIV reverse transcriptase associated ribonuclease H and polymerase. *European Journal of Medicinal Chemistry* 133: 85–96.

58 Tang, J., Maddali, K., Dreis, C.D. et al. (2011). *N*-3 hydroxylation of pyrimidine-2,4-diones yields dual inhibitors of HIV reverse transcriptase and integrase. *ACS Medicinal Chemistry Letters* 2: 63–67.

59 Tang, J., Maddali, K., Metifiot, M. et al. (2011). 3-Hydroxypyrimidine-2,4-diones as an inhibitor scaffold of HIV integrase. *Journal of Medicinal Chemistry* 54: 2282–2292.

60 Tang, J., Maddali, K., Dreis, C.D. et al. (2011). 6-Benzoyl-3-hydroxypyrimidine-2,4-diones as dual inhibitors of HIV reverse transcriptase and integrase. *Bioorganic and Medicinal Chemistry Letters* 21: 2400–2402.

61 Hopkins, A.L., Ren, J., Esnouf, R.M. et al. (1996). Complexes of HIV-1 reverse transcriptase with inhibitors of the HEPT series reveal conformational changes relevant to the design of potent non-nucleoside inhibitors. *Journal of Medicinal Chemistry* 39: 1589–1600.

62 Tang, J., Kirby, K.A., Huber, A.D. et al. (2017). 6-Cyclohexylmethyl-3-hydroxypyrimidine-2,4-dione as an inhibitor scaffold of HIV reverase transcriptase: Impacts of the 3-OH on inhibiting RNase H and polymerase. *European Journal of Medicinal Chemistry* 128: 168–179.

63 Tang, J., Liu, F., Nagy, E. et al. (2016). 3-hydroxypyrimidine-2,4-diones as selective active site inhibitors of HIV reverse transcriptase-associated RNase H: design, synthesis, and bochemical evaluations. *Journal of Medicinal Chemistry* 59: 2648–2659.

64 Wang, L., Tang, J., Huber, A.D. et al. (2018). 6-Biphenylmethyl-3-hydroxypyrimidine-2,4-diones potently and selectively inhibited HIV reverse transcriptase-associated RNase H. *European Journal of Medicinal Chemistry* 156: 680–691.

65 Wang, L., Tang, J., Huber, A.D. et al. (2018). 6-Arylthio-3-hydroxypyrimidine-2,4-diones potently inhibited HIV reverse transcriptase-associated RNase H with antiviral activity. *European Journal of Medicinal Chemistry* 156: 652–665.

66 Tang, J., Do, H.T., Huber, A.D. et al. (2019). Pharmacophore-based design of novel 3-hydroxypyrimidine-2,4-dione subtypes as inhibitors of HIV reverse transcriptase-associated RNase H: Tolerance of a nonflexible linker. *European Journal of Medicinal Chemistry* 166: 390–399.

67 Wang, L., Sarafianos, S.G., and Wang, Z. (2020). Cutting into the substrate dominance: pharmacophore and structure-based approaches toward inhibiting human immunodeficiency virus reverse transcriptase-associated ribonuclease H. *Accounts of Chemical Research* 53: 218–230.

68 Vernekar, S.K.V., Tang, J., Wu, B. et al. (2017). double-winged 3-hydroxy-pyrimidine-2,4-diones: potent and selective inhibition against HIV-1 RNase H with significant antiviral activity. *Journal of Medicinal Chemistry* 60: 5045–5056.

69 Beilhartz, G.L., Ngure, M., Johns, B.A. et al. (2014). Inhibition of the ribonuclease H activity of HIV-1 reverse transcriptase by GSK5750 correlates with slow enzyme-inhibitor dissociation. *Journal of Biological Chemistry* 289: 16270–16277.

70 Himmel, D.M., Myshakina, N.S., Ilina, T. et al. (2014). Structure of a dihydroxycoumarin active-site inhibitor in complex with the RNase H domain of HIV-1 reverse transcriptase and structure-activity analysis of inhibitor analogs. *Journal of Molecular Biology* 426: 2617–2631.

71 Messore, A., Corona, A., Madia, V.N. et al. (2021). Quinolinonyl non-diketo acid derivatives as inhibitors of HIV-1 ribonuclease H and polymerase functions of reverse transcriptase. *Journal of Medicinal Chemistry* 64: 8579–8598.

72 Zhang, L., Wei, F., Borrego, D. et al. (2022). Design, synthesis, and biological evaluation of novel double-winged galloyl derivatives as HIV-1 RNase H inhibitors. *European Journal of Medicinal Chemistry* 240: 114563.

73 Ito, Y., Lu, H., Kitajima, M. et al. (2023). Sticklac-derived natural compounds inhibiting RNase H activity of HIV-1 reverse transcriptase. *Journal of Natural Products* 86: 2487–2495.

74 Gao, P., Cheng, X., Sun, L. et al. (2019). Design, synthesis and biological evaluation of 3-hydroxyquinazoline-2,4(1H,3H)-diones as dual inhibitors of HIV-1 reverse transcriptase-associated RNase H and integrase. *Bioorganic and Medicinal Chemistry* 27: 3836–3845.

75 Dusheiko, G., Agarwal, K., and Maini, M.K. (2023). New approaches to chronic hepatitis B. *New England Journal of Medicine* 388: 55–69.

76 Pérez-Pérez, M.-J., Saiz, J.-C., Priego, E.-M., and Martín-Acebes, M.A. (2022). Antivirals against (Re)emerging flaviviruses: should we target the virus or the host? *ACS Medicinal Chemistry Letters* 13: 5–10.

77 Microbiology A D O M; Immunology S L U L C, Saint Louis University School of Medicine, Saint Louis, Mo, USA.; Microbiology A D O M; Immunology S L U L C, Saint Louis University School of Medicine, Saint Louis, Mo, USA.; Microbiology A D O M; Immunology S L U L C, Saint Louis University School of Medicine, Saint Louis, Mo, USA (2019). Shedding light on RNaseH: a promising target for hepatitis B virus (HBV). *Expert Opinion on Therapeutic Targets* 23: 559–563.

78 Wei, F.J., Kang, D.W., Cherukupalli, S. et al. (2020). Discovery and optimizing polycyclic pyridone compounds as anti-HBV agents. *Expert Opinion on Therapeutic Targets* 30: 715–721.

79 Lok, A.S.F., Mcmahon, B.J., Brown, R.S. et al. (2016). Antiviral therapy for chronic hepatitis B viral infection in adults: a systematic review and meta-analysis. *Hepatology* 63: 284–306.

80 Hu Y; Cheng X; Huang A; Tavis J (2013). β-thujaplicinol inhibits hepatitis B virus by blocking the viral ribonuclease H activity. In *compilation of papers from the 16th National Academic Conference on viral hepatitis and liver disease of the chinese medical association.*

81 Lu, G., Lomonosova, E., Cheng, X. et al. (2015). Hydroxylated tropolones inhibit hepatitis B virus replication by blocking viral ribonuclease H activity. *Antimicrobial Agents and Chemotherapy* 59: 1070–1079.

82 Omoto, S., Speranzini, V., Hashimoto, T. et al. (2018). Characterization of influenza virus variants induced by treatment with the endonuclease inhibitor baloxavir marboxil. *Scientific Reports* 8: 9633.

83 Cai, C.W., Lomonosova, E., Moran, E.A., and Cheng, X. (2014). Hepatitis B virus replication is blocked by a 2-hydroxyisoquinoline-1,3(2H,4H)-dione (HID) inhibitor of the viral ribonuclease H activity. *Antiviral Research* 108: 48–55.

84 Edwards, T.C., Lomonosova, E., Patel, J.A. et al. (2017). Inhibition of hepatitis B virus replication by N-hydroxyisoquinolinediones and related polyoxygenated heterocycles. *Antiviral Research* 143: 205–217.

85 Ma Ruize, C.Z. (2023). The latest progress of small molecule anti-SARS-CoV-2 drugs. *Chinese Journal of Pharmacovigilance* 20: 961–966.

86 Newman, J.A., Douangamath, A., Yazdani, S. et al. Structure, mechanism and crystallographic fragment screening of the SARS-CoV-2 NSP13 helicase. *Nature Communications* 11: 4848.

87 White, M.A., Lin, W., and Cheng, X. (2020). Discovery of COVID-19 inhibitors targeting the SARS-CoV-2 Nsp13 helicase. *Journal of Physical Chemistry Letters* 11: 9144–9151.

88 Ruan, Z., Liu, C., Guo, Y., and Yang, T. (2020). SARS-CoV-2 and SARS-CoV: Virtual screening of potential inhibitors targeting RNA-dependent RNA polymerase activity (NSP12). *Journal of Medical Virology* 93: 389–400.

89 Callahan, L., Hall, M.E., Wright, R.D. et al. (2005). Characterization of AMN107, a selective inhibitor of native and mutant Bcr-Abl. *Cancer Cell* 7: 129–141.

90 Ugurel, O.M., Mutlu, O., Sariyer, E. et al. (2020). Evaluation of the potency of FDA-approved drugs on wild type and mutant SARS-CoV-2 helicase (Nsp13). *International Journal of Biological Macromolecules* 163: 1687–1696.

91 Yuan, S., Wang, R., Chan, J. et al. (2020). Metallodrug ranitidine bismuth citrate suppresses SARS-CoV-2 replication and relieves virus-associated pneumonia in Syrian hamsters. *Nature Microbiology* 5: 1439–1448.

92 Jingkun, Z., Florian, W., Bertolin, A.P. et al. (2021). Identifying SARS-CoV-2 antiviral compounds by screening for small molecule inhibitors of nsp13 helicase. *The Biochemical Journal* 478: 2405–2423.

93 Vivek, B., Fakhara, A., Shreelekha, A. et al. (2006). Synthesis, molecular characterization, and biological activity of novel synthetic derivatives of chromen-4-one in human cancer cells. *Journal of Medicinal Chemistry* 49: 3800–3808.

94 Eloise, M., Stefania, M., Jacopo, F. et al. (2014). Delivery of suramin as an antiviral agent through liposomal systems. *ChemMedChem* 9: 933–939.

95 Angela, C., Krzysztof, W., Carmine, T. et al. (2022). Natural compounds inhibit SARS-CoV-2 nsp13 unwinding and ATPase enzyme activities. *ACS Pharmacology & Translational Science* 5: 226–239.

96 Kuzikov, M., Reinshagen, J., Wycisk, K. et al. (2024). Drug repurposing screen to identify inhibitors of the RNA polymerase (nsp12) and helicase (nsp13) from SARS-CoV-2 replication and transcription complex. *Virus Research* 343: 199356–199356.

97 Lian, L., Yun, P., Huiqiao, Y. et al. (2022). Punicalagin as an allosteric NSP13 helicase inhibitor potently suppresses SARS-CoV-2 replication in vitro. *Antiviral Research* 206: 105389–105389.

98 Wang, M., Wu, M., Liu, X. et al. (2022). Pyroptosis Remodeling tumor microenvironment to enhance pancreatic cancer immunotherapy driven by membrane anchoring photosensitizer. *Advanced Science (Weinheim, Baden-Wurttemberg, Germany)* 9: e2202914.

99 Xiaoai, W., Xiuli, W., Qizheng, S. et al. (2017). Progress of small molecular inhibitors in the development of anti-influenza virus agents. *Theranostics* 7: 826–845.

100 Han, J., Jian, Z., Boshi, H. et al. (2017). Inhibitors of influenza virus polymerase acidic (PA) endonuclease: contemporary developments and perspectives. *Journal of Medicinal Chemistry* 60: 3533–3551.

101 Young-A, H. (2018). Baloxavir: first global approval. *Drugs* 78: 693–697.

102 Zhan, P., Pannecouque, C., De Clercq, E., and Liu, X. (2016). Anti-HIV drug discovery and development: current innovations and future trends. *Journal of Medicinal Chemistry* 59: 2849–2878.

103 Jinrui, Z. and Ye, W. (2020). Bilobetin, a novel small molecule inhibitor targeting influenza virus polymerase acidic (PA) endonuclease was screened from plant extracts. *Natural Product Research* 35: 1–4.

104 Shuofeng, Y., Hin, C., Kailash, S. et al. (2016). A novel small-molecule inhibitor of influenza A virus acts by suppressing PA endonuclease activity of the viral polymerase. *Scientific Reports* 6: 22880.

105 Zhihao, L., Shuyin, G., Xiang, Z. et al. (2022). Discovery and optimization of new 6, 7-dihydroxy-1, 2, 3, 4-tetrahydroisoquinoline derivatives as potent influenza virus PAN inhibitors. *European Journal of Medicinal Chemistry* 227: 113929–113929.

106 Ruan, J., Lu, K., He, J. et al. (2024). Optimization and biological evaluation of l-DOPA derivatives as potent influenza PAN endonuclease inhibitors with multi-site binding characteristics. *Bioorganic Chemistry* 144: 107139.

107 Staras, S.A.S., Dollard, S.C., Radford, K.W. et al. (2006). Seroprevalence of cytomegalovirus infection in the United States, 1988–1994. *Clinical Infectious Diseases : An Official Publication of the Infectious Diseases Society of America* 43: 1143–1151.

108 Britt, W.J. (2017). Congenital human cytomegalovirus infection and the enigma of maternal immunity. *Journal of Virology* 91: e02392–16.

109 Lazzarotto, T., Blázquez-Gamero, D., Delforge, M.-L. et al. (2020). Congenital cytomegalovirus infection: a narrative review of the issues in screening and management from a panel of European experts. *Frontiers in Pediatrics* 8: 13.

110 Revello, M.G. and Gerna, G. (2004). Pathogenesis and prenatal diagnosis of human cytomegalovirus infection. *Journal of Clinical Virology : The Official Publication of the Pan American Society For Clinical Virology* 29: 71–83.

111 Gianella, S. and Letendre, S. (2016). Cytomegalovirus and HIV: a dangerous pas de deux. *The Journal of Infectious Diseases* 214 (Suppl 2): S67–S74.

112 Perello, R., Vergara, A., Monclus, E. et al. (2019). Cytomegalovirus infection in HIV-infected patients in the era of combination antiretroviral therapy. *BMC Infectious Diseases* 19: 1030.

113 Limaye, A.P., Babu, T.M., and Boeckh, M. (2020). Progress and challenges in the prevention, diagnosis, and management of cytomegalovirus infection in transplantation. *Clinical Microbiology Reviews* 34: e00043-19.

114 Faulds, D. and Heel, R.C. (1990). Ganciclovir. A review of its antiviral activity, pharmacokinetic properties and therapeutic efficacy in cytomegalovirus infections. *Drugs* 39: 597–638.

115 Hakki, M. (2020). Moving past ganciclovir and foscarnet: advances in CMV therapy. *Current Hematologic Malignancy Reports* 15: 90–102.

116 Zeichner, S.L. (1998). Foscarnet. *Pediatrics in Review* 19: 399–400.

117 Kim, E.S. (2018). Letermovir: first global approval. *Drugs* 78: 147–152.

118 Mullard, A. (2022). FDA approves first drug for common form of dwarfism. *Nature Reviews Drug Discovery* 21: 9.

119 Chou, S. (2017). A third component of the human cytomegalovirus terminase complex is involved in letermovir resistance. *Antiviral Research* 148: 1–4.

120 Chou, S., Song, K., Wu, J. et al. (2022). Drug resistance mutations and associated phenotypes detected in clinical trials of maribavir for treatment of cytomegalovirus infection. *The Journal of Infectious Diseases* 226: 576–584.

121 Bogner, E., Radsak, K., and Stinski, M.F. (1998). The gene product of human cytomegalovirus open reading frame UL56 binds the pac motif and has specific nuclease activity. *Journal of Virology* 72: 2259–2264.

122 Yang, Y., Yang, P., Wang, N. et al. (2020). Architecture of the herpesvirus genome-packaging complex and implications for DNA translocation. *Protein & Cell* 11: 339–351.

123 Scheffczik, H., Savva, C.G.W., Holzenburg, A. et al. (2002). The terminase subunits pUL56 and pUL89 of human cytomegalovirus are DNA-metabolizing proteins with toroidal structure. *Nucleic Acids Research* 30: 1695–1703.

124 Neuber, S., Wagner, K., Goldner, T. et al. (2017). Mutual interplay between the human cytomegalovirus terminase subunits pUL51, pUL56, and pUL89 promotes terminase complex formation. *Journal of Virology* 91: e02384–16.

125 Selvarajan Sigamani, S., Zhao, H., Kamau, Y.N. et al. (2013). The structure of the herpes simplex virus DNA-packaging terminase pUL15 nuclease domain suggests an evolutionary lineage among eukaryotic and prokaryotic viruses. *Journal of Virology* 87: 7140–7148.

126 Sun, S., Gao, S., Kondabagil, K. et al. (2012). Structure and function of the small terminase component of the DNA packaging machine in T4-like bacteriophages. *Proceedings of the National Academy of Sciences of the United States of America* 109: 817–822.

127 Ostapchuk, P., Almond, M., and Hearing, P. (2011). Characterization of empty adenovirus particles assembled in the absence of a functional adenovirus IVa2 protein. *Journal of Virology* 85: 5524–5531.

128 Underwood, M.R., Harvey, R.J., Stanat, S.C. et al. (1998). Inhibition of human cytomegalovirus DNA maturation by a benzimidazole ribonucleoside is mediated through the UL89 gene product. *Journal of Virology* 72: 717–725.

129 Buerger, I., Reefschlaeger, J., Bender, W. et al. (2001). A novel nonnucleoside inhibitor specifically targets cytomegalovirus DNA maturation via the UL89 and UL56 gene products. *Journal of Virology* 75: 9077–9086.

130 Nadal, M., Mas, P.J., Blanco, A.G. et al. (2010). Structure and inhibition of herpesvirus DNA packaging terminase nuclease domain. *Proceedings of the National Academy of Sciences of the United States of America* 107: 16078–16083.

131 Bongarzone, S., Nadal, M., Kaczmarska, Z. et al. (2018). Structure-driven discovery of α,γ-diketoacid inhibitors against UL89 herpesvirus terminase. *ACS Omega* 3: 8497–8505.

132 Jagtap, A.D., Geraghty, R.J., and Wang, Z. (2023). Inhibiting HCMV pUL89-C endonuclease with metal-binding compounds. *Journal of Medicinal Chemistry* 66: 13874–13887.

133 Wang, Y., Mao, L., Kankanala, J. et al. (2017). Inhibition of human cytomegalovirus pUL89 terminase subunit blocks virus replication and genome cleavage. *Journal of Virology* 91: e02152–e02116.

134 Wang, Y., Tang, J., Wang, Z., and Geraghty, R.J. (2018). Metal-chelating 3-hydroxypyrimidine-2,4-diones inhibit human cytomegalovirus pUL89 endonuclease activity and virus replication. *Antiviral Research* 152: 10–17.

135 Wang, L., Edwards, T.C., Sahani, R.L. et al. (2021). Metal binding 6-arylthio-3-hydroxypyrimidine-2,4-diones inhibited human cytomegalovirus by targeting the pUL89 endonuclease of the terminase complex. *European Journal of Medicinal Chemistry* 222: 113640.

136 He, T., Edwards, T.C., Majima, R. et al. (2022). Repurposing N-hydroxy thienopyrimidine-2,4-diones (HtPD) as inhibitors of human cytomegalovirus pUL89 endonuclease: Synthesis and biological characterization. *Bioorganic Chemistry* 129: 106198.

137 He, T., Edwards, T.C., Xie, J. et al. (2022). 4,5-dihydroxypyrimidine methyl carboxylates, carboxylic acids, and carboxamides as inhibitors of human cytomegalovirus pUL89 endonuclease. *Journal of Medicinal Chemistry* 65: 5830–5849.

138 Santos, M.A., Marques, S.M., and Chaves, S. (2012). Hydroxypyridinones as "privileged" chelating structures for the design of medicinal drugs. *Coordination Chemistry Reviews* 256: 240–259.

139 Hayden, F.G., Sugaya, N., Hirotsu, N. et al. (2018). Baloxavir marboxil for uncomplicated influenza in adults and adolescents. *The New England Journal of Medicine* 379: 913–923.

140 Johns, B.A., Kawasuji, T., Weatherhead, J.G. et al. (2013). Carbamoyl pyridone HIV-1 integrase inhibitors 3. A diastereomeric approach to chiral nonracemic tricyclic ring systems and the discovery of dolutegravir (S/GSK1349572) and (S/GSK1265744). *Journal of Medicinal Chemistry* 56: 5901–5916.

11

Drug Discovery Targeting Carbonic Anhydrase

Weina Zhong, Xueying Li, Wenli Zhang, and Wukun Liu

Nanjing University of Chinese Medicine, Jiangsu Collaborative Innovation Center of Chinese Medicinal Resources Industrialization, School of Medicine, 138 Xianlin Rd, Nanjing, 210023, P. R. China

11.1 Introduction

Carbonic anhydrase (CA) is a family of zinc-containing metalloenzymes that are crucial for various physiological processes in the human body. These enzymes are known for their ability to catalyze the reversible hydration of CO_2 to HCO_3^- and H^+, a reaction that is pivotal in maintaining the acid–base balance within the body.

There are several isoforms of CA, with at least 16 distinct genes identified in humans. They are classified into different families and subfamilies based on their structures, functions, and evolutionary relationships. The predominant isoform, CA II, exhibits the highest catalytic efficiency among human CA (HCA) and is primarily localized in erythrocytes. Comparative enzymatic studies have demonstrated that both CA II and CA IX display superior catalytic activity relative to other HCA [1–4]. CA plays a critical role in respiration, where it helps to facilitate the exchange of gases in the lungs by converting CO_2 into HCO_3^- for transport in the blood. It is also involved in the formation of cerebrospinal fluid, the regulation of pH in various tissues, and the process of bone remodeling.

Due to its importance in physiological processes, CA has been extensively studied as a target for therapeutic interventions. Inhibitors of CA are used in the treatment of glaucoma, to reduce intraocular pressure and in altitude sickness to prevent the symptoms associated with rapid ascent to high altitudes. Additionally, CA inhibitors (CAIs) are being investigated for their potential use in treating various cancers, as well as neurological and cardiovascular diseases. Research into CA continues to provide insights into its diverse functions and the potential for developing new drugs that can modulate its activity for therapeutic benefit.

Drug Discovery Targeting Metalloenzymes: Strategies and Applications, First Edition. Edited by Guo-Bo Li.

Table 11.1 CAs encoded by eight gene families and their corresponding organisms.

Family	Organisms
α-CA	Algae, bacteria, plants, protozoa, and vertebrates
β-CA	Algae, archaea, fungi, plants, and protozoa
γ-CA	Algae, bacteria, and plants
δ-CA & ζ-CA	Marine diatoms
η-CA	Protozoa
θ-CA	Algae and plants
ι-CA	Bacteria

11.2 Categories, Structures, Functions, and Roles of CA

11.2.1 Categories of CA

CA is found in a variety of organisms. This class of enzymes is present in almost all organisms investigated so far from the prokaryote and eukaryote domains. They are encoded by at least eight distinct genetic families, with all except ι-CA being metalloenzymes [5–8]. Table 11.1 illustrates these CAs encoded by distinct genetic families and the organisms in which they are present.

11.2.2 Structural Differences of CA

Although CA catalyzes similar reactions and is highly conserved at the base of their active sites, they can be distinguished by differences in the amino acid sequences at the entrance of their active sites. This distinction provides a molecular basis for developing inhibitors targeting different CA.

In CA I, the critical His200 is tightly bound to the active site through hydrogen bonds, stabilizing a structured hydration network [9]. In CA II, the shuttling group His64 mediates proton transfer. While CA II and CA III are structurally similar, there are significant sequence differences between them [10]. The crystal structures of CA VII and CA II are nearly identical, with a root mean square deviation (RMSD) of only 0.4 $Å^2$ [11]. CA XIII shares a highly similar 3D structure with CA II due to their conserved secondary structures. The most notable difference between them is the insertion of Asp126 in CA XIII, which induces a conformational change in the Ser125-Pro129 sequence [12].

CA XIV exists in a monomeric conformation as a transmembrane isoenzyme. Sequence variations in CA XIV result in structural differences compared to CA XII, particularly in the insertion of the Gly151-Glu153 loop segment and the deletion of the Thr233-Pro240 loop region [13].

Both CA IX and CA XII are dimers composed of two CA monomers. However, CA IX dimers are stabilized by disulfide bonds between two cysteine residues, whereas CA XII dimers are maintained through interactions between evolutionarily conserved Gln249. Additionally, the active site of CA XII is located in the extracellular environment, and its C-terminus is connected to the cell membrane, both of which facilitate catalytic reactions [2, 14].

11.2.3 The Structure and the Mechanism of HCA

A key reaction in maintaining pH balance in the human body is the synthesis of HCO_3^- and H^+ from CO_2 and H_2O, a process catalyzed by CA. Numerous studies have reported the catalytic mechanism of CA in this reaction. The 15 HCAs identified in the human body all contain a highly conserved catalytic domain. This domain is characterized by a zinc-binding site formed through the coordinated interaction of imidazole side chains from three histidine residues [15]. Figure 11.1 illustrates the molecular mechanism by which HCA II regulates pH in human physiological processes [16]. The Zn^{2+}-binding OH^- performs a nucleophilic attack on incoming CO_2, leading to the generation of HCO_3^- (Figure 11.1a). Due to the relatively weak binding between OH^- and Zn^{2+}, H_2O readily displaces HCO_3^- and is released into the solvent environment (Figure 11.1b). Finally, a proton transfer event activates the zinc-binding H_2O, converting it to OH^- (Figure 11.1c), generating an inactive enzyme complex. This transformation not only produces the catalytically active form of the enzyme but also regenerates its capability to catalyze CO_2 hydration. This step represents the rate-determining step in the CA catalytic cycle.

HCA II has a conical active site cavity, extending from the surface to the center of the protein. The catalytic Zn^{2+} is coordinated by three evolutionarily conserved histidine residues that form the structural foundation of the active site cavity [17, 18]. Variations in amino acid sequences mainly occur at the edge of this cavity, which is also the part where HCAs differ [2, 19]. HCA II and HCA IX are the most catalytically active among the 15 HCAs. Through structural and dynamic studies, HCA II and HCA IX have emerged as promising therapeutic targets for pharmacological intervention. Although the structures of most HCAs have been identified, the 3D structure of all HCAs is not yet available. Extensive research has demonstrated a high degree of evolutionary conservation in the catalytic domains across all HCAs [12, 20].

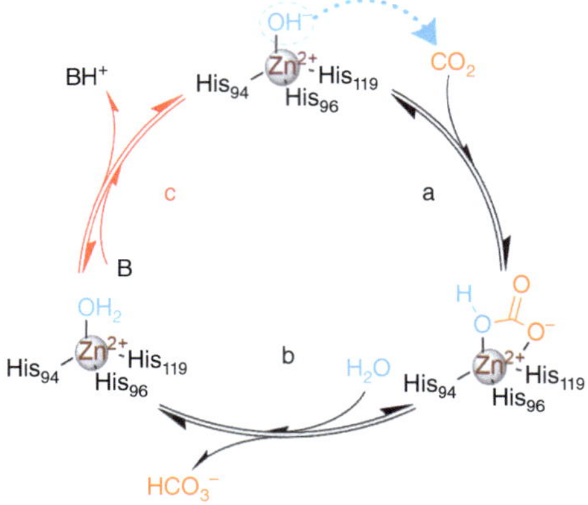

Figure 11.1 Molecular mechanism of pH regulation by HCA II in human physiology. His; Histidine, Zn; Zinc, CO_2; Carbon dioxide, H_2O; Hydrogen dioxide, HCO_3; Bicarbonate, B; Base, BH^+; the conjugate acid of the base, Chemical Equation; $BH^+ = B + H^+$. The Bronsted Lowry acid and base theory states that an acid donates a proton (hydrogen ion, H^+), while a base accepts a proton.

11.2.4 Isozymes of HCA

Research on mammalian CA has revealed the existence of 16 genetically distinct isoenzymes, each exhibiting unique structural characteristics, specific subcellular distributions, and diverse catalytic properties across various tissue types and organ systems [11, 21, 22]. Among these 16 CAs expressed in mammals, the human genome notably lacks CA XV, resulting in the expression of only the 15 functional variants in humans (Table 11.2) [23]. Catalytically active CA shares a conserved active site, typically composed of a Zn^{2+}, three histidine residues, and H_2O/OH^- [24]. However, three CAs (CA VIII, CA X, and CA XI) are classified as CA-related proteins (CARPs) due to their catalytic inactivity in the CO_2 hydration/dehydration reaction, which is attributed to the absence of one or more residues in the zinc-coordinating histidine cluster [11]. Based on their subcellular localization, the 15 catalytically active HCAs are categorized into cytoplasmic HCA, membrane-associated HCA, mitochondrial HCA, and secreted HCA (Table 11.2) [23].

Table 11.2 Subcellular localization and tissue-specific expression patterns of HCA.

HCA	Subcellular localization	Tissue-specific expression patterns
HCA VI	Secreted	Salivary and mammary glands
HCA VA	Mitochondria	Liver
HCA VB	Mitochondria	Heart muscle, skeletal muscle, kidney, pancreas, spinal cord, and gastrointestinal tract
HCA IV	Plasma membrane	Brain, eye, erythrocytes, lung, heart muscle, kidney, pancreas, colon, testis, and osteoclasts
HCA IX	Plasma membrane	Tumors
HCA XII	Plasma membrane	Central nervous system (CNS), eye, kidney, intestine, reproductive epithelia, and tumor cells
HCA XIV	Plasma membrane	Brain, bladder, eye, liver, kidney, skeletal muscle, and spinal cord
HCA I	Cytosol	Eye, gastrointestinal tract, erythrocytes
HCA II	Cytosol	Brain, eye, erythrocytes, gastrointestinal tract, lung, kidney, testis, and osteoclasts
HCA III	Cytosol	Adipocytes and skeletal muscle
HCA VII	Cytosol	Brain, CNS, skeletal muscle liver, and colon
HCA VIII	Cytosol	CNS
HCA X	Cytosol	CNS
HCA XI	Cytosol	CNS
HCA XIII	Cytosol	CNS, eye, kidney, intestine, reproductive epithelia, and tumor cells

11.2.5 Dysregulation of HCA

HCA is an enzyme indispensable for numerous normal physiological activities in the human body, which implies that various types of HCA are distributed throughout different tissues of the body. However, when diseases occur in the human body, the normal signaling pathways are correspondingly altered, and these changes may lead to abnormal expression patterns of pathway-associated HCA under various disease conditions. Under certain special pathological conditions, the normal distribution of HCA in the human body can become imbalanced, such as an increase or decrease in expression levels in specific tissue regions, as shown in Table 11.3. Based on the various characteristics of HCA in the human body, HCAs have gradually become potential diagnostic biomarkers for multiple pathological conditions and systemic diseases [25].

11.3 CA Inhibitors (CAIs)

According to the chemical structure of CAIs, they can be divided into coumarins, phthalocyanines, phenols, selenols, and sulfonamides.

11.3.1 Coumarins

Coumarin derivatives are widely present in nature and have the ability to effortlessly engage with numerous enzymes and receptors within cancer cells through mild non-covalent bonds. As a result, the coumarin scaffold **1** (Figure 11.2) is regarded as a highly favored pharmacophore for creating innovative anticancer medications [26]. In earlier work, Onyilmaz et al. conducted a pioneering investigation into isocoumarins (an isomer of coumarins), as potent CAIs. Their research focused on examining the interactions of a range of isocoumarins **2a–2j** (Figure 11.2) with HCA I, HCA II, HCA IX, and HCA XII [27].

The X-ray crystal structure of the adduct between CA II and the coumarin derivative **3** (Figure 11.2) revealed that it is actually the hydrolysis product of coumarin, specifically a cis-2-hydroxycinnamic acid derivative, that binds to the active site of the enzyme, rather than the original coumarin compound. The binding of the inhibitor effectively seals off the access to the active site of CA without engaging with the Zn^{2+} crucial for catalysis. This unusual binding pattern, in which there is no interaction between the inhibitor molecule and Zn^{2+}, is unprecedented in this enzyme class and presents fresh avenues for future drug development endeavors [28]. For instance, Chandak et al. synthesized four distinct series of sulfonamide–coumarin hybrids **4–7** (Figure 11.2) to enhance the inhibitory efficacy by combining the synergistic effects of the aromatic sulfonamide and coumarin functional groups. Despite the lack of consistency in selectivity ratios observed in the inhibitory results, numerous compounds demonstrated superior performance compared to the reference sulfonamide-based antitumor drug, acetazolamide (AZA).

Table 11.3 HCA-related dysregulation and diseases.

HCAs	Pathological condition	Expression levels
HCA I	Breast cancer, early stage of NSCLC, prostate cancer, and diabetes	Cancer cells and urine: increases
HCA II	Erythrocyte hemolysis and gastrointestinal mesenchymal tumor (GIST)	Blood and GIST cells: increases
HCA III	Liver injury, skeletal muscle injury, acute myocardial infarction (AMI), and polyangiitis (MPA)	MPA: increases
		Liver injury: decreases
		AMI: unchanged
HCA IV	AMI, appendicitis, autoimmune pancreatitis (AIP)	Blood: increases
HCA V	Hyperammonemia, pancreatic cancer	Pancreatic cancer cells: increases
		Hyperammonemia: decreases
HCA VI	Early childhood caries (ECC), dryness disease (SD)	SD: increases
		ECC: decreases
HCA VII	Rectal cancer, colorectal cancer	Rectal cancer and colorectal cancer: increases
HCA VIII	Colorectal and lung cancers	Colorectal and lung cancer cells: increases
HCA IX	Head and neck cancer, breast cancer, lung cancer, NSCLC, pancreatic cancer, renal cell carcinoma (RCC), rectal cancer, colorectal cancer, and ovarian cancer	Cancer cells: increases
HCA X	Diffuse invasive gliomas, acute disseminated encephalomyelitis	Diffused invasive glioma cells: increases
		Acute disseminated encephalomyelitis: decreases
HCA XI	GIST, diffuse invasive gliomas	GIST cells and diffused invasive glioma cells: increases
HCA XII	Brain cancer, esophageal squamous cell carcinoma (ESCC), breast cancer, NSCLC, kidney cancer, cervical cancer, colorectal cancer, and diffused astrocytoma	Cancer cells: increases
HCA XIII	Colorectal tumor, renal acidification	Renal acidification: increases
		Cancer cells: decreases
HCA XIV	Cystoid retinal edema, uric acidification, modulating excitatory synaptic transmission in the brain	Cystoid retinal, proximal tubules and rodent nephron: increases

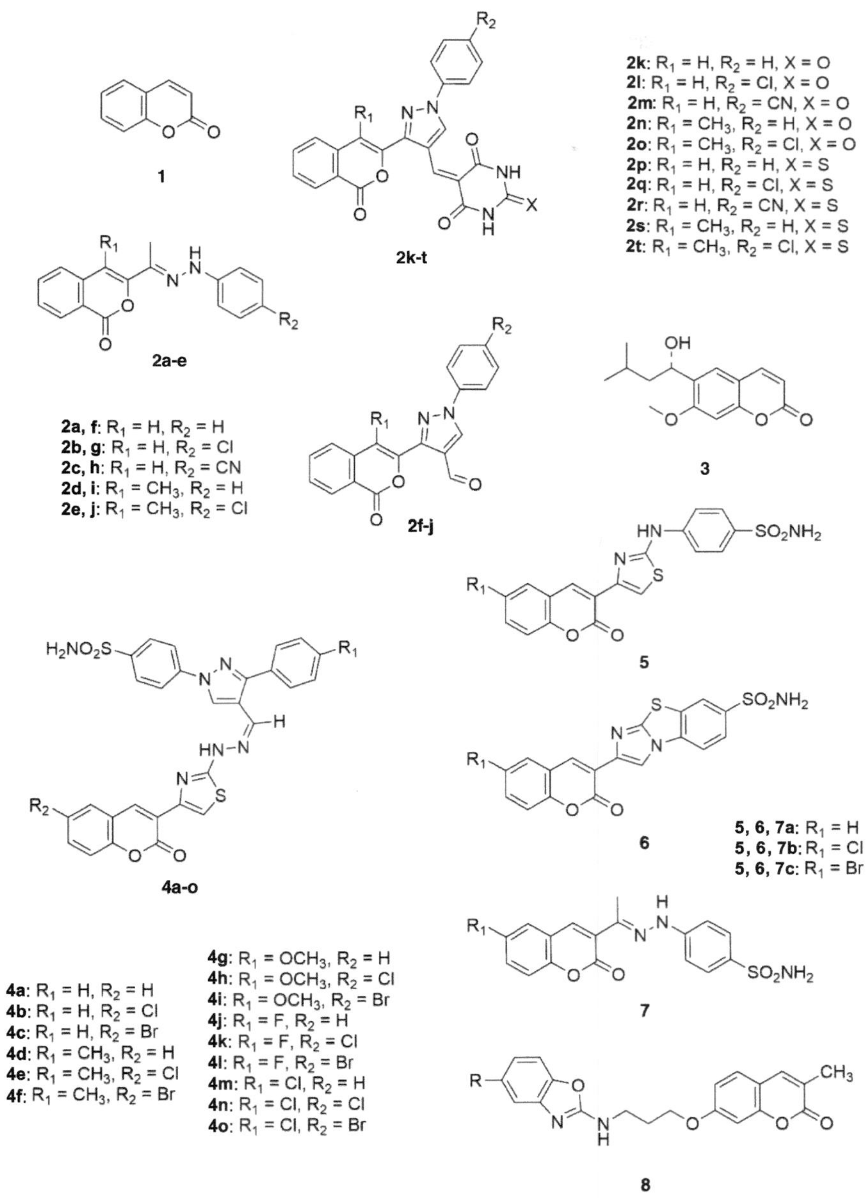

Figure 11.2 Compounds **1–8**, which inhibit CA based on coumarin.

One derivative, **5b** (Figure 11.2) from series **5** with R_1 = Cl, has demonstrated significant promise for advancement as an anticancer therapeutic with reduced adverse effects [29].

Likewise, Fuentes-Aguilar et al. reported the suppressive impact of newly synthesized 2-aminobenzoxazole-coupled coumarins on the inhibitory effects against HCA IX and HCA XII. To this end, they investigated the structural relationships by altering the substituents at the C-3 and C-4 positions of coumarin scaffolds that contain benzoxazole moieties. The results showed that compound **8** (Figure 11.2) had the best activity. In this case, incorporating a chlorine atom situated at the C-3 position in the structure of coumarin is expected to boost the antiproliferative efficacy [30]. Consequently, to develop CA IX inhibitors with heightened inhibitory potency and improved selectivity, researchers have incorporated benzenesulfonamide and coumarin into the design of CA IX inhibitory compounds. The modification strategies for coumarins as CAIs primarily involve the introduction of diverse substituents, expansion of the ring system, and optimization of the substitution patterns. Through these structural modifications, the inhibitory activity and selectivity of coumarins toward specific CA, particularly cancer-related CA IX and CA XII, can be significantly enhanced.

11.3.2 Phthalocyanines

In the first study on phthalocyanine inhibition of CA, Arslan et al. synthesized a new silicon phthalocyanine with axial substitution **9a–c** (Figure 11.3) and its quaternized derivative **10a–c** (Figure 11.3), which demonstrates significant inhibitory effects on HCA I and CA II [31]. Unlike traditional sulfonamide and sulfamate inhibitors, silicon phthalocyanines demonstrate a fundamentally different interaction profile within the CA active site, particularly at the phenol-binding region. This unique interaction suggests that derivatives of silicon phthalocyanine have the potential to be advanced into pharmaceuticals exhibiting more potent CA inhibitory effects [32].

The improvement of water solubility may lead to better inhibitory effects on CA. Guzel et al. reported for the first time on the inhibitory properties of CA and paraoxonase by water-soluble zinc and gallium phthalocyanine complexes **11a–b** (Figure 11.3). The incorporation of sulfonated phenoxy groups into the phthalocyanine structure facilitates excellent water solubility and inhibitory effects on CA I and CA II [33]. This suggests that with enhanced solubility, these phthalocyanine derivatives could potentially be advanced into more effective CAIs for cancer treatment. The favorable aqueous solubility profile of these compounds, surpassing that of traditional synthetic CAIs, provides distinct advantages for achieving optimal inhibitory activity.

11.3.3 Phenols and Selenols

In human daily diets, phenols play a significant role as trace components and are associated with various essential physiological functions. The structural and chemical characteristics of phenolic compounds allow these molecules to act as multifunctional ligands, capable of interacting with multiple targets. CA is a significant target among them, as simple phenolic compounds and polyamines could interact with H_2O/OH^- bond to Zn^{2+}, thereby exerting a suppressive influence [34]. Phenolic and polyphenolic natural products exhibit the potential to serve as potent CAIs. They bind to CA through various mechanisms, including competitive inhibition, hydrogen bonding, and hydrophobic interactions, demonstrating notable inhibitory activity. Notably, gallic acid, caffeic acid, and ferulic acid stand out due to their unique structural characteristics and robust binding capabilities. These natural products, with their low toxicity and wide availability, hold significant potential

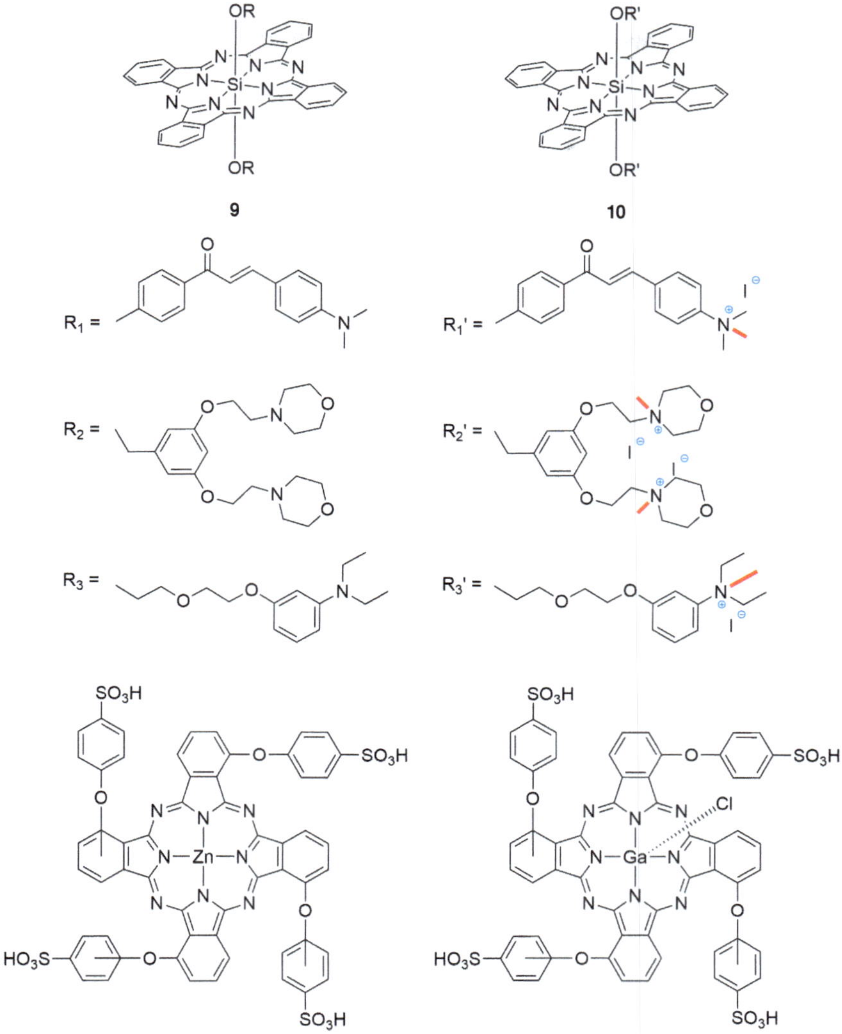

Figure 11.3 Compounds **9–10**, which inhibit CA based on silicon phthalocyanine. Compound **11**, which inhibits CA based on zinc and gallium phthalocyanine.

for drug development and therapeutic applications [34]. The introduction of a free hydroxyl group at the 4′ position coupled with the conjugated double bond within the phenylpropanoid framework, as exemplified by *p*-coumaric acid **12** (Figure 11.4), demonstrates markedly superior inhibitory potency compared to basic phenolic structures. This structural advantage was corroborated in subsequent investigations involving limited monophenolic derivatives, where three natural products **14–16** exhibited enhanced efficacy relative to fundamental phenolic analogs like benzoic acid **13** (Figure 11.4) [35].

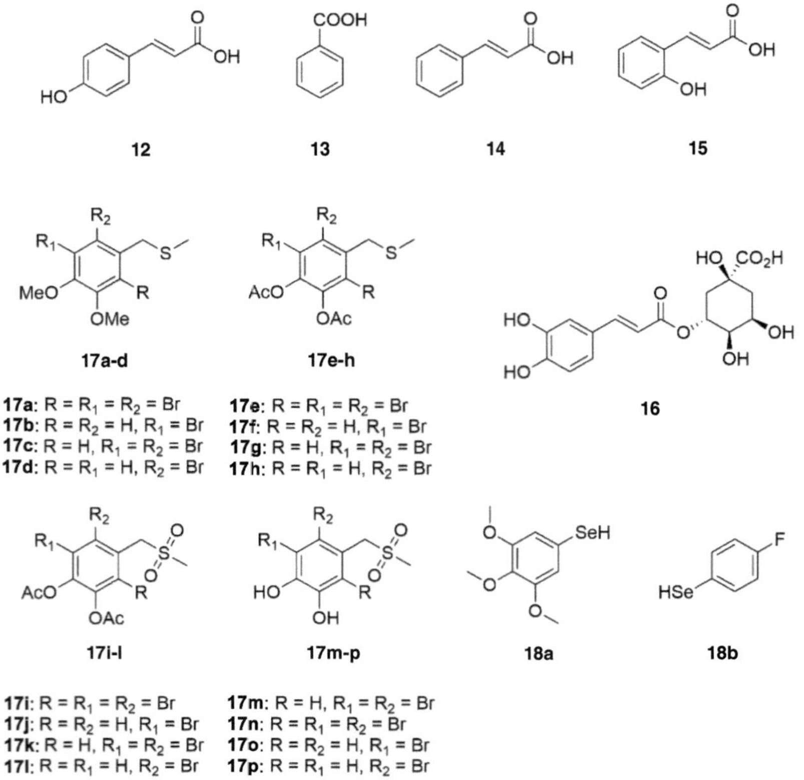

Figure 11.4 Compounds **12–18**, which inhibit CA based on phenol or polyphenol.

Bayrak et al. reported that in their study, the synthesized benzyl(methyl) thioether derivatives of bromophenol **17a–p** (Figure 11.4) exhibited significant HCA I and HCA II inhibitory activity. Among them, compound **17o** (Figure 11.4) has proven to be the most effective CAI, exhibiting exceptionally high inhibitory activity against HCA II, approximately 5.34-fold stronger than AZA [36].

Selenols represent a novel class of CAIs, inhibiting HCA I, HCA II, HVA VII, and HCA IX. Andrea Angeli and colleagues synthesized a series of innovative selenol-based CAIs, among which compound **18a** (Figure 11.4) exhibited significant inhibitory effects against CA I, CA II, and CA VII, while compound **18b** showed better inhibition only against CA VII and CA IX [37].

11.3.4 Sulfonamides

Sulfonamide-based CAIs have emerged as a pivotal class of therapeutic agents, with AZA **19** (Figure 11.5) pioneering clinical use in 1954 [38]. As a pan-inhibitor, **19** exhibits potent nanomolar inhibitory activity against most HCAs, primarily used as a diuretic by enhancing the excretion of bicarbonate, sodium ions, and water through renal CA inhibition, thereby alkalinizing urine pH [38, 39].

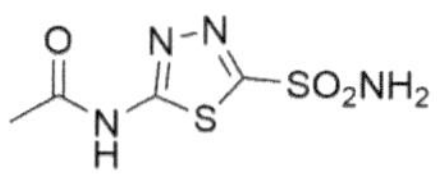

19

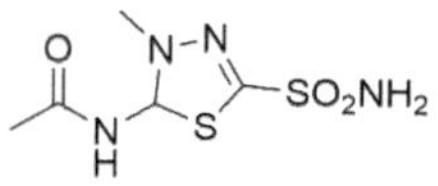

20

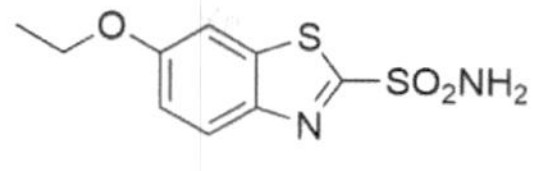

21

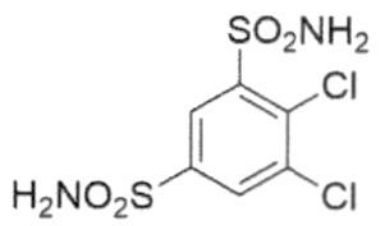

22

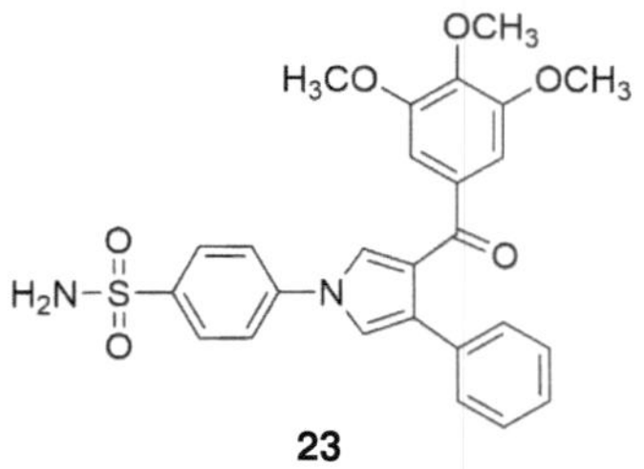

23

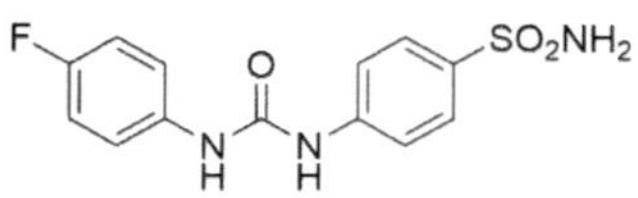

24

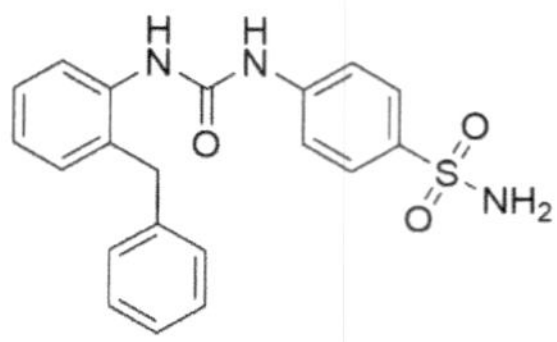

25

Figure 11.5 Compounds **19–25**, which inhibit CA based on sulfonamide.

However, long-term diuretic use is associated with the development of tolerance, although the mechanism remains unclear, leading to a decline in its diuretic application. Methazolamide **20** (Figure 11.5), a lipophilic variant, has shown promise in improving metabolic complications of COVID-19 when combined with tyrosine kinase inhibitors [40] and in treating acute mountain sickness due to its hypoxia-alleviating effects [41, 42]. Ethazolamide **21** (Figure 11.5), though less frequently used as a diuretic [43, 44], has garnered interest as an anti-infective agent against pathogens like *Neisseria gonorrhoeae* [45] and *Helicobacter pylori* [46, 47], and it exhibits synergistic activity with β-lactamase inhibitors against multidrug-resistant *Acinetobacter baumannii* [48]. Dichlorophenamide **22** (Figure 11.5), traditionally an antiglaucoma drug [43, 44], has found efficacy in managing primary periodic paralysis and other neuromuscular genetic disorders [49, 50], albeit with an incompletely understood mechanism.

Recent advancements in sulfonamide CAI research have ventured into dual-targeting strategies. For instance, a novel compound **23** (Figure 11.5), which simultaneously targets both CA and the Wnt/β-catenin signaling pathway, has demonstrated potent activity against multidrug-resistant cancer cells [51], highlighting a new therapeutic direction. Additionally, SLC-0111 **24** (Figure 11.5), a selective CAI for CA IX and CA XII, is undergoing clinical trials for hypoxic, advanced metastatic tumors [52, 53], exhibiting synergistic antitumor effects when combined with various chemotherapy drugs [54–60] and enhancing immunotherapy responses by modulating the tumor microenvironment [61–63].

Moreover, the design of sulfonamide derivatives incorporating hydantoin moieties [64], sugar and iminosugar decorations [65], and phthalimide caps [66] has significantly enhanced selectivity for specific CAs, such as CA I, CA IX, and CA XII. These modifications not only improve the therapeutic index but also broaden the application spectrum of sulfonamide CAIs, including in the treatment of gastric cancer and other malignancies. Compound **25** (Figure 11.5) further exemplifies the precision in targeting specific CA, underscoring the ongoing evolution in sulfonamide CAI design [67].

Collectively, these advancements underscore the versatility and potential of sulfonamide CAIs, which continue to evolve through structural innovations and combination therapies, offering promising new paradigms in the treatment of resistant infections, neuromuscular disorders, and precision oncology.

11.4 CAI Complexes for Tumor-Targeted Therapy

At present, some researchers have developed a variety of antitumor treatments, such as chemotherapy drugs and photodynamic therapy (PDT). However, hypoxia in tumor tissues can influence the stability, permeability, and biological processes of numerous drugs, reduce the effectiveness of oxygen-dependent photodynamic therapy, and greatly limit the effectiveness of metal drugs, photosensitizers. CA is involved in regulating pathophysiological processes such as pH, CO_2, and HCO_3^- transport, and CAIs can improve the hypoxia and acidic microenvironment in solid tumors. Based on this, some researchers have developed several CAIs to augment the treatment efficacy of chemotherapy and photodynamic therapy against hypoxic tumors.

11.4.1 Pt(IV)–CA IX Inhibitors Hybrid Complexes

Hypoxia and acidic microenvironment are the main features of solid tumors, which play crucial roles in enhancing tumor growth, the development of new blood vessels, and the process of metastasis [68–70]. Meanwhile, the stability, permeability, and biological functions of numerous chemotherapeutic drugs can be impacted by hypoxia and acidic conditions, which severely restrict the effectiveness of DNA-targeted drugs, including cisplatin. The metal-like drug cisplatin is a first-line treatment for solid tumors [71, 72]. Therefore, it has far-reaching clinical significance and application value for the development of new platinum drugs to overcome hypoxia and regulate the microenvironment.

CA IX is a transmembrane protein that is overexpressed during tumor development and invasion, and it is promoted by HIF-1α [4, 73]. Inhibition of CA IX can regulate not only the exclusive hypoxia and acidic microenvironment of tumor cells but also interfere with tumor metabolism. Some investigators have developed a tetravalent Pt(IV) inhibitor as an axial ligand, named as CA IX platins (Figure 11.6) [74]. These prodrugs have strong affinity and inhibitory activity, overcoming hypoxia and acidic conditions, while also inhibiting the metabolic pathways in

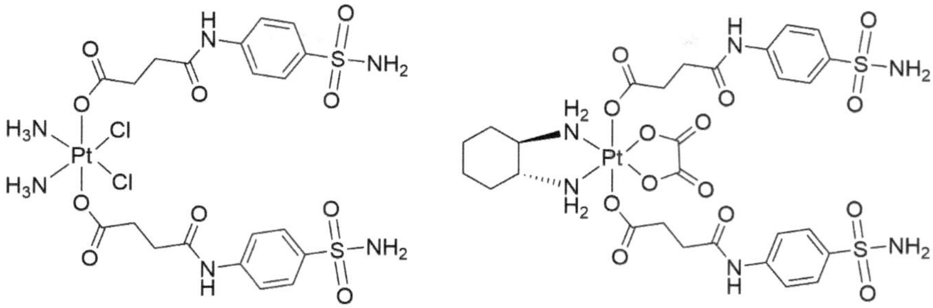

Figure 11.6 Structures of Pt^{IV}–CA IX inhibitor hybrid complexes [72].

hypoxic cancer cells, significantly increasing the therapeutic efficacy against hypoxic MDA-MB-231 tumors. By targeting CA IX, Pt(IV) prodrugs overcome the challenges of poor selectivity, suboptimal efficacy, and severe side effects associated with traditional Pt-based therapies, presenting a viable drug development approach for managing hypoxic and aggressive tumors, particularly triple-negative breast cancer.

11.4.2 CA–Re Complex

An optimal cancer therapy should not only eliminate the primary tumor but also enhance the immunogenicity of the tumor microenvironment to promote effective antitumor immune responses [75]. Recently, PDT has also been shown to produce immune stimulation [76, 77], but the hypoxia and very low immunogenicity of tumor tissue seriously restrict the full activation of adaptive immunity during PDT [78–80]. Consequently, there is a pressing demand to design innovative photosensitizers that maintain high photodynamic efficiency under hypoxia and can effectively enhance tumor immunogenicity in hypoxia.

Some researchers have designed CA–Re, a photosensitizer that is anchored to CA IX and based on Re(I) (Figure 11.7). This compound contains the pyridine ligand of phensulfonamide tail, which is usually combined with the Zn^{2+} active center of CA IX [75]. CA–Re displays outstanding photostability with no pyridine ligand dissociation observed even after irradiation. In addition, CA–Re has the CA IX anchor and intervention capability, facilitating *in situ* generation of membrane-ruptured reactive oxygen species (ROS) while self-reporting the loss of membrane integrity. Remarkably, it shows nanomolar phototoxicity under hypoxic conditions. Additionally, CA–Re can promote Gasdermin D (GSDMD)-mediated pyroptotic cell death and greatly enhance the immunogenicity of tumor cells.

The novel CA IX-anchored Re(I) photosensitizer, CA–Re, stands as the inaugural pyroptosis inducer, based on a metal complex, and is recognized for its ability to efficiently stimulate the antitumor immune response within living organisms, providing critical information for the future development of potent metal-based immunotherapies.

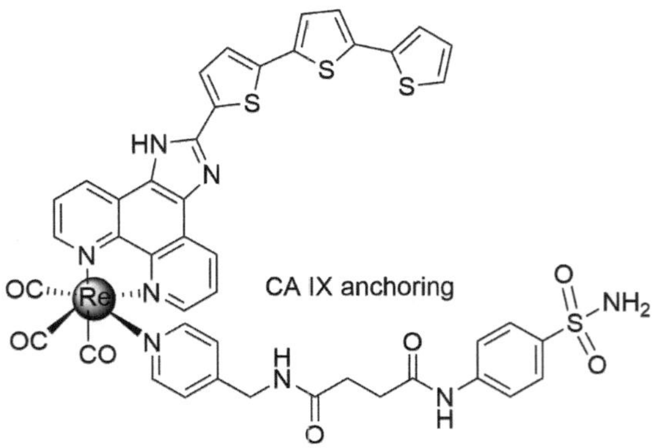

Figure 11.7 Structure of CA-Re [75].

11.4.3 The CAI SA-Tz Combined with Photosensitizer 775NP-Tz

PDT can promote the production of cytotoxic ROS and has shown good results in the treatment of malignant tumors [81–84]. However, the scarcity of antigens or receptors on cancer cells and the hypoxic environment of solid tumors hinder PDT's efficacy [85–88].

In order to overcome the above deficiencies, some researchers proposed a tumor-pretargeted theranostic approach, through the sequential process of *in situ* self-assembly driven by alkaline phosphatase (ALP) and Diels–Alder (IEDDA) reaction, to improve the enrichment of photosensitizer and CAIs in tumor tissues and achieve multimodal imaging guided photodynamic therapy [89]. The tumor-pretargeted theranostic approach first uses ALP to catalyze dephosphorylation and self-assembly of P-FFGd-TCO, which contains trans-cyclooctene (TCO), to synthesize fluorescent and magnetic nanoparticles (FMNPs-TCO) and retain them on the cancer cell membrane, introducing nearly 1 billion "artificial antigens" to each tumor cell. Then, tetrazine-decorated nanophotosensitizer, 775NP-Tz, and small-molecule CAI, Small Antagonist (SA) - Tetrazine (Tz), are captured by IEDDA reaction (Figure 11.8). Through this two-step pre-targeting process, FMNPs-TCO were regrown into particulate FMNPs-775/SA on the tumor cell membrane, thus enabling dual FL (710 and 780 nm) and MRI dual-mode imaging guided by persistently blocking CA activity and ameliorating tumor hypoxia (Figure 11.8).

Through *in situ* self-assembly and biologically orthogonal chemical transformation cascade regulation of a tumor-pretargeted theranostic approach, it effectively overcomes the scarcity of natural antigens or receptors on the surface of tumor cells. At the same time, it improves the photosensitizer and CAIs in the tumor area enrichment. This pre-targeting method can be expanded to increase the buildup of other therapeutic agents within tumors and carry out accurate and efficient treatment of tumors guided by multimodal imaging.

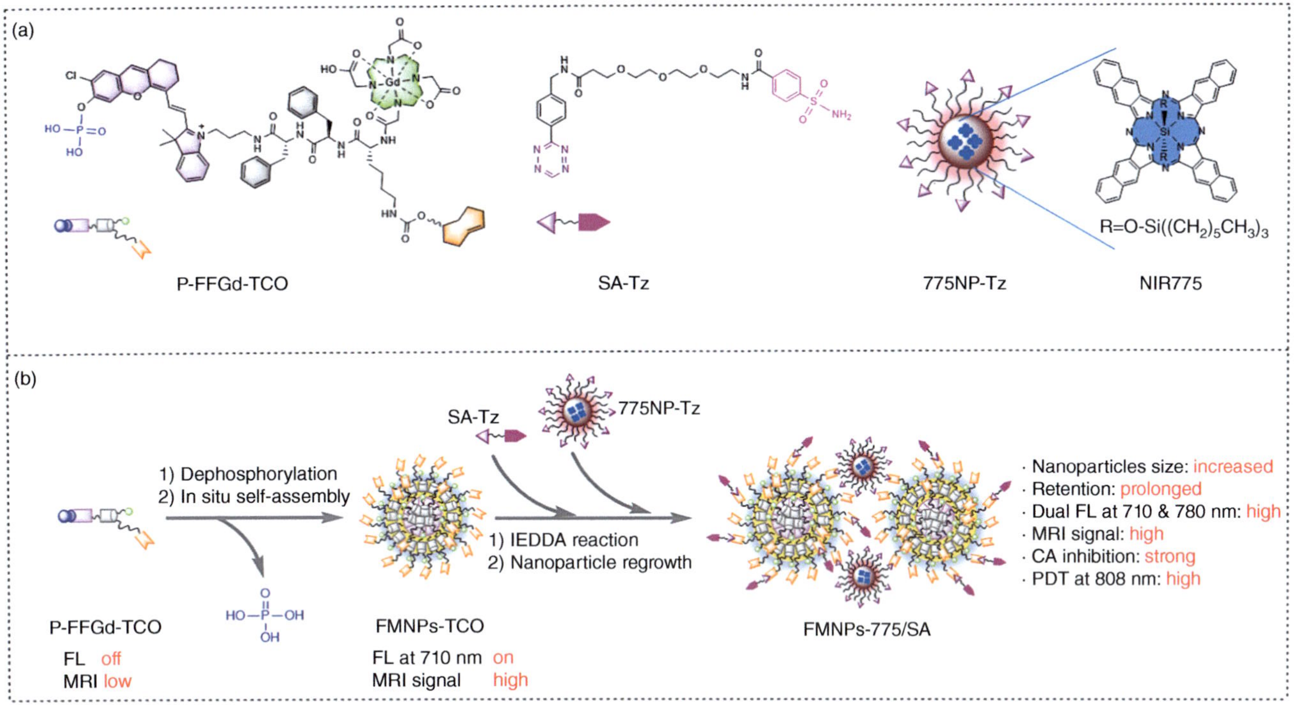

Figure 11.8 (a) The structures and cartoon illustrations. (b) The process for self-assembly *in situ* [89].

11.5 Concluding Remarks and Future Perspectives

CA is a class of zinc-containing metalloenzymes that are extensively involved in various physiological activities of the human body, including respiration, acid–base balance, and bone metabolism. Multiple isoforms of CA exist, which are expressed in different tissues and perform specific biological functions. Currently, there is relatively little research in the field of CA activators (CAAs). CAAs are a class of heterogeneous compounds, but they all possess protonatable molecules capable of participating in proton transfer from the zinc-coordinating H_2O at the active site of CA to the environment, thereby facilitating the rate-determining step in the cycle catalyzed by CA [90, 91]. Although there are no CAAs currently on the market, numerous studies have shown that CAAs exhibit pro-cognitive effects, making them useful in memory therapy and in modulating emotional/social/extinction memories, among other areas [92–96].

CAIs are already used clinically to treat diseases such as glaucoma, certain types of epilepsy, and obesity. Research is exploring the role of CA in cancer development, especially CA IX and CA XII, which are highly expressed on the surface of some tumor cells. The development of new CAIs focuses on improving isoform selectivity to reduce side effects and enhance efficacy. The potential of CAIs for anti-infective purposes is being studied, particularly targeting CA in pathogens. The potential role of CA in neurological diseases is being explored, such as its application in Alzheimer's disease and cerebral ischemia. Pharmacological tools such as activators or inhibitors of CA help to validate the role of these enzymes in diseases. In addition to being a drug target, the levels or activity of CA also serve as disease markers, aiding in diagnosis and monitoring disease progression. Despite progress in certain areas with CAIs, more research is needed to fully understand their complex roles in various diseases and to develop safer and more effective treatment strategies.

References

1 Supuran, C.T., Nocentini, A. et al. (2019). Carbonic anhydrases: biochemistry and pharmacology of an evergreen pharmaceutical target. In: *Academic Press*, 2–539.

2 Alterio, V., Hilvo, M., Di Fiore, A. et al. (2009). Crystal structure of the catalytic domain of the tumor-associated human carbonic anhydrase IX. *Proceedings of the National Academy of Sciences of the United States of America* 106 (38): 16233–16238.

3 Opavský, R., Pastoreková, S., Zelník, V. et al. (1996). HumanMN/CA9Gene, a novel member of the carbonic anhydrase family: structure and exon to protein domain relationships. *Genomics* 33 (3): 480–487.

4 Supuran, C.T. and Winum, J.Y. (2015). Carbonic anhydrase IX inhibitors in cancer therapy: an update. *Future Medicinal Chemistry* 7 (11): 1407–1414.

5 Aspatwar, A., Tolvanen, M.E.E., Barker, H. et al. (2022). Carbonic anhydrases in metazoan model organisms: molecules, mechanisms, and physiology. *Physiological Reviews* 102 (3): 1327–1383.

6 Supuran, C.T. (2023). A simple yet multifaceted 90 years old, evergreen enzyme: carbonic anhydrase, its inhibition and activation. *Bioorganic & Medicinal Chemistry Letters* 93: 129411.

7 Nocentini, A., Supuran, C.T., Capasso, C. et al. (2021). An overview on the recently discovered iota-carbonic anhydrases. *Journal of Enzyme Inhibition and Medicinal Chemistry* 36 (1): 1988–1995.

8 Smith, K.S., Jakubzick, C., Whittam, T.S. et al. (1999). Carbonic anhydrase is an ancient enzyme widespread in prokaryotes. *Proceedings of the National Academy of Sciences of the United States of America* 96 (26): 15184–15189.

9 Srivastava, D.K., Jude, K.M., Banerjee, A.L. et al. (2007). Structural analysis of charge discrimination in the binding of inhibitors to human carbonic anhydrases I and II. *Journal of the American Chemical Society* 129 (17): 5528–5537.

10 Eriksson, A.E. and Liljas, A. (1993). Refined structure of bovine carbonic anhydrase III at 2.0 Å resolution. *Proteins: Structure, Function, and Bioinformatics* 16 (1): 29–42.

11 Hassan, M.I., Shajee, B., Waheed, A. et al. (2013). Structure, function and applications of carbonic anhydrase isozymes. *Bioorganic & Medicinal Chemistry* 21 (6): 1570–1582.

12 Di Fiore, A., Monti, S.M., Hilvo, M. et al. (2009). Crystal structure of human carbonic anhydrase XIII and its complex with the inhibitor acetazolamide. *Proteins-Structure Function and Bioinformatics* 74 (1): 164–175.

13 Whittington, D.A., Grubb, J.H., Waheed, A. et al. (2004). Expression, assay, and structure of the extracellular domain of murine carbonic anhydrase XIV: implications for selective inhibition of membrane-associated isozymes. *The Journal of Biological Chemistry* 279 (8): 7223–7228.

14 Jones, S., Marin, A., Thornton, J.M. et al. (2000). Protein domain interfaces: characterization and comparison with oligomeric protein interfaces. *Protein Engineering, Design and Selection* 13 (2): 77–82.

15 Avvaru, B.S., Kim, C.U., Sippel, K.H. et al. (2010). A short, strong hydrogen bond in the active site of human carbonic anhydrase II. *Biochemistry* 49 (2): 249–251.

16 Aggarwal, M. and McKenna, R. (2012). Update on carbonic anhydrase inhibitors: a patent review (2008–2011). *Expert Opin on Ther Pat* 22 (8): 903–915.

17 Christianson, D.W. and Fierke, C. (1996). Carbonic anhydrase: evolution of the Zinc binding site by nature and by design. *Accounts of Chemical Research* 29: 331–339.

18 Håkansson, K., Carlsson, M., Svensson, L.A. et al. (1992). Structure of native and apo carbonic anhydrase II and structure of some of its anion-ligand complexes. *Journal of Molecular Biology* 227 (4): 1192–1204.

19 Whittington, D.A., Waheed, A., Ulmasov, B. et al. (2001). Crystal structure of the dimeric extracellular domain of human carbonic anhydrase XII, a bitopic membrane protein overexpressed in certain cancer tumor cells. *Proceedings of the National Academy of Sciences of the United States of America* 98 (17): 9545–9550.

20 Mishra, C.B., Tiwari, M., Supuran, C.T. et al. (2020). Progress in the development of human carbonic anhydrase inhibitors and their pharmacological applications: where are we today? *Medicinal Research Reviews* 40 (6): 2485–2565.

21 Esbaugh, A.J. and Tufts, B.L. (2006). The structure and function of carbonic anhydrase isozymes in the respiratory system of vertebrates. *Respiratory Physiology & Neurobiology* 154 (1–2): 185–198.

22 Supuran, C.T. (2008). Carbonic anhydrases – an overview. *Current Pharmaceutical Design* 14 (7): 603–614.

23 Hilvo, M., Tolvanen, M., Clark, A. et al. (2005). Characterization of CA XV, a new GPI-anchored form of carbonic anhydrase. *Biochemical Journal* 392: 83–92.

24 Clare, B.W. and Supuran, C.T. (2006). A perspective on quantitative structure-activity relationships and carbonic anhydrase inhibitors. *Expert Opinion on Drug Metabolism & Toxicology* 2 (1): 113–137.

25 Zamanova, S., Shabana, A.M., Mondal, U.K. et al. (2019). Carbonic anhydrases as disease markers. *Expert Opinion on Therapeutic Patents* 29 (7): 509–533.

26 Song, X.F., Fan, J., Liu, L. et al. (2020). Coumarin derivatives with anticancer activities: an update. *Archiv der Pharmazie* 353 (8): e2000025.

27 Onyılmaz, M., Koca, M., Bonardi, A. et al. (2022). Isocoumarins: a new class of selective carbonic anhydrase IX and XII inhibitors. *Journal of Enzyme Inhibition and Medicinal Chemistry* 37 (1): 743–748.

28 Maresca, A., Temperini, C., Vu, H. et al. (2009). Non-zinc mediated inhibition of carbonic anhydrases: coumarins are a new class of suicide inhibitors. *Journal of the American Chemical Society* 131 (8): 3057–3062.

29 Chandak, N., Ceruso, M., Supuran, C.T. et al. (2016). Novel sulfonamide bearing coumarin scaffolds as selective inhibitors of tumor associated carbonic anhydrase isoforms IX and XII. *Bioorganic & Medicinal Chemistry* 24 (13): 2882–2886.

30 Fuentes-Aguilar, A., Merino-Montiel, P., Montiel-Smith, S. et al. (2022). 2-Aminobenzoxazole-appended coumarins as potent and selective inhibitors of tumour-associated carbonic anhydrases. *Journal of Enzyme Inhibition and Medicinal Chemistry* 37 (1): 168–177.

31 Arslan, T., Bıyıklıoğlu, Z., Senturk, M. et al. (2018). The synthesis of axially disubstituted silicon phthalocyanines, their quaternized derivatives and first inhibitory effect on human cytosolic carbonic anhydrase isozymes hCA I and II. *RSC Advances* 8 (19): 10172–10178.

32 Zhou, X.Q., Xian-Li, M., and Ariffin, N.S. (2024). The potential of carbonic anhydrase enzymes as a novel target for anti-cancer treatment. *European Journal of Pharmacology* 976: 176677.

33 Güzel, E., SÖnmez, F., Erkan, S. et al. (2020). Evaluation of carbonic anhydrase and paraoxonase inhibition activities and molecular docking studies of highly water-soluble sulfonated phthalocyanines. *Turkish Journal of Chemistry* 44 (6): 1565–1573.

34 Karioti, A., Carta, F., Supuran, C.T. et al. (2016). Phenols and polyphenols as carbonic anhydrase inhibitors. *Molecules* 21 (12): 1649.

35 Poulsen, S.A. and Davis, R.A. (2014). Natural products that inhibit carbonic anhydrase. *Sub-cellular Biochemistry* 75: 325–347.

36 Bayrak, C., Taslimi, P., Karaman, H.S. et al. (2019). The first synthesis, carbonic anhydrase inhibition and anticholinergic activities of some bromophenol derivatives with S including natural products. *Bioorganic Chemistry* 85: 128–139.

37 Angeli, A., Tanini, D., Nocentini, A. et al. (2019). Selenols: a new class of carbonic anhydrase inhibitors. *Chemical Communications* 55 (5): 648–651.

38 Maren, T.H. (1967). Carbonic anhydrase: chemistry, physiology, and inhibition. *Physiological Reviews* 47 (4): 595–781.

39 Tsikas, D. (2024). Acetazolamide and human carbonic anhydrases: retrospect, review and discussion of an intimate relationship. *Journal of Enzyme Inhibition and Medicinal Chemistry* 39 (1): 2291336.

40 Li, Z.L., Peng, M., Chen, P. et al. (2022). Imatinib and methazolamide ameliorate COVID-19-induced metabolic complications via elevating ACE2 enzymatic activity and inhibiting viral entry. *Cell Metabolism* 34 (3): 424–440.

41 Lu, H., Zhang, H., Jiang, Y. et al. (2020). Methazolamide in high-altitude illnesses. *European Journal of Pharmaceutical Sciences* 148: 105326.

42 Subudhi, A.W., Evero, O., Reitinger, J. et al. (2021). Combined methazolamide and theophylline improves oxygen saturation but not exercise performance or altitude illness in acute hypobaric hypoxia. *Experimental Physiology* 106 (1): 117–125.

43 Supuran, C.T. (2016). Drug interaction considerations in the therapeutic use of carbonic anhydrase inhibitors. *Expert Opinion on Drug Metabolism & Toxicology* 12 (4): 423–431.

44 Supuran, C.T. (2020). An update on drug interaction considerations in the therapeutic use of carbonic anhydrase inhibitors. *Expert Opinion on Drug Metabolism & Toxicology* 16 (4): 297–307.

45 Abutaleb, N.S., Elhassanny, A.E.M., Nocentini, A. et al. (2022). Repurposing FDA-approved sulphonamide carbonic anhydrase inhibitors for treatment of Neisseria gonorrhoeae. *Journal of Enzyme Inhibition and Medicinal Chemistry* 37 (1): 51–61.

46 Modak, J.K., Tikhomirova, A., Gorrell, R.J. et al. (2019). Anti-activity of ethoxzolamide. *Journal of Enzyme Inhibition and Medicinal Chemistry* 34 (1): 1660–1667.

47 Rahman, M.M., Tikhomirova, A., Modak, J.K. et al. (2020). Antibacterial activity of ethoxzolamide against strains SS1 and 26695. *Gut Pathogens* 12 (1): 20.

48 Colquhoun, J.M., Farokhyfar, M., Anderson, A.C. et al. (2023). Collateral changes in cell physiology associated with ADC-7 β-lactamase expression in acinetobacter baumannii. *Microbiology Spectrum* 11 (3): e0464622.

49 Sansone, V.A., Johnson, N., Hanna, M.G. et al. (2021). Long-term efficacy and safety of dichlorphenamide for treatment of primary periodic paralysis. *Muscle & Nerve* 64 (3): 342–346.

50 Gupta, A., Iyadurai, S., Roggenbuck, J. et al. (2021). Marked reduction in paralytic attacks in a patient with Andersen-Tawil syndrome switched from acetazolamide to dichlorphenamide. *Neuromuscular Disorders* 31 (7): 656–659.

51 Masci, D., Puxeddu, M., Di Magno, L. et al. (2023). 4-(3-Phenyl-4-(3,4,5-trimethoxybenzoyl)-1H-pyrrol-1-yl)benzenesulfonamide, a novel carbonic anhydrase and Wnt/β-catenin signaling pathway dual-targeting inhibitor with potent activity against multidrug resistant cancer cells. *Journal of Medicinal Chemistry* 66 (21): 14824–14842.

52 McDonald, P.C., Chia, S., Bedard, P.L. et al. (2020). A phase 1 study of SLC-0111, a novel inhibitor of carbonic anhydrase IX, in patients with advanced solid tumors. *American Journal of Clinical Oncology-Cancer Clinical Trials* 43 (7): 484–490.

53 Angeli, A., Carta, F., Nocentini, A. et al. (2020). Carbonic anhydrase inhibitors targeting metabolism and tumor microenvironment. *Metabolites* 10 (10): 412.

54 Ruzzolini, J., Laurenzana, A., Andreucci, E. et al. (2020). A potentiated cooperation of carbonic anhydrase IX and histone deacetylase inhibitors against cancer. *Journal of Enzyme Inhibition and Medicinal Chemistry* 35 (1): 391–397.

55 Andreucci, E., Biagioni, A., Peri, S. et al. (2023). The CAIX inhibitor SLC-0111 exerts anti-cancer activity on gastric cancer cell lines and resensitizes resistant cells to 5-Fluorouracil, taxane-derived, and platinum-based drugs. *Cancer Letters* 571: 216338.

56 Rotermund, A., Brandt, S., Staege, M.S. et al. (2023). Differential CMS-related expression of cell surface carbonic anhydrases IX and XII in colorectal cancer models-implications for therapy. *International Journal of Molecular Sciences* 24 (6): 5787.

57 Eloranta, K., Pihlajoki, M., Liljeström, E. et al. (2023). SLC-0111, an inhibitor of carbonic anhydrase IX, attenuates hepatoblastoma cell viability and migration. *Frontiers in Oncology* 13: 1118268.

58 Sarnella, A., Ferrara, Y., Auletta, L. et al. (2022). Inhibition of carbonic anhydrases IX/XII by SLC-0111 boosts cisplatin effects in hampering head and neck squamous carcinoma cell growth and invasion. *Journal of Experimental & Clinical Cancer Research* 41 (1): 122.

59 Sarnella, A., Ferrara, Y., Albanese, S. et al. (2023). Inhibition of bone marrow-mesenchymal stem cell-induced carbonic anhydrase IX potentiates chemotherapy efficacy in triple-negative breast cancer cells. *Cells* 12 (2): 298.

60 Huo, Z.H., Bilang, R., Supuran, C.T. et al. (2022). Perfusion-based bioreactor culture and isothermal microcalorimetry for preclinical drug testing with the carbonic anhydrase inhibitor SLC-0111 in patient-derived neuroblastoma. *International Journal of Molecular Sciences* 23 (6): 3128.

61 Yin, L., Lu, Y., Cao, C. et al. (2021). CA9-related acidic microenvironment mediates CD8+ T cell related immunosuppression in pancreatic cancer. *Frontiers in Oncology* 11: 832315.

62 Zheng, C.X., Song, Q., Zhao, H. et al. (2021). A nanoplatform to boost multi-phases of cancer-immunity-cycle for enhancing immunotherapy. *Journal of Controlled Release* 339: 403–415.

63 Chen, X., Ding, J.C., Hu, G.S. et al. (2023). Estrogen-induced LncRNA, LINC02568, promotes estrogen receptor-positive breast cancer development and drug resistance through both in trans and in cis mechanisms. *Advanced Science* 10 (25): e2206663.

64 Abdoli, M., De Luca, V., Capasso, C. et al. (2022). Benzenesulfonamides incorporating hydantoin moieties effectively inhibit eukaryoticand human carbonic anhydrases. *International Journal of Molecular Sciences* 23 (22): 14115.

65 Davighi, M.G., Matassini, C., Goti, A. et al. (2023). Mono- and three-tailed sugar and iminosugar decorated benzenesulfonamide carbonic anhydrase inhibitors. *Organic & Biomolecular Chemistry* 21 (21): 4491–4503.

66 Shilkar, D., Mohd Siddique, M.U., Bua, S. et al. (2023). Carbonic anhydrase inhibitory activity of phthalimide-capped benzene sulphonamide derivatives. *Journal of Enzyme Inhibition and Medicinal Chemistry* 38 (1): 2235089.

67 Denner, T.C., Angeli, A., Ferraroni, M. et al. (2023). Ureidobenzenesulfonamides as selective carbonic anhydrase I, IX, and XII inhibitors. *Molecules* 28 (23): 7782.

68 Gatenby, R.A., Smallbone, K., Maini, P.K. et al. (2007). Cellular adaptations to hypoxia and acidosis during somatic evolution of breast cancer. *British Journal of Cancer* 97 (5): 646–653.

69 Wilson, W.R. and Hay, M.P. (2011). Targeting hypoxia in cancer therapy. *Nature Reviews Cancer* 11 (6): 393–410.

70 Swietach, P., Vaughan-Jones, R.D., and Harris, A.L. (2007). Regulation of tumor pH and the role of carbonic anhydrase 9. *Cancer and Metastasis Reviews* 26 (2): 299–310.

71 Marmion, C.J., Sigel, A., Sigel, H., and Sigel, R.K.O. (2014). interrelations between essential metal ions and human diseases. Vol. 13 of Metal ions in life sciences. *Transition Metal Chemistry* 39 (8): 971–972.

72 Sadler, P.J. et al. (2020). Advances in inorganic chemistry. In: *Academic Press*, vol. 75, 2–496.

73 De Simone, G., Supuran, C.T. et al. (2010). Carbonic anhydrase IX: biochemical and crystallographic characterization of a novel antitumor target. *Biochimica et Biophysica Acta (BBA) – Proteins and Proteomics* 1804 (2): 404–409.

74 Cao, Q., Zhou, D.J., Pan, Z.Y. et al. (2020). CAIXplatins: highly potent platinum(IV) prodrugs selective against carbonic anhydrase IX for the treatment of hypoxic tumors. *Angewandte Chemie International Edition* 59 (42): 18556–18562.

75 Su, X.X., Wang, W.J., Cao, Q. et al. (2022). A carbonic anhydrase IX (CAIX)-anchored rhenium(I) photosensitizer evokes pyroptosis for enhanced anti-tumor immunity. *Angewandte Chemie-International Edition* 61 (8): 105–129.

76 Deng, Z., Wang, N., Liu, Y. et al. (2020). A photocaged, water-oxidizing, and nucleolus-targeted Pt(IV) complex with a distinct anticancer mechanism. *Journal of the American Chemical Society* 142 (17): 7803–7812.

77 Castano, A.P., Mroz, P., and Hamblin, M.R. (2006). Photodynamic therapy and anti-tumour immunity. *Nature Reviews Cancer* 6 (7): 535–545.

78 Chen, Z., Liu, L., Liang, R. et al. (2018). Bioinspired hybrid protein oxygen nanocarrier amplified photodynamic therapy for eliciting anti-tumor immunity and abscopal effect. *ACS Nano* 12 (8): 8633–8645.

79 Garg, A.D., Nowis, D., Golab, J., and Agostinis, P. (2010). Photodynamic therapy: illuminating the road from cell death towards anti-tumour immunity. *Apoptosis* 15 (9): 1050–1071.

80 Xu, J., Xu, L., Wang, C. et al. (2017). Near-infrared-triggered photodynamic therapy with multitasking upconversion nanoparticles in combination with checkpoint blockade for immunotherapy of colorectal cancer. *ACS Nano* 11 (5): 4463–4474.

81 Zhou, Z., Song, J., Nie, L., and Chen, X. (2016). Reactive oxygen species generating systems meeting challenges of photodynamic cancer therapy. *Chemical Society Reviews* 45 (23): 6597–6626.

82 Xie, J., Wang, Y., Choi, W., and Paramesh, J. (2021). Overcoming barriers in photodynamic therapy harnessing nano-formulation strategies. *Chemical Society Reviews* 50 (16): 9152–9201.

83 Li, X., Lovell, J.F., Yoon, J., and Chen, X. (2020). Clinical development and potential of photothermal and photodynamic therapies for cancer. *Nature Reviews Clinical Oncology* 17 (11): 657–674.

84 Ng, K.K. and Zheng, G. (2015). Molecular interactions in organic nanoparticles for phototheranostic applications. *Chemical Reviews* 115 (19): 11012–11042.

85 Valencia-Hernandez, A.M., Ng, W.Y., Ghazanfari, N. et al. (2020). A natural peptide antigen within the plasmodium ribosomal protein RPL6 confers liver T(RM) cell-mediated immunity against malaria in mice. *Cell Host & Microbe* 27 (6): 950–962.

86 Leko, V. and Rosenberg, S.A. (2020). Identifying and targeting human tumor antigens for T Cell-based immunotherapy of solid tumors. *Cancer Cell* 38 (4): 454–472.

87 Bhandari, V., Hoey, C., Liu, L.Y. et al. (2019). Molecular landmarks of tumor hypoxia across cancer types. *Nature Genetics* 51 (2): 308–318.

88 Singleton, D.C., Macann, A., and Wilson, B. (2021). Therapeutic targeting of the hypoxic tumour microenvironment. *Nature Reviews Clinical Oncology* 18 (12): 751–772.

89 Wen, X., Zeng, W., Zhang, J. et al. (2024). Cascade in situ self-assembly and bioorthogonal reaction enable the enrichment of photosensitizers and carbonic anhydrase inhibitors for pretargeted cancer theranostics. *Angewandte Chemie International Edition* 63 (4): e202314039.

90 Supuran, C.T. (2018). Carbonic anhydrase activators. *Future Medicinal Chemistry* 10 (5): 561–573.

91 Fiorentino, F., Carta, F., Rotili, D. et al. (2023). State of the art of carbonic anhydrase activators. *Future Medicinal Chemistry* 15 (22): 2025–2028.

92 Blandina, P., Provensi, G., Passsani, M.B. et al. (2020). Carbonic anhydrase modulation of emotional memory. Implications for the treatment of cognitive disorders. *Journal of Enzyme Inhibition and Medicinal Chemistry* 35 (1): 1206–1214.

93 Provensi, G., Costa, A., Rani, B. et al. (2022). New β-arylchalcogeno amines with procognitive properties targeting Carbonic Anhydrases and Monoamine Oxidases. *European Journal of Medicinal Chemistry* 244: 114828.

94 Schmidt, S.D., Nachtigall, E.G., Marcondes, L.A. et al. (2022). Modulation of carbonic anhydrases activity in the hippocampus or prefrontal cortex differentially affects social recognition memory in rats. *Neuroscience* 497: 184–195.

95 Provensi, G., Nocentini, A., Passani, M.B. et al. (2021). Activation of carbonic anhydrase isoforms involved in modulation of emotional memory and cognitive disorders with histamine agonists, antagonists and derivatives. *Journal of Enzyme Inhibition and Medicinal Chemistry* 36 (1): 719–726.

96 Schmidt, S.D., Costa, A., Rani, B. et al. (2020). The role of carbonic anhydrases in extinction of contextual fear memory. *Proceedings of the National Academy of Sciences of the United States of America* 117 (27): 16000–16008.

12

Targeting Autotaxin for Therapeutic Intervention

Yangyang Chen, Maolin Duan, Jifa Zhang, and Liang Ouyang

Sichuan University, State Key Laboratory of Biotherapy and Cancer Center, Laboratory of Neuro-system and Multimorbidity, West China Hospital, LinYin street, Chengdu 610041, P.R. China

12.1 Introduction

Autotaxin, also known as ATX, identified as one of the ecto-nucleotide pyrophosphatase/phosphodiesterase-2 (ENPP2) family, is distinguished as the sole extracellular enzyme within this group that exhibits lysophospholipase D (lysoPLD) activity [1, 2]. Since its initial isolation in 1992 from A2058 melanoma cells, autotaxin has garnered significant research interest due to its critical biofunction, such as cell survival, distribution, invasion, and neovascularization [3]. Functionally, it is primarily acknowledged for its capacity to participate in the decomposition of extracellular lysophosphatidylcholine (LPC), producing active lysophosphatidic acid (LPA), releasing choline as a byproduct [4]. LPA is a multifunctional phospholipid molecule. It is produced by two major pathways: the hydrolysis of phosphatidic acid by PLA1/2 and the hydrolysis of LPC by ATX, which is the major pathway [5]. Once generated, LPA binds to G protein–coupled lysophosphatidic acid receptor, which are differentially expressed with overlapping and distinct signaling properties, thereby transducing the signal, initiating and/or activating specific cell signaling cascades [6]. The LPA receptor family is categorized into two distinct classes: the endothelial differentiation gene (EDG) family, which includes LPA1-5, and the non-EDG family, comprising LPA6 (P2Y5) and LPA7 (P2Y10) [7–9]. The primary signaling pathways involve calcium mobilization, the Ras-MAPK/ERK pathway, which regulates the proliferation of cells, the PI3K-AKT survival pathway to prevent apoptosis, and the Rho pathway, which participates in cytoskeletal reorganization and cellular deformation [10] (Figure 12.1). Therefore, targeting the ATX pathway cascade is considered a promising strategy for therapeutic intervention in various and serious diseases, including autoimmune diseases [11], cancer [12], fibroproliferative diseases [13], inflammation [14], metabolic syndrome [15], and neurodegeneration, among others. Consequently, academia and industrial communities have worked to develop novel chemical targeting the ATX pathway over the past decades. These endeavors have resulted in the discovery of various ATX

Drug Discovery Targeting Metalloenzymes: Strategies and Applications, First Edition. Edited by Guo-Bo Li.

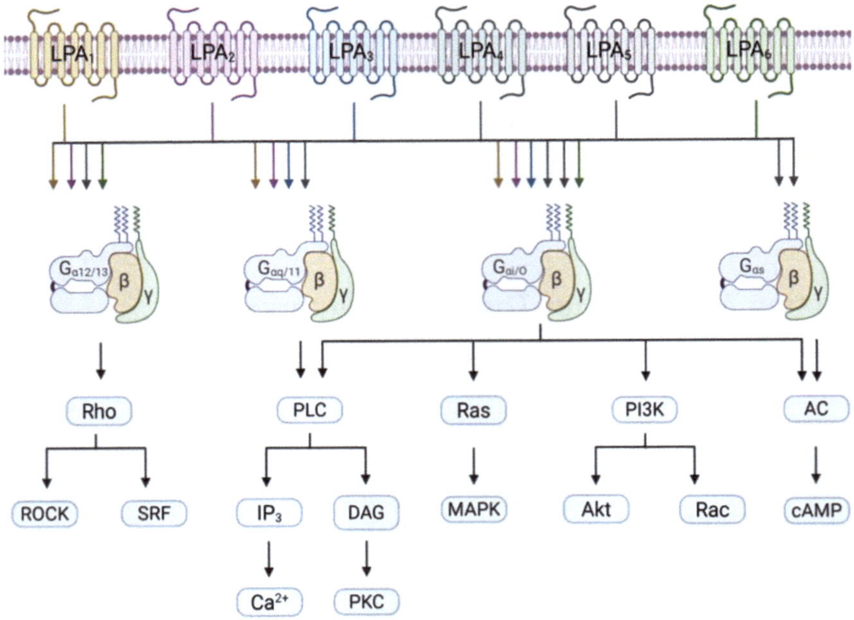

Figure 12.1 Signaling pathways activated by LPA_{1-6}. Rho; Ras homology, ROCK; Rho-associated coiled-coil kinase, SRF; Serum Response Factor, PLC; Phospholipase C, IP3; Inositol Triphosphate, DAG; Diacylglycerol, PKC; Protein Kinase C, RAS; Rat Sarcoma, MAPK; Mitogen-Activated Protein Kinase, PI3K: Phosphatidylinositol 3-kinase, AKT; Protein Kinase B, RAC; ras-related c3 botulinum toxin substrate, AC; Adenylate cyclase, cAMP; Cyclic Adenosine Monophosphate.

inhibitors and a few lysophosphatidic acid receptor (LPAR) antagonists, although these are limited in number.

Moreover, ATX has been identified as the potential biomarkers for a range of human illnesses, including glaucoma [16], calcific aortic valve stenosis [17], pancreatic cancer [18], acute and chronic liver failure [19], Graves' disease [20], and so on. ATX is mainly in the central nervous system and reproductive organs, and the reduction of ATX levels leading to reduced LPA concentration can lead to itching [21]. Recently, multiple studies have demonstrated that inhibition of ATX shows promising therapeutic effects for many diseases, for example, central nervous system disease [22, 23], cardiovascular disease [24], breast cancer [25], oral squamous cell carcinoma [26], and more. It was demonstrated that ATX participates in the development of embryos, potentially serving as the sole pathway for LPA production during the early stages of development [27]. Embryos homozygous for the knockout (KO) mutation in the ATX gene will die in 10 days, with the most common cause of death being vascular and neural tube defects [28]. Based on the above, ATX represents a relatively promising treatment pathway for a broad spectrum of diseases, although further extensive research is necessary to confirm its efficacy and safety.

Medicinal chemists have dedicated significant efforts to discovering new therapeutic agents that target ATX, with several of these compounds advancing to clinical trials. Among these, GLPG1690 exhibited significant efficacy in phase II clinical trials, demonstrating its potential for treating idiopathic pulmonary fibrosis (IPF); however, it was discontinued due to its lower activity, higher dosage, and a higher and dose-dependent increase in the risk of death in patients with IPF who had been on the drug for 6–9 months compared to those who had been on placebo [29]. Based on GLPG1690, HNC664, a new ATX inhibitor modified through pharmacochemical design, has significantly improved ATX inhibitory activity and drug metabolism compared with GLPG1690 and has completed phase I clinical trials. BBT-877 and BLD-0409 are being used in IPF patients in clinical trials. Although the ATX inhibitors showed promising prospects in clinical trials, as of now, there are no Food and Drug Administration (FDA)- or European Medicines Agency (EMA)-approved therapies utilizing ATX inhibitors currently available.

The progress in developing ATX inhibitors has faced several obstacles, such as structural similarities among compounds, suboptimal drug-like properties, and limited selectivity of the inhibitors. Consequently, innovative techniques and strategies are essential to advance the development of novel therapeutics, such as multi-target inhibitors and targeted degraders. Additionally, combining drugs presents a viable approach to amplify anticancer efficacy and mitigate tumor resistance.

This perspective focuses on the medicinal chemistry of compounds targeting ATX. It aims to offer a thorough review of the key strategies employed by the scientific community thus far in the pursuit of developing novel ATX inhibitors. It is hoped that this comprehensive review, including development in previous ATX inhibitors, along with insights into related drug development strategies, will provide valuable guidance and inspire further research in the field of ATX inhibitor discovery.

12.2 Autotaxin

12.2.1 ATX Structure and Functions

Due to its significant therapeutic potential, a lot of studies have been done to elucidate the structure and function of ATX. The ATX gene is expressed across a wide range of species and encodes a 125 kDa protein. The human ATX gene is located on chromosome 8, long arm (8q24.1). In both mice and humans, five distinct isoforms of ATX have been identified and characterized, referring to ATXα, ATXβ, ATXγ, ATXδ, and ATXε [30]. All these ATX isoforms exhibit similar lysoPLD activities and substrate preferences [31, 32]. ATXα, the first discovered subtype, was initially discovered from the human A2058 cell line. This form is found in low concentrations in the nervous system [33]. In addition, ATXα has a unique nonspecific protease cleavage site in comparison to other isoforms [31]. ATXβ, 863 amino acids, is the most extensively studied and important isoform. Unlike ATXα, ATXβ was initially isolated from human teratocarcinoma cell line, and high expression levels are observed in peripheral tissues of both mice and humans. Beyond its plasma lysoPLD activity, ATXβ has the ability to bind to integrins, enhancing cell proliferation and directional movement. These characteristics are associated with the somatomedin B (SMB) domain, which will be explored in detail in subsequent sections [34, 35]. The ATXγ isoform, consisting of 889 amino acid residues, was identified from animal brain and exhibits higher expression in the human neurological system. ATXδ and ATXε were initially derived from ATXβ and ATXα, respectively. Notably, ATXδ is the second most prominent isoform after ATXβ. All ATX isoforms retain catalytic activity.

After characterizing all these ATX isomers, the structures of ATX were identified in both humans and mice by Nishimasu and Hausmann 15 years ago [36]. Three main domains were found (Figure 12.2): The structure includes two SMB domains, referred to as SMB1 and SMB2, a nuclease-like domain (NUC), and a catalytic phosphodiesterase (PDE) domain. The SMB domain is rich in cysteine and participates in integrin binding. Furthermore, research has demonstrated that the SMB domain is essential in catalytic activity and is believed to participate in the later release process. The central PDE domain includes an active site that catalyzes LPC hydrolysis. Further analysis of the active site revealed that a hydrophobic pocket, a hydrophobic channel, and a catalytic site containing two zinc ions form a "T" shape. PDE domain is not only hydrophobic but also hydrophilic, and is also capable of binding steroids and LPA [37, 38]. Although the NUC domain lacks catalytic activity, it participates in the formation of the complete structural PDE domain [39]. Additionally, two linkers, known as the L1 and L2 linkers, were identified. These linkers connect the SMB2 domain to the PDE domain and the PDE domain to the NUC domain, respectively, thereby stabilizing the protein's structure and preserving its active conformation.

As previously noted, ATX has been identified as the enzyme responsible for hydrolyzing phospholipids like LPC, and research has confirmed that ATX exhibits greater efficiency as a phospholipid hydrolase compared to its activity as a nucleotide pyrophosphatase/PDE. However, this is not its only function, as it is also able to hydrolyze other types of phospholipids. ATX also facilitates the

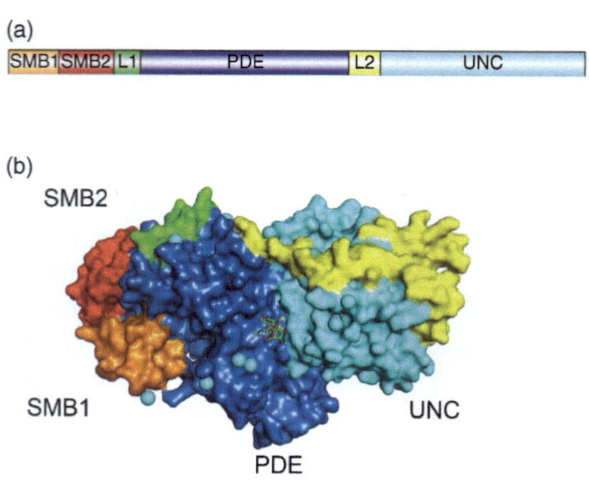

Figure 12.2 The domains and structure of ATX.

conversion of sphingosylphosphorylcholine (SPC) into sphingosine-1-phosphate (S1P), which exhibits signaling properties akin to LPA and mediates a diverse array of signaling effects through other receptor families [40, 41]. However, this pathway is not the main route for the production of S1P [42]. Furthermore, unlike other isoforms, ATX possesses the unique ability to hydrolyze both phospholipid substrates and nucleotides *in vitro*.

12.3 Disease Implications

As mentioned above, the ATX pathway is involved in multiple human pathologies. Nevertheless, the most widely studied diseases are mainly focused on cancer [12] and fibrotic diseases [13], such as IPF, which is the most widely studied disease linked to the –autotaxin–lysophosphatidic acid (ATX–LPA) pathway.

It has been shown that ATX plays a role in stimulating chemotaxis and haptotaxis in melanoma cells, suggesting its involvement in cancer initiation, progression, survival, and metastasis [3]. The experimental outcome also proved that ATX significantly influences movement-related processes, including invasion and metastasis [43]. Moreover, it is evident that ATX has an overexpression in non-small cell lung [44], hepatocellular [45], renal [46], breast [47], thyroid [48], and ovarian cancer tissues. Furthermore, genetic deletion of ENPP2 in hepatocytes resulted in reduced development of hepatocellular carcinoma, further highlighting the significance of the ATX autocrine pathway in hepatocyte metabolism. Other reviews have elegantly discussed the connection between ATX and human cancer in more detail [49, 50], focusing on the role of ATXs and LPAs in the development of cancer and in the ability of tumor cells to invade and metastasize. Consequently, targeting tumor metastasis through the design of ATX inhibitors represents a promising therapeutic strategy.

The ATX–LPA axis also participates in the pathogenesis of numerous fibrotic illnesses, such as those affecting the liver [51], kidney [52], adipose tissue [53], synovial joints [54], retina [55], and lungs [56]. In these human diseases, elevated levels of LPA generated by ATX drive various pathological processes linked to pulmonary fibrosis. The processes are marked by excessive production of an extracellular matrix, irreversible lung disability, loss of tissue structure, and the degradation of lung function. The overexpression of ATX has been observed in patients with IPF [57]. Studies have confirmed the critical role of ATX in fibrotic pathology, as evidenced by the resistance of mice with macrophage-specific ATX deficiency to bleomycin-induced pulmonary fibrosis. Consistent with the above, genetic deletion of the LPA1 receptor did not lead to the development of disease in the mouse model, while the use of an LPA1 receptor antagonist significantly improved pathological hallmarks and indices [58, 59]. It has been reported that the ATX–LPA signaling pathway is also involved in the progression of fibrosis in lung allografts. This renders the targeting of this pathway for the treatment of fibroproliferative diseases a very attractive prospect [60]. Finally, from a therapeutic point of view, all ATX inhibitors currently in clinical trials are being developed for the treatment of IPF and have demonstrated promising therapeutic effects. This progress underscores the feasibility and validity of targeting the ATX–LPA pathway, positioning it as a leading focus in drug discovery. The mechanism through which the LPA pathway contributes to fibrotic processes in the lung is complex, but key factors include the increase of lung cells due to enhanced migration and proliferation and increased vascular permeability [13]. It has been found that ATX participates in the development of liver fibrosis [61]. Specifically, positive correlations have been observed between the progression of fibrosis and elevated serum levels of ATX in a mouse fibrosis disease model [62]. Furthermore, elevated concentration of ATX has been identified in patients with some liver diseases stemming from various causes, and this increase is associated with reduced overall survival. In contrast, studies in rats have demonstrated that ATX expression contributes to the intensification of fibrotic signaling pathways [63]. Moreover, the elevated ATX level can also be a reliable predictor of cirrhosis [51]. In addition to the lung and liver, the overexpressed ATX level has also been detected in kidney and skin fibrosis [64, 65].

The ATX–LPA signaling pathway has also made progress in chronic inflammatory diseases. Emerging experimental data increasingly indicate that individuals with multiple sclerosis exhibit higher levels of ATX and LPA in both serum and cerebrospinal fluid. Conversely, the progression of experimental autoimmune encephalomyelitis has been markedly reduced when ATX is pharmacologically inhibited [66, 67]. Similarly, it has also been shown that inhibition or gene deletion of ATX leads to attenuation of arthritis in animal models [68]. Moreover, ATX was found to upregulate the pain-associated proteins via the LPA1 receptor, thus correlating with neuropathic pain [69]. Overall, targeting the ATX pathway provides strong evidence as a therapeutic way due to its role as a modulator of immune response and the capacity to convert monocytes into macrophages [70]. In conclusion, while the involvement of ATX and LPA in some human diseases has been established, the other ATX functions in metabolic processes and disease mechanisms remain insufficiently explored. Additionally, the existing clinical findings on this subject are inconsistent [71].

12.4 ATX Inhibitors Identification Assays

Developing some new methods for evaluating ATX inhibitory potency is crucial for the design of potent compounds targeting ATX. Various assays have been designed to measure ATX activity, which were broadly categorized into two groups based on the type of substrate used: those employing the enzyme's natural LPC and those utilizing synthetic substrates.

As previously noted, ATX hydrolyzes LPC into LPA and choline, both of which can be quantified to assess ATX activity. This measurement can be accomplished through various techniques, such as radiolabeled substrates, liquid chromatography–tandem mass spectrometry (LC–MS/MS), and the choline release method. Among these, the choline release assay is the most widely used. However, care must be exercised when employing this method, as small molecules may interfere with the dye or inhibit key enzymes (e.g. horseradish peroxidase [HRP] or choline oxidase), potentially leading to false-positive results [72].

The use of unnatural substrates is an alternative way of testing for ATX inhibition, including CPF4, thymidine 5′-monophosphate *p*-nitrophenyl ester (pNP-TMP), FS-3, and bis(*p*-nitrophenyl) phosphate (bis-pNPP). Among these synthetic substrates, pNP-TMP and bis-pNPP offer the simplest method for measuring lysoPLD activity. However, using unnatural substrates instead of the natural substrate can pose a problem: there is a chance that ATX will not be specific for phosphatases. Studies have shown that these substrates can be easily broken down by other enzymes, which may compromise the accuracy of the assay. Consequently, it is recommended that these assays be used exclusively in the presence of purified enzymes in order to ensure the rigor of output data [73]. Overall, lysoPLD assays using the natural substrate LPC and the nonnatural substrate bis-pNPP are the two most common methods for measuring ATX activity in the above assays using both natural and nonnatural substrates. Moreover, besides the substrate specificity, the nonnatural substrates have different interactions with ATX than normal LPC substrates. Subsequent molecular modeling studies confirmed this hypothesis [40]. It can be argued that the data produced by the various ATX assays indicate that utilizing a series of assays to evaluate the test compounds in order to confirm their activity is more prudent than solely relying on a single assay.

12.5 Autotaxin Inhibitor Discovery

Based on their binding mechanisms to ATX, autotaxin inhibitors are primarily classified into five categories: type I–V inhibitors. Among these, type I inhibitors interact with the hydrophobic pocket and catalytic site of ATX without occupying its hydrophobic channel. Type II inhibitors exclusively occupy the hydrophobic pocket of ATX, leaving both the hydrophobic channel and catalytic site unbound, thereby preventing LPC from accessing the catalytic site. In contrast, type III inhibitors specifically bind to the hydrophobic channel of ATX, while the hydrophobic pocket and catalytic site remain unoccupied. Type IV inhibitors, also known as metastable inhibitors, function by interacting with both the ATX channel and hydrophobic pocket, thereby effectively inhibiting ATX activity. Recently, a completely different class of steroid derivatives, which interacted with a new catalytic site, has been found as the type V autotaxin inhibitors. This paper mainly analyzed and summarized the structural features, discovery process, and pharmacological properties of these different kinds of ATX inhibitors.

12.5.1 Type I Autotaxin Inhibitors

Several patents from Merck KGA69 and Novartis have revealed a common structural pattern for ATX inhibitors, characterized by a lipophilic chain, a core linker, and a head group (Figure 12.3). PF-8380 **(1)** was found as an ATX inhibitor by Gierse et al. in 2010 (IC_{50} = 2.8 nM) [74]. The benzoxazolinone moiety binds

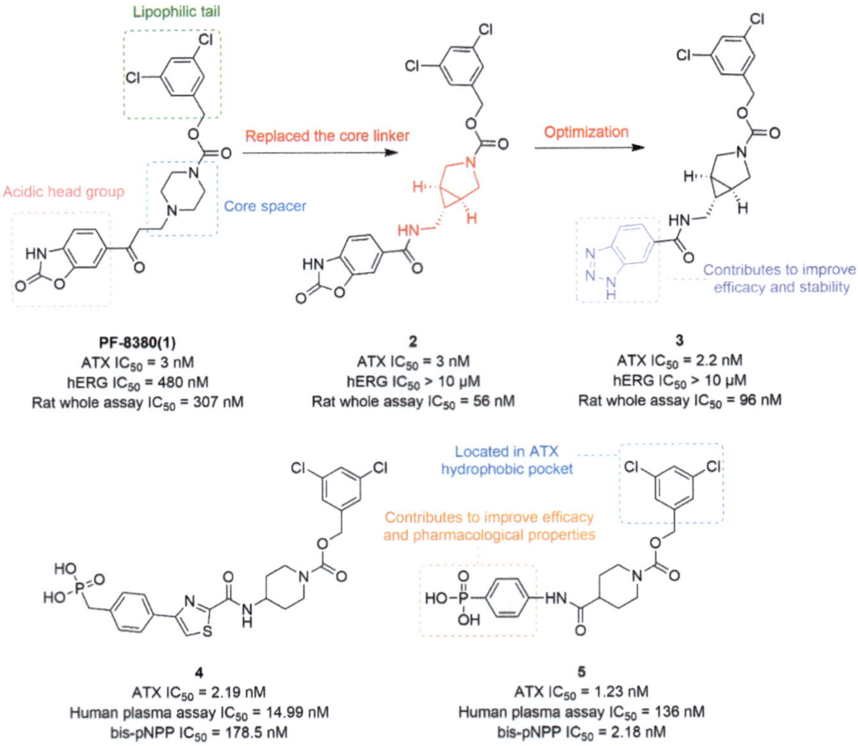

Figure 12.3 Structural modification of compounds **1–3** and chemical structure of compounds **4** and **5**.

to the pocket, binding with zinc. PF-8380 demonstrated inhibition of human ether-a-go-go-related gene (hERG) access with an IC_{50} value of 480 nM but showed poor metabolic stability in human liver microsomes [75]. Besides, PF-8380 also showed good oral bioavailability and exhibited good *in vivo* potency [3]. Compounds **2** and BI-2545 (**3**) were developed by substituting the piperazine nitrogen group with a [3.1.0]-bicyclic group, resulting in IC_{50} values of 3 nM and 2.2 nM, respectively. The structure–activity relationship (SAR) study revealed that the benzotriazole group enhances both activity and stability in rat blood. **2** demonstrated improved compound stability, while compound **3** exhibited higher potency and better metabolic stability *in vivo*. Currently, compound **3** is in preclinical development [76].

In addition, the 4-phenylthiazole portion was also used in the design of ATX inhibitors. Balupuri et al. identified compounds **4** and **5** as ATX inhibitors with a 4-phenylthiazole core. Compounds **4** and **5** demonstrated potent inhibitory activity against human ATX. The methylphosphonic acid group established an electrostatic interaction with the zinc ion, while the 3,5-dichlorophenyl group was positioned within the ATX hydrophobic pocket. However, the higher molecular weight of **4** gives it poor pharmacokinetic properties. In order to improve this property, compound **5** was obtained by modifying the linkage chain. Compared with **4**,

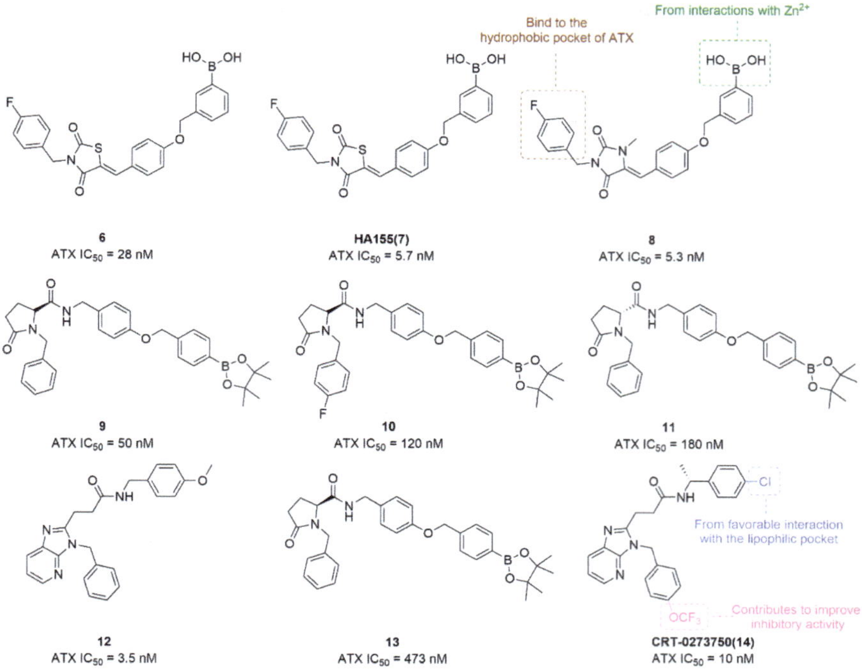

Figure 12.4 Chemical structure of compounds **6–14**.

compound **5** exhibited better inhibitory activity and was more conducive to absorption. **5** also exhibited inhibitory effects on some melanoma cells, and its favorable pharmacokinetic properties highlight its potential for further research and therapeutic applications [77, 78].

Harald and colleagues discovered that certain thiazolidinedione derivatives act as type I ATX inhibitors. Notably, compounds **6** and **HA155 (7)** demonstrated efficacy by significantly lowering plasma LPA levels (Figure 12.4). Additionally, compounds **6** and **7** share a similar binding mode with ATX. The phenyl fraction occupies the same ATX pocket, while the boronic acid group interacts with the zinc ion. The SAR showed that the boronic acid group in the para position contributes to the improvement of ATX inhibitory activity. The best thiazolidinedione derivative **8** exhibited powerful inhibitory activity with an IC_{50} value of 5.3 nM. The flexible structure of compound **8** enables its 4-fluorophenyl group to interact with a distinct region within the same pocket, which suggests that enhancing interactions within the ATX pocket is promising for optimizing future ATX inhibitors [79–81].

Gerokonstantis et al. found some 2-pyrrolidone and pyrrolidine derivatives as ATX inhibitors. Compounds **9–12** were synthesized, yielding IC_{50} values of 50 nM, 120 nM, 180 nM, and 3.5 nM, respectively. Notably, compounds **9** and **11** demonstrated enhanced inhibitory activity in their s-configuration at the stereocenter. Additionally, compound **12** exhibits a binding mode with ATX similar to that of compound **7** [82].

High-throughput screening has led to compound **13** with a novel pyridine-like scaffold. Compound **13** demonstrated promising inhibitory activity (IC_{50} = 473 nM). The SAR study revealed that introducing a chlorine atom at position 4 of the benzene ring enhances inhibitory potency by establishing favorable interactions with the lipophilic pocket of the binding site. However, the substituted groups in positions 2 or 3 of the benzene ring and chain extensions of the *p*-phenylethyl substituent cause some loss of the inhibitory potency. **CRT-0273750 (14)**, featuring a trifluoromethyl ether group, exhibited enhanced inhibitory activity against ATX. The crystal structure of murine ATX (mATX) in complex with **14** revealed that it interacted with ATX by occupying the LPA channel and alkyl chain of ATX, while avoiding exposure to the Zn^{2+}. This unique binding mode provides a significant advantage over other inhibitors (PDB 5LIA). Additionally, **14** effectively regulates LPA levels in human plasma and has demonstrated favorable pharmacokinetic properties in *in vivo* studies, highlighting its therapeutic potential [83].

12.5.2 Type II Autotaxin Inhibitors

Pantsard et al. have identified some type II compounds through virtual screening. Among them, compound **15** inhibited hATX with an IC_{50} value of 134 nM (Figure 12.5). The SAR study indicated that the benzene ring and pyrazole moiety were essential for its activity, and relatively small electron-withdrawing substituents at the meta- and para-positions are essential for its activity [84].

Subsequently, using some methods including quantitative structure activity relationship (QSAR) analysis, virtual screening, high-throughput and *in silico* searching,

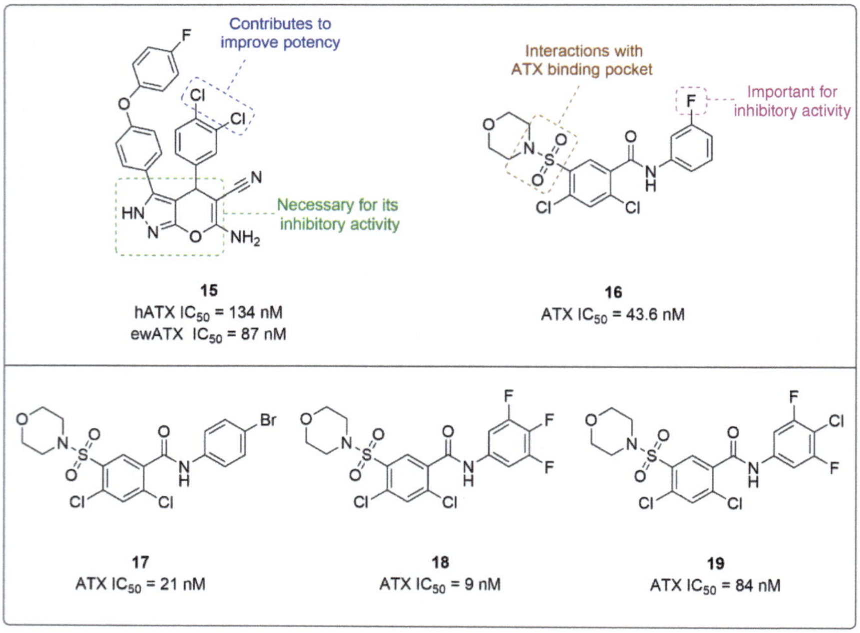

Figure 12.5 Chemical structures of compounds **15–19**.

some compounds with benzenesulfonamide structure have been identified as type II ATX inhibitors by James and Banerjee et al. Among them, compound **16–19** exhibited promising inhibitory potency against ATX with IC_{50} values of 43.6, 21, 9, 84 nM. The sulfonamide structure in these inhibitors plays a critical role in interacting with ATX, which is important for their activity. The SAR showed that aromatic rings of these compounds may be involved in Π–Π interactions. Furthermore, targeting hydrophobic pockets may lead to better ATX inhibitors [72, 85–87].

12.5.3 Type III Autotaxin Inhibitors

Most of the type III ATX inhibitors have a 1H-pyrazole structure. Compound **20**, with a 1H-pyrazole structure, was first reported by Bain et al. compound **20** can effectively inhibit ATX potency, and it has good oral bioavailability (Figure 12.6). Compound **20** also maximally inhibited ATX potency in grain plasma and exhibited potent anti-fibrotic potency in the CDAHFD study. Additionally, compound **20** demonstrated the ability to inhibit pulmonary fibrosis in some mouse models.

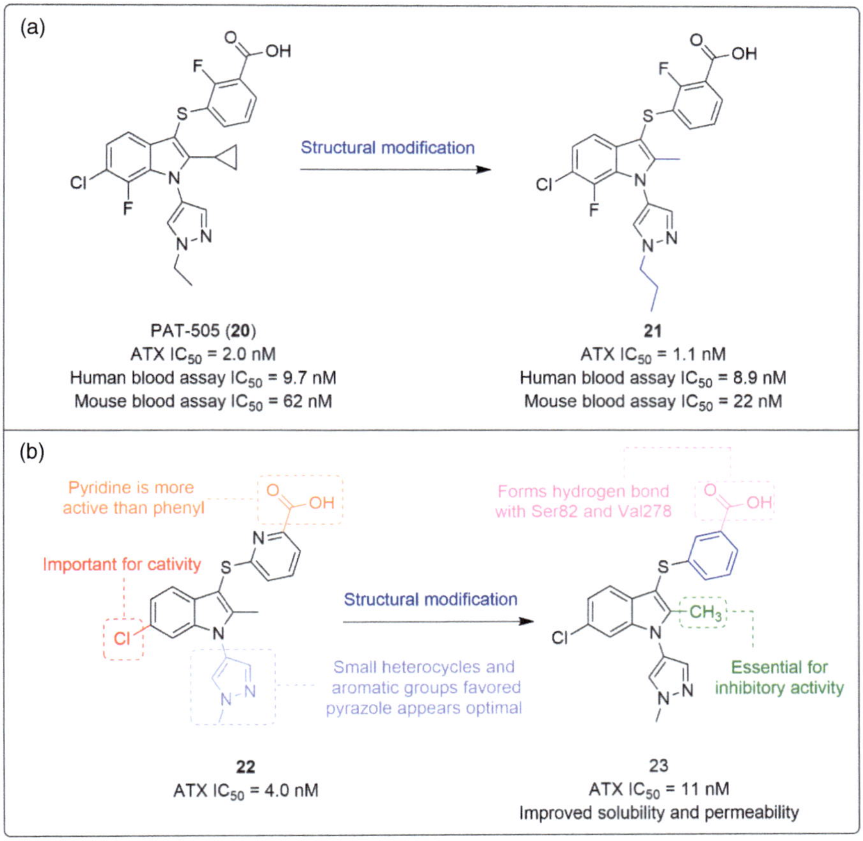

Figure 12.6 (a) Structural modification of inhibitors **20–21**. (b) Structural modification of inhibitors **22–23**.

Notably, studies have shown that **20** primarily decreases ATX potency by interacting with the same ATX channel. Another compound **21** exhibited increased inhibitory activity through the ATX lysoPLD activity assay. However, it has shown no efficiency in reducing bleomycin-induced pulmonary fibrosis [88, 89]. Amira Pharmaceuticals has reported an inhibitor **22** with an IC_{50} value of 4 nM. Subsequently, compound **23**, with a similar scaffold like **22**, was obtained by replacing the pyridine ring with a benzene ring. Compound **23** inhibited ATX with an IC_{50} value of 11 nM and exhibited improved solubility and permeability compared with **22**. The SAR study showed that the substituent group at the 6-position and the ring position of the indole ring are important for the inhibitory potency. The addition of aromatic substituents enhances potency. Additionally, the methylpyrazole moiety is essential for maintaining potency, as its removal results in a complete loss of inhibitory activity. The docking study has shown that **23** inhibits ATX by interacting with the hydrophobic channels of ATX. The acidic group of compound **23** directly interacted with Ser^{82} and Val^{278}, which are essential for its inhibitory potency against ATX [90]. This highlights that ATX hydrophobic channels can serve as a valuable starting orientation for designing new compounds targeting ATX, offering important insights for the future.

12.5.4 Type IV Autotaxin Inhibitors

Joncour et al. firstly reported that compound **24** weakly inhibited the production of LPA in rat plasma with an IC_{50} value of 122 nM (Figure 12.7). In accordance with the structural characteristics of **24**, it can be concluded that the inhibitory potency can be enhanced when its 6-position is replaced by a basic amine and a hydrogen bond acceptor. The SAR study demonstrated that the thiazole ring plays a pivotal role in activity. With compound **24** as a precursor, it has been demonstrated that administration of compound **25** in an oral formulation, results in a reduction in the rat LPA level (IC_{50} = 27 nM). Subsequently, GLPG1690 (**26**) was obtained by introducing a nitrogen atom and a methyl group. GLPG1690 has been demonstrated to have the capacity to reduce serum LPA levels in mice in a continuous manner at a dose of 3 mg/kg. In addition, it has been shown to have strong inhibitory activity against ATX, with an IC_{50} value of 131 nM. Furthermore, it has been shown to have remarkable potency in the mouse fibrosis model [91]. Furthermore, it has been established that GLPG1690, an ATX inhibitor, has the capacity to reduce inflammation to a comparable degree to conventional chronic obstructive pulmonary disease (COPD) therapies, as determined using a mouse steroid-resistant tobacco smoke model. Consequently, GLPG1690 was clinically utilized in treating some IPF disease. GLPG1690 has successfully concluded the initial human phase 1 clinical trial and is well tolerated in humans [92, 93]. The crystal structure of **26** in complex with human ATX was examined, revealing that **26** interacted with ATX through a V-shaped binding pattern.

Subsequently, compound **27**, with a benzoic acid structure, was first synthesized with an IC_{50} value of 3.3 μM against ATX. Then the author has examined the conformational relationships of these inhibitors by introducing different amide groups.

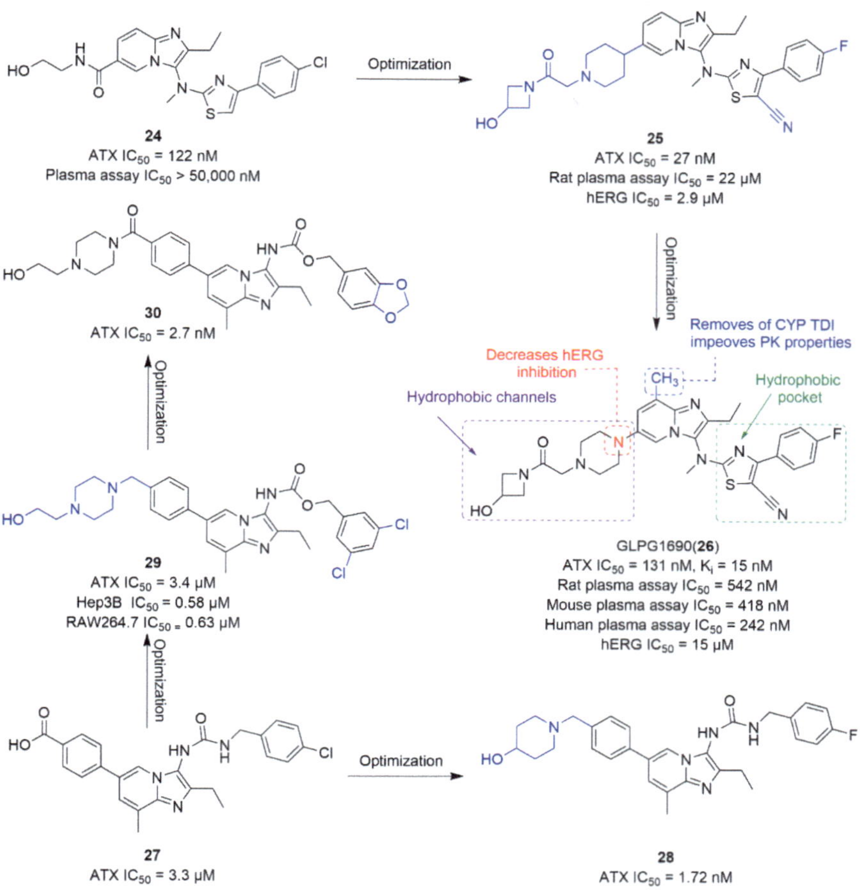

Figure 12.7 Structural optimization of inhibitors **24–26** and **27–30**.

It was shown that the introduction of a terminal hydroxyl group contributes to increasing inhibitory activity and efficacy. In addition, the molecular docking study showed that a spatial conflict has been identified between Trp^{255} and the amide group. To improve this point, the authors replaced the carbon chain with a methylene group. Among them, the best inhibitor **28** was obtained by introducing a 4-fluorobenzene group. Compound **28** demonstrated the capacity to inhibit ATX (IC_{50} = 1.72 nM). In addition, **28** exhibited a notable protective effect in a model of pulmonary fibrosis in mice treated with bleomycin (BLM). In addition, **28** exhibited superior drug-like properties, providing a basis for the design of ATX inhibitors in the future [94]. Meanwhile, the authors have found that changing the length of the terminal aliphatic amine can adjust inhibitory potency by modulating the extent to which the inhibitor binds ATX. Therefore, further modification led to two new ATX inhibitors **29–30** with IC_{50} values of 3.4 and 2.7 nM [25, 26]. Among them, compound **29** was the most effective at fighting tumors in the Hep3B and RAW264.7 cell lines, which had high levels of ATX mRNA(IC_{50} = 0.58 and 0.63 μM, respectively).

Compound **29** also dose-dependently suppressed the migration rate of RAW264.7 cells in a wound healing assay and significantly inhibited the colony formation of RAW264.7 cells [95]. In order to enhance the π–π interactions between the inhibitor and adjacent residues, the piperazine group in **26** was replaced with a phenyl ring. Compound **30** was obtained by utilizing a hybrid strategy. Compound **30** has been shown to reduce the severity of fibrosis tissues and effectively reduce the deposition of fibrotic biomarker α-Smooth muscle actin (α-SMA). In addition, **30** was also observed to be as potent or more potent than **26** with superior ATX inhibitory potency [96]. Docking studies demonstrated that **29** and **30** exhibited a similar binding paradigm to compound **26**. The hydroxyl group of **30** interacted with Trp^{255}, while the carbonyl group formed hydrogen bonds with Trp^{276}. Furthermore, another hydrogen bond was observed between the dioxane group and the Phe306 residue, which results in the superior inhibitory activity of this inhibitor. Consequently, **29** and **30** can be confirmed as potential candidates for the regulation of fibrosis-related diseases.

Another ATX inhibitor called Indole-1 (**31**), with an indole-like structure, was discovered by Lei et al. through high-throughput screening, and it inhibited ATX with an IC_{50} value of 740 nM (Figure 12.8). The SAR study demonstrated that a terminal hydroxyl group is beneficial for increasing the inhibitory potency of these inhibitors. Based on the structure of **31**, compound **32**, with the carbamate group as a linker, was synthesized. Subsequently, promising inhibitors **33** and **34** were obtained by further optimizing the carboxylic acid structure as the linker of the internal skeleton and hydrophobic pocket. **33** and **34** showed improved inhibitory activity. Among them, inhibitor **34** demonstrated superior antithrombin (ATX) inhibitory effects, exhibiting a lower fluorescence absorption value (approximately 3.25) in comparison to GLPG1690 (approximately 4.04). Additionally, it exhibited a more effective protective function on injured lung tissues. There is an important hydrogen bond interaction between the carbamate group and the residue Phe274. Meanwhile, hydroxyl group–containing amines effectively occupied part of the hydrophobic tunnel and formed another H-bond with the Gly256 [97].

Based on the structure of **31**, compound **35**, with an acylhydrazone linkage chain, was identified as an ATX inhibitor by Jia et al. However, **35** showed no enhanced inhibitory potency. To better fit the hydrophobic pocket, some ATX inhibitors were designed by introducing a flexible urea moiety. Among them, compound **36** showed a huge improvement in ATX inhibitory potency compared with the precursor compound **35**. To reduce the cLogP of these compounds, the authors replaced the thiazole ring with a benzamide while keeping the urea linker unchanged. The benzamide derivative **37**, featuring a 4-hydroxy piperidine fragment, demonstrated significant inhibitory activity against ATX (IC_{50} = 2.3 nM). Compound **37** also exhibited the highest ligand-lipophilicity efficiency (LLE) of 4.61, outperforming GLPG1690 (3.1 nM). The crystal structure of **37** bound to ATX revealed that the benzyl urea fragment occupied the hydrophobic pocket formed by Phe^{274}, Ser^{170}, Tyr^{307}, and surrounding residues. A hydrogen bond was observed between the single bond hydroxyl group and Trp255, and two fundamental hydrogen bond interactions were formed between the urea moiety of **37** and Phe^{274} and Trp^{276}.

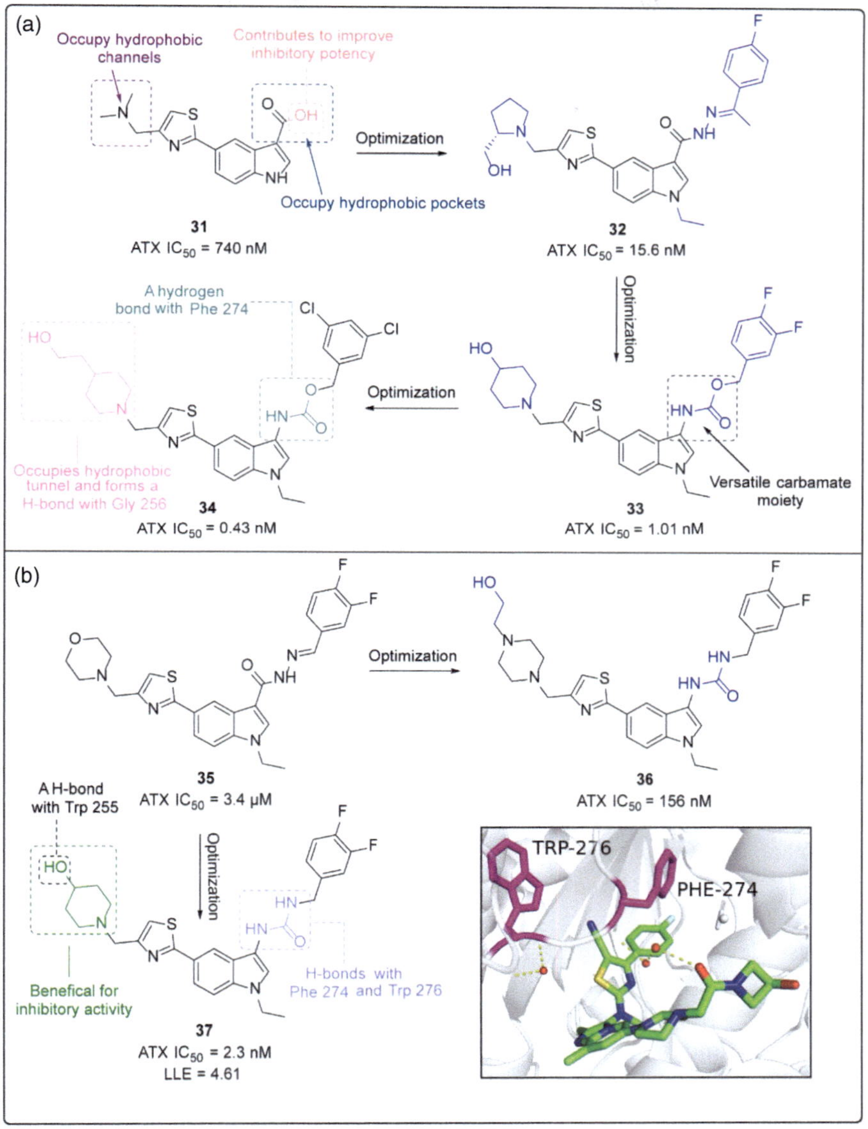

Figure 12.8 (a) Structural optimization of inhibitors **31–34** (b) Structural optimization of inhibitors **35–37,** and the crystal structure of **37** in complex with ATX(PDB: 5MHP).

In addition, the 4-hydroxy piperidine moiety of **37** extended into the solvent region, potentially facilitating interactions that could assist in the efficient binding of **37** with the ATX cavity (PDB 5MHP) [98].

In 2022, Lei et al. reported a series of indole-based carbamate derivatives as ATX inhibitors. Among them, the best compound **38,** bearing a morpholine moiety, showed the optimal inhibitory potency (Figure 12.9). However, the pharmacokinetic properties and degree of absorption of **38** represent significant obstacles to

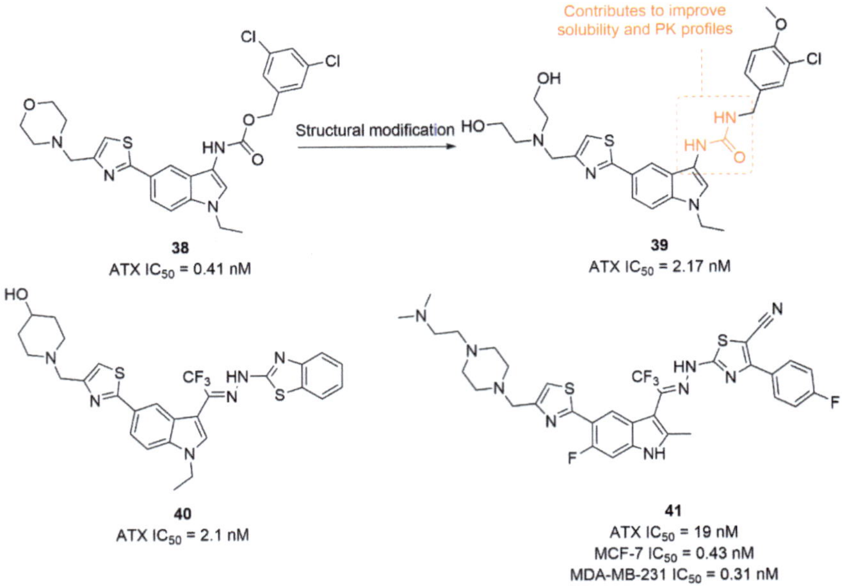

Figure 12.9 Chemical structures of compounds **38–41**.

its further development. To resolve the intractable issue, other inhibitors were synthesized by introducing a urea moiety as a surrogate of carbamate. Among them, **39** exhibited excellent drug-like properties and moderate activity (IC_{50} = 2.17 nM). Compound **39** was also assessed for its anti-fibrotic effects in a mouse model. Treatment with **39** significantly downregulated *in vivo* ATX activity in both lung homogenate and bronchoalveolar lavage fluid (BALF) samples. These promising biological effects suggest that **39** has potential applications in treating fibrotic diseases [99].

Scientists developed other ATX inhibitor structures by anchoring the benzothiazole group of **26** onto the indole group. Among them, compound **40** was obtained by introducing a cyclic benzothiazole fragment to reduce the space conflicts of these compounds. Compound **40** effectively inhibited ATX with an IC_{50} value of 2.1 nM. To further improve the hydrophilicity of compound **40,** other inhibitors were obtained by introducing a piperazine and a piperidine group. Among these inhibitors, the representative inhibitor **41** exhibited potent inhibition against ATX. In addition, Inhibitor **40** also exhibited optimal inhibitory activity on MCF-7 and MDA-MB-231 cell lines with IC_{50} values of 0.43 and 0.31 μM. Accordingly, inhibitors **40** and **41** merited further investigation as prospective lead compounds, with the potential to confirm their applications in due course [100].

Kawaguchi et al. identified some highly efficient and selective compounds as ATX inhibitors by screening a large chemical library. Compound **42**, with imidazopyrimidone scaffold-like structure, potently inhibits ATX activity (IC_{50} = 4.2 nM) (Figure 12.10). The primary mechanism of action of the compound under investigation involves interacting with these hydrophobic channels and pockets, thereby improving the *in vivo* inhibitory potency against ATX. Meanwhile, **42** specifically

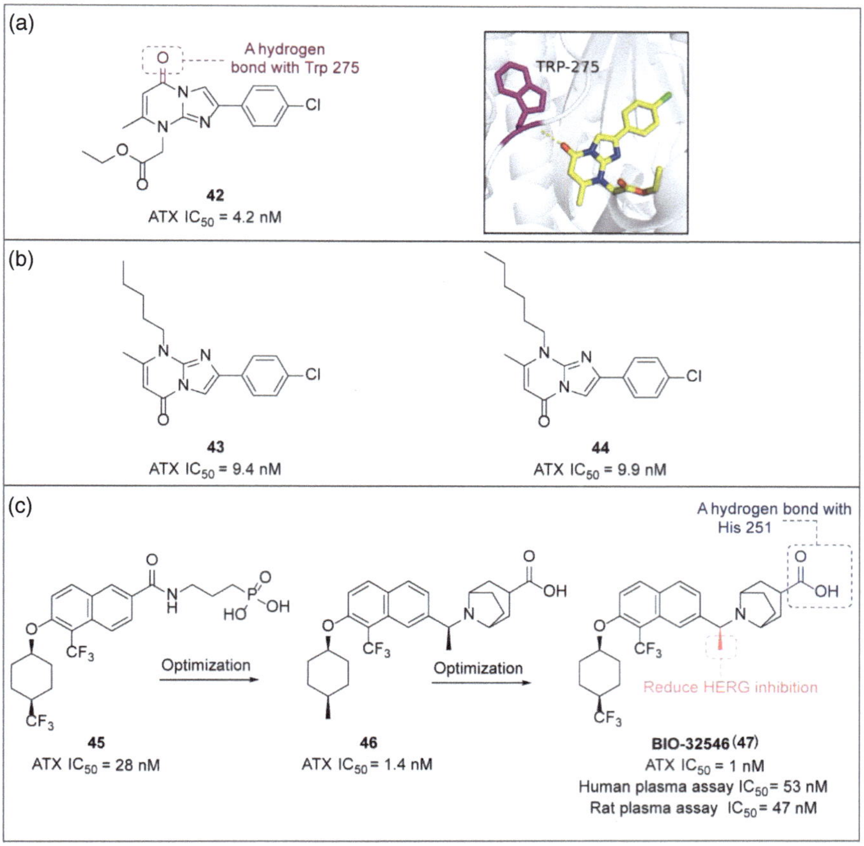

Figure 12.10 (a) Chemical structure of compound **42** and the crystal structure of **42** in complex with ATX (PDB 6LEH). (b) Chemical structures of inhibitors **43** and **44**. (c) Structural optimization of compounds **45–47**.

inhibits ATX. However, the ester functional group of **42** may be a significant impediment to stability, and the compound was unable to suppress ATX-mediated LPA production in the incubated plasma of mice. Consequently, further modifications are required to develop these compounds with better plasma stability and potency. The crystal structure of the ATX and **42** complex revealed that the chlorobenzene moiety and the imidazopyrimidinone scaffold of **42** are positioned within the hydrophobic pocket formed by Ile^{167}, Leu^{213}, Leu^{216}, Ala^{217}, Trp^{260}, Phe^{273}, Phe^{274}, Ala^{304}, Tyr^{306}, and Met^{512}. Additionally, the carbonyl group forms a hydrogen bond with the main-chain amide group of Trp^{275}. The 8-ethyl acetate moiety interacts with the hydrophobic channel formed by Phe^{210}, Tyr^{214}, Trp^{254}, Trp^{260}, and Phe^{274}(PDB 6LEH). Because there are ester bonds in mouse plasma that can easily break down, the ester group was changed to an alkyl group, which makes it more stable in the body. Compounds **43** and **44** were synthesized by replacing the 4-chloro group with the pentyl or hexyl group at the 8-position and exhibited potent inhibitory activity with IC_{50} values of 9.4 and 9.9 nM. Moreover, **43** and **44** can effectively block the rise of plasma LPA during the incubation process. They can also reduce the levels of LPA in the blood of mice. The SAR study demonstrated that the substituent groups at the 8-position can impact hydrogen interactions by influencing the conformation of these compounds in space, thereby exerting an additional influence on the inhibitory activity against ATX. The 5-carbonyl group is essential for the inhibitory potency of these inhibitors. Furthermore, the introduction of hydrophobic groups at the 8-position contributes to an improvement in the inhibitory activity, while the hydrophilic substituents cause a loss of potency. Interestingly, the 8-substituent is the most active when the side chain contains five carbon atoms, while longer alkyl side chains could result in loss of effectiveness. The author posited that a promising strategy for developing potent and selective inhibitors is to target multiple sites of ATX, namely the hydrophobic pocket, the hydrophobic channel, and the Trp^{275} main-chain amide group, without chelating the zinc ions in the catalytic center [101].

In 2021, Ma et al. reported other ATX inhibitors. Among them, lead compound **45** showed potent inhibition against ATX in fluorescence resonance energy transfer (FRET) experiments with an IC_{50} value of 28 nM. Nevertheless, it has been demonstrated to exhibit poor *in vivo* activity, likely due to a lack of promising oral bioavailability. To address this issue, the authors first replaced the phosphonic acid with a carboxylic acid, which resulted in a reduction in inhibitory potency. The process of conversion to amino acids has been demonstrated to result in a moderate increase in efficacy. Following this, compound **46** was synthesized with the objective of solving the issue of hERG inhibition resulting from the α-methylation of the benzylamine position and showed improved inhibition against ATX with an IC_{50} value of 1.4 nM compared with inhibitor **45**. Furthermore, **46** also showed adequate solubility and favorable drug-like properties. To improve the metabolic stability of **46**, the best inhibitor **47** was synthesized by introducing a CF_3 group. Compound **47**, also named BIO-32546, potently inhibited ATX with an IC_{50} value of 1 nM. The cocrystal structure of **47** in complex with mouse ATX revealed a binding mode similar to that of GLPG1690. The tail of **47** occupies the hydrophobic pocket, while the bicyclic head portion binds to the hydrophobic channel. A hydrogen bond interaction was formed between the carboxylate group and His^{251}. Importantly, **47** does not interact with the zinc ion. Moreover, **47** has been demonstrated to exhibit *in vivo* efficacy in a model of acute pain, a property that is currently being investigated in preclinical studies. Due to the potent, selective, orally bioavailable, brain-penetrable properties of **47**, it could be used to treat acute pain in a medical setting [102].

12.5.5 Type V Allosteric Autotaxin Inhibitors

In 2022, Jamieson and colleagues introduced a novel series of analogs targeting a different catalytic site, representing a distinct class of ATX inhibitors classified as type V. Among these, the representative compounds **48** and **49** demonstrated a remarkable 400-fold increase in potency compared to the progenitor steroid, with IC_{50} values of 50 nM and 30 nM, respectively (Figure 12.11). The authors

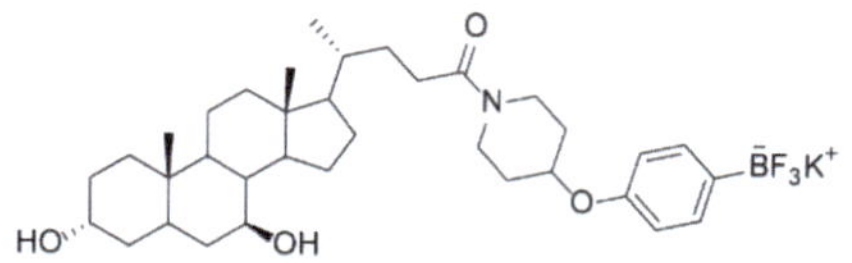

48
ATX IC_{50} = 50 nM

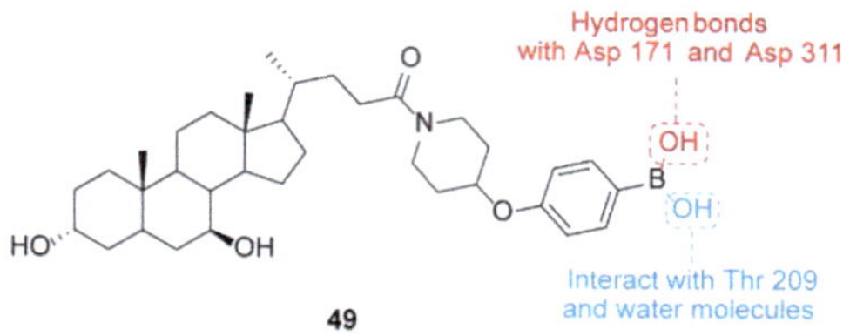

49
ATX IC_{50} = 30 nM

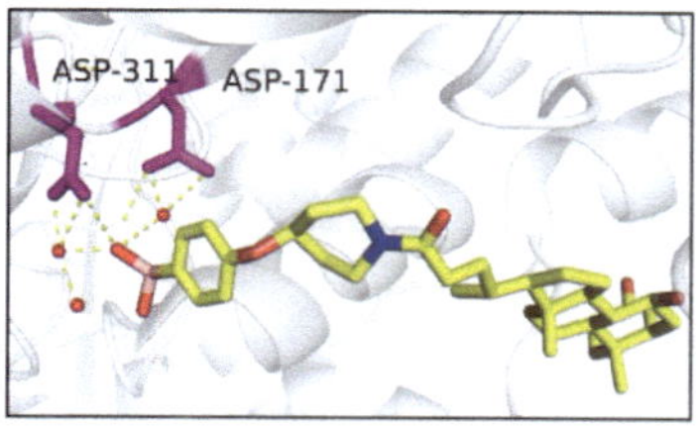

Figure 12.11 Chemical structures of compounds **48** and **49** and the crystal structure of **42** in complex with ATX (PDB 7ZON).

confirmed that by attaching an active warhead to the weak endogenous steroid, the inhibitory mechanism was successfully altered from noncompetitive to competitive. Furthermore, the compounds **48** and **49** have been demonstrated to effectively decrease the LPA receptor, thereby demonstrating excellent efficacy in inhibiting LPA-dependent pathways across a variety of cell lines. The SAR demonstrated that the use of a three-carbon linker as a spacer is beneficial for enhancing inhibitory activity. Furthermore, the conversion of the sulfonamide to boron-containing warheads played a pivotal role in achieving complete inhibition of ATX. The crystal structure of **48** and **49** in complex with ATX showed that the trifluoroborate warhead of **48** closely resembled the binding mode of LPA. Specifically, one of the fluorine atoms formed H-bond with Asn^{230} and Thr^{209}, and another fluorine atom coordinated with Zn^{2+}(PDB 7ZOM). The binding mode of **49**, featuring a boronic acid warhead, showed significant similarity to that of HA^{155}. Specifically, γ-hydroxyl group formed a reversible covalent bond with the Thr^{209} residue through the proximity effect of the boron atom. The hydroxyl groups of the boronic acid group formed H-bond with Asp^{171}, Asp^{311}, and Thr^{209}. This intricate network of bonds effectively blocked the ATX active site, which is responsible for the high potency of inhibitor **49** (PDB 7ZON). The comparison of the two binding modes of the inhibitors revealed that both **48** and **49** exhibited similar interactions. The authors hypothesized that the preferred binding mode within the tunnel involves both steroid hydroxyl groups forming hydrogen bonds with Trp^{260} and Tyr^{82}. Additionally, numerous hydrophobic interactions are established between these compounds and the residues lining the ATX tunnel. Nowadays, **48** and **49** are undergoing further investigation as type V ATX inhibitors [103].

12.5.6 Potential Inhibitors of ATX

A series of derivatives featuring pyridine and pyrimidine structures were discovered as ATX inhibitors, showing efficacy in curing some human diseases. Inhibitor **50**,

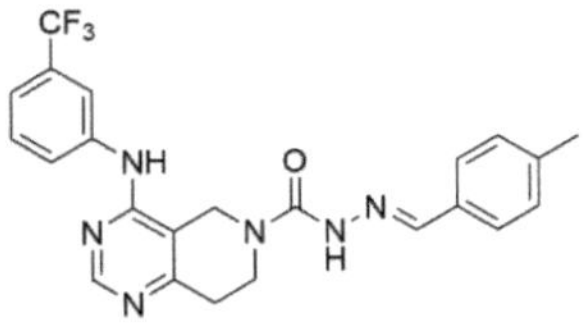

51
ATX IC_{50} = 29.1 nM
EGFR IC_{50} = 24.2 nM

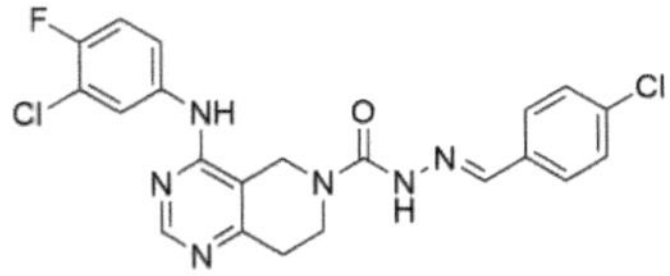

52
ATX IC_{50} = 24.2 nM

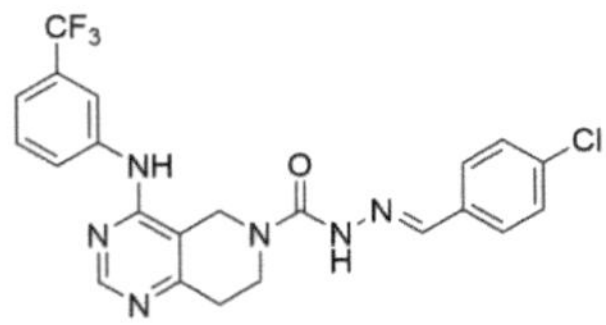

53
ATX IC_{50} = 15.3 nM

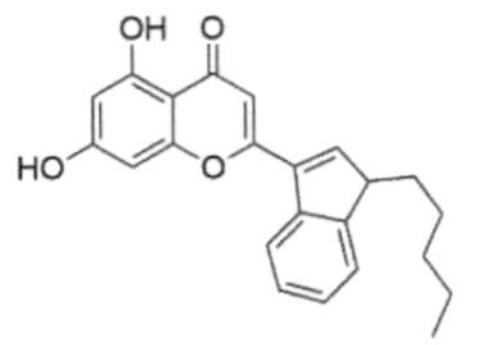

54
hATX-β IC_{50} = 0.46 μM
hATX-γ IC_{50} = 1.099 μM

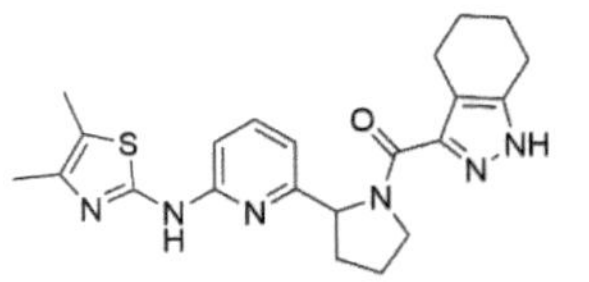

55
ATX IC_{50} = 2.53 μM

Figure 12.12 Chemical structures of compounds **51–55**.

characterized by a long-chain linker and a nonrigid backbone, demonstrated powerful potency against fibrillation (Figure 12.12). Jing et al. identified a series of compounds possessing semicarbazone moiety as ATX–EGFR dual inhibitors. Among these, compound **51** was developed by substituting the original THPPs (the original chemical structure) with a 4-aminoquinazoline backbone and incorporating hemicarbazone linker chains. This modification resulted in a spatial conformation that closely overlaps with epidermal growth factor receptor (EGFR) inhibitors, enhancing its potential therapeutic relevance. Compound **51** demonstrated strong inhibitory activity against both ATX and EGFR. It also effectively inhibited the CF cells in the determination of anti-fibrosis efficacy with an IC_{50} value of 1.49 μM. Compound **51** exhibited significant antitumor activity against A^{549}, H^{1975}, MKN-45, and SGC cancer cells. Reverse transcription-polymerase chain reaction (RT-PCR) studies revealed that **51** downregulated the mRNA expression of TGF-β and TNF-α in a dose-dependent manner. The SAR studies indicated that introducing an aliphatic ring reduced pharmacological activity compared to aromatic structures. Among aromatic groups, aniline demonstrated superior inhibitory activity in A^{549} cells. Halogenation at the 4-position of the benzene ring enhanced potency, with polyhalogenated structures outperforming mono-halogenated ones. Docking studies of **51** with EGFR revealed that it binds to the adenosine triphosphate (ATP) pocket similarly to gefitinib, forming hydrogen bonds with residues Met^{793} and Cys^{797}. The 3-trifluoromethylphenyl fragment extended into the hydrophobic pocket composed of Val^{726}, Lys^{745}, Met^{790}, and Leu^{788}, engaging in alkyl and halogen interactions. These findings highlight **51** as a promising dual inhibitor of ATX and EGFR, offering potential therapeutic benefits for idiopathic pulmonary fibrosis with lung cancer (IPF-LC) treatment [104].

Other inhibitors **52** and **53** were obtained by introducing halogen groups. Compared with **51**, **52** and **53** showed improved inhibitory potency against ATX. Both **52** and **53** can modulate collagen levels at a concentration of 10 μM/l. Specifically, **52** reduces collagen levels by 74.4%, demonstrating a strong inhibitory effect on a peculiar cardiac fibrosis. Docking studies showed that the carbonyl group of the SCZ fragment forms favorable hydrogen bond interactions with TRP276, further supporting its mechanism of action. Overall, inhibitors **52** and **53** hold great potential as effective candidate compounds for the treatment of cardiac and hepatic fibrosis, respectively [105].

Mathias et al. screened a large chemical library sharing chemical similarities with the cannabinoid tetrahydrocannabinol (THC) to obtain a novel potential inhibitor **54**. Compound **54** showed moderate inhibition against hATX-β and hATX-γ with IC_{50} values of 0.46 and 1.099 μM, respectively. In addition, **54** also showed promising physicochemical properties. The unique structure of **54**, distinct from previously reported ATX inhibitors, holds promise for the development of novel drugs targeting the ATX–LPA axis with reduced side effects [106]. Another inhibitor **55** was also obtained by screening a compound library. Compound **55** exhibited moderate inhibitory activity against ATX in the low micromolar range. In conclusion, compound 55 is a promising "hit" for further evaluation [107].

12.6 Conclusion and Perspective

In summary, ATX plays a pivotal role as a regulator of LPA metabolic processes, influencing a wide range of biological activities such as cell proliferation, survival, migration, and motility through the conversion of LPC into LPA. LPA exerts its biological effects by binding to specific G-protein-coupled receptors, triggering and activating downstream cellular signaling pathways. The ATX–LPA signaling axis has been implicated in the progression of various human diseases, including cancer, inflammation, and fibroproliferative disorders. Consequently, targeting LPA has emerged as a promising therapeutic strategy, demonstrating significant potential for the treatment of these conditions.

To date, numerous novel inhibitors of ATX have been designed and identified by medicinal chemists, with some demonstrating therapeutic potential. Among these, **GLPG1690** has advanced to phase 3 clinical trials for the treatment of IPF, while another ATX inhibitor, **IOA-289**, has also progressed to clinical trials targeting pancreatic cancer. Nowadays, research on ATX inhibitors has achieved great progress, yet there also remain some unresolved issues that require further attention. Future efforts in ATX inhibitor design should focus on enhancing both *in vitro* and *in vivo* potency, optimizing kinetic properties, and exploring additional functional roles of ATX. The application of artificial intelligence (AI) methods can be instrumental in analyzing known ATX inhibitors, enabling a deeper understanding of drug mechanisms and the factors influencing pharmacological efficacy. This approach could significantly advance the development of more effective and targeted therapies. A comprehensive approach to drug design, examining

SAR studies and exploring various functional groups that impact the pharmacokinetic properties of ATX inhibitors *in vivo*, could facilitate the development of innovative ATX inhibitors. Moreover, designing drugs that target multiple aspects of disease pathogenesis may offer a promising avenue for research. In terms of safety, multi-target inhibitors have an advantage over drug combinations because they can achieve good pharmacological activity at lower doses. Moreover, these inhibitors exhibit predictable pharmacodynamic (PD) and pharmacokinetic (PK) properties. For instance, compound **51** has shown promise as a dual inhibitor targeting both ATX and EGFR, presenting a potential therapeutic strategy for IPF-LC. However, their large molecular size poses a challenge for further development. The design of multi-target inhibitors should aim to optimize pharmacophore overlap while maintaining molecular simplicity to enhance drug-like properties.

As the structural and molecular mechanisms of ATX become increasingly understood, it is anticipated that novel ATX inhibitors with unique chemical frameworks will be developed using advanced techniques such as virtual high-throughput screening (VHTS) and artificial intelligence–assisted drug design (AIDD). These approaches hold great promise for accelerating the discovery of innovative and effective therapeutic agents. To summarize, ATX continues to be an extremely valuable focus for drug development, and we expect the creation and utilization of more powerful compounds of ATX for the betterment of patients in clinical settings.

Glossary

Signaling cascade Also referred to as the signaling pathway, this process involves the transmission of extracellular signals into the cell through membrane-bound receptors. These signals trigger a cascade of enzymatic reactions, culminating in specific physiological changes within the cell.

Domain It is the basic unit that forms the structure of proteins and the functional unit of proteins.

Homology It refers to genes and their products that have evolved from a common ancestor.

Biomarker It is an indicator that signifies alterations or potential alterations in the structure or function of systems, organs, tissues, cells, and subcellular components.

Orphan drug status (ODD) It refers to special legal protection for drug treatments for diseases that affect a very small number of people.

Isoforms They are different transcripts produced from the same gene code, which can contain different combinations of exons during the splicing process and therefore produce a variety of different mRNAs and proteins.

References

1 Tokumura, A., Majima, E., Kariya, Y. et al. (2002). Identification of human plasma lysophospholipase D, a lysophosphatidic acid-producing enzyme, as autotaxin, a multifunctional phosphodiesterase. *Journal of Biological Chemistry* 277: 39436–39442.

2 Stefan, C., Jansen, S., and Bollen, M. (2006). Modulation of purinergic signaling by NPP-type ectophosphodiesterases. *Purinergic Signal* 2: 361–370.
3 Stracke, M.-L., Krutzsch, H.-C., Unsworth, E.-J. et al. (1992). Identification, purification, and partial sequence analysis of autotaxin, a novel motility-stimulating protein. *Journal of Biological Chemistry* 267: 2524–2529.
4 Tokumura, A., Harada, K., Fukuzawa, K., and Tsukatani, H. (1986). Involvement of lysophospholipase D in the production of lysophosphatidic acid in rat plasma. *Biochimica et Biophysica Acta* 875: 31–38.
5 Matralis, A.-N., Afantitis, A., and Aidinis, V. (2019). Development and therapeutic potential of autotaxin small molecule inhibitors: From bench to advanced clinical trials. *Medicinal Research Reviews* 39: 976–1013.
6 Lin, M.-E., Herr, D.-R., and Chun, J. (2010). Lysophosphatidic acid (LPA) receptors: signaling properties and disease relevance. *Prostaglandins & Other Lipid Mediators* 91: 130–138.
7 Zhao, Y. and Natarajan, V. (2009). Lysophosphatidic acid signaling in airway epithelium: role in airway inflammation and remodeling. *Cellular Signalling* 21: 367–377.
8 Yanagida, K., Kurikawa, Y., Shimizu, T., and Ishii, S. (2013). Current progress in non-Edg family LPA receptor research. *Biochimica et Biophysica Acta (BBA) – Molecular and Cell Biology of Lipids* 1831: 33–41.
9 Chun, J., Hla, T., Lynch, K.-R. et al. (2010). International union of basic and clinical pharmacology. LXXVIII. Lysophospholipid receptor nomenclature. *Pharmacological Reviews* 62: 579–587.
10 Mills, G.-B. and Moolenaar, W.-H. (2003). The emerging role of lysophosphatidic acid in cancer. *Nature Reviews Cancer* 3: 582–591.
11 Bourgoin, S.-G. and Zhao, C. (2010). Autotaxin and lysophospholipids in rheumatoid arthritis. *Current Opinion in Investigational Drugs* 11: 515–526.
12 Willier, S., Butt, E., and Grunewald, T.-G. (2013). Lysophosphatidic acid (LPA) signalling in cell migration and cancer invasion: a focussed review and analysis of LPA receptor gene expression on the basis of more than 1700 cancer microarrays. *Biology of the Cell* 105: 317–333.
13 Tager, A.-M., LaCamera, P., Shea, B.-S. et al. (2008). The lysophosphatidic acid receptor LPA1 links pulmonary fibrosis to lung injury by mediating fibroblast recruitment and vascular leak. *Nature Medicine* 14: 45–54.
14 Zhao, Y. and Natarajan, V. (2013). Lysophosphatidic acid (LPA) and its receptors: role in airway inflammation and remodeling. *Biochimica et Biophysica Acta (BBA) – Molecular and Cell Biology of Lipids* 1831: 86–92.
15 D'Souza, K., Paramel, G.-V., and Kienesberger, P.-C. (2018). Lysophosphatidic acid signaling in obesity and insulin resistance. *Nutrients* 10: 399.
16 Igarashi, N., Honjo, M., Asaoka, R. et al. (2021). Aqueous autotaxin and TGF-βs are promising diagnostic biomarkers for distinguishing open-angle glaucoma subtypes. *Scientific Reports* 11: 1408.
17 Bourgeois, R., Devillers, R., Perrot, N. et al. (2020). Interaction of autotaxin with lipoprotein(a) in patients with calcific aortic valve stenosis. *JACC: Basic to Translational Science* 5: 888–897.

18 Chen, J., Li, H., Xu, W., and Guo, X. (2021). Evaluation of serum ATX and LPA as potential diagnostic biomarkers in patients with pancreatic cancer. *BMC Gastroenterology* 21: 58.

19 Nie, C., Zhang, L., Chen, X. et al. (2020). Autotaxin: an early warning biomarker for acute-on-chronic liver failure. *Journal of Clinical and Translational Hepatology* 8: 240–245.

20 Nojiri, T., Kurano, M., Araki, O. et al. (2019). Serum autotaxin levels are associated with Graves' disease. *Endocrine Journal* 66: 409–422.

21 Magkrioti, C., Galaris, A., Kanellopoulou, P. et al. (2019). Autotaxin and chronic inflammatory diseases. *Journal of Autoimmunity* 104: 102327.

22 Ninou, I., Sevastou, I., Magkrioti, C. et al. (2020). Genetic deletion of Autotaxin from CD11b+ cells decreases the severity of experimental autoimmune encephalomyelitis. *PLoS One* 15: e0226050.

23 Herr, D.-R., Chew, W.-S., Satish, R.-L., and Ong, W.-Y. (2020). Pleotropic roles of autotaxin in the nervous system present opportunities for the development of novel therapeutics for neurological diseases. *Molecular Neurobiology* 57: 372–392.

24 Zhao, Y., Hasse, S., Zhao, C., and Bourgoin, S.-G. (2019). Targeting the autotaxin – lysophosphatidic acid receptor axis in cardiovascular diseases. *Biochemical Pharmacology* 164: 74–81.

25 Brindley, D.-N., Tang, X., Meng, G., and Benesch, M.-G.-K. (2020). Role of adipose tissue-derived autotaxin, lysophosphatidate signaling, and inflammation in the progression and treatment of breast cancer. *International Journal of Molecular Sciences* 21: 5938.

26 Abdul Rahman, M., Tan, M.-L., Johnson, S.-P. et al. (2020). Deregulation of lysophosphatidic acid metabolism in oral cancer promotes cell migration via the up-regulation of COX-2. *PeerJ* 8: e10328.

27 Fukui, M., Tsutsumi, T., Yamamoto-Mikami, A. et al. (2020). Distinct contributions of two choline-producing enzymatic activities to lysophosphatidic acid production in human amniotic fluid from pregnant women in the second trimester and after parturition. *Prostaglandins & Other Lipid Mediators* 150: 106471.

28 van Meeteren, L.-A., Ruurs, P., Stortelers, C. et al. (2006). Autotaxin, a secreted lysophospholipase D, is essential for blood vessel formation during development. *Molecular and Cellular Biology* 26: 5015–5022.

29 Maher, T.-M., van der Aar, E.-M., Van de Steen, O. et al. (2018). Safety, tolerability, pharmacokinetics, and pharmacodynamics of GLPG1690, a novel autotaxin inhibitor, to treat idiopathic pulmonary fibrosis (FLORA): a phase 2a randomised placebo-controlled trial. *The Lancet Respiratory Medicine* 6: 627–635.

30 Albers, H.-M. and Ovaa, H. (2012). Chemical evolution of autotaxin inhibitors. *Chemical Reviews* 112: 2593–2603.

31 Giganti, A., Rodriguez, M., Fould, B. et al. (2008). Murine and human autotaxin alpha, beta, and gamma isoforms: gene organization, tissue distribution, and biochemical characterization. *Journal of Biological Chemistry* 283: 7776–7789.

32 Hashimoto, T., Okudaira, S., Igarashi, K. et al. (2012). Identification and biochemical characterization of a novel autotaxin isoform, ATXδ, with a four-amino acid deletion. *The Journal of Biochemistry* 151: 89–97.

33 Houben, A.-J., van Wijk, X.-M., van Meeteren, L.-A. et al. (2013). The polybasic insertion in autotaxin α confers specific binding to heparin and cell surface heparan sulfate proteoglycans. *Journal of Biological Chemistry* 288: 510–519.

34 Perrakis, A. and Moolenaar, W.-H. (2014). Autotaxin: structure-function and signaling. *Journal of Lipid Research* 55: 1010–1018.

35 Wu, T., Kooi, C.-V., Shah, P. et al. (2014). Integrin-mediated cell surface recruitment of autotaxin promotes persistent directional cell migration. *The FASEB Journal* 28: 861–870.

36 Hausmann, J., Kamtekar, S., Christodoulou, E. et al. (2011). Structural basis of substrate discrimination and integrin binding by autotaxin. *Nature Structural & Molecular Biology* 18: 198–204.

37 Keune, W.-J., Hausmann, J., Bolier, R. et al. (2016). Steroid binding to Autotaxin links bile salts and lysophosphatidic acid signalling. *Nature Communications* 7: 11248.

38 Salgado-Polo, F., Fish, A., Matsoukas, M.-T. et al. (2018). Lysophosphatidic acid produced by autotaxin acts as an allosteric modulator of its catalytic efficiency. *The Journal of Biological Chemistry* 293: 14312–14327.

39 Nishimasu, H., Okudaira, S., Hama, K. et al. (2011). Crystal structure of autotaxin and insight into GPCR activation by lipid mediators. *Nature Structural & Molecular Biology* 18: 205–212.

40 Clair, T., Aoki, J., Koh, E. et al. (2003). Autotaxin hydrolyzes sphingosylphosphorylcholine to produce the regulator of migration, sphingosine-1-phosphate. *Cancer Research* 63: 5446–5453.

41 van Meeteren, L.-A., Ruurs, P., Christodoulou, E. et al. (2005). Inhibition of autotaxin by lysophosphatidic acid and sphingosine 1-phosphate. *Journal of Biological Chemistry* 280: 21155–21161.

42 Hait, N.-C., Oskeritzian, C.-A., Paugh, S.-W. et al. (2006). Sphingosine kinases, sphingosine 1-phosphate, apoptosis and diseases. *Biochimica et Biophysica Acta* 1758: 2016–2026.

43 Nam, S.-W., Clair, T., Campo, C.-K. et al. (2000). Autotaxin (ATX), a potent tumor motogen, augments invasive and metastatic potential of ras-transformed cells. *Oncogene* 19: 241–247.

44 Yang, Y., Mou, L., Liu, N., and Tsao, M.-S. (1999). Autotaxin expression in non-small-cell lung cancer. *American Journal of Respiratory Cell and Molecular Biology* 21: 216–222.

45 Zhang, G., Zhao, Z., Xu, S. et al. (1999). Expression of autotaxin mRNA in human hepatocellular carcinoma. *Chinese Medical Journal* 112: 330–332.

46 Stassar, M.-J., Devitt, G., Brosius, M. et al. (2001). Identification of human renal cell carcinoma associated genes by suppression subtractive hybridization. *British Journal of Cancer* 85: 1372–1382.

47 Panupinthu, N., Lee, H.-Y., and Mills, G.-B. (2010). Lysophosphatidic acid production and action: critical new players in breast cancer initiation and progression. *British Journal of Cancer* 102: 941–946.

48 Kehlen, A., Englert, N., Seifert, A. et al. (2004). Expression, regulation and function of autotaxin in thyroid carcinomas. *International Journal of Cancer* 109: 833–838.

49 Barbayianni, E., Kaffe, E., Aidinis, V., and Kokotos, G. (2015). Autotaxin, a secreted lysophospholipase D, as a promising therapeutic target in chronic inflammation and cancer. *Progress in Lipid Research* 58: 76–96.

50 Benesch, M.-G.K., MacIntyre, I.-T.-K., McMullen, T.-P.-W., and Brindley, D.-N. (2018). Coming of age for autotaxin and lysophosphatidate signaling: clinical applications for preventing, detecting and targeting tumor-promoting inflammation. *Cancers (Basel)* 10: 73.

51 Nakagawa, H., Ikeda, H., Nakamura, K. et al. (2011). Autotaxin as a novel serum marker of liver fibrosis. *Clinica Chimica Acta* 412: 1201–1206.

52 Pradère, J.-P., Klein, J., Grès, S. et al. (2007). LPA1 receptor activation promotes renal interstitial fibrosis. *Journal of the American Society of Nephrology* 18: 3110–3118.

53 Rancoule, C., Viaud, M., Gres, S. et al. (2014). Pro-fibrotic activity of lysophosphatidic acid in adipose tissue: in vivo and in vitro evidence. *Biochimica et Biophysica Acta* 1841: 88–96.

54 Wu, L., Petrigliano, F.-A., Ba, K. et al. (2015). Lysophosphatidic acid mediates fibrosis in injured joints by regulating collagen type I biosynthesis. *Osteoarthritis and Cartilage* 23: 308–318.

55 Abu El-Asrar, A.-M., Mohammad, G., Nawaz, M.-I. et al. (2013). Expression of lysophosphatidic acid, autotaxin and acylglycerol kinase as biomarkers in diabetic retinopathy. *Acta Diabetologica* 50: 363–371.

56 Tager, A.-M. (2012). Autotaxin emerges as a therapeutic target for idiopathic pulmonary fibrosis: limiting fibrosis by limiting lysophosphatidic acid synthesis. *American Journal of Respiratory Cell and Molecular Biology* 47: 563–565.

57 Oikonomou, N., Mouratis, M.-A., Tzouvelekis, A. et al. (2012). Pulmonary autotaxin expression contributes to the pathogenesis of pulmonary fibrosis. *American Journal of Respiratory Cell and Molecular Biology* 47: 566–574.

58 Huang, L.-S., Fu, P., Patel, P. et al. (2013). Lysophosphatidic acid receptor-2 deficiency confers protection against bleomycin-induced lung injury and fibrosis in mice. *American Journal of Respiratory Cell and Molecular Biology* 49: 912–922.

59 Swaney, J.-S., Chapman, C., Correa, L.-D. et al. (2010). A novel, orally active LPA(1) receptor antagonist inhibits lung fibrosis in the mouse bleomycin model. *British Journal of Pharmacology* 160: 1699–1713.

60 Cao, P., Aoki, Y., Badri, L. et al. (2017). Autocrine lysophosphatidic acid signaling activates β-catenin and promotes lung allograft fibrosis. *The Journal of Clinical Investigation* 127: 1517–1530.

61 Ikeda, H. and Yatomi, Y. (2012). Autotaxin in liver fibrosis. *Clinica Chimica Acta* 413: 1817–1821.

62 Watanabe, N., Ikeda, H., Nakamura, K. et al. (2007). Plasma lysophosphatidic acid level and serum autotaxin activity are increased in liver injury in rats in relation to its severity. *Life Sciences* 81: 1009–1015.

63 Kaffe, E., Katsifa, A., Xylourgidis, N. et al. (2017). Hepatocyte autotaxin expression promotes liver fibrosis and cancer. *Hepatology* 65: 1369–1383.

64 Pradère, J.-P., Gonzalez, J., Klein, J. et al. (2008). Lysophosphatidic acid and renal fibrosis. *Biochimica et Biophysica Acta* 1781: 582–587.

65 Castelino, F.-V., Bain, G., Pace, V.-A. et al. (2016). An autotaxin/lysophosphatidic acid/interleukin-6 amplification loop drives scleroderma fibrosis. *Arthritis & Rheumatology* 68: 2964–2974.

66 Zahednasab, H., Balood, M., Harirchian, M.-H. et al. (2014). Increased autotaxin activity in multiple sclerosis. *Journal of Neuroimmunology* 273: 120–123.

67 Schmitz, K., Brunkhorst, R., de Bruin, N. et al. (2017). Dysregulation of lysophosphatidic acids in multiple sclerosis and autoimmune encephalomyelitis. *Acta Neuropathologica Communications* 5: 42.

68 Nikitopoulou, I., Kaffe, E., Sevastou, I. et al. (2013). A metabolically-stabilized phosphonate analog of lysophosphatidic acid attenuates collagen-induced arthritis. *PLoS One* 8: e70941.

69 Inoue, M., Ma, L., Aoki, J. et al. (2008). Autotaxin, a synthetic enzyme of lysophosphatidic acid (LPA), mediates the induction of nerve-injured neuropathic pain. *Molecular Pain* 4: 6.

70 Sun, S., Wang, R., Song, J. et al. (2017). Blocking gp130 signaling suppresses autotaxin expression in adipocytes and improves insulin sensitivity in diet-induced obesity. *Journal of Lipid Research* 58: 2102–2113.

71 Rancoule, C., Dusaulcy, R., Tréguer, K. et al. (2014). Involvement of autotaxin/lysophosphatidic acid signaling in obesity and impaired glucose homeostasis. *Biochimie* 96: 140–143.

72 Fells, J.-I., Lee, S.-C., Fujiwara, Y. et al. (2013). Hits of a high-throughput screen identify the hydrophobic pocket of autotaxin/lysophospholipase D as an inhibitory surface. *Molecular Pharmacology* 84: 415–424.

73 Morris, A.-J. and Smyth, S.-S. (2007). Measurement of autotaxin/lysophospholipase D activity. *Methods in Enzymology* 434: 89–104.

74 Gierse, J., Thorarensen, A., Beltey, K. et al. (2010). A novel autotaxin inhibitor reduces lysophosphatidic acid levels in plasma and the site of inflammation. *Journal of Pharmacology and Experimental Therapeutics* 334: 310–317.

75 Ninou, I., Kaffe, E., Müller, S. et al. (2018). Pharmacologic targeting of the ATX/LPA axis attenuates bleomycin-induced pulmonary fibrosis. *Pulmonary Pharmacology & Therapeutics* 52: 32–40.

76 Kuttruff, C.-A., Ferrara, M., Bretschneider, T. et al. (2017). Discovery of BI-2545: a novel autotaxin inhibitor that significantly reduces LPA levels in vivo. *ACS Medicinal Chemistry Letters* 8: 1252–1257.

77 Balupuri, A., Lee, D.-Y., Lee, M.-H. et al. (2017). Design, synthesis, docking and biological evaluation of 4-phenyl-thiazole derivatives as autotaxin (ATX) inhibitors. *Bioorganic & Medicinal Chemistry Letters* 27: 4156–4164.

78 Balupuri, A., Lee, M.-H., Chae, S. et al. (2018). Discovery and optimization of ATX inhibitors via modeling, synthesis and biological evaluation. *European Journal of Medicinal Chemistry* 148: 397–409.

79 Albers, H.-M., Dong, A., van Meeteren, L.-A. et al. (2010). Boronic acid-based inhibitor of autotaxin reveals rapid turnover of LPA in the circulation. *Proceedings of the National Academy of Sciences of the United States of America* 107: 7257–7262.

80 Albers, H.-M., van Meeteren, L.-A., Egan, D.-A. et al. (2010). Discovery and optimization of boronic acid based inhibitors of autotaxin. *Journal of Medicinal Chemistry* 53: 4958–4967.

81 Albers, H.-M., Hendrickx, L.-J., van Tol, R.-J. et al. (2011). Structure-based design of novel boronic acid-based inhibitors of autotaxin. *Journal of Medicinal Chemistry* 54: 4619–4626.

82 Gerokonstantis, D.-T., Nikolaou, A., Magkrioti, C. et al. (2020). Synthesis of novel 2-pyrrolidinone and pyrrolidine derivatives and study of their inhibitory activity against autotaxin enzyme. *Bioorganic & Medicinal Chemistry* 28: 115216.

83 Shah, P., Cheasty, A., Foxton, C. et al. (2016). Discovery of potent inhibitors of the lysophospholipase autotaxin. *Bioorganic & Medicinal Chemistry Letters* 26: 5403–5410.

84 Pantsar, T., Singha, P., Nevalainen, T.-J. et al. (2017). Design, synthesis, and biological evaluation of 2,4-dihydropyrano[2,3-c]pyrazole derivatives as autotaxin inhibitors. *European Journal of Pharmaceutical Sciences* 107: 97–111.

85 Banerjee, S., Norman, D.-D., Deng, S. et al. (2020). Molecular modelling guided design, synthesis and QSAR analysis of new small molecule non-lipid autotaxin inhibitors. *Bioorganic Chemistry* 103: 104188.

86 Fells, J.-I., Lee, S.-C., Norman, D.-D. et al. (2014). Targeting the hydrophobic pocket of autotaxin with virtual screening of inhibitors identifies a common aromatic sulfonamide structural motif. *The FEBS Journal* 281: 1017–1028.

87 Banerjee, S., Norman, D.-D., Lee, S.-C. et al. (2017). Highly potent non-carboxylic acid autotaxin inhibitors reduce melanoma metastasis and chemotherapeutic resistance of breast cancer stem cells. *Journal of Medicinal Chemistry* 60: 1309–1324.

88 Bain, G., Shannon, K.-E., Huang, F. et al. (2017). Selective inhibition of autotaxin is efficacious in mouse models of liver fibrosis. *Journal of Pharmacology and Experimental Therapeutics* 360: 1–13.

89 Black, K.-E., Berdyshev, E., Bain, G. et al. (2016). Autotaxin activity increases locally following lung injury, but is not required for pulmonary lysophosphatidic acid production or fibrosis. *The FASEB Journal* 30: 2435–2450.

90 Miller, L.-M., Keune, W.-J., Castagna, D. et al. (2017). Structure-activity relationships of small molecule autotaxin inhibitors with a discrete binding mode. *Journal of Medicinal Chemistry* 60: 722–748.

91 Desroy, N., Housseman, C., Bock, X. et al. (2017). Discovery of 2-[[2-Ethyl-6-[4-[2-(3-hydroxyazetidin-1-yl)-2-oxoethyl] piperazin-1-yl]-8-methylimidazo [1, 2-a] pyridin-3-yl] methylamino]-4-(4-fluorophenyl) thiazole-5-carbonitrile (GLPG1690), a first-in-class autotaxin inhibitor undergoing clinical evaluation for the treatment of idiopathic pulmonary fibrosis. *ACS Publications* 60: 3580–3590.

92 Blanque, R., Desroy, N., Dupont, S. et al. (2015). Pharmacological profile and efficacy of GLPG1690, a novel ATX inhibitor for COPD treatment. *European Respiratory Society* 46: PA2129.

93 Van der Aar, E., Fagard, L., Desrivot, J. et al. (2015). Favorable human safety, pharmacokinetics and pharmacodynamics of the autotaxin inhibitor GLPG1690, a potential new treatment in COPD. *European Respiratory Society* 46: OA484.

94 Chen, Y., Lei, H., Li, T. et al. (2021). Design, synthesis and anti-fibrosis evaluation of imidazo[1,2-a]pyridine derivatives as potent ATX inhibitors. *Bioorganic & Medicinal Chemistry* 46: 116362.

95 Lei, H., Wang, X., Zhao, G. et al. (2022). Design, synthesis and promising anti-tumor efficacy of novel imidazo[1,2-a]pyridine derivatives as potent autotaxin allosteric inhibitors. *European Journal of Medicinal Chemistry* 236: 114307.

96 Lei, H., Li, Z., Li, T. et al. (2022). Novel imidazo[1,2-a]pyridine derivatives as potent ATX allosteric inhibitors: design, synthesis and promising in vivo anti-fibrotic efficacy in mice lung model. *Bioorganic Chemistry* 120: 105590.

97 Lei, H., Guo, M., Li, X. et al. (2020). Discovery of novel indole-based allosteric highly potent ATX inhibitors with great in vivo efficacy in a mouse lung fibrosis model. *Journal of Medicinal Chemistry* 63: 7326–7346.

98 Jia, F., Lei, H., Chen, Y. et al. (2020). Structure-based linker exploration: discovery of 1-ethyl-1H-indole analogs as novel ATX inhibitors. *Bioorganic & Medicinal Chemistry* 28: 115795.

99 Lei, H., Cao, Z., Wu, H. et al. (2022). Structural and PK-guided identification of indole-based non-acidic autotaxin (ATX) inhibitors exhibiting high in vivo anti-fibrosis efficacy in rodent model. *European Journal of Medicinal Chemistry* 227: 113951.

100 Lei, H., Li, C., Yang, Y. et al. (2020). Structure guided design of potent indole-based ATX inhibitors bearing hydrazone moiety with tumor suppression effects. *European Journal of Medicinal Chemistry* 201: 112456.

101 Kawaguchi, M., Okabe, T., Okudaira, S. et al. (2020). Identification of potent in vivo autotaxin inhibitors that bind to both hydrophobic pockets and channels in the catalytic domain. *Journal of Medicinal Chemistry* 63: 3188–3204.

102 Ma, B., Zhang, L., Sun, L. et al. (2021). Discovery of potent selective nonzinc binding autotaxin inhibitor BIO-32546. *ACS Medicinal Chemistry Letters* 12: 1124–1129.

103 Clark, J.-M., Salgado-Polo, F., Macdonald, S.-J.-F. et al. (2022). Structure-based design of a novel class of autotaxin inhibitors based on endogenous allosteric modulators. *Journal of Medicinal Chemistry* 65: 6338–6351.

104 Jing, T., Miao, X., Jiang, F. et al. (2018). Discovery and optimization of tetrahydropyrido[4,3-d]pyrimidine derivatives as novel ATX and EGFR dual inhibitors. *Bioorganic & Medicinal Chemistry* 26: 1784–1796.

105 Jiang, N., Zhou, Y., Zhu, M. et al. (2020). Optimization and evaluation of novel tetrahydropyrido[4,3-d]pyrimidine derivatives as ATX inhibitors for cardiac and hepatic fibrosis. *European Journal of Medicinal Chemistry* 187: 111904.

106 Eymery, M.-C., Nguyen, K.-A., Basu, S. et al. (2024). Discovery of potent chromone-based autotaxin inhibitors inspired by cannabinoids. *European Journal of Medicinal Chemistry* 263: 115944.

107 Stylianaki, E.-A., Mouchlis, V.-D., Magkrioti, C. et al. (2024). Identification of two novel chemical classes of Autotaxin (ATX) inhibitors using Enalos Asclepios KNIME nodes. *Bioorganic & Medicinal Chemistry Letters* 103: 129690.

13

Targeting ENPP1 for Therapeutic Intervention

Yuyan Han[1,2], *Yaoliang Sun*[1], *and Shilin Xu*[1,2]

[1] *Department of Medicinal Chemistry, Shanghai Institute of Materia Medica, Chinese Academy of Sciences, 555 Zuchongzhi Rd., Shanghai 201203, P.R. China*
[2] *University of Chinese Academy of Science, 19 Yuquan Road, Beijing 100049, P.R. China*

Section I

13.1 Introduction

Ecto-nucleotide pyrophosphatase/phosphodiesterase 1 (ENPP1), also known as CD203a/PC-1, is a metalloenzyme that contains two zinc ions in the catalytic site. ENPP1 is encoded by the *ENPP1* gene located at the 6q22-q23 locus [1]. It is situated on the cell membrane as a homodimer and can also be secreted extracellularly as an enzymatically active monomer [2, 3]. ENPP1 is expressed in various cell types within multiple tissues, including osteoblasts, osteocytes, chondrocytes, smooth muscle cells, proximal tubule epithelial cells of the kidney, mature plasma cells, and skin fibroblasts [4]. ENPP1 plays a key role in regulating purinergic signaling by hydrolyzing extracellular adenosine triphosphate (ATP) and guanosine triphosphate (GTP) into adenosine monophosphate (AMP) and guanosine monophosphate (GMP), respectively, while releasing inorganic pyrophosphate (PPi). Alterations in the *ENPP1* gene, such as deletion, mutation, or overexpression, are associated with the occurrence and development of multiple diseases, including bone and metabolic diseases. Notably, recent studies have demonstrated that ENPP1 is overexpressed in various tumors, where it downregulates the cyclic GMP–AMP synthase (cGAS)–stimulator of interferon genes (STING) signaling pathway by hydrolyzing 2′3′-cyclic guanosine monophosphate–adenosine monophosphate (2′3′-cGAMP), resulting in immunosuppression within the tumor microenvironment. This discovery has sparked significant interest in the pharmaceutical community, leading to the development of numerous small-molecule inhibitors targeting ENPP1. In this

Drug Discovery Targeting Metalloenzymes: Strategies and Applications, First Edition. Edited by Guo-Bo Li.

chapter, we will introduce the structure, catalytic mechanism, and related diseases of ENPP1, as well as the current progress in developing small-molecule inhibitors targeting ENPP1.

13.2 Structure and Catalytic Mechanism

13.2.1 Structure of ENPP1

ENPP1 belongs to the ecto-nucleotide pyrophosphatase/phosphodiesterase (ENPP) family, characterized by their ability to hydrolyze pyrophosphate or phosphodiester bonds in nucleotides [5]. The ENPP enzymes are classified based on localization, substrate specificity, and the order of discovery. They exhibit distinct structural configurations, as depicted in Figure 13.1a. From the perspective of structure and evolution, ENPPs can be categorized into two subgroups: ENPP1–3 and ENPP4–7. ENPP1–3 are multidomain proteins, comprising two tandem N-terminal somatomedin B-like domains (SMB), followed by the phosphodiesterase domain (PDE) and a C-terminal nuclease-like domain (NUC). Notably, ENPP1 and ENPP3 are single-pass type II membrane proteins, while ENPP2 (also known as Autotaxin,

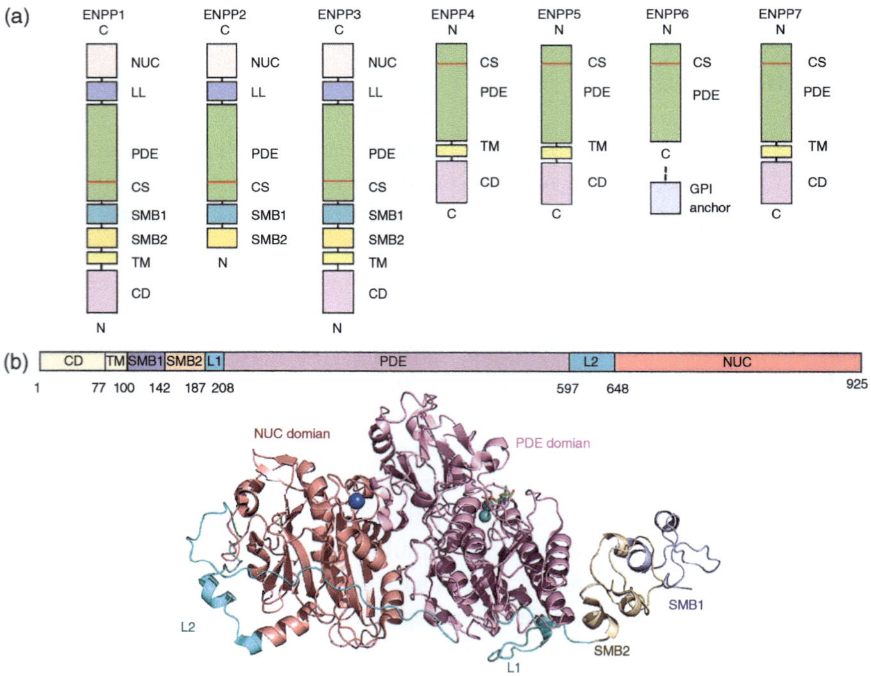

Figure 13.1 Schematics and structure of ENPPs. (a) Schematic diagrams of ENPP1–ENPP7. PDE, phosphodiesterase domain; CS, catalytic site; SMB1/2, somatomedin B-like domain 1/2; NUC, nuclease-like domain; LL, lasso loop; TM, transmembrane domain; CD, cytoplasmic domain. (b) Three-dimensional structure of human ENPP1 (PDB: 6WFJ), with zinc ions represented as green spheres and the calcium ion as blue spheres.

ATX) is a secreted protein [6, 7]. In contrast, ENPP4–7 contain only a single PDE domain in their extracellular domain. ENPP4, ENPP5, and ENPP7 are classified as single-pass type I membrane proteins, whereas ENPP6 is anchored to the plasma membrane via a glycosylphosphatidylinositol (GPI) linkage [8, 9].

Human ENPP1 is a single-chain metalloenzyme comprising over 900 amino acids, along with one calcium ion and two zinc ions, as illustrated in Figure 13.1b. The extracellular domain of ENPP1 includes two SMB domains (SMB1–2), a PDE domain, and a NUC domain. Moreover, two linker regions (L1 and L2) are believed to strengthen the interaction between the PDE domain and the NUC domain. The transmembrane domain (TM) consists of a hydrophobic region that traverses the plasma membrane, followed by a cytoplasmic domain (CD).

The two SMB domains of ENPP1 are tightly bound by a disulfide bond and are structurally similar to the SMB domain of vitronectin, which is known to promote the adhesion, extension, and proliferation of endothelial cells, as well as the differentiation of various normal and cancer cells [10]. Although the SMB domains do not participate in the catalytic function of ENPP1, they facilitate homodimerization, which is crucial for the membrane localization and stability of the enzyme [11, 12]. Additionally, the PDE domain resides in the extracellular space, where it cleaves high-energy phosphate bonds in nucleotide triphosphates (e.g., ATP, GTP) to generate extracellular PPi and nucleotide monophosphates (e.g., AMP, GMP), as well as cyclic nucleotides such as 2′3′-cGAMP, generating 5′-AMP and 5′-GMP. The catalytic site of the PDE domain is centrally located within a β-sheet structure and flanked by an α-helix. This catalytic site contains two zinc ions situated within a shallow groove where substrate binding occurs. The zinc ions are coordinated by seven residues: Zn1 is coordinated by two histidines and an aspartate, while Zn2 is coordinated by two aspartates, a histidine, and a threonine (Figure 13.2a).

The NUC domain is characterized by a six-stranded antiparallel β-sheet surrounded by eight α-helices, and shares structural similarities with bacterial nonspecific endonucleases, such as Nuclease A [13]. Despite this similarity, the NUC domain of ENPP1 does not exhibit endonuclease activity [14]. The NUC

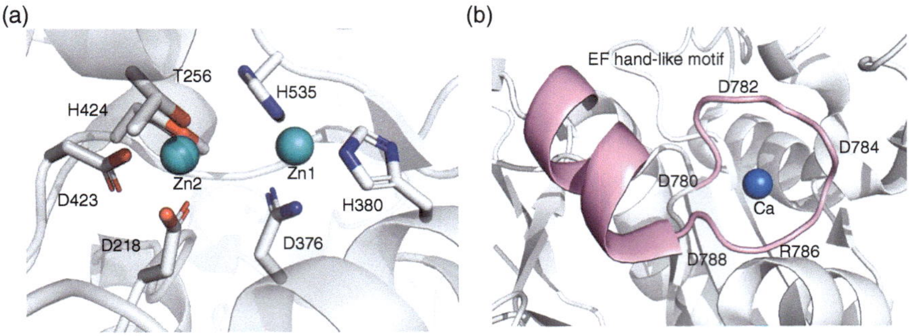

Figure 13.2 Structural diagrams of the catalytic site and EF-hand-like motif in ENPP1. (a) The chelation of zinc ions within the active site of ENPP1 (PDB: 6WFJ). (b) The EF-hand-like motif in the NUC domain of ENPP1 (PDB: 4GTW).

domain features an EF-hand-like motif, as shown in Figure 13.2b. This EF-hand-like motif in mouse ENPP1, which binds a calcium ion, is composed of Asp780, Asp782, Asp784, Arg786, and Asp788 [5]. Notably, the interaction between Asp780 in the NUC domain and Lys479 in the PDE domain is vital for ENPP1's stability and enzymatic activity [15].

13.2.2 Catalytic Mechanism of ENPP1

ENPP1 primarily catalyzes the hydrolysis of ATP to AMP and PPi, as well as the conversion of 2′3′-cGAMP to 5′-AMP and 5′-GMP (Figure 13.3). Additionally, ENPP1 can hydrolyze a range of other substrates, such as GTP, cytidine triphosphate (CTP), uridine triphosphate (UTP), diadenosine 5′,5‴-P1,P3-triphosphate (Ap3A), diadenosine 5′,5‴-P1,P4-tetraphosphate (Ap4A), diadenosine 5′,5‴-P1,P5-pentaphosphate (Ap5A), diguanosine 5′,5‴-P1,P4-triphosphate (Gp4G), nicotinamide adenine dinucleotide (NAD^+), and cyclic adenosine monophosphate (cGMP) [5]. As ATP approaches the ENPP1 protein, its adenine base is accommodated in the nucleotide-binding pocket (N-pocket) [16], and the α-phosphate group interacts with the two zinc ions in the active site of ENPP1, initiating the bond cleavage process to yield AMP and PPi [12]. Analysis of the co-crystal structure of ENPP1 with AMP (Figure 13.4a, PDB: 6WFJ), reveals that the nucleotide base is positioned between Tyr340 and Phe257, forming a π–π interaction with Tyr340. Additionally, the N1 atom of AMP forms a hydrogen bond with Lys295, and the phosphonate group of AMP interacts with the zinc ion in the catalytic site. AMP also exhibits close interactions with other residues, including Asn277, Asn376, His380, His424, and His535.

ENPP1 employs distinct mechanisms to hydrolyze 2′3′-cGAMP. Initially, ENPP1 binds the adenine and guanine bases of 2′3′-cGAMP in the N-pocket

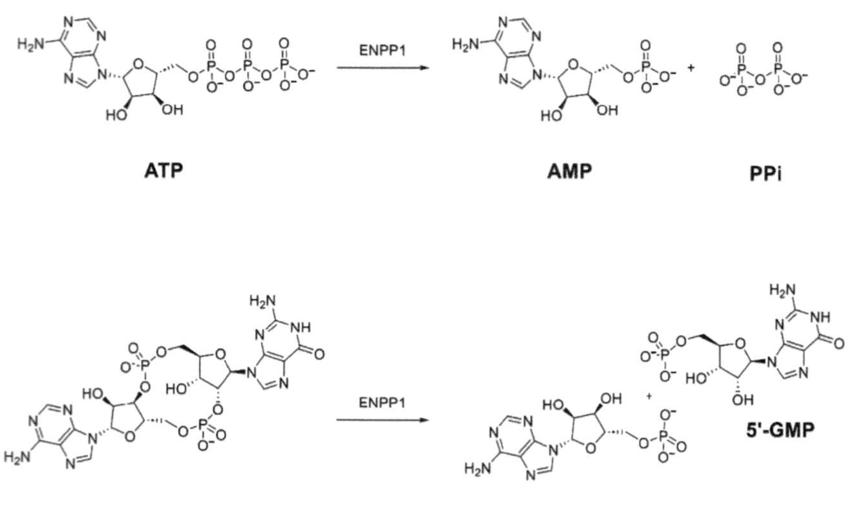

ATP AMP PPi

5'-GMP

2'3'-cGAMP 5'-AMP

Figure 13.3 Hydrolysis of ATP and 2′3′-cGAMP catalyzed by ENPP1.

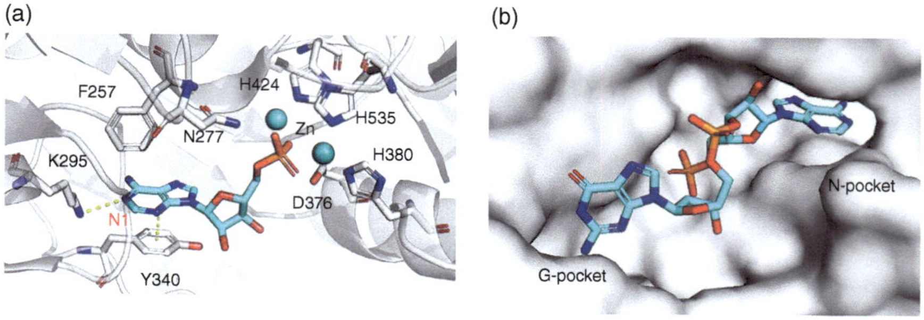

Figure 13.4 Structure of ENPP1 in complex with AMP and pApG. (a) Co-crystal structure of ENPP1 bound to AMP (PDB: 6WFJ). (b) Co-crystal structure of ENPP1 bound to pApG (PDB: 6AEK).

and the guanine-binding pocket (G-pocket), respectively (Figure 13.4b). The 2′-5′ phosphodiester bond is activated by the zinc ions (Figure 13.5a), and the oxygen atom of Thr238 nucleophilically attacks the phosphorus atom in this bond, yielding pApG (Figure 13.5a). Subsequently, the guanine base of pApG flips over and fits into the N-pocket, similar to the binding model of GMP in the ENPP1–GMP complex structure (Figure 13.5b) [17]. In this binding model, the 3′-5′ phosphodiester bond of pApG is positioned within the catalytic center (Figure 13.5c). Finally, ENPP1 hydrolyzes pApG to form 5′-AMP and 5′-GMP (Figure 13.5d). Notably, the intermediate state of pApG is transient, indicating the rapid processing by ENPP1 [18, 19].

13.3 ENPP1-Related Diseases

Dysfunction of ENPP1 is associated with a variety of diseases. Inactivating mutations in the *ENPP1* gene cause generalized arterial calcification of infancy (GACI), a condition with high mortality rates [20]. The downregulation of ENPP1 activity potentially correlates with the pathogenesis of atherosclerosis and osteoarthritis [21–25]. Mutations such as Cys120Arg and Cys164Ser within the SMB1 and SMB2 domains are implicated in Cole disease [26]. Furthermore, both overexpression and mutations of ENPP1 have been linked to systemic insulin resistance and diabetes [27]. Recent studies have also identified aberrant ENPP1 as a contributing factor in tumor onset and progression [28].

13.3.1 ENPP1 and Biomineralization Disorders

Dysregulation of the extracellular purine metabolic pathway is implicated in various diseases associated with biomineralization disorders, with ENPP1 playing a pivotal role in this process (Figure 13.6). ATP-binding cassette subfamily C member 6 (ABCC6) facilitates the transport of ATP into the blood, where ENPP1 hydrolyzes it into AMP and PPi. Subsequently, cluster of differentiation 73 (CD73) converts AMP into adenosine and inorganic phosphate, while tissue-nonspecific alkaline phosphatase (TNAP) catalyzes the hydrolysis of PPi into inorganic

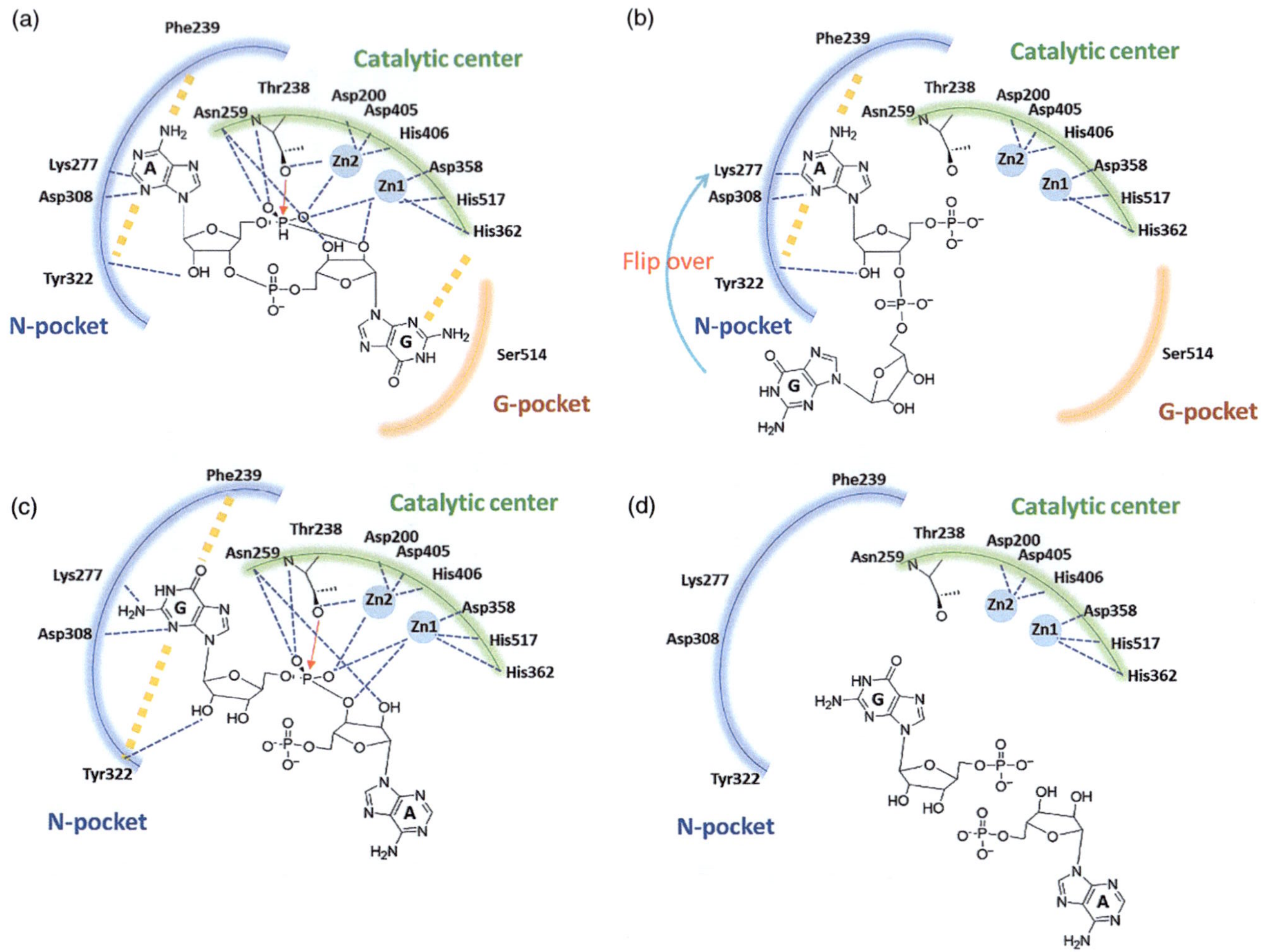

(a)
Phe239
Catalytic center
Thr238
Asn259
Asp200
Asp405
His406
Asp358
His517
His362
Zn2
Zn1
Lys277
Asp308
Tyr322
N-pocket
Ser514
G-pocket
(b)
Flip over
(c)
(d)

Figure 13.5 Hydrolysis of 2′3′-cGAMP by ENPP1. (a) The adenine and guanine bases of 2′3′-cGAMP are positioned in the N-pocket and G-pocket, respectively. The nucleophilic attack of Thr238 to the phosphorus atom results in the cleavage of 2′-5′ phosphodiester bond and yields pApG; (b) The guanine base of pApG undergoes a conformational change. (c) The guanine base of pApG is then accommodated in the N-pocket, and the 3′-5′ phosphodiester bond is positioned in the catalytic center. The 3′-5′ phosphodiester bond is cleaved similarly to the 2′-5′ phosphodiester bond; (d) The final products, 5′-AMP and 5′-GMP, are released from ENPP1.

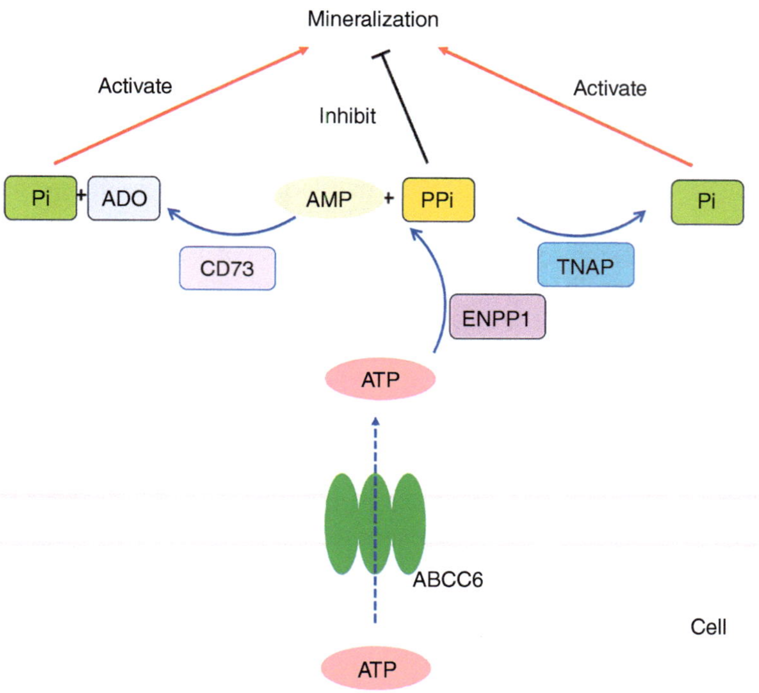

Figure 13.6 Extracellular purine metabolic pathway. Pi, inorganic phosphate; ADO, adenosine; AMP, adenosine monophosphate; CD73, cluster of differentiation 73; TNAP, tissue-nonspecific alkaline phosphatase; ENPP1, ecto-nucleotide pyrophosphatase/phosphodiesterase 1; ATP, adenosine triphosphate; ABCC6, ATP-binding cassette subfamily C member 6.

phosphate (Pi). The resulting Pi combines with calcium to form hydroxyapatite, which constitutes the hard mineral phase of bone. However, PPi can replace the Pi in hydroxyapatite to prevent the formation of crystals, thereby inhibiting biomineralization. Thus, maintaining the balance between PPi and Pi, regulated by the key regulator ENPP1, is critical for normal biomineralization.

Inactivation of ENPP1 reduces PPi in the plasma, resulting in several serious conditions, including GACI, autosomal recessive hyperphosphatemic rickets type 2 (ARHR2), and ossification of the posterior longitudinal ligament (OPLL) of the spine. GACI is characterized by vascular calcification that threatens the life of the infant during the second trimester. Affected infants typically experience stroke, severe hypertension, and heart failure within the first week of life. Those who survive often develop ARHR2 and enthesopathy of the extremities and spine, with progressive worsening over time [18]. Other biomineralization disorders associated with ENPP1 dysfunction include calcified coronary artery lesions, early-onset osteoporosis in middle-aged adults, elastic fibrous pseudotumor, and others [29–31].

13.3.2 ENPP1 and Insulin Resistance

Overexpression and mutations of the *ENPP1* gene significantly affect insulin signaling. The SMB2 region of the ENPP1 protein binds directly to the alpha subunit of the insulin receptor, inducing a structural alteration in the receptor's beta subunit. This alteration hinders the beta subunit's autophosphorylation, consequently blocking downstream signaling cascades involving phosphoinositide 3-kinase (PI3K) and protein kinase B (Akt). As a result, the normal translocation of glucose transporter type 4 (GLUT4) to the plasma membrane is disrupted, leading to impaired glucose uptake, disrupted cellular glucose regulation, and the onset of diabetes and obesity [32, 33]. Furthermore, insulin resistance may be correlated with genetic mutations in ENPP1. For instance, the K121Q mutation within the SMB2 domain of ENPP1 is associated with obesity and type 2 diabetes [33], although the mechanism remains unclear.

13.3.3 ENPP1 and Cancer

The *ENPP1* gene is located at the 6q22-q23 locus, a region frequently amplified in various tumors [34, 35]. Elevated ENPP1 expression has been observed in numerous solid tumors, including ovarian cancer [36], breast cancer [37, 38], glioblastoma [39], and non-small cell lung cancer (NSCLC) [40]. Moreover, clinical specimens reveal that ENPP1 protein levels increase during different stages of tumorigenesis, with stronger expression correlating with later stages and poorer cell differentiation [36]. ENPP1 is also highly expressed in several immunosuppressive cells, such as neutrophils and M2 macrophages, which promotes tumor progression. In contrast, low levels of expression are detected in natural killer cells (NK cells), dendritic cells (DCs), monocytes, and T and B cells.

Overexpression of ENPP1 mainly affects antitumor immunity through two mechanisms [41]. First, ENPP1 hydrolyzes extracellular 2′3′-cGAMP, suppressing the activation of the cGAS–STING signaling pathway in immune cells, thereby facilitating immune evasion (Figure 13.7). Second, ENPP1 degrades extracellular 2′3′-cGAMP, ATP, and NAD^+ into AMP, which is subsequently hydrolyzed into adenosine, promoting immunosuppression (Figure 13.8).

ENPP1 has recently been identified as a key regulator of the cGAS–STING pathway by hydrolyzing 2′3′-cGAMP. Specifically, pathogen invasion, mitochondrial damage, or genome instability can cause the accumulation of cytoplasmic double-stranded DNA (dsDNA), which is recognized by the DNA receptor cGAS. Upon recognition, cGAS catalyzes the formation of the secondary messenger 2′3′-cGAMP from GTP and ATP [42]. The 2′3′-cGAMP subsequently binds to the receptor protein STING, which is a stable dimer on the endoplasmic reticulum membrane, triggering STING oligomerization and conformational changes that

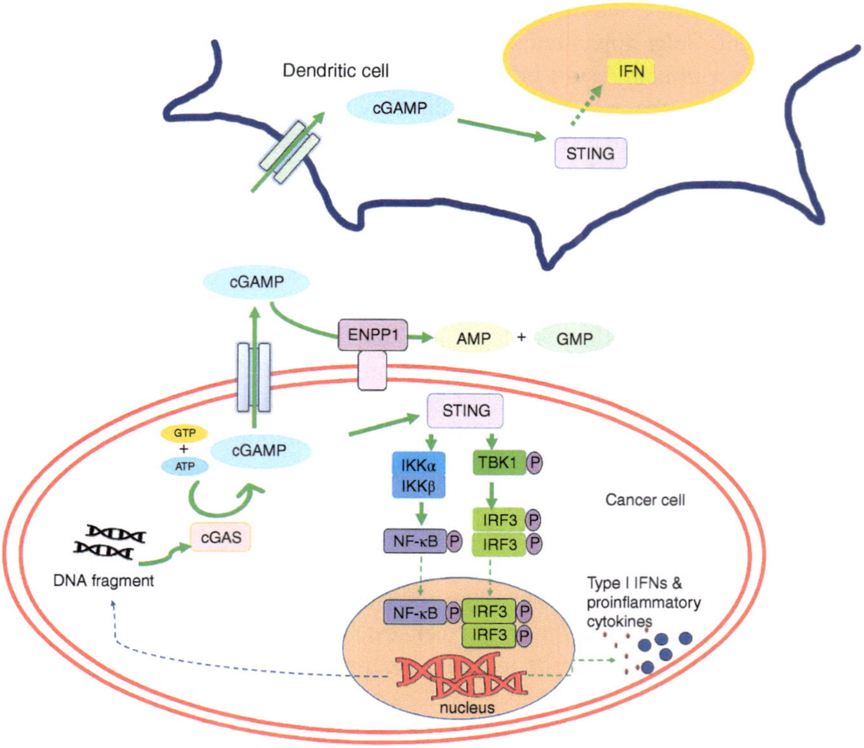

Figure 13.7 ENPP1 interacts with the STING pathway in the tumor microenvironment. 2′3′-cGAMP, cyclic GMP–AMP; STING, stimulator of interferon genes; IFN, Interferon; ENPP1, ecto-nucleotide pyrophosphatase/phosphodiesterase 1; AMP, adenosine monophosphate; GMP, guanosine monophosphate; GTP, guanosine triphosphate; ATP, adenosine triphosphate; cGAS, cyclic GMP–AMP synthase; IKK, IκB kinase; TBK1, TANK-binding kinases 1; IRF3, interferon regulatory factor 3; NF-κB, nuclear factor kappa-B.

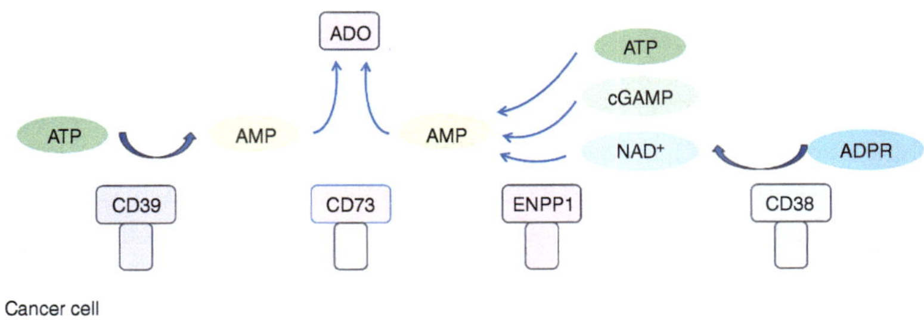

Figure 13.8 ENPP1 participates in the generation of adenosine in the tumor microenvironment. ATP, adenosine 5′-triphosphate; AMP, adenosine monophosphate; ADO, adenosine; 2′3′-cGAMP, cyclic GMP–AMP; NAD^+, nicotinamide adenine dinucleotide; ADPR, adenosine diphosphate ribose; CD39, cluster of differentiation 39; CD73, cluster of differentiation 73; ENPP1, ecto-nucleotide pyrophosphatase/phosphodiesterase 1; CD38, cluster of differentiation 38.

lead to its activation. Once activated, STING translocates from the endoplasmic reticulum to the Golgi apparatus [43], where it recruits TANK-binding kinase 1 (TBK1). This recruitment results in TBK1 autophosphorylation and the subsequent phosphorylation of the nearby STING dimer within the same oligomer [44]. Phosphorylated STING then recruits interferon regulatory factor 3 (IRF3), which is subsequently phosphorylated by TBK1. Phosphorylated IRF3 forms dimers and translocates to the nucleus, thereby promoting the transcription, translation, and secretion of type I interferons (IFNs) [45], which are effective antiviral and antitumor cytokines. In Parallel, STING recruits IκB kinase (IKK), resulting in translocation of nuclear factor kappa-B (NF-κB) into the nucleus and expression of proinflammatory cytokines such as IL-6 and tumor necrosis factor (TNF) [46, 47]. STING activation triggers the activation of dendritic cells, enhances the cytotoxic functions of natural killer cells, and promotes the proliferation of cytotoxic $CD8^+$ T cells, ultimately leading to the elimination of cancer cells [47]. Intracellular 2′3′-cGAMP has been verified to be continuously exported into the tumor microenvironment, where it is taken up by neighboring cells, activating the STING signaling pathway and inducing a robust antitumor immune response [48]. Notably, accumulating evidence indicates that cancer cells have evolved to overexpress ENPP1, which hydrolyzes the extracellular 2′3′-cGAMP into AMP and GMP, thereby counteracting the tumor cell–extrinsic STING signaling pathway and eventually promoting tumor immune escape and metastasis [48, 49]. Very recent research has also uncovered ENPP3 as the second 2′3′-cGAMP hydrolase and proposed that dual inhibition of both ENPP1 and ENPP3 could be a valuable strategy for benefiting a broader population of cancer patients [50].

Apart from downregulating the cGAS–STING signaling, ENPP1 also participates in the generation of adenosine in the tumor microenvironment, thus fostering immune suppression [51]. Extracellular adenosine can be generated through the ENPP1–CD73-dependent pathway. For example, ENPP1 hydrolyzes 2′3′-cGAMP or ATP, which is abundant in the tumor microenvironment due to necrosis, apoptosis, and cellular stress, into AMP. This AMP is subsequently hydrolyzed by membrane-bound CD73 to generate adenosine [52], leading to its accumulation in the tumor microenvironment. Another pathway involves the cluster of differentiation 38 (CD38)–ENPP1–CD73 axis, where CD38 converts NAD^+ into adenosine diphosphate ribose (ADPR), followed by ENPP1-mediated conversion of ADPR into AMP, which is then processed by CD73 into adenosine. Additionally, adenosine can also be generated through ENPP1-independent pathways, such as the cluster of differentiation 39 (CD39)–CD73 pathway. The accumulated extracellular adenosine exerts its regulatory functions by binding to and stimulating adenosine receptors, such as adenosine 2a receptor (A2AR) and adenosine A2B receptor (A2BR), which in turn upregulate adenylate cyclase activity and trigger cAMP-dependent signaling. In T cells, extracellular adenosine inhibits T cell receptor signaling, T-cell-specific surface glycoprotein (CD28) co-stimulation, and IL-2R signaling through A2AR activation, thereby affecting the activation, proliferation, survival, cytokine production (such as IFN-γ, TNFα, and IL-2), and cytotoxic activity of effector T cells. Moreover, A2AR activation induces the expression of co-inhibitory molecules like programmed death 1 (PD-1) and Lymphocyte Activation Gene-3

(LAG-3) and promotes the differentiation of CD4+ T cells into regulatory T cells (Tregs) [53]. Extracellular adenosine also impairs the priming ability of $CD8^+$ T cells by affecting the differentiation of DCs. Overall, the overexpression of ENPP1 facilitates the adenosine accumulation in the tumor microenvironment, which hinders antitumor immune responses by suppressing immune-active cells and enhancing tumor-promoting activities.

13.4 ENPP1 Inhibitor Discovery

Given the potential roles of ENPP1 in human diseases, the development of its small-molecule inhibitors could present a significant therapeutic opportunity and offer chemical tools to explore its biological functions. Over the past decades, numerous ENPP1 inhibitors have been developed, which can be primarily classified into two categories: nucleoside-based and non-nucleoside inhibitors. Currently, four small-molecule inhibitors of ENPP1 have progressed into clinical research for cancer treatment. In this section, we will systematically introduce these inhibitors.

13.4.1 Nucleoside-Based ENPP1 Inhibitors

The unique catalytic activity of ENPP1 on nucleotide substrates results in the formation of products like AMP and uridine monophosphate (UMP), which can act as inhibitors of ENPP1. Therefore, a series of substrate analogs have been synthesized as ENPP1 inhibitors, which primarily function through competitive binding. Among these, adenine and uridine nucleotide derivatives have drawn significant interest and attention for their potential inhibitory effects [54].

Several adenine nucleotide derivatives, including α,β-metADP (**1**), α,β-metATP (**2**), γ-S-α,β-metATP derivative (**3**), α-borano-β,γ-metATP derivative (**4**), ARL67156 (**5**), and bzATP (**6**), have been identified as inhibitors of human ENPP1 (Figure 13.9). Their inhibitory efficacy was determined using human soluble ENPP1 with ATP or p-Nph-5′-TMP as substrates. The K_i values for these inhibitors ranged from 0.5 to 16.5 μM, indicating moderate potency [55]. Moreover, 2-methylthio-adenine derivatives 2-MeSADP (**7**) and 2-MeSATP (**8**) showed weaker inhibition against ENPP1 with K_i values exceeding 25 μM. Additionally, dialADP (**9**) and dialATP (**10**), obtained by opening the ribose ring, retained their inhibitory activity. This suggests that modifications to ring and chain architectures may be a pivotal alternative strategy for developing nucleotide analog-based ENPP1 inhibitors.

Eliahu et al. reported a series of novel dinucleotide analogs (**11–14**) as ENPP1 inhibitors [56], demonstrating moderate inhibitory activity (Figure 13.10). These analogs were able to completely inhibit ENPP1 activity in HTB-85 and HT29 cells using pNP-TMP as the substrate, at a concentration of 100 μM. Since uracil nucleotide analogs are recognized by fewer proteins as substrates, they may have a reduced potential for off-target effects. Therefore, Zelikman et al. developed a series of uridine 5′-$P_{\alpha,\alpha}$-dithiophosphate analogs, exemplified by compound **15**, which exhibited a K_i of 27 nM. Furthermore, at a concentration of 100 μM, compound **15** was selective for ENPP1 over human nucleoside triphosphate diphosphohydrolase 1 (NTPDase 1), nucleoside triphosphate diphosphohydrolase 2 (NTPDase 2),

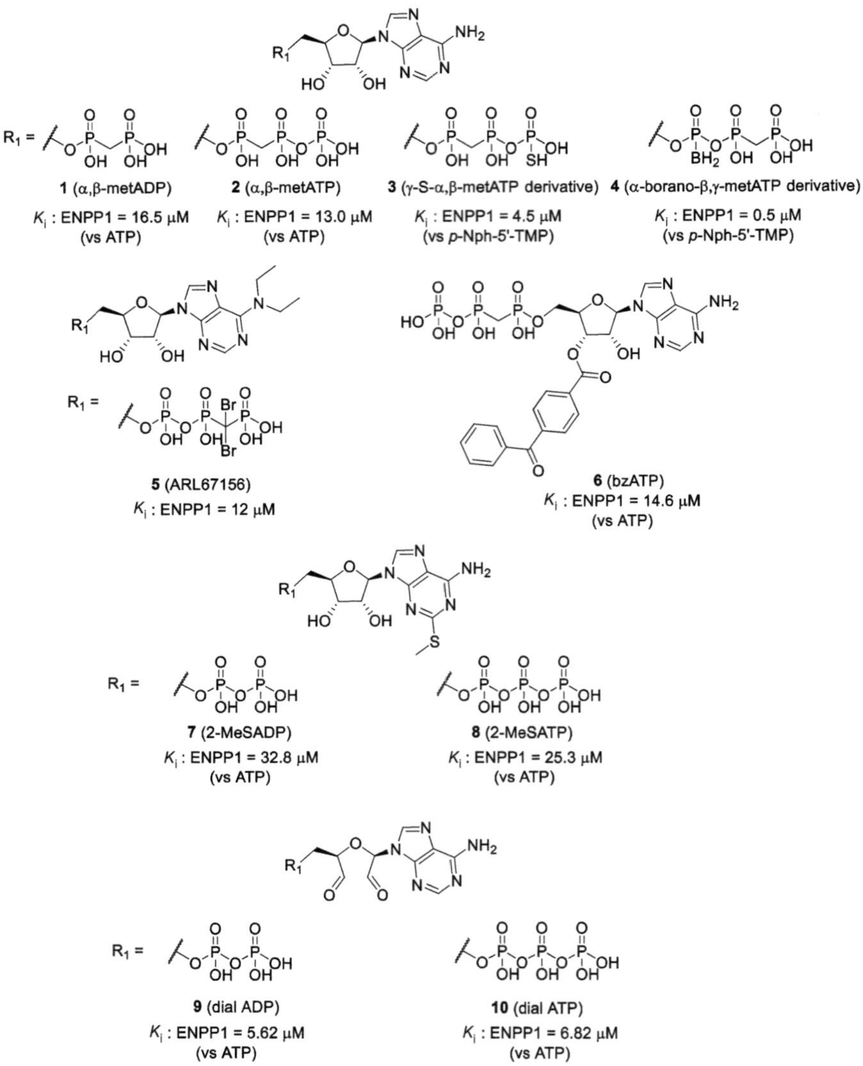

Figure 13.9 Structures of ENPP1 inhibitors based on adenine nucleotide derivatives.

and nucleoside triphosphate diphosphohydrolase 8 (NTPDase 8), indicating that it is an active, selective, and stable ENPP1 inhibitor [57].

Despite their potency, nucleotide analogs exhibit a high level of acidity, which results in poor permeability and low oral bioavailability. Furthermore, these inhibitors show limited selectivity for ENPP1 compared to other members of the ectonucleotidase family. The structural similarities between these inhibitors and endogenous substrates raise concerns about potential off-target interactions, including inadvertent stimulation of P2 purinergic receptors, which could increase the risk of adverse effects. As a result, nucleotide-based inhibitors may not be ideal candidates for developing clinically effective ENPP1-targeting therapeutics.

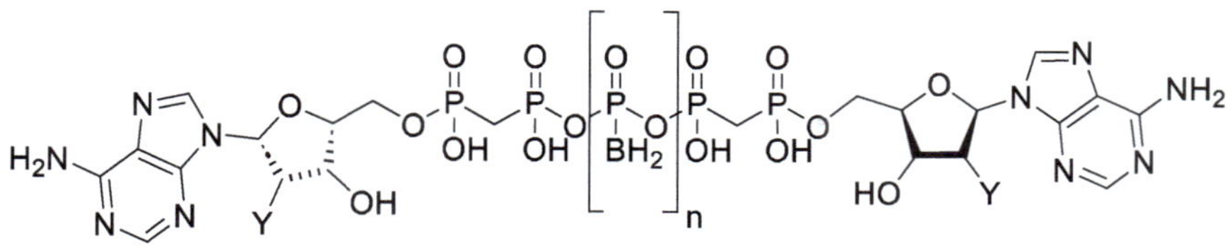

11 Y = OH X = CH_2 n = 1 IC_{50} = 63 μM
12 Y = H X = CH_2 n = 1 IC_{50} = 13 μM
13 Y = OH X = CH_2 n = 0 IC_{50} = 33 μM
14 Y = H X = CH_2 n = 0 IC_{50} = 50 μM

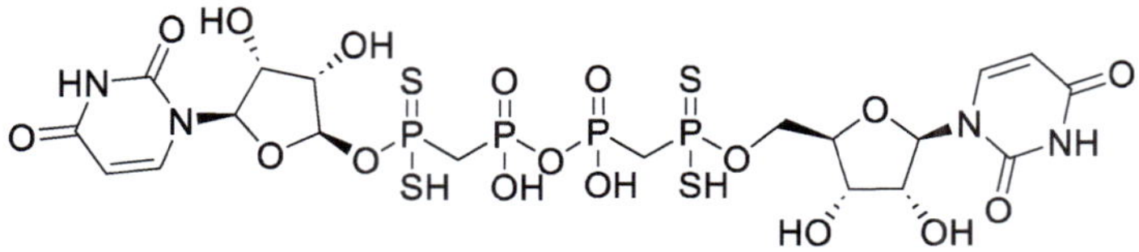

15 K_i : ENPP1 = 27 nM
(vs pNP-TMP)

Figure 13.10 Structures of dinucleotide ENPP1 inhibitors.

13.4.2 Non-Nucleoside ENPP1 Inhibitors

Nucleoside-derived ENPP1 inhibitors encounter significant challenges, including poor water solubility, limited oral bioavailability, and potential off-target effects. Conversely, non-nucleoside ENPP1 inhibitors present a promising alternative to address these issues. Reported non-nucleoside ENPP1 inhibitors typically feature three pharmacophore components: a central core, a zinc-binding group, and a linker (Figure 13.11). The central core usually consists of fused aromatic rings that anchor into the N-pocket, while the zinc-binding group, often composed of polar functional groups, coordinates with zinc ions in the catalytic pocket. The linker connects these two components. In addition, some inhibitors lack a well-defined

Figure 13.11 Pharmacophore components of typical non-nucleoside ENPP1 inhibitors.

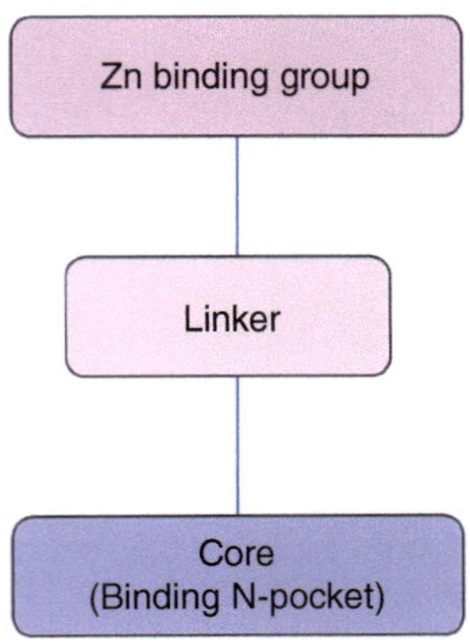

zinc ion–binding group, and their binding modes with the protein remain unclear. These inhibitors will be discussed separately in the following sections.

13.4.2.1 ENPP1 Inhibitors Based on Sulfamide, Sulfonamide and Sulfonimidamide Group

QS1 (**16**) was the first quinazoline-based small molecule reported to exhibit potent inhibitory activity against ENPP1, with an IC_{50} of 36 nM, as measured by an *in vitro* Kinase-Glo assay monitoring the consumption of ATP by the ENPP1 enzyme. However, QS1 also acted as a ligand for human ether-a-go-go-related gene (hERG) potassium channels, with an affinity of 601 nM in the tritiated dofetilide binding assay. This off-target effect would lead to cardiovascular side effects and QT prolongation [58].

To improve the safety profile of QS1, a structure–activity relationship (SAR) study was performed (Figure 13.12). The investigation revealed that minor alterations to the quinazoline ring did not effectively reduce the compounds' ability to inhibit hERG. For instance, compound **17**, featuring a 7-OMe substitution on the quinazoline ring, demonstrated a higher hERG binding affinity with an IC_{50} of 120 nM. Compound **18**, with a modification at the 2-position of the quinazoline ring, demonstrated effective ENPP1 inhibition while preserving submicromolar potency against hERG. Conversely, the introduction of a 6-methylimidazole moiety into the pyrimidine ring (**19**) completely abolished hERG binding activity but led to a significant loss of ENPP1 inhibitory activity. Consequently, the focus shifted to modifying the linker. Shortening the linker from 4-ethyl piperidine to 4-methylene piperidine or piperidine resulted in derivatives that showed no measurable hERG

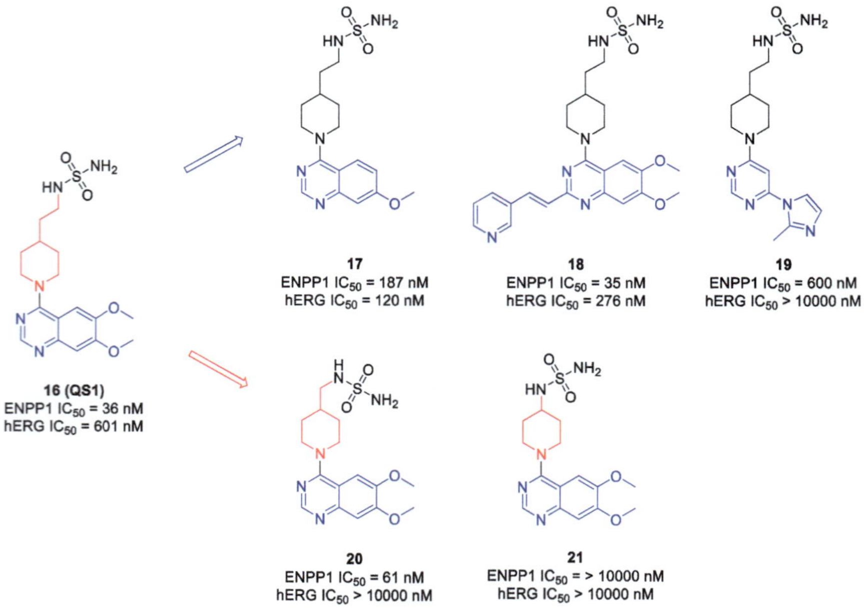

Figure 13.12 Modifications to the quinazoline region and linker lengths in QS1 (**16**). *Source:* MDPI / CC BY 4.0.

binding affinity. For example, compound **20** with 4-methylene piperidine as linker maintained ENPP1 inhibitory properties, while completely abolishing its hERG binding activity. However, compound **21** with a piperidine linker exhibits a complete loss in ENPP1 inhibitory activity despite showing no activity to hERG. This observation highlights the crucial role of the linker in modulating both ENPP1 inhibition and hERG binding activity. Shayhidin et al. also investigated the inhibitory potencies of QS1 and compound **20** against ENPP1, revealing K_i values of 59.3 nM and 110 nM, respectively [59]. Additionally, QS1 demonstrated excellent selectivity, showing no significant activity against ENPP3, NTPDase 1, NTPDase 2, nucleoside triphosphate diphosphohydrolase 3 (NTPDase 3), alkaline phosphatase (ALP), or CD73.

The co-crystal structure of compound **20** with the ENPP1 catalytic domain (PDB: 6WEV) provided detailed insight into its binding interactions (Figure 13.13) [60]. The sulfamide group of **20** established a robust hydrogen bonding network with water and amino acid residues surrounding the two zinc ions. The quinazoline core scaffold was located in the hydrophobic pocket, where it was stabilized by π–π stacking interactions with Phe257 and Tyr340. Furthermore, the methoxy group at the 8-position of the quinazoline ring formed a hydrogen bond with Tyr322, while the nitrogen atom of the aromatic ring established another hydrogen bond with Lys295. This co-crystal structure not only elucidates the mode of action of compound **20** but also provides a structural basis for the design of similar ENPP1 inhibitors.

Building on the structure of QS1, Jung and colleagues identified two classes of ENPP1 inhibitors, characterized by 3,4-dihydropyrimido[4,5-*d*]pyrimidin-2(1*H*)-one and 3,4-dihydropyrido[2,3-*d*]pyrimidin-2(1*H*)-one as their central cores (Figure 13.14) [61]. The lead compound, **22**, exhibited moderate potency with an IC_{50} value of 766 nM in the AMP-Glo assay. Compound **23**, featuring an *m*-benzyl linker, showed enhanced activity with an IC_{50} of 525 nM. Further improvements were seen with compound **24**, which contained a *p*-benzyl linker and demonstrated

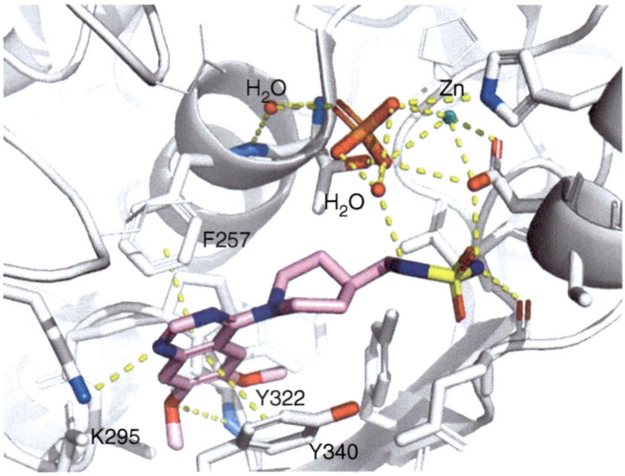

Figure 13.13 The co-crystal structure of compound **20** with ENPP1 (PDB: 6WEV).

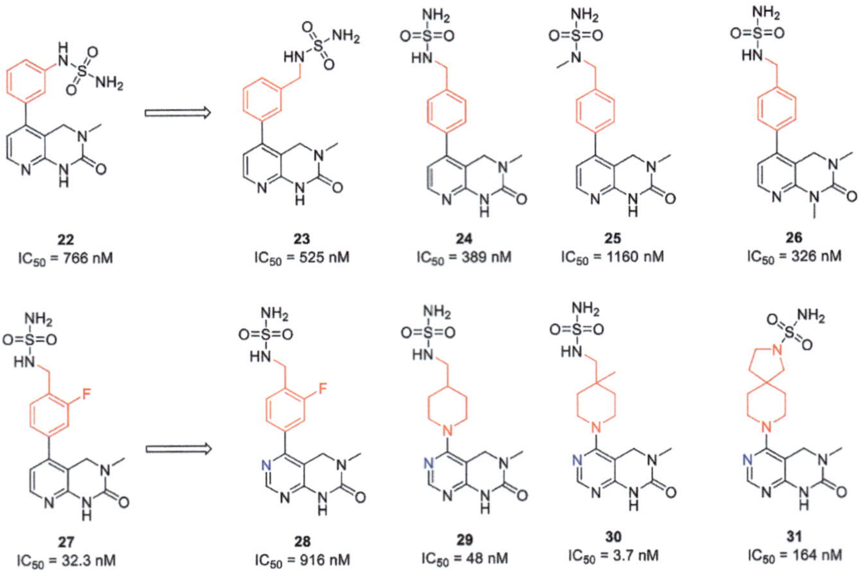

Figure 13.14 The structures of inhibitors based on 3,4-dihydropyrimido[4,5-*d*]pyrimidin-2(1*H*)-one and 3,4-dihydropyrido[2,3-*d*]pyrimidin-2(1*H*)-one cores.

an IC_{50} of 389 nM. However, the introduction of a methyl group to the sulfamide moiety resulted in reduced activity, as compound **25** displayed a higher IC_{50} of 1160 nM. Adding an additional methyl group on the dihydropyrimidine ring was tolerable, with compound 26 showing slightly increased activity (IC_{50} = 326 nM). Compound **27**, which incorporated a fluoro-phenyl linker, exhibited the strongest inhibition within the series, with an IC_{50} of 32.3 nM. When the central core was replaced with a 3,4-dihydropyrimido[4,5-*d*]pyrimidin-2(1*H*)-one scaffold, resulting in compound **28**, a slight decrease in potency was observed (IC_{50} = 916 nM) compared to compound **27**. Notably, the replacement of a piperidine linker (**29**) resulted in an obvious increase in potency (IC_{50} of 48 nM). Furthermore, adding a methyl group to the piperidine ring in compound **30** significantly enhanced its inhibitory activity against ENPP1 (IC_{50} = 3.7 nM). Conversely, the spirocyclic compound **31** exhibited a decrease in potency, with an IC_{50} value of 164 nM.

The microsomal stability of compounds **26** and **30** was evaluated using liver microsomes from humans, rats, and mice. The results demonstrated that both compounds exhibited favorable stability profiles across all species. Furthermore, neither compound **26** nor compound **30** showed significant inhibition of the five primary cytochrome P450 enzymes (CYP1A2, CYP2C9, CYP2C19, CYP2D6, and CYP3A4), as detailed in Table 13.1. These findings suggest that both compounds possess favorable stability and safety profiles, supporting their potential for further development.

Shortly thereafter, Hand and colleagues reported novel pyrrolopyrimidine derivatives as ENPP1 inhibitors, conducting an comprehensive study of their SARs (Figure 13.15) [62]. Compound **32** was designed by substituting the quinazoline

Table 13.1 Microsomal stabilities and CYP inhibition profile of compounds **26** and **30**.

Compound	Microsomal stability (%)[a)] Human	Rat	Mouse	CYP remaining activity (%)[b)] 1A2	2C9	2C19	2D6	3A4
26	86.9	86.7	91.1	>100	>100	>100	>100	>100
30	85.9	82.3	96.4	94.3	89.4	>100	90.9	89.7

a) % remaining during 30 min at 1 μM.
b) % of control activity at 10 μM.

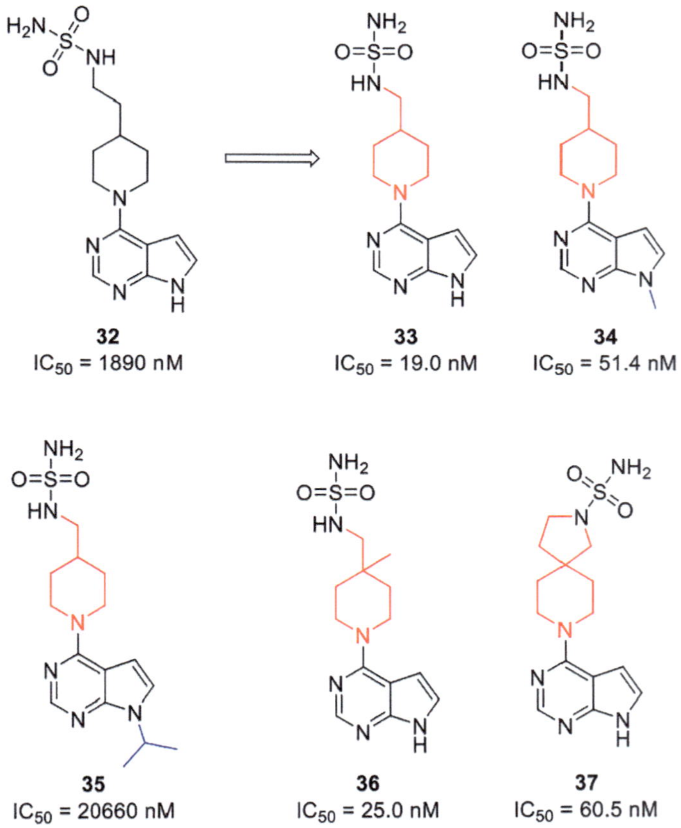

Figure 13.15 Structures of ENPP1 inhibitors featuring a pyrrolopyrimidine core.

core of QS1 with a pyrrolopyrimidine core. In an *in vitro* assay using recombinant human ENPP1 and the AMP-Glo method, compound **32** demonstrated an IC_{50} of 1890 nM. Notably, shortening this linker led to a substantial increase in potency, with compound **33** presenting an IC_{50} of 19.0 nM. While N-methylated pyrrolopyrimidine (**34**) retained high efficacy (IC_{50} = 51.4 nM), the isopropyl derivative **35** exhibited a substantial reduction in activity (IC_{50} = 20,660 nM). Additionally, the piperidine derivative **36**, featuring a quaternary carbon center, showed comparable ENPP1 inhibitory activity (IC_{50} = 25.0 nM) to **33**. However, introducing a spiro ring structure into the linker induced a threefold decrease in potency, as compound **37** exhibited an IC_{50} value of 60.5 nM.

To further investigate the immune-enhancing effects of compound **36**, its impact was assessed in THP-1 human monocytes containing an interferon-stimulated response element (ISRE) luciferase reporter system. When cells were treated with a low concentration of 2′3′-cGAMP (1 μg/ml), only a modest induction of the luciferase signal was observed. However, co-administration of compound **36** significantly amplified the 2′3′-cGAMP-induced ISRE activation in a dose-dependent manner, as demonstrated by enzyme-linked immunosorbent assay (ELISA) measurements of IFN-β and IP-10. The combination of compound **36** with 2′3′-cGAMP led to enhanced cytokine secretion in THP-1 cells compared to treatment with 2′3′-cGAMP alone. Real-time polymerase chain reaction (PCR) further revealed that co-treatment with compound **36** and 2′3′-cGAMP upregulated the expression of various interferon-stimulated genes (ISGs), including C-X-C Motif Chemokine Ligand 10 (CXCL10), 2′-5′-oligoadenylate synthetase 1 (OAS1), and interferon-inducible transmembrane (IFITM1). Western blot analysis confirmed a dose-dependent increase in the phosphorylation levels of IRF3 and signal transducer and activator of transcription 1 (STAT1) in THP-1 cells upon concurrent treatment with 2′3′-cGAMP and compound **36**. These results collectively demonstrate that compound **36** robustly activates the STING signaling pathway in a dose-dependent manner. Furthermore, the pharmacokinetic (PK) evaluation of compound **36** in mice revealed excellent oral bioavailability, a moderately extended half-life ($T_{1/2}$), and a substantial plasma concentration of 1698 ng*h/ml following oral administration at a dose of 10 mg/kg. Given its favorable PK profile and stability in liver microsomes, compound **36** was evaluated as a monotherapy in a 4T1 mouse cancer model. When administered orally at a dose of 40 mg/kg daily for two weeks, compound **36** achieved a tumor growth inhibition (TGI) rate of 39% by day 14. Notably, no adverse effects, such as body weight loss, were observed in the treated mice, underscoring the compound's therapeutic potential.

Recently, Cho and colleagues have reported a new series of ENPP1 inhibitors with a novel phthalazin-1(2*H*)-one core (Figure 13.16) [63]. The inhibitory effects of these compounds on 2′3′-cGAMP hydrolysis by recombinant human ENPP1 were evaluated using an *in vitro* AMP-Glo assay. Compound **38** exhibited moderate inhibition with an IC_{50} of 139 nM. In contrast, compound **39**, which contains a 1,2,3,4-tetrahydroisoquinoline structure, showed reduced potency, with an IC_{50} of 2220 nM. Compound **40**, incorporating a piperidine linker, also demonstrated moderate inhibition against ENPP1, with an IC_{50} of 441 nM. Notably, compound **41**, which features a benzyl linker, displayed highly potent ENPP1 inhibition with an IC_{50} of 39 nM. Compound **42**, with a 2-methylphthalazin-1(2*H*)-one moiety, also showed strong potency, with an IC_{50} of 68 nM. Finally, compound **43**, characterized by a 6,7-dimethoxy substituted phthalazin-1(2*H*)-one core, inhibited ENPP1 with an IC_{50} of 69 nM. In cellular assays, compounds **41**, **42**, and **43** at 100 μM showed 1.85-, 3.63-, and 2.49-fold increases in ISRE activity, respectively, relative to the DMSO vehicle control.

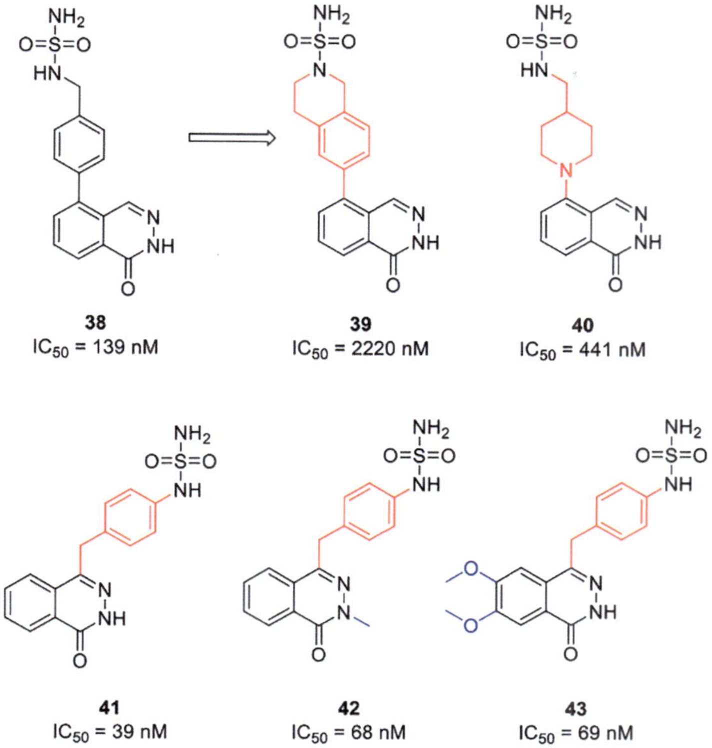

Figure 13.16 Structures of ENPP1 inhibitors with a phthalazin-1(2*H*)-one core.

Compound **42** also exhibited remarkable PK characteristics following both intravenous injection (IV) and oral administration (PO) routes, as shown in Table 13.2. Notably, oral administration of compound **42** resulted in high oral bioavailability (65%), a favorable $T_{1/2}$ of 2.80 hours, and notable exposure levels, as evidenced by a peak plasma concentration (C_{max}) of 12.71 μg/ml and an AUC_{0-t} value of 79.38 μg/ml. Compound **42** demonstrated moderate metabolic stability in mouse liver microsomes and was stable in human liver microsomes. Furthermore, the compound demonstrated a very low inhibitory potential against key human cytochrome P450 enzymes, with IC_{50} values exceeding 10 μM for five different isoforms (CYP1A2, CYP2C9, CYP2C19, CYP2D6, and CYP3A4). In a CT26 BALB/c mouse model, compound **42** displayed significant antitumor efficacy. Oral administration at a dose of 200 mg/kg daily for two weeks resulted in a TGI rate of 55% by day 14. Importantly, compound **42** enhanced the efficacy of anti-PD-L1 therapy, with the combination-treated group (**42**: PO, 200 mg/kg daily; anti-PD-L1: Intraperitoneal injection ([IP]), 5 mg/kg, day 1 and day 8) achieving a TGI rate of 69% by day 15. Furthermore, compound **42** was capable of triggering immunological memory. When CT26 cells were re-inoculated into the treated group and tumor growth was monitored without further administration, the rechallenged tumors completely regressed in all tested mice in the **42**-treated group.

Table 13.2 Pharmacokinetic profile in male ICR mice for compound **42**[a].

Parameter	PO (20 mg/kg)	IV (5 mg/kg)
$T_{1/2}$ (h)	2.80 ± 0.11	3.61 ± 1.28
T_{max} (h)	1.67 ± 0.11	0.08 ± 0.00
C_{max} (μg/ml)	12.71 ± 1.53	9.54 ± 0.53
$AUC_{0\text{-}t}$ (μg·h/ml)	79.38 ± 11.86	30.36 ± 9.82
$AUC_{0-\infty}$ (μg·h/ml)	79.57 ± 11.89	30.94 ± 10.69
MRT_{0-t} (h)	3.75 ± 0.27	2.83 ± 0.94
$MRT_{0-\infty}$ (h)	3.81 ± 0.28	3.21 ± 1.47
V_{ss} (l/kg)		0.51 ± 0.05
CL (ml/min/kg)		2.88 ± 0.83
F (%)	65.36 ± 9.77	

a) All of the values were reported as mean ± SD of three independent experiment.

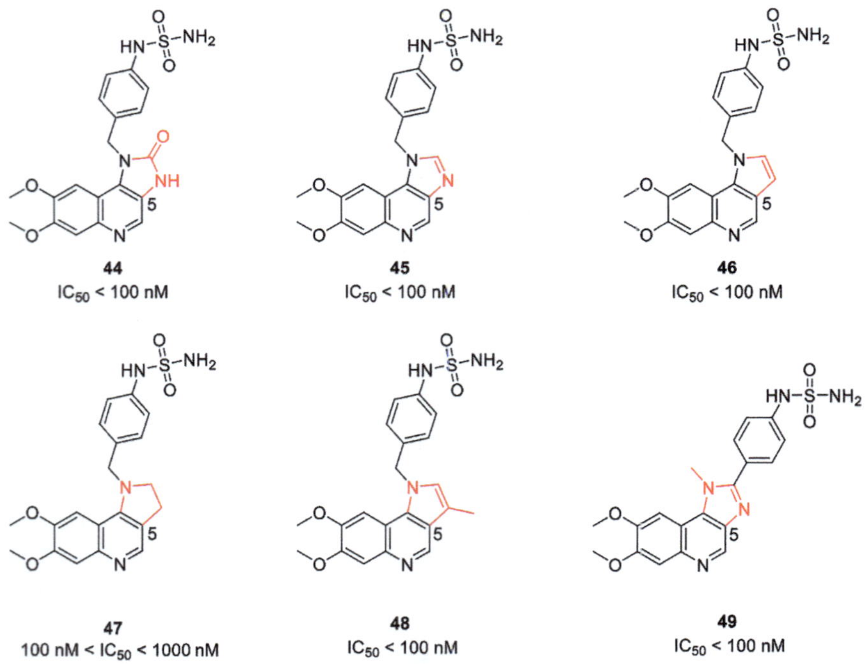

Figure 13.17 Structures of ENPP1 inhibitors featuring a tricyclic core developed by Mavupharma.

Mavupharma (acquired by AbbVie in 2019) disclosed a novel class of ENPP1 inhibitors featuring tricyclic structures in a patent [64], as shown in Figure 13.17. These derivatives were synthesized by cycloalkylation of QS1 at the linker attachment site on the quinoline core, specifically at the 5-position. For example, compound **44**, featuring a 2-oxo-2,3-dihydro-1*H*-imidazo ring, demonstrated an impressive IC_{50} of less than 100 nM in an ENPP1 enzyme assay using 2′3′-cGAMP as the substrate. Modification of the five-membered ring to a 1*H*-imidazo moiety yielded compound **45**, while conversion to a 1*H*-pyrrolo ring resulted in compound **46**, both of which retained significant inhibitory potency. However, reducing the pyrrolo ring to a 2,3-dihydro-1*H*-pyrrolo ring in compound **47** led to a decrease in inhibitory capacity, with an IC_{50} value exceeding 100 nM but remaining below 1000 nM. Additionally, the introduction of a methyl group at the pyrrolo ring did not diminish inhibitory activity, as evidenced by compound **48**, which preserved its potency. Finally, altering the linker position did not compromise inhibition efficacy, with compound **49** effectively suppressing ENPP1 activity.

In 2021, scientists from Nanjing Zenshine Pharma revealed a series of tricyclic ENPP1 inhibitors employing a sulfonamide group as the key component for zinc ion coordination (Figure 13.18) [65]. Among them, compound **50** exhibited IC_{50} values of 1.7 and 5.9 nM when tested under pH 9.5 conditions using p-NP-TMP and p-NP-AMP as substrates, respectively. In MDA-MB-231 cell lines, compound **50** demonstrated an IC_{50} of 2.9 μM against ENPP1 with p-NP-TMP as the substrate. However, in HEK-293 and Saos-2 cells, it inhibited ENPP1 by only 19% and 32%, respectively, at a concentration of 20 μM. Structural modifications led to the development of compound **51**, which showed improved enzymatic inhibition of ENPP1 with an IC_{50} of 0.55 μM in MDA-MB-231 cells. Notably, compound **51**'s efficacy in HEK-293 and Saos-2 cells was significantly enhanced, with IC_{50} values of 2.3 μM

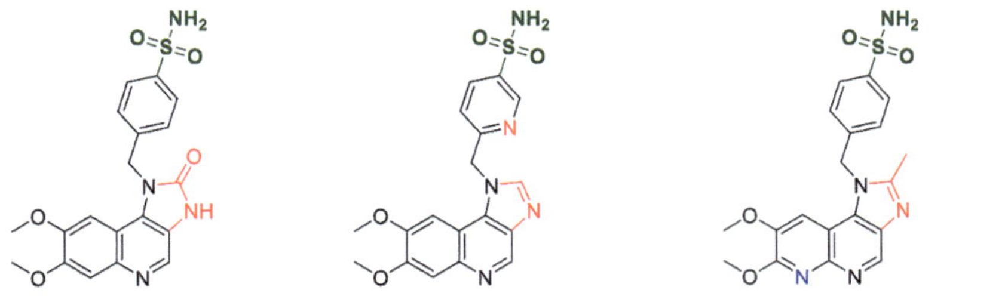

50
IC_{50} = 1.7 nM (vs p-NP-TMP)
IC_{50} = 5.9 nM (vs p-NP-AMP)

51
IC_{50} = 1.2 nM (vs p-NP-TMP)
IC_{50} = 3.9 nM (vs p-NP-AMP)
IC_{50} = 0.55 μM (in MDA-MB-231 cells)
IC_{50} = 2.3 μM (in HEK 293 cells)
IC_{50} = 1.0 μM (in Saos-2 cells)

52
IC_{50} = 0.29 nM (vs p-NP-TMP)
IC_{50} = 0.44 nM (vs p-NP-AMP)
IC_{50} = 0.55 μM (in MDA-MB-231 cells)
IC_{50} = 0.67 μM (in HEK 293 cells)
$T_{1/2}$ = 0.33 h
CL = 70 mL/min/kg

Figure 13.18 Structures of ENPP1 inhibitors featuring a tricyclic core developed by Nanjing Zenshine Pharma.

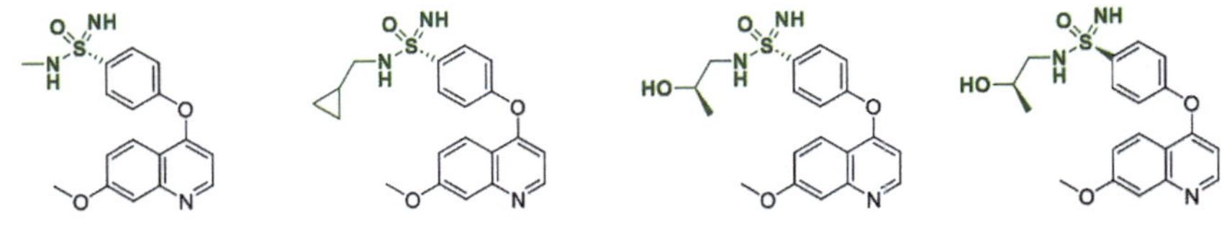

53 IC_{50} < 10 nM (vs cGAMP, pH = 8.0)
54 IC_{50} < 10 nM (vs cGAMP, pH = 8.0)
55 IC_{50} < 10 nM (vs cGAMP, pH = 8.0)
56 IC_{50} < 10 nM (vs cGAMP, pH = 8.0)

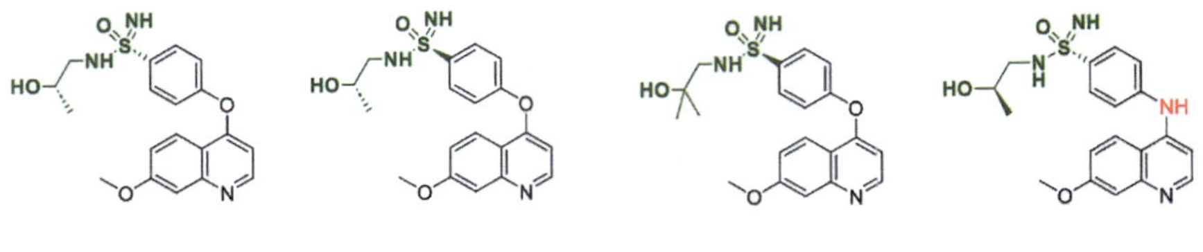

57 10 nM < IC_{50} < 100 nM (vs cGAMP, pH = 8.0)
58 IC_{50} < 10 nM (vs cGAMP, pH = 8.0)
59 10 nM < IC_{50} < 100 nM (vs cGAMP, pH = 8.0)
60 IC_{50} < 10 nM (vs cGAMP, pH = 8.0)

Figure 13.19 Structures of EBNPP1 inhibitors based on sulfonimidamide.

and 1.0 μM, respectively. Further modification, including the introduction of a methyl group within the imidazole ring, yielded compound **52**, which exhibited enzymatic IC_{50} values of 0.29 and 0.44 nM. At the cellular level, compound **52** maintained inhibitory activity with IC_{50} values of 0.55 μM in MDA-MB-231 cells and 0.67 μM in HEK-293 cells. However, compound **52** encountered PK challenges, specifically a short $T_{1/2}$ of 0.33 hours and a high clearance rate (CL) of 70 ml/min/kg, indicating rapid elimination *in vivo*.

A patent from Vir Biotechnology disclosed several ENPP1 inhibitors with sulfonimidamide as a zinc-binding group [66], as shown in Figure 13.19. Compound **53** showed excellent potency in the enzymatic assay when tested under pH 8.0 with 2′3′-cGAMP as substrate. Compound **54** with a cyclopropylmethyl group and compound **55** with **a** hydroxypropyl group maintained similar potency. The stereochemistry of the zinc ion–coordinating group appeared to have minimal impact on binding activity, as **55**, **56**, and **57** showed comparable activities, with only a slight reduction observed for isomer **57**. Introduction of a methyl group to compound **56** resulted in a decrease in binding activity, producing compound **59** with a slightly higher IC_{50} value. Substituting the linking atom from oxygen to nitrogen in compound **55** to yield compound **60** retained activity. Both compounds **55** and **60** effectively inhibited tumor growth in mice bearing MC38 tumor xenografts, enhancing survival rates. Furthermore, treatment with compound **60** significantly increased the expression of IFNβ, IP-10, MIP-1β, MCP-3, and eotaxin in the tumors of these mice. These results suggest that compound **60** is an effective *in vivo* ENPP1 inhibitor.

In addition to the detailed ENPP1 inhibitors mentioned above, numerous patents have also disclosed a wide variety of ENPP1 inhibitors based on the sulfonamide and sulfonimidamide groups. A summary of representative compounds from these patents, including their reported activities and the disclosing companies, is provided in Table 13.3.

Table 13.3 Inhibitors derived from sulfamide, sulfonamide and sulfonimidamide.

Structure	Potency	Originator
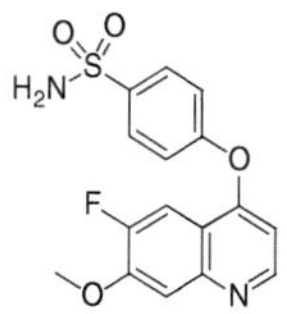	K_i < 100 nM (vs 2′3′-cGAMP)	AbbVie [67]
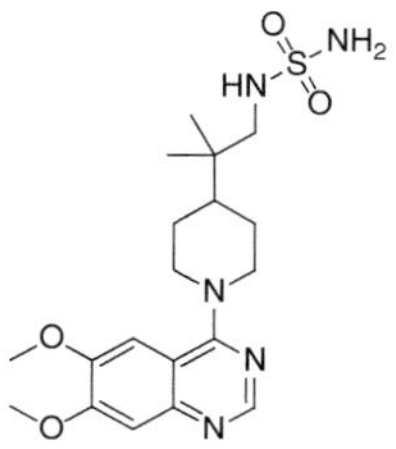	IC_{50} = 2.39 nM (vs pNP-TMP)	Stingray Therapeutics [68]
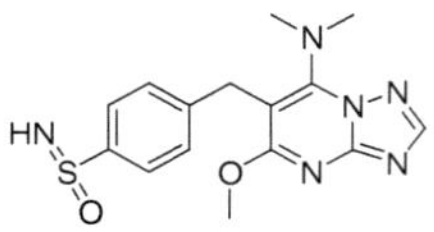	K_i = 5.86 pM (vs 2′3′-cGAMP)	Volastra Therapeutics [69]
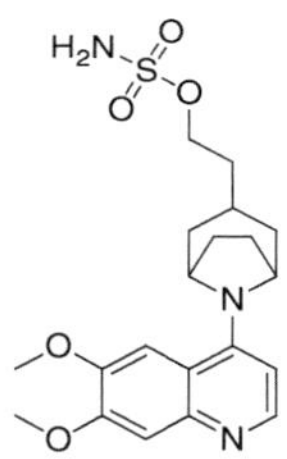	IC_{50} = 2.5 nM (vs pNP-TMP)	Betta Pharmaceuticals [70]
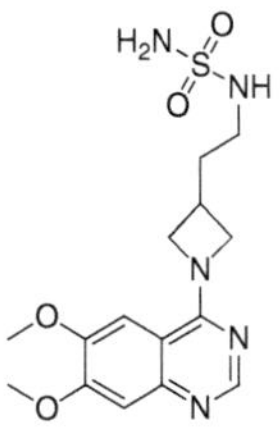	IC_{50} = 8.0 nM (vs 2′3′-cGAMP)	Integral BioSciences [71]
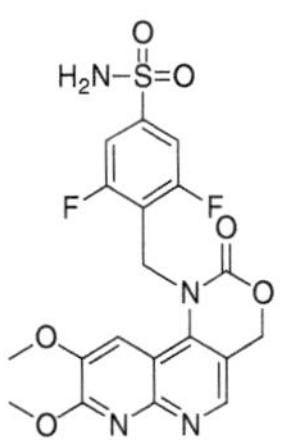	0.1 nM <= IC_{50} <= 0.5 nM (vs pNP-TMP)	Innovstone Therapeutics [72]

(Continued)

Table 13.3 (Continued)

Structure	Potency	Originator
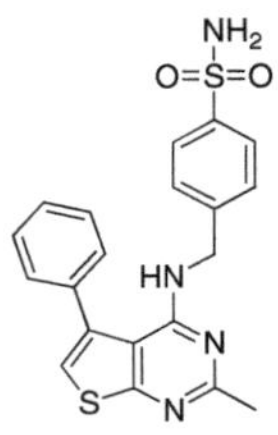	$IC_{50} < 100\,nM$ (ATP assay)	Sanford Burnham Prebys Medical [73]
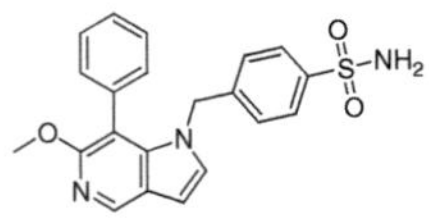	$IC_{50} <= 1.0\,nM$ (vs 2′3′-cGAMP)	Insilico Medicine [74]
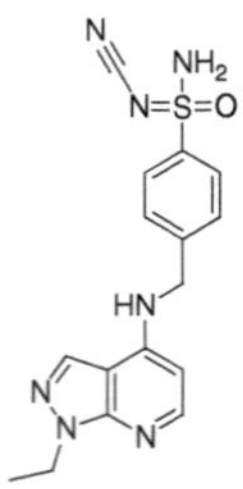	$IC_{50} < 10\,nM$ (vs 2′3′-cGAMP)	Gossamer Bio [75]
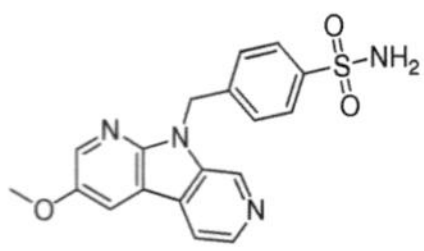	$IC_{50} <= 1000\,nM$ (vs 2′3′-cGAMP)	LegoChem Biosciences [76]

References

1 Grobben, B., De Deyn, P., and Slegers, H. (2002). Rat C6 glioma as experimental model system for the study of glioblastoma growth and invasion. *Cell and Tissue Research* 310 (3): 257–270.

2 Bischoff, E., Tran-Thi, T.-A., and Decker, K.F.A. (1975). Nucleotide pyrophosphatase of rat liver. A Comparative study on the enzymes solubilized and purified from plasma membrane and endoplasmic reticulum. *European Journal of Biochemistry* 51 (2): 353–361.

3 Jansen, S., Perrakis, A., Ulens, C. et al. (2012). Structure of NPP1, an ectonucleotide pyrophosphatase/phosphodiesterase involved in tissue calcification. *Structure* 20 (11): 1948–1959.

4 Goding, J.W., Grobben, B., and Slegers, H. (2003). Physiological and pathophysiological functions of the ecto-nucleotide pyrophosphatase/phosphodiesterase

family. *Biochimica et Biophysica Acta (BBA) - Molecular Basis of Disease* 1638 (1): 1–19.
5 Borza, R., Fernando, S.-P., Moolenaar, W.H. et al. (2022). Structure and function of the ecto-nucleotide pyrophosphatase/phosphodiesterase (ENPP) family: Tidying up diversity. *Journal of Biological Chemistry* 298 (2): 101526.
6 Moolenaar, W.H. (2002). Lysophospholipids in the limelight. *The Journal of Cell Biology* 158 (2): 197–199.
7 Jansen, S., Stefan, C., Creemers, J.W. et al. (2005). Proteolytic maturation and activation of autotaxin (NPP2), a secreted metastasis-enhancing lysophospholipase D. *Journal of Cell Science* 118 (14): 3081–3089.
8 Guan, D., Fang, L., Feng, M. et al. (2024). Ecto-nucleotide pyrophosphatase/phosphodiesterase 1 inhibitors: research progress and prospects. *European Journal of Medicinal Chemistry* 267: 116211.
9 Greiner-Tollersrud, L., Berg, T., Stensland, H.M. et al. (2012). Bovine brain myelin glycerophosphocholine choline phosphodiesterase is an alkaline lysosphingomyelinase of the eNPP-family regulated by lysosomal sorting. *Neurochemical Research* 38 (2): 300–310.
10 Zhou, A., Huntington, J.A., Pannu, N.S. et al. (2003). How vitronectin binds PAI-1 to modulate fibrinolysis and cell migration. *Nature Structural & Molecular Biology* 11: 541–544.
11 Gorelik, A., Randriamihaja, A., Illes, K. et al. (2018). Structural basis for nucleotide recognition by the ectoenzyme CD203c. *The FEBS Journal* 285 (13): 2481–2494.
12 Kato, K., Nishimasu, H., Okudaira, S. et al. (2012). Crystal structure of Enpp1, an extracellular glycoprotein involved in bone mineralization and insulin signaling. *Proceedings of the National Academy of Sciences* 109 (42): 16876–16881.
13 Ghosh, M., Meiss, G., Pingoud, A. et al. (2005). Structural insights into the mechanism of nuclease A, a ββα metal nuclease from anabaena. *Journal of Biological Chemistry* 280 (30): 27990–27997.
14 Stefan, C., Jansen, S., and Bollen, M. (2005). NPP-type ectophosphodiesterases: unity in diversity. *Trends in Biochemical Sciences* 30 (10): 542–550.
15 Koyama, M., Nishimasu, H., Ishoitani, R. et al. (2012). Molecular dynamics simulation of autotaxin: roles of the nuclease-like domain and the glycan modification. *The Journal of Physical Chemistry B* 116 (39): 11798–11808.
16 Onyedibe, K.I., Wang, M., and Sintim, H.O. (2019). ENPP1, an old enzyme with new functions, and small molecule inhibitors – a STING in the tale of ENPP1. *Molecules* 24 (22): 4192.
17 Ferretti, E., Horentein, A.L., Canzonetta, C. et al. (2019). Canonical and non-canonical adenosinergic pathways. *Immunology Letters* 205: 25–30.
18 Kato, K., Nishimasu, H., Oikawa, D. et al. (2018). Structural insights into cGAMP degradation by ecto-nucleotide pyrophosphatase phosphodiesterase 1. *Nature Communications* 9 (1): 1–8.
19 Namasivayam, V., Lee, S.-Y., and Müller, C.E. (2017). The promiscuous ectonucleotidase NPP1: molecular insights into substrate binding and hydrolysis. *Biochimica et Biophysica Acta (BBA) - General Subjects* 1861 (3): 603–614.

20 Haffner, D., Emma, F., Seefried, L. et al. (2019). Clinical practice recommendations for the diagnosis and management of X-linked hypophosphataemia. *Nature Reviews Nephrology* 15 (7): 435–455.

21 Nakahara, T., Dweck, M.R., Narula, N. et al. (2017). Coronary artery calcification: from mechnaism to molecular imaging. *JACC: Cardiovascular Imaging* 10 (5): 582–593.

22 Jin, Y., Cong, Q., Gvozdenovic-Jeremic, J. et al. (2018). Enpp1 inhibits ectopic joint calcification and maintains articular chondrocytes by repressing hedgehog signaling. *Development* 145 (18): dev164830.

23 Nitschke, Y., Hartmann, S., Torsello, G. et al. (2011). Expression of NPP1 is regulated during atheromatous plaque calcification. *Journal of Cellular and Molecular Medicine* 15 (2): 220–231.

24 Lin, A.C., Seeto, B.L., Bartoszko, J.M. et al. (2009). Modulating hedgehog signaling can attenuate the severity of osteoarthritis. *Nature Medicine* 15 (12): 1421–1425.

25 Regard, J.B., Malhotra, D., Gvozdenovic-Jeremic, J. et al. (2013). Activation of Hedgehog signaling by loss of GNAS causes heterotopic ossification. *Nature Medicine* 19 (11): 1505–1512.

26 Chourabi, M., Liew, M.S., Lim, S. et al. (2018). ENPP1 mutation causes recessive cole disease by altering melanogenesis. *Journal of Investigative Dermatology* 138 (2): 291–300.

27 Meyre, D., Bouatia-Naji, N., Tounian, A. et al. (2005). Variants of ENPP1 are associated with childhood and adult obesity and increase the risk of glucose intolerance and type 2 diabetes. *Nature Genetics* 37 (8): 863–867.

28 Vincent, T., Neve, E.P., Johnson, J.R. et al. (2009). A SNAIL1–SMAD3/4 transcriptional repressor complex promotes TGF-β mediated epithelial–mesenchymal transition. *Nature Cell Biology* 11 (8): 943–950.

29 Furukawa, H., Oka, S., Kondo, N. et al. (2022). The contribution of deleterious rare alleles in ENPP1 and osteomalacia causative genes to atypical femoral fracture. *The Journal of Clinical Endocrinology & Metabolism* 107 (5): e1890–e1898.

30 Ferreira, C.R., Carpenter, T.O., and Braddock, D.T. (2024). ENPP1 in blood and bone: skeletal and soft tissue diseases induced by ENPP1 deficiency. *Annual Review of Pathology: Mechanisms of Disease* 19 (1): 507–540.

31 Thumbigere-Math, V., Alqadi, A., Chalmers, N.I. et al. (2017). Hypercementosis associated with ENPP1 mutations and GACI. *Journal of Dental Research* 97 (4): 432–441.

32 El Achhab, Y., Meyre, D., Bouatia-Naji, N. et al. (2009). Association of the ENPP1 K121Q polymorphism with type 2 diabetes and obesity in the Moroccan population. *Diabetes & Metabolism* 35 (1): 37–42.

33 Dimatteo, C., Marucci, A., Palazzo, A. et al. (2013). Role of somatomedin-B-like domains on ENPP1 inhibition of insulin signaling. *Biochimica et Biophysica Acta (BBA) – Molecular Cell Research* 1833 (3): 552–558.

34 Petersen, C.B., Nygard, A.B., Viuff, B. et al. (2007). Porcine ecto-nucleotide pyrophosphatase/phosphodiesterase 1 (NPP1/CD203a): Cloning, transcription,

expression, mapping, and identification of an NPP1/CD203a epitope for swine workshop cluster 9 (SWC9) monoclonal antibodies. *Developmental & Comparative Immunology* 31 (6): 618–631.
35 Hsiao, T.-J. and Lin, E. (2016). The ENPP1 K121Q polymorphism is associated with type 2 diabetes and related metabolic phenotypes in a Taiwanese population. *Molecular and Cellular Endocrinology* 433: 20–25.
36 H, W., Ye, F., Cheng, Q. et al. (2021). High expression of ENPP1 in high-grade serous ovarian carcinoma predicts poor prognosis and as a molecular therapy target. *PLoS One* 16 (2): e0245733.
37 Bageritz, J., Puccio, L., Piro, R.M. et al. (2014). Stem cell characteristics in glioblastoma are maintained by the ecto-nucleotidase E-NPP1. *Cell Death and Differentiation* 21 (6): 929–940.
38 Aerts, I., Martin, J.J., De Devn, P.P. et al. (2011). The expression of ecto-nucleotide pyrophosphatase/phosphodiesterase 1 (E-NPP1) is correlated with astrocytic tumor grade. *Clinical Neurology and Neurosurgery* 113 (3): 224–229.
39 Hu, M., Guo, W., Liao, Y. et al. (2019). Dysregulated ENPP1 increases the malignancy of human lung cancer by inducing epithelial mesenchymal transition phenotypes and stem cell features. *American Journal of Cancer Research* 9 (1): 134–144.
40 Takahashi, R.U., Miyazaki, H., Takeshita, F. et al. (2015). Loss of microRNA-27b contributes to breast cancer stem cell generation by activating ENPP1. *Nature Communications* 6 (1): 7318.
41 Huang, R., Ning, Q., Zhao, J. et al. (2024). Targeting ENPP1 for cancer immunotherapy: killing two birds with one stone. *Biochemical Pharmacology* 220: 116006.
42 Ritchie, C., Carozza, J.A., and Li, L. (2022). Biochemistry, cell biology, and pathophysiology of the innate immune cGAS–cGAMP–STING pathway. *Annual Review of Biochemistry* 91 (1): 599–628.
43 Ishikawa, H., Ma, Z., and Barber, G.N. (2009). STING regulates intracellular DNA-mediated, type I interferon-dependent innate immunity. *Nature* 461 (7265): 788–792.
44 Zhang, C., Shang, G., Gui, X. et al. (2019). Structural basis of STING binding with and phosphorylation by TBK1. *Nature* 567 (7748): 394–398.
45 Chen, Q., Sun, L., and Chen, Z.J. (2016). Regulation and function of the cGAS–STING pathway of cytosolic DNA sensing. *Nature Immunology* 17 (10): 1142–1149.
46 Kwon, J. and Bakhoum, S.F. (2020). The cytosolic DNA-sensing cGAS–STING pathway in cancer. *Cancer Discovery* 10 (1): 26–39.
47 Huang, R., Ning, Q., Zhang, J. et al. (2022). Targeting STING for cancer immunotherapy: from mechanisms to translation. *International Immunopharmacology* 113.
48 Carozza, J.A., Bohnert, V., Nguyen, K.C. et al. (2020). Extracellular cGAMP is a cancer-cell-produced immunotransmitter involved in radiation-induced anticancer immunity. *Nature Cancer* 1 (2): 184–196.

49 Mekers, V.E., Kho, V.M., Ansems, M., and Adema, G.J. (2022). cGAS/cGAMP/STING signal propagation in the tumor microenvironment: key role for myeloid cells in antitumor immunity. *Radiotherapy and Oncology* 174: 158–167.

50 Mardjuki, R., Kho, V.M., Ansems, M. et al. (2024). Identification of the extracellular membrane protein ENPP3 as a major cGAMP hydrolase and innate immune checkpoint. *Cell Reports* 43 (5): 158–167.

51 Ghalamfarsa, G., Kasemi, M.H., Raoofi Mohseni, S. et al. (2018). CD73 as a potential opportunity for cancer immunotherapy. *Expert Opinion on Therapeutic Targets* 23 (2): 127–142.

52 Li, L., Yin, Q., Kuss, P. et al. (2014). Hydrolysis of 2′3′-cGAMP by ENPP1 and design of nonhydrolyzable analogs. *Nature Chemical Biology* 10 (12): 1043–1048.

53 Leone, R.D., Sun, I.M., Oh, M.H. et al. (2018). Inhibition of the adenosine A2a receptor modulates expression of T cell coinhibitory receptors and improves effector function for enhanced checkpoint blockade and ACT in murine cancer models. *Cancer Immunology, Immunotherapy* 67 (8): 1271–1284.

54 Lee, S.-Y. and Müller, C.E. (2017). Nucleotide pyrophosphatase/phosphodiesterase 1 (NPP1) and its inhibitors. *MedChemComm* 8 (5): 823–840.

55 Lecka, J., Ben-David, G., Simhaev, L. et al. (2013). Nonhydrolyzable ATP analogues as selective inhibitors of human NPP1: a combined computational/experimental study. *Journal of Medicinal Chemistry* 56 (21): 8308–8320.

56 Eliahu, S., Lecka, J., Reiser, G. et al. (2010). Diadenosine 5′,5″-(boranated)polyphosphonate analogues as selective nucleotide pyrophosphatase/phosphodiesterase inhibitors. *Journal of Medicinal Chemistry* 53 (24): 8485–8497.

57 Zelikman, V., Pelletier, J., Simhaev, L. et al. (2018). Highly selective and potent ectonucleotide pyrophosphatase-1 (NPP1) inhibitors based on uridine 5′-Pα,α-dithiophosphate analogues. *Journal of Medicinal Chemistry* 61 (9): 3939–3951.

58 Patel, S.D., Habeski, W.M., Cheng, A.C. et al. (2009). Quinazolin-4-piperidin-4-methyl sulfamide PC-1 inhibitors: Alleviating hERG interactions through structure based design. *Bioorganic & Medicinal Chemistry Letters* 19 (12): 3339–3343.

59 Shayhidin, E.E., Forcellini, E., Boulanger, M.C. et al. (2015). Quinazoline-4-piperidine sulfamides are specific inhibitors of human NPP1 and prevent pathological mineralization of valve interstitial cells. *British Journal of Pharmacology* 172 (16): 4189–4199.

60 Dennis, M.L., Newman, J., Dolezal, O. et al. (2020). Crystal structures of human ENPP1 in apo and bound forms. *Acta Crystallographica Section D Structural Biology* 76 (9): 889–898.

61 Jung, J.E., Jang, Y., Jeong, H.J. et al. (2022). Discovery of 3,4-dihydropyrimido[4,5-d]pyrimidin-2(1H)-one and 3,4-dihydropyrido[2,3-*d*]pyrimidin-2(1H)-one derivatives as novel ENPP1 inhibitors. *Bioorganic & Medicinal Chemistry Letters* 75: 128947.

62 Jeong, H.J., Lee, H.L., Kim, S.J. et al. (2022). Identification of novel pyrrolopyrimidine and pyrrolopyridine derivatives as potent ENPP1 inhibitors. *Journal of Enzyme Inhibition and Medicinal Chemistry* 37 (1): 2434–2451.

63 Cho, Y., Kang, M., Ji, S.H. et al. (2023). Discovery of orally bioavailable phthalazinone analogues as an ENPP1 inhibitor for STING-mediated cancer immunotherapy. *Journal of Medicinal Chemistry* 66 (22): 15141–15170.

64 Gallatin, W.M., Odingo, J., Dietsch, G.N. et al. (2019). Imidazoquinolines as ectonucleotide pyrophosphatase-phosphodiesterase 1 (ENPP-1) inhibitors and their preparation WO2019177971.

65 Hao, X. (2021). Preparation of tricyclic heterocyclic compounds as phosphodiesterase inhibitors for treating ENPP1-related disorders WO2021061803.

66 Saito, R.D. and W.C. Tse (2023). Preparation of enantiomeric quinoline and quinazolines as ENPP1 modulators WO2023086638.

67 Gallatin, W.M., Odingo, J., Dietsch, G.N. et al. (2019). Preparation quinolinyl and quinazolinyl benzenesulfamides and analogs as ectonucleotide pyrophosphatase-phosphodiesterase 1 (ENPP-1) inhibitors as antitumor antiviral WO2019046778.

68 Vankayalapati, H., Sharma, S.; Kaadige, M. et al. (2020). Preparation of quinoline and quinazoline compounds as ENPP1 inhibitors and methods of use thereof WO2020190912.

69 Cogan, D.A., Bettigole, S., Su, M. et al. (2021). Triazolopyrimidine and imidazolopyrimidine inhibitors of ENPP1 WO2021257614.

70 Fu, B., Bettigole, S., Su, M. et al. (2021). Synthesis of heterocyclic ENPP1 inhibitors treating cancers and infectious diseases. WO2021203772.

71 Pujala, B., Ansari, A., Sapra, S. et al. (2022). Preparation of substituted quinazoline and pyrrolotriazine compounds as ectonucleotide pyrophosphatase-phosphodiesterase-1 (ENPP1) inhibitors and uses thereof. WO2022091048.

72 Song, Y., Zhou, Y., Fu, Y. et al. (2023). Preparation of arylheterocylic derivatives as ENPP1 inhibitors. CN116262750.

73 Pinkerton, A., Sergienko, E., Kiyotsuka, Y. et al. (2021). Preparation of bicyclic heteroaryls, especially thienopyrimidines, as ectonucleotide pyrophosphatase/phosphodiesterase 1 (ENPP1) modulators. WO2021133915.

74 Cheng, X., Liu, Y., Qin, L. et al. (2023) Preparation of pyrrolo[3,2-c]pyridine derivatives as ectonucleotide pyrophosphatase-phosphodiesterase 1 inhibitors and uses thereof. WO2023143520.

75 Rowbottom, M.W., Lu, K., Michels, T. et al. (2023). Preparation of pyrrolopyrimidine compounds as ENPP1 modulators and products and uses thereof. WO2023220402.

76 Kim, J.H., Jung, E.M., Lee, Y.H. et al. (2023). Preparation of substituted pyridoindoles as ectonucleotide pyrophosphatase-phosphodiesterase-1 inhibitors, and pharmaceutical compositions comprising the same. WO2023242631.

Section II

13.4.2.2 ENPP1 Inhibitors Based on Phosphate Group

In addition to the sulfamide, sulfonamide, and sulfonimidamide-based ENPP1 inhibitors previously discussed, new zinc ion–binding groups have been developed, which significantly diversified the types of ENPP1 inhibitors. Carozza et al. determined the K_i value of QS1 using ATP as a substrate at pH 7.4 and found a 145-fold decrease in potency (K_i = 1600 nM) compared to pH 9 [1]. They attributed this reduction to the difficulty of deprotonating QS1's sulfamide group (with a pKa in the range of 7–8) at pH 7.4, which impaired binding to the zinc ions in ENPP1's catalytic center. To address this issue, various alternative zinc-binding groups were explored as replacements for the sulfonamide group, as illustrated in Figure 13.20. Among these, urea-based compound **61** and carboxylic acid **62** demonstrated lower potency compared to QS1 under physiological pH conditions. However, significant improvements were observed with boronic acid derivative **64** (K_i = 560 nM), hydroxamic acid **65** (K_i = 240 nM), and particularly phosphate **63** (K_i = 33 nM).

Subsequently, the linker was explored to achieve optimal spatial arrangement between the zinc-binding phosphate head and the quinazoline tail, both of which are critical for interaction with the ENPP1 protein pocket. Reversing the piperidine ring led to a dramatic decrease in potency, with compound **66** exhibiting a K_i value of 8700 nM. Replacement of the piperidine with a benzyl group (**67**) led to an approximately fivefold decrease in potency (K_i = 150 nM) compared to **63**. Extending this benzyl group to a benzylamine-containing linker (**68**) improved the Ki value to 26 nM. Modification of the quinazoline core through substitution studies revealed that a single 6-methoxy group significantly reduced potency by 100-fold (compound **69**, K_i = 2900 nM), while the 7-methoxy substituent alone (compound **70**) resulted in a K_i value of 43 nM. Notably, the 8-methoxy quinazoline derivative (compound **71**) demonstrated exceptional potency, with a K_i value of less than 2 nM, which approached the assay's limit of quantification with a 3 nM concentration of ENPP1. These findings highlight the critical role of the methoxy group at the 8-position in enhancing inhibitor binding to the protein pocket.

Co-crystal structural analysis illustrated that compound **63** effectively bound to the substrate-binding pocket, engaging in extensive interactions with zinc ions and surrounding catalytic site residues (Figure 13.21). Specifically, two phosphonate oxygen atoms coordinated with both zinc ions, while the third established a hydrogen bond with Asn259. The quinazoline moiety was positioned between Tyr322 and Phe239, facilitating π–π stacking interactions with these aromatic residues. An additional hydrogen bond was observed between the side chain of Lys277 and the 8-methoxy oxygen, which also had a potential hydrogen bond interaction with Asp308.

In mouse plasma, compound **71** displayed potent enzyme inhibitory activity vs 2′3′-cGAMP with an IC_{50} value of 4 nM and showed minimal intracellular nontarget effects within cells due to the phosphate-induced poor permeability. However,

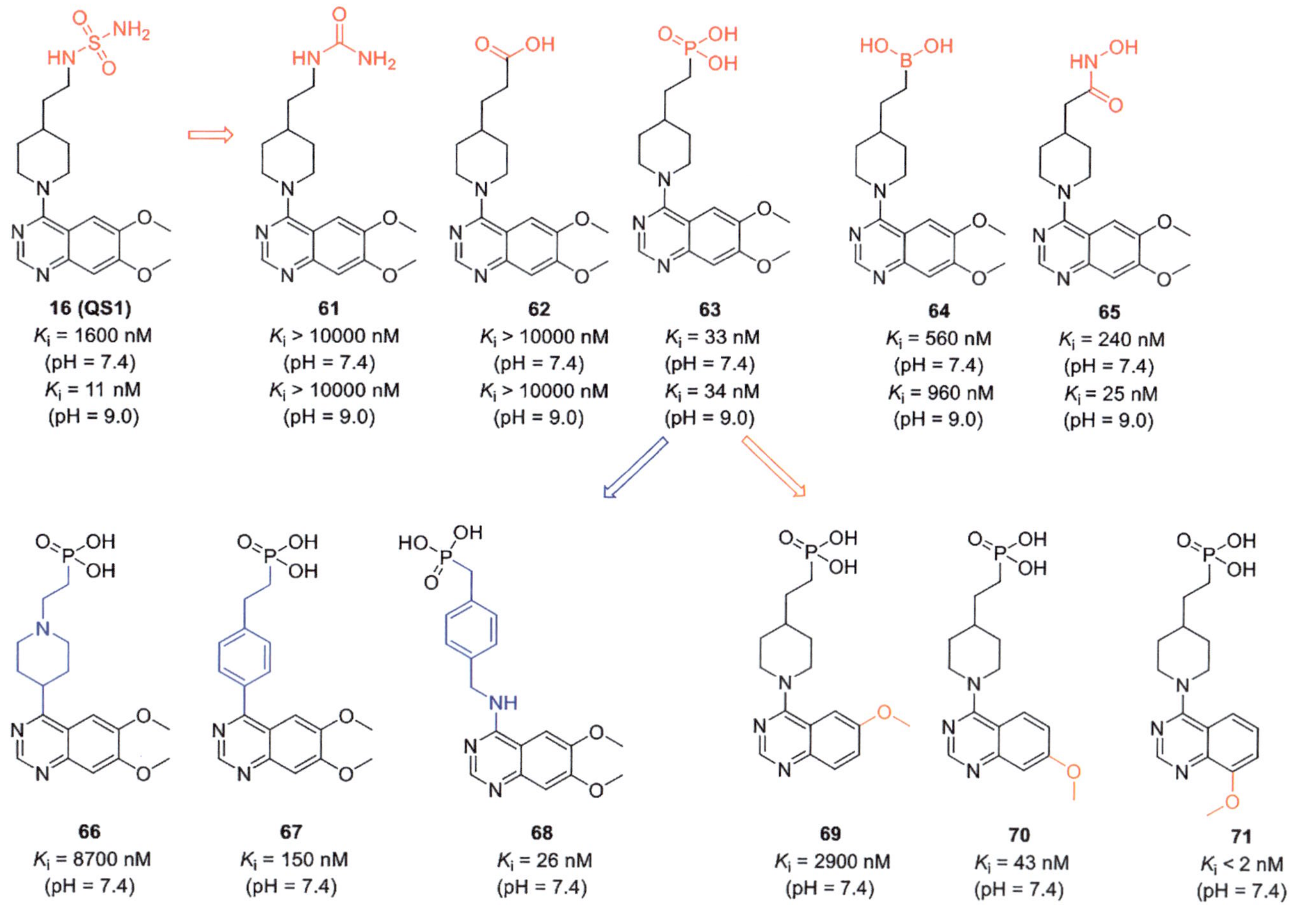

Figure 13.20 ENPP1 inhibitors based on the phosphate group.

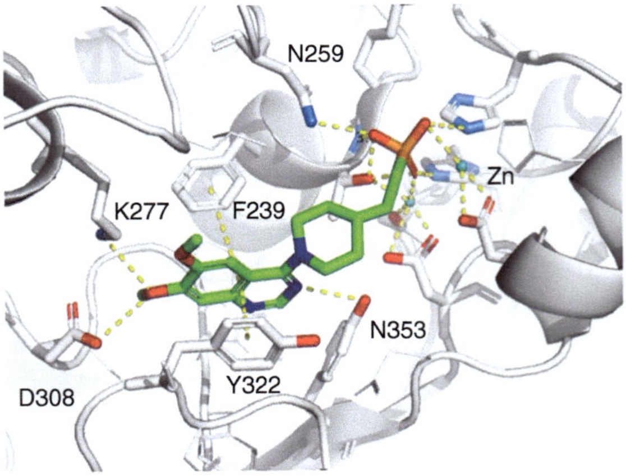

Figure 13.21 The co-crystal structure of compound **63** with ENPP1 (PDB: 6XKD).

after treatment with compound **71** at 10 mg/kg to mice, the serum concentrations of **71** declined to 10 nM or less within eight hours, regardless of whether it was treated via IV or subcutaneous injection (SC). The half-life of compound **71** was only 10–15 minutes, indicating rapid excretion. Despite the poor PK properties, **71** still exhibited antitumor efficacy in the orthotopic and syngeneic E0771 triple-negative breast cancer (TNBC) model. Notably, mice treated with compound **71** at a dose of 300 mg/kg via the SC route for six days showed a significant delay in tumor growth compared to controls, and experienced prolonged survival.

To develop highly active ENPP1 inhibitors, Sun et al. employed a scaffold-hopping strategy, resulting in the design of inhibitor **72**, as shown in Figure 13.22. This compound was developed by replacing the quinazoline core of **63** with a privileged heterocyclic scaffold, pyrido[2,3-*d*]pyrimidin-7-one. The NH group at the 8-position of this new scaffold has the potential to form a hydrogen bond with the carboxyl group of Asp326. Compound **72** demonstrated remarkable inhibitory activity against ENPP1, with an enzymatic IC_{50} of 0.3 nM against human ENPP1 using 2′3′-cGAMP as the substrate at pH 7.5. Further molecular modifications revealed that the conformation of the linker significantly affects inhibitor potency. Inhibitors with a rigid linker, such as compound **73**, demonstrated both strong enzymatic inhibition (IC_{50} = 0.09 nM) and cellular ENPP1 inhibition (IC_{50} = 8.8 nM).

When combined with 2′3′-cGAMP, compound **73** significantly enhanced and prolonged the phosphorylation of TBK1 and IRF3 in human monocytic THP-1 cells. Notably, compound **73** demonstrated greater efficacy in stimulating the STING signaling pathway compared to compound **63**, which correlates with its superior inhibition of ENPP1 enzymatic activity. The activation of STING led to both interferon responses and inflammatory processes. Treatment with compound **73** for 18 hours resulted in a marked increase in the expression of the IFNB1 and CXCL10 genes in THP-1 cells.

To elucidate the role of compound **73** in the immune response mediated by the 2′3′-cGAMP–STING axis, human breast cancer MDA-MB-231 cells were co-treated with 2′3′-cGAMP and compound **73** for 36 hours. The resulting conditioned medium from these cells exhibited a dose-dependent activation of the ISRE reporter in THP1-Dual cells, indicating that compound **73** effectively inhibited ENPP1 of

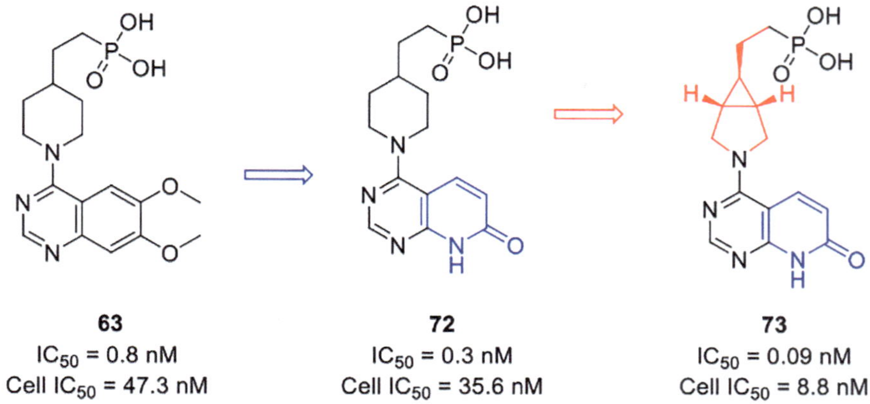

Figure 13.22 The structures of ENPP1 inhibitors with pyrido[2,3-*d*]pyrimidin-7-one core.

MDA-MB-231 cells, thereby preventing the hydrolysis of 2′3′-cGAMP in culture. Furthermore, the absence of the ISRE reporter signal in STING-lacking THP1-Dual cells exposed to the conditioned medium confirmed that STING is essential for the immune response triggered by compound **73**.

The PK profile of compound **73** in male Institute of Cancer Research (ICR) mice, administered orally at 25 mg/kg or intravenously at 5 mg/kg, revealed a low oral bioavailability for compound **73** (4.2%) and a short half-life of less than one hour, suggesting that alternative administration methods may be needed to achieve therapeutic concentrations. Despite its low oral bioavailability, compound **73** proved effective as a monotherapy via subcutaneous injection in inhibiting tumor progression and dissemination in a 4T1 triple-negative breast cancer syngeneic mouse model. At doses of 50 mg/kg and 100 mg/kg, compound **73** significantly reduced 4T1 tumor growth, with T/C percentages of 58.87% and 55.40%, respectively. Importantly, no significant reduction in body weight was observed in treated mice, indicating a favorable safety profile. Additionally, administration of 100 mg/kg of compound **73** resulted in a substantial decrease in both the number of lung metastatic lesions and intra-abdominal nodules, demonstrating its efficacy in hindering the metastasis of 4T1 breast cancer cells.

Since phosphonate compounds carry at least one negative charge under physiological conditions, they exhibit poor permeability. This property hinders phosphonate-based ENPP1 inhibitors from traversing cellular membranes and intestinal mucosa, leading to low oral bioavailability [2–4]. Additionally, their high polarity and water solubility make them prone to rapid renal clearance, resulting in a very short half-life [5]. In order to overcome the limitations of phosphonates, researchers have been working to enhance the PK properties of phosphonate-based ENPP1 inhibitors.

Researchers at Qilu Pharmaceutical Research Center introduced substitutions to the α-position of the phosphate group, resulting in compounds **74** and **75**, which demonstrated IC_{50} values of less than 10 nM [6], as detailed in Table 13.4. Remarkably, this modification significantly enhanced the PK properties of

Table 13.4 Enzymatic inhibitory activity and pharmacokinetic profile of compounds **74–75, 71**.

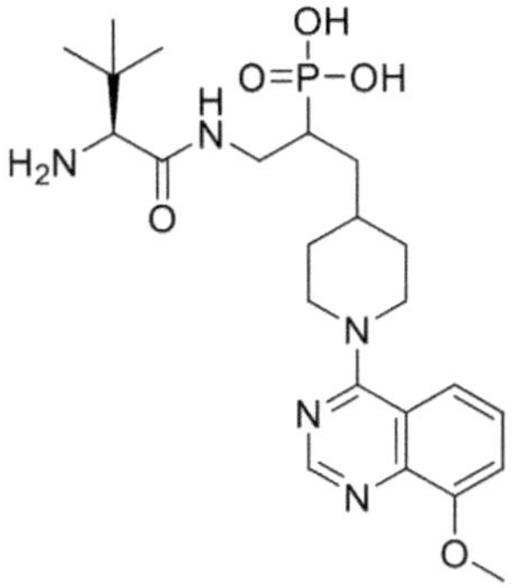

74

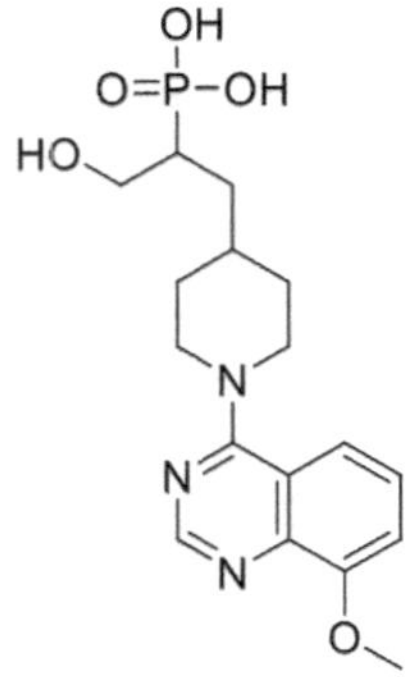

75

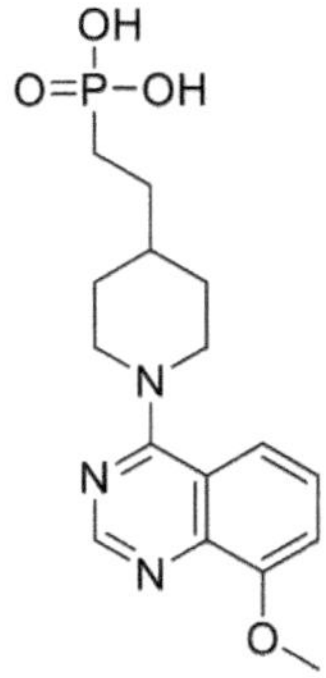

71

Compound	**74**	**75**	**71**
Human ENPP1 enzymatic assay (2′3′-cGAMP) (nM)	<10 nM	<10 nM	/
dosage	PO 50 mg/kg	PO 50 mg/kg	PO 50 mg/kg
AUC_{last} (h*ng/ml)	4134	941	344
C_{max} (ng/ml)	1680	337	67.2

phosphonate-based ENPP1 inhibitors. Compared to compound **71**, the value of AUC_{last} improved substantially, rising from 344 h*ng/ml to 4134 h*ng/ml for compound **74**. Additionally, compound **74** exhibited a substantial increase in C_{max}, reaching a value of 1680 ng/ml, which represents a 25-fold improvement over compound **71**. Compound **75** only exhibited a slight increase in AUC_{last} and C_{max}, reaching 941 h*ng/ml and 337 ng/ml. The results of compounds **74** and **75** revealed that the improvement of PK properties came from the introduction of additional amino acid groups.

To enhance oral bioavailability and facilitate intracellular delivery of phosphonates, various prodrug strategies have been explored [3]. Researchers at HaiHe Biopharma first reported compound **76**, shown in Figure 13.23, as a potent ENPP1 inhibitor with an IC_{50} value of 1.2 nM. Subsequently, the bis-pivaloyloxymethyl (bis-POM) prodrug **77** was developed based on **76**, demonstrating favorable PK characteristics in both rats and dogs (Table 13.5) [7]. Compound **77** was administered to rats via both IV (1 mg/kg) and PO (5 mg/kg) routes. Of note, oral administration of **77** resulted in a bioavailability of approximately 40%, supported by a favorable $T_{1/2}$ of 4.48 hours and notable exposure levels. The C_{max} after oral administration was 4420 ng/ml, with an AUC_{0-t} of 5014 ng/ml for oral and 5984 ng/ml for IV

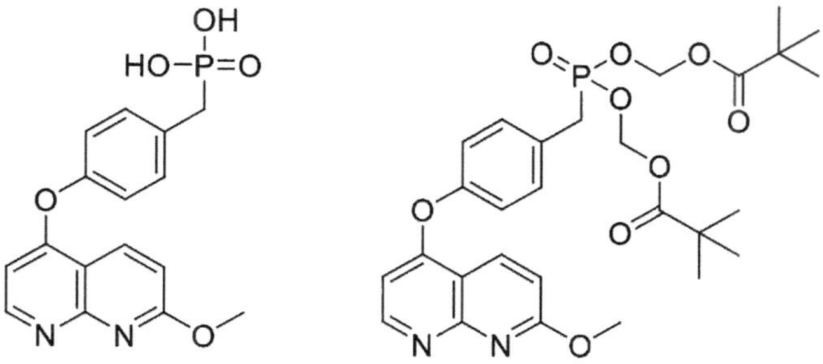

76 **77**

Figure 13.23 Structures of ENPP1 inhibitor featuring phosphonic acid and its prodrug.

Table 13.5 Pharmacokinetic profile of compound **77**.

Parameter	Rat	Dog
CL(ml/min/kg) IV	3.36	3.40
V_{ss}(ml/kg) IV	278	217
$T_{1/2}$ (h) IV	4.48	1.2
$AUC_{0\text{-}t}$ (ng·h/ml) IV	5014	4890
$AUC_{0\text{-}t}$ (ng·h/ml) PO	5984	741
C_{max} (ng/ml) PO	4420	488
T_{max} (h) PO	0.25	0.33
Oral BA (%F)	40	21

routes. In dogs, compound **77** was also administered via intravenous (1 mg/kg) and oral (2 mg/kg) routes, which revealed a bioavailability of about 21%. Overall, these results provided sufficient exposure for further *in vivo* efficacy studies of compound **77** and demonstrated that prodrug strategies could effectively enhance the PK profile of phosphonate-based ENPP1 inhibitors.

In addition to the phosphonate ENPP1 inhibitors mentioned above, other related patents have disclosed various structural variants, which are summarized in Table 13.6. These inhibitors generally exhibit good enzymatic inhibitory activity; however, no additional *in vitro* or *in vivo* data have been disclosed for these compounds.

13.4.2.3 ENPP1 Inhibitors Based on Boronic Acid Groups

In 2020, researchers from Riboscience introduced a novel set of ENPP1 inhibitors featuring a boronic acid moiety as the zinc-binding group in a patent, some of which are shown in Figure 13.24. In this patent, they only mentioned that the formate of compound **78** exhibited a K_i value below 5 nM, without providing further details on the efficacy of the entire series [12]. During the same year, the company disclosed

Table 13.6 Other ENPP1 inhibitors based on phosphonate.

Structure	Potency	Originator
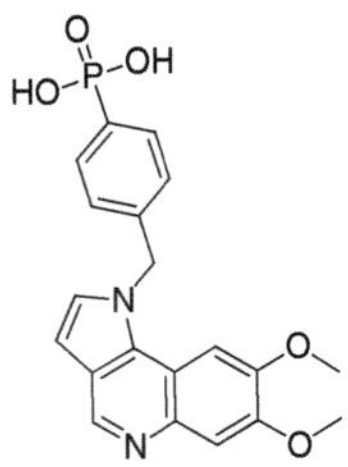	unknown	Stingray Therapeutics [8]
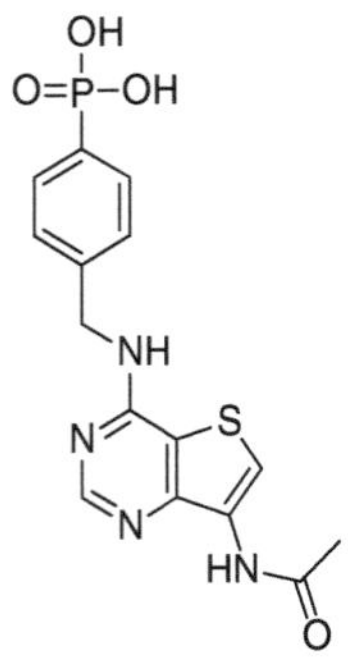	K_i < 100 nM (vs pNP-TMP)	Riboscience [9]
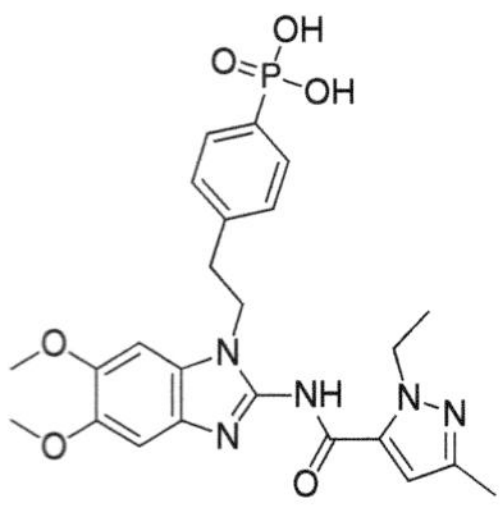	IC_{50} = 127 nM (vs 2′3′-cGAMP)	China Pharmaceutical University Shanghai Institute of Materia Medica [10]
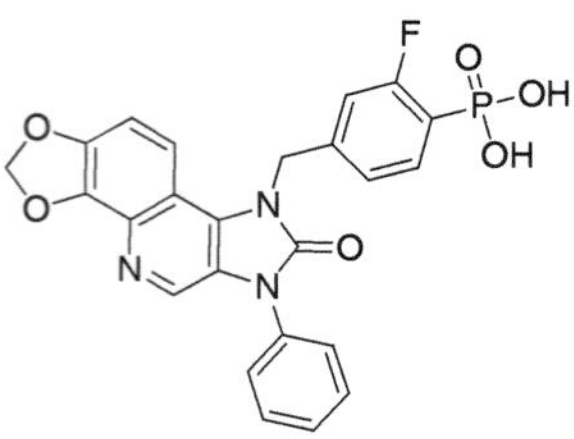	IC_{50} < 10 nM (vs 2′3′-cGAMP)	Shanghai Qilu Pharmaceutical Research and Development Centre [11]

another set of ENPP1 inhibitors based on a benzimidazole core, with the linker moiety attached to the nitrogen atom of the benzimidazole. Compounds **79–81** were obtained by incorporating lactam, cyanide, and acylamide modifications onto the benzimidazole core, and their values of K_i were all below 10 nM [13]. Two years later, another patent from the same company provided a series of bicyclic heteroaryl compounds. The boronic acid moiety was attached to the pyrimidine

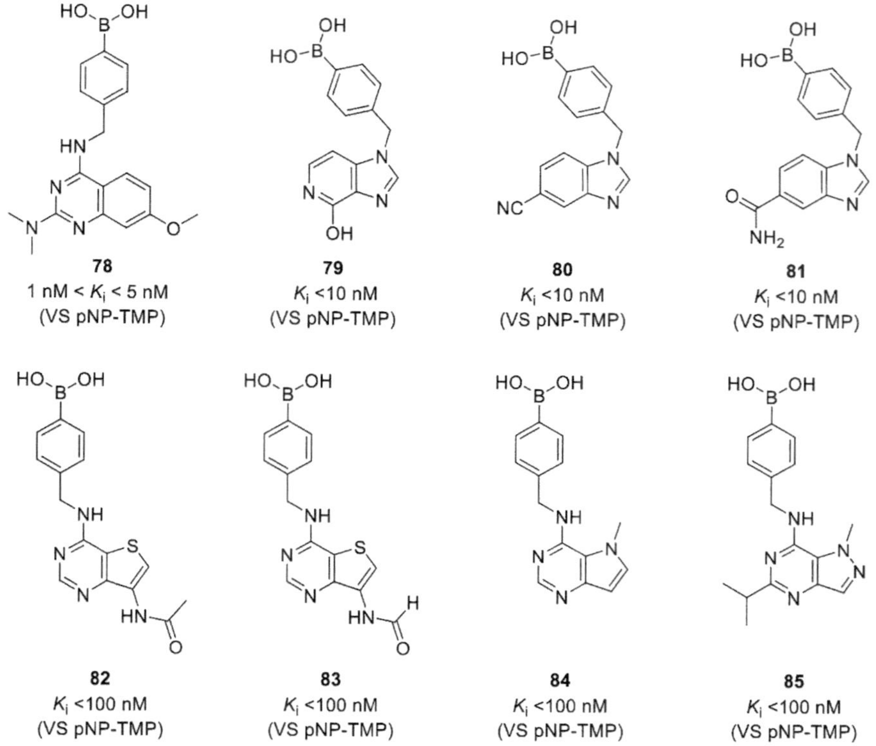

Figure 13.24 Structures of boronic acid derivatives as ENPP1 inhibitors.

ring by benzylamine as a linker, and the pyrimidine ring was fused with different five-membered heterocycles to provide compounds **82–85**, which exhibited K_i values below 100 nM [14].

13.4.2.4 ENPP1 Inhibitors Based on Hydroxamic Acid

Hydroxamic acid is a well-established metal-binding moiety commonly used in histone deacetylase (HDAC) inhibitors, such as Belinostat and Panobinostat, both of which are Food and Drug Administration (FDA)-approved for cancer treatment. This raises the hypothesis that substituting sulfonamide groups with hydroxamic acid could lead to the development of novel and effective ENPP1 inhibitors. Pioneering research by Arjun and colleagues introduced compounds **86** and **87** as potential ENPP1 inhibitors [15, 16], as shown in Figure 13.25. Although their patent did not provide comprehensive details on the enzymatic potency of these compounds, compounds **86** and **87** demonstrated a modest inhibitory effect, suppressing 30% of human ENPP1 enzyme activity when ATP served as the substrate.

Scientists from HaiHe Biopharma have introduced a novel series of ENPP1 inhibitors, demonstrating the efficacy of hydroxamic acid as a zinc-binding group within ENPP1's catalytic core (Table 13.7) [17]. Compound **88** displayed remarkable inhibitory activity (IC_{50} = 1.9 nM) against ENPP1 when using 2′3′-cGAMP as the substrate. Further improvements in inhibitory potency were observed with

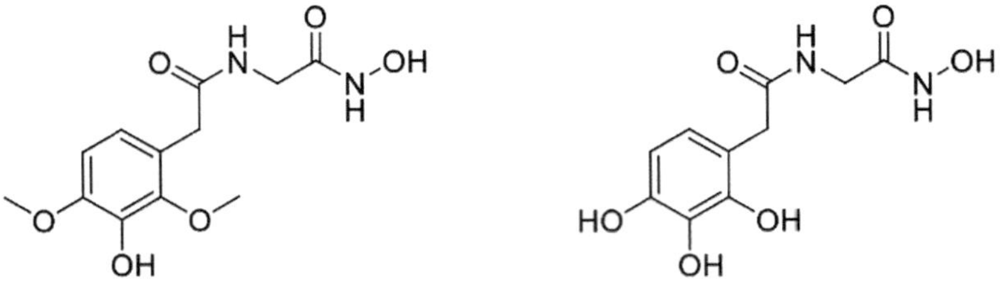

86 **87**

Figure 13.25 The structures of hydroxamic acid ENPP1 inhibitors.

Table 13.7 Enzymatic inhibitory activity and pharmacokinetic profile of compounds 88–92.

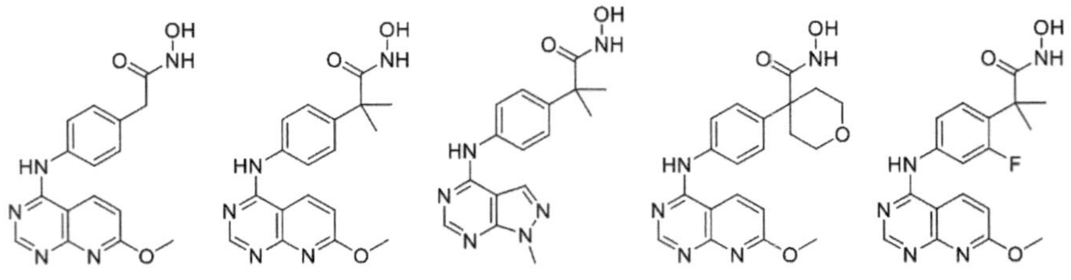

88 **89** **90** **91** **92**

Compound	**88**	**89**	**90**	**91**	**92**
Human ENPP1 enzymatic assay (2′3′-cGAMP) (nM)	1.9	1	4.8	2.2	2.2
$T_{1/2}$ (h)	3.26	1.30	2.44	2.0	3.9
C_{max} (ng/ml)	736	1488	244	640	2370
$AUC_{0\text{-}t}$ (h*ng/ml)	619	887	161	463	1589
F%	57.2	46.0	20.2	23.5	46.3

the introduction of two methyl groups at the α-position of the hydroxamic acid in compound **89**, likely due to favorable conformational adjustments in the linker region. However, the addition of methyl groups induced alterations in the *in vivo* metabolic profile, reducing the half-life to 1.3 hours, yet elevating the C_{max} from 736 ng/ml to 1488 ng/ml. Replacing methoxypyridine with *N*-methyl pyrazole in compound **90** resulted in diminished enzymatic inhibition and altered metabolic characteristics. Compound **91**, which involved cyclizing the two methyl groups into a tetrahydropyran ring, did not show improved metabolic characteristics *in vivo*. Conversely, compound **92**, created by adding a fluorine atom to the benzene ring of compound **89**, maintained its enzymatic potency and significantly enhanced the metabolic profile compared to compounds **88** and **89**. This work highlights that hydroxamic acid can be an effective zinc ion–binding group for developing promising ENPP1 inhibitors.

13.4.2.5 Other ENPP1 Inhibitors

In 2014, Chang and colleagues utilized a spectrophotometric assay employing p-Nph-5′-TMP as the substrate to evaluate ENPP1 inhibition efficiency, leading to the discovery of compound **93** with a K_i of 217 nM under pH 9.0 through high-throughput screening [18], as illustrated in Figure 13.26. The thioacetamide moiety of **93** appears to serve a dual function as both a linker and a zinc ion chelator. Subsequent SAR optimization highlighted the importance of the 3,4-dimethoxyphenyl group for effective ENPP1 inhibition. Compounds **94–96** obtained by removing or replacing these two methoxy groups, completely lost their activity (K_i > 10 μM). In contrast, the opposite side of the bicyclic framework was more tolerant of modifications. This optimization led to the synthesis of compounds **97** and **98**, which demonstrated K_i values of 29.6 nM and 5.00 nM vs p-Nph-5′-TMP, respectively. However, the inhibitory capacity of compounds **93**, **97**, and **98** was significantly reduced when tested against ATP, the native substrate of ENPP1.

Gangar and colleagues conducted a screening that yielded the identification of compound **99**, which exhibited a K_i value of 3.866 μM when tested with p-Nph-5′-TMP as the substrate at pH 9.0 [19], as shown in Figure 13.27. Their SAR

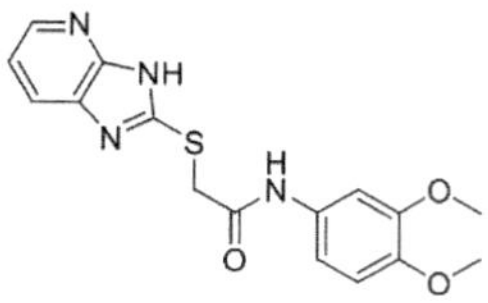

93
ENPP1 K_i = 217 nM (vs p-Nph-5'TMP)
ENPP1 K_i = 22.3 μM (vs ATP)

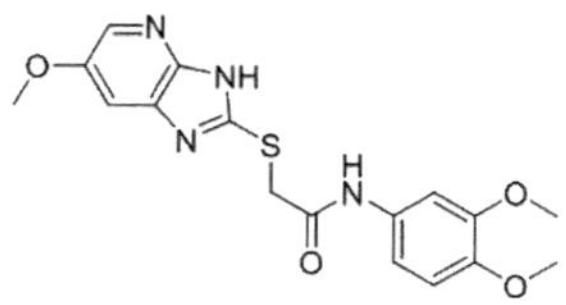

94
ENPP1 K_i = 29 nM (vs p-Nph-5'TMP)
ENPP1 K_i = 5.34 μM (vs ATP)

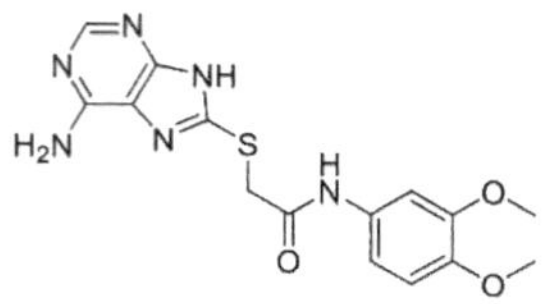

95
ENPP1 K_i = 5 nM (vs p-Nph-5'TMP)
ENPP1 K_i = 18.0 μM (vs ATP)

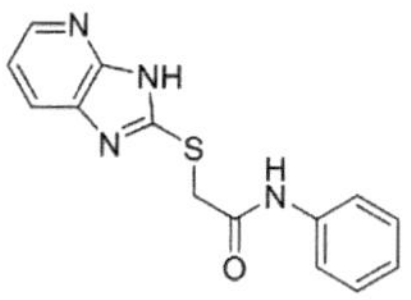

96
ENPP1 K_i > 10 μM (vs p-Nph-5'TMP)

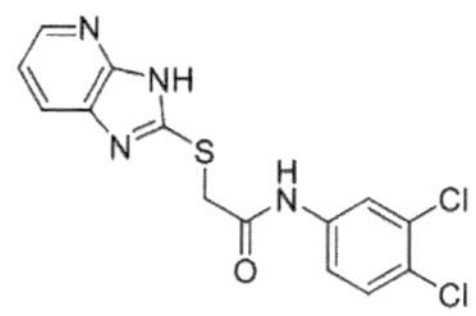

97
ENPP1 K_i > 10 μM (vs p-Nph-5'TMP)

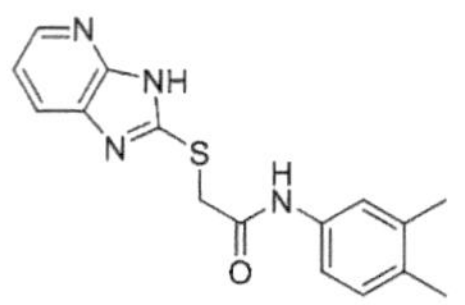

98
ENPP1 K_i > 10 μM (vs p-Nph-5'TMP)

Figure 13.26 Structures of ENPP1 inhibitors **93–98**.

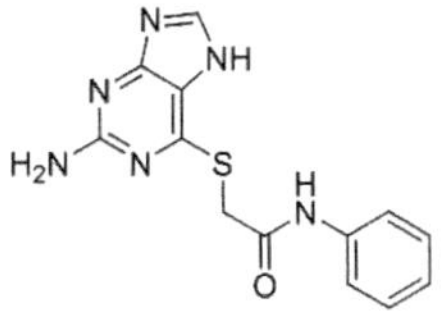

99
ENPP1 K_i = 3.866 μM

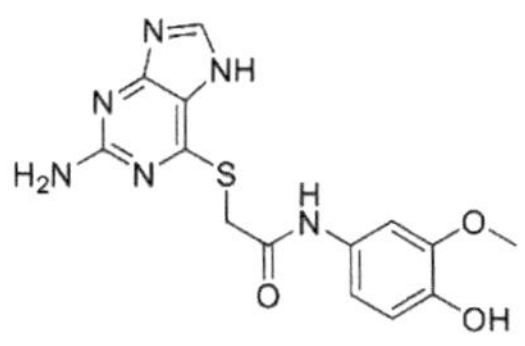

100
ENPP1 K_i = 0.038 μM

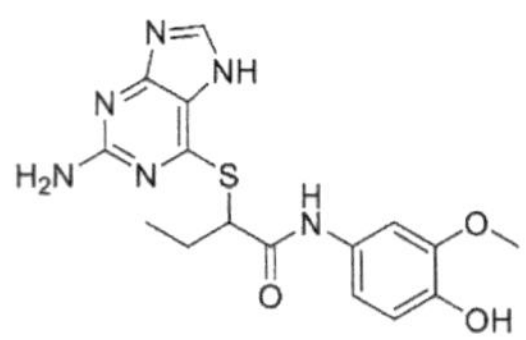

101
ENPP1 K_i = 0.041 μM

Figure 13.27 Structures of ENPP1 inhibitors **99–101**.

studies revealed that incorporating a methoxy group at the 3-position of the aromatic ring enhanced the compound's activity, while a hydroxyl substitution at the 4-position dramatically increased potency. Building on these findings, they synthesized compound **100**, which achieved a K_i value of 0.038 μM. However, compound **100** suffered from poor oral bioavailability (F <1%). To address this issue, the linker was modified by introducing an ethyl group at the α-position of the amide linkage, resulting in compound **101**. This modification not only preserved the inhibitory activity but also enhanced bioavailability. Compound **101** demonstrated favorable PK properties, with a half-life of 1.04 hours and AUC_{inf} of 1032.66 h*ng/ml. Moreover, in a mouse model of Lewis Lung Carcinoma Line 1 (LLC1) xenografts, compound **101** effectively inhibited tumor growth by approximately 50% upon systemic administration, highlighting its substantial potential as an ENPP1 inhibitor.

Building upon sulofenur, Saif Ullah and colleagues developed a series of pyrrolo[2,3-*b*]pyridine derivatives embedded with the sulfamide group [20], as shown in Figure 13.28. While these derivatives exhibited only moderate ENPP1 inhibitory potency, SAR studies provided valuable insights. Compound **102**, which includes a strong electron-withdrawing -NO_2 group, demonstrated selective inhibition of ENPP1 with an IC_{50} of 0.80 μM, compared to ENPP3, which was moderately inhibited with an IC_{50} of 1.17 μM. Compound **103**, containing a pyrrolopyridine core with chlorine at 4-position, was more favorable for inhibition of isoenzyme ENPP1 with an IC_{50} value of 1.08 μM, whereas its inhibition of ENPP3 was less effective, with an IC_{50} of 26.09 μM. Compound **102** stood out for its pronounced antiproliferative effect against the MCF-7 cell line, inhibiting growth by 70.66%. Similarly, compound **103** demonstrated a moderate suppressive effect on HT-29 cells, with a 47.57% inhibition rate. Molecular docking provided by the article revealed that the sulfonamide and carbonyl amide functionalities of these coordinated with the Zn^{2+} ion, establishing metal ion coordination. This research introduces a novel molecular design paradigm for targeting the ENPP1 protein pocket.

In addition to the ENPP1 inhibitors discussed above, several other compounds have demonstrated enzymatic inhibitory activity against ENPP1. Due to the

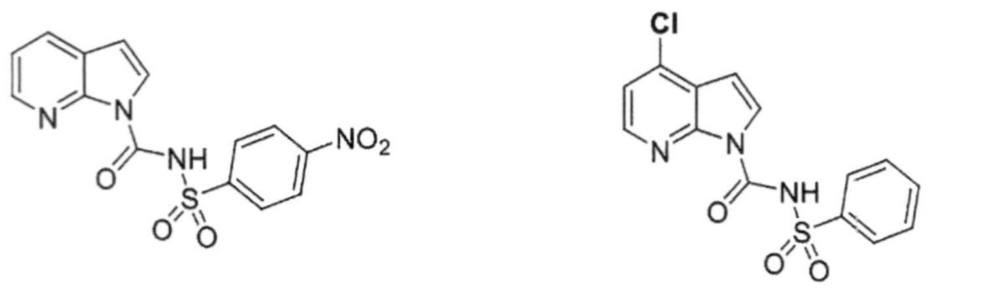

102
ENPP1 IC_{50} = 0.80 μM
ENPP3 IC_{50} = 1.17 μM
MCF-7 70.66% inhibition at 10 μM
HT-29 18.92% inhibition at 10 μM

103
ENPP1 IC_{50} = 1.08 μM
ENPP3 IC_{50} = 26.09 μM
MCF-7 3.32% inhibition at 10 μM
HT-29 47.57% inhibition at 10 μM

Figure 13.28 The structures of ENPP1 inhibitors **102** and **103**.

unclear mechanisms underlying the enzymatic inhibition of these compounds and their subsequent discontinuation as targeted ENPP1 drug candidates, we have summarized these compounds in a table without further detailed discussion (Table 13.8).

13.4.3 Clinical Molecules of ENPP1

To date, four ENPP1 inhibitors – RBS-2418 [28], TXN10128 [29], SR-8541A [30], and ZX-8177 [31, 32] – have progressed to clinical trials. Notably, the structures of these clinical compounds have not been disclosed. In this section, we will provide an update on their preclinical data and the latest clinical developments.

RBS-2418, developed by Riboscience, is the first ENPP1 inhibitor to reach Phase I clinical trials. This study (NCT05270213) is an open-label, non-randomized Phase 1 study for the treatment of adult patients with advanced, unresectable, recurrent, or metastatic solid tumors who have either progressed on or are ineligible for standard therapies. The results demonstrated that RBS-2418, administered at doses ranging from 100 mg twice daily (BID) to 400 mg BID in combination with pembrolizumab, was safe and well-tolerated, with no adverse safety events attributed to the drug. RBS-2418 showed excellent oral bioavailability, with plasma concentrations exceeding the serum EC_{90} level for ENPP1 by more than 17-fold at the 100 mg BID dose and over 40-fold at the 200 mg BID dose. Furthermore, the therapy enhanced DCs activation, promoted the proliferation of both $CD4^+$ and $CD8^+$ T lymphocytes, and led to a significant expansion of T cell receptors (TCR) clonotypes in peripheral blood. It also upregulated genes encoding cytotoxic granule proteins in T cells, indicating a shift from a nonresponsive tumor state to an activated immune phenotype. Collectively, these encouraging outcomes support the ongoing development of RBS-2418, spearheading a new generation of immunotherapeutic agents [33].

TXN10128, another promising candidate, entered Phase I clinical trials in 2023 (NCT05978492). The clinical trial primarily aims to evaluate the safety and tolerability of TXN10128, while also assessing its PKs, pharmacodynamics, and potential antitumor efficacy in patients with locally advanced, inoperable, or metastatic solid tumors. Notably, preclinical investigations have illustrated TXN10128's remarkable capability to inhibit ENPP1 with nanomolar potency *in vitro* and to activate the cGAS–STING signaling cascade in cellular assays. The *in vivo* efficacy was further validated in an MC38 syngeneic mouse model, where oral administration of TXN10128, in combination with intravenous anti-PD-L1 therapy, not only potently suppressed ENPP1 activity at sub-nanomolar concentrations but also promoted STING pathway activation. These collective findings underscore TXN10128 as a compelling candidate for clinical exploration, particularly in synergy with established immunotherapeutic regimens [34].

SR-8541A is a highly selective and potent ENPP1 inhibitor that enhances the therapeutic efficacy of immune checkpoint inhibitors (ICIs) in colorectal cancer models. Preliminary research showed that the combination therapy of SR-8541A with ICIs *in vivo* significantly improved overall therapeutic outcomes compared to

Table 13.8 Other ENPP1 inhibitors.

Name	Structure	Potency	Originator
$[TiW_{11}CoO_{40}]^{8-}$	/	1.46 nM (vs ATP)	Lee et al. [21]
Reactive Blue 2	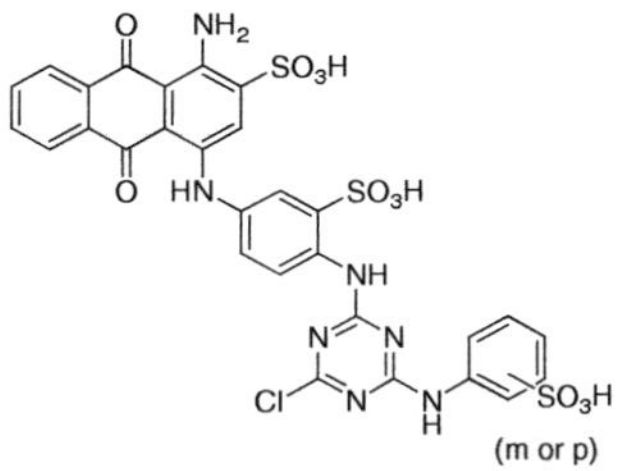	ENPP1 $K_i = 140\,nM$	Iqbal et al. [22]
Suramin	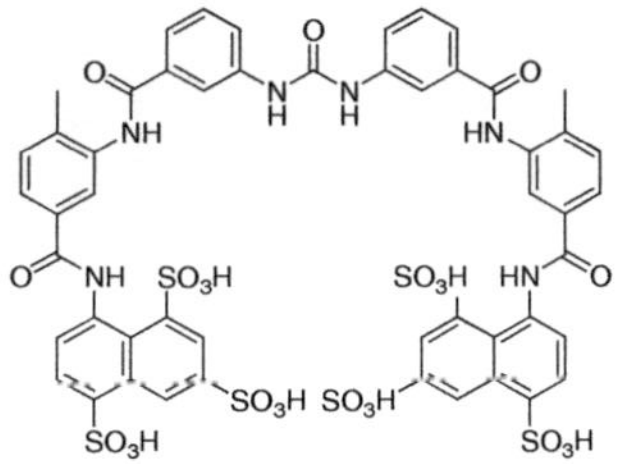	ENPP1 $K_i = 260\,nM$	Iqbal et al. [22]
PPADS	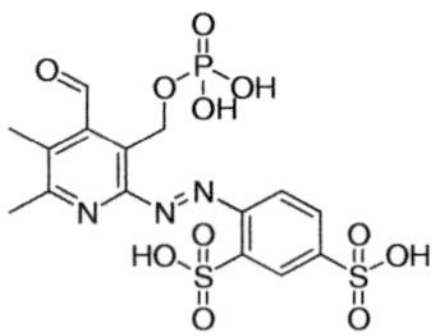	$IC_{50} = 15\,\mu M$	Grobben et al. [23]

Heparin	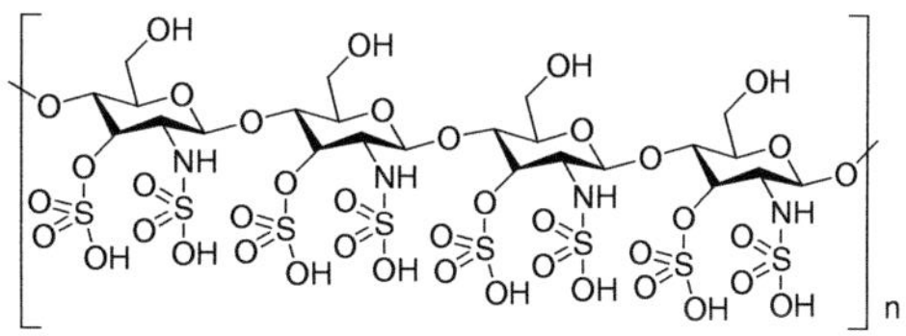	$IC_{50} = < 1\ \mu M$	Lopez et al. [24]
Raloxifene derivative	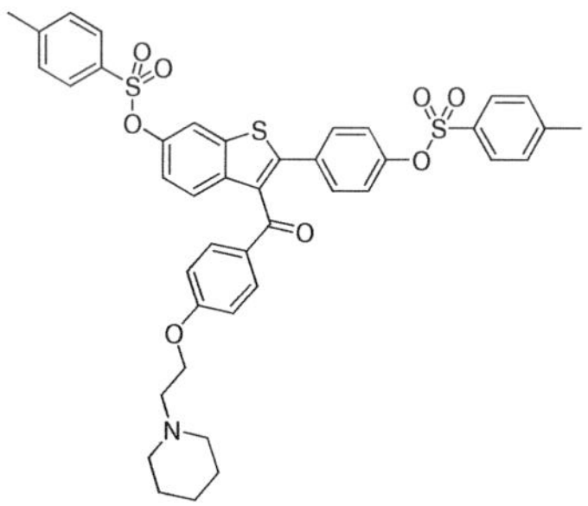	$IC_{50} = 290\ nM$	El-Gamal et al. [25]
Benzothiophene derivative	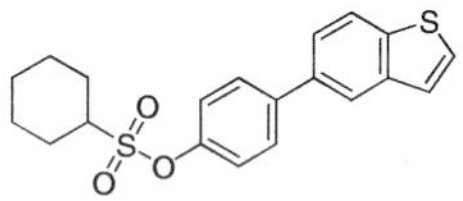	$IC_{50} = 120\ nM$	Anbar et al. [26]
Thiazolobenzimidazolone derivative	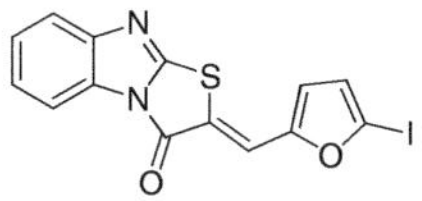	ENPP1 $K_i = 467\ nM$	Lee et al. [27]

ICIs alone. Tumors treated with this combination exhibited increased infiltration of $CD3^+$ and $CD8^+$ T cells, heightened IFN response, and reduced adenosine levels [35]. The phase I clinical trial of SR-8541A was designed to assess its safety, tolerability, and PKs when administered orally as a monotherapy in patients with solid tumors (NCT06063681). Initial evaluations have confirmed the safety, tolerability, and favorable oral bioavailability of SR-8541A, supporting dose escalation in the ongoing Phase I trial and the continued clinical evaluation of SR-8541A [36].

ZX-8177, developed by Nanjing Zenshine Pharma, exhibits high potency in both biochemical and MDA-MB-231 cell-based enzymatic assays, with IC_{50} values of 9.5 nM and 11 nM, respectively. In various syngeneic mouse models, ZX-8177 administered intraperitoneally at 2 mg/kg twice daily resulted in a TGI ranging from 37% to 60%. This treatment also significantly increased the presence of NK cells, Granzyme B^+ $CD8^+$ T cells, and enhanced the M1/M2 macrophage ratio within the tumor microenvironment. In the CT-26 model, a synergistic antitumor effect was observed when ZX-8177 (25 mg/kg, orally, twice daily) was combined with Mitomycin C (0.5 mg/kg, twice weekly). Similarly, in the 4T1 and Pan02 models, combining ZX-8177 (25 mg/kg, orally, twice daily) with Cisplatin (5 mg/kg, twice weekly) enhanced antitumor efficacy. Flow cytometry analysis revealed an increase in tumor-infiltrating NK cells in the tumor tissues treated with ZX-8177. Additionally, these tumor tissues exhibited elevated levels of 2′3′-cGAMP and increased IFN-related gene expression, such as CCL5 and CXCL10. In the Pan02 syngeneic mouse model, combining ZX-8177 (25 mg/kg, orally, twice daily) with 20 Gy radiation showed superior antitumor efficacy compared to radiation alone, achieving 100% TGI vs 78.5% TGI ($p < 0.005$). These *in vivo* studies demonstrated that combining ZX-8177 with radiation or chemotherapy synergistically inhibited tumor growth by activating STING-mediated innate immunity [37]. Recently, ZX-8177 has been approved for clinical trial by the National Medical Products Administration (NMPA, China) [37].

13.5 Concluding Remarks and Future Perspectives

ENPP1, through its nucleotide pyrophosphatase and phosphodiesterase activities, plays a crucial role in various diseases, including biomineralization disorders, diabetes, and cancers. Despite its significance, the precise physiological roles of ENPP1 remain not fully understood, warranting further investigation. Recently, the role of ENPP1 in tumor immunotherapy has received extensive attention. In the tumor microenvironment, ENPP1 contributes to immune suppression by hydrolyzing 2′3′-cGAMP, thereby downregulating the cGAS–STING pathway, and by participating in the adenosine synthesis pathway. Inhibiting ENPP1 activity can mitigate immune suppression, thereby enabling the partial restoration of the body's immune response and enhancing its ability to combat tumors. Thus, developing small-molecule inhibitors of ENPP1 is an effective strategy for tumor immunotherapy. Currently, four ENPP1 inhibitors are in clinical stages, and available data highlight their potential therapeutic efficacy. Consequently, ENPP1 stands as a promising target for the next wave of cancer immunotherapies, underscoring the value of designing and discovering small-molecule ENPP1 inhibitors.

Various ENPP1 inhibitors have recently been developed and have shown great potential for cancer immunotherapy, paving the way for new research in this field. To further enhance the *in vitro* and *in vivo* activity of current ENPP1 small-molecule inhibitors, improve their PK profiles, and enhance selectivity, we believe it is essential to carefully choose zinc-ion coordinating groups and refine the conformation of linkers. Given that the ENPP1 protein has multiple functional domains, some with nonenzymatic activities, the development of targeted protein degraders against ENPP1 could yield additional biological effects and provide more comprehensive inhibition of protein function. Moreover, exploring inhibitors that target other functional domains of ENPP1 may also be a viable strategy for modulating its activity. Additionally, investigating the combinations of ENPP1-targeted therapies with other cancer treatments is crucial for maximizing ENPP1's therapeutic potential and should be a key focus for future research.

As a metalloenzyme, the physiological function of ENPP1 mainly relies on the catalytic center, which contains two zinc ions. When designing small-molecule inhibitors for ENPP1, it is essential to consider the interaction between these molecules and the zinc ions. Up to now, approximately 70 small-molecule inhibitors targeting metalloenzymes have received clinical approval. The majority of these inhibitors employ specific chemical structures, typically referred to as metal-binding groups, to form direct coordination bonds with the metal ion(s) at the active site [38, 39]. Research on the functions of ENPP1 and its small-molecule inhibitors will provide valuable insights for the development of drugs targeting metalloenzymes.

Glossary

ABCC6 ATP-binding cassette subfamily C member 6
ADO adenosine
ADPR adenosine diphosphate ribose
Akt protein kinase B
ALP alkaline phosphatase
AMP adenosine monophosphate
Ap3A diadenosine 5′,5‴-P1, P3-triphosphate
Ap4A diadenosine 5′,5‴-P1, P4-tetraphosphate
Ap5A diadenosine 5′,5‴-P1, P5-pentaphosphate
ARHR2 autosomal recessive hyperphosphatemic rickets type 2
A2AR adenosine A2A receptor
A2BR adenosine A2B receptor
ATP adenosine triphosphate
ATX autotaxin
BID twice daily
cAMP cyclic adenosine monophosphate

CD cytoplasmic domain
CD28 T-cell-specific surface glycoprotein
CD38 cluster of differentiation 38
CD39 cluster of differentiation 39
CD73 cluster of differentiation 73
cGAS cyclic GMP–AMP synthase
CL clearance rate
C_{max} peak plasma concentration
CS catalytic site
CTP cytidine triphosphate
CXCL10 C-X-C Motif Chemokine Ligand 10
DCs dendritic cells
dsDNA double-stranded DNA
ENPP ecto-nucleotide pyrophosphatase/phosphodiesterase
ENPP1 ecto-nucleotide pyrophosphatase/phosphodiesterase 1
ELISA enzyme-linked immunosorbent assay
GACI generalized arterial calcification of infancy
GLUT4 glucose transporter type 4
GMP guanosine monophosphate
GPI glycosylphosphatidylinositol
Gp3G diguanosine 5′,5‴-P1, P4- triphosphate
GTP guanosine triphosphate
G-pocket guanine-binding pocket
HDAC histone deacetylase
ICIs immune checkpoint inhibitors
IFITM1 interferon-inducible transmembrane
IFN Interferon
IKK IκB kinase
IRF3 interferon regulatory factor 3
ISGs interferon-stimulated genes
ISRE interferon-stimulated response element
IP intraperitoneal injection
IV intradermal injection
LAG-3 lymphocyte activation gene-3
NAD$^+$ nicotinamide adenine dinucleotide
NF-κB nuclear factor kappa-B
NK natural killer (cell)
NMPA National Medical Products Administration
NSCLC non-small cell lung cancer
NTPDase 1 nucleoside triphosphate diphosphohydrolase 1
NTPDase 2 nucleoside triphosphate diphosphohydrolase 2
NTPDase 3 nucleoside triphosphate diphosphohydrolase 3
NTPDase 8 nucleoside triphosphate diphosphohydrolase 8
NUC nuclease-like domain
N-pocket nucleotide-binding pocket

OAS1 2′-5′-oligoadenylate Synthetase 1
OPLL ossification of the posterior longitudinal ligament
PDE phosphodiesterase domain
PD-1 programmed death 1
PK pharmacokinetic
Pi inorganic phosphate
PI3K phosphoinositide 3-kinase
PO oral administration
PPi pyrophosphate
SAR structure–activity relationship
SC subcutaneous injection
SMB somatomedin B-like domain
STAT1 signal transducer and activator of transcription 1
STING stimulator of interferon genes
TBK1 TANK-binding kinase 1
TCR T cell receptors
TGI tumor growth inhibition
TNBC triple-negative breast cancer
TM transmembrane domain
TNAP tissue-nonspecific alkaline phosphatase
TNF tumor necrosis factor
$T_{1/2}$ half-life
UMP uridine monophosphate
UTP uridine triphosphate
VICs valvular interstitial Cells
2′3′-cGAMP 2′3′- cyclic guanosine monophosphate–adenosine monophosphate

References

1 Carozza, J.A., Brown, J.A., Bohnert, V. et al. (2020). Structure-aided development of small-molecule inhibitors of ENPP1, the extracellular phosphodiesterase of the immunotransmitter cGAMP. *Cell Chemical Biology* 27 (11): 1347–1358.
2 Yang, W., Lipert, M., and Nofsinger, R. (2023). Current screening, design, and delivery approaches to address low permeability of chemically synthesized modalities in drug discovery and early clinical development. *Drug Discovery Today* 28 (9): 103685.
3 Hecker, S.J. and Erion, M.D. (2008). Prodrugs of phosphates and phosphonates. *Journal of Medicinal Chemistry* 51 (8): 2328–2345.
4 Caroff, E., Hubler, F., Meyer, E. et al. (2015). 4-((R)-2-{[6-((S)-3-Methoxy-pyrrolidin-1-yl)-2-phenylpyrimidine-4-carbonyl]amino}-3-phosphonopropionyl) piperazine-1-carboxylic acid butyl ester (ACT-246475) and its prodrug (ACT-281959), a novel P2Y12 receptor antagonist with a wider therapeutic

window in the rat than clopidogrel. *Journal of Medicinal Chemistry* 58 (23): 9133–9153.
5 Smith, D.A., Beaumont, K., Maurer, T.S. et al. (2019). Clearance in drug design. *Journal of Medicinal Chemistry* 62 (5): 2245–2255.
6 Yan, Q., J. Pan, and D. Sun. (2022). Application of ENPP1 inhibitor in preparation of medicine for treating ENPP1-mediated disease comprising solid tumor cancer. CN115536696.
7 Gao, S., Hou, Y., Li, J. et al. (2023). Phosphonic acid compound and prodrug thereof, and preparation methods for and uses of phosphonic acid compound and prodrug thereof. WO2023138637.
8 Kasibhatla, S.R., Sharma, S., Kaadige, M. et al. (2022). Phosphonates as inhibitors of ENPP1 and CdnP. WO2022125614.
9 Hawley, R. (2022). Bicyclic heteroaryl phosphonate derivatives as ectonucleotide pyrophosphatase phosphodiesterase 1 inhibitors. WO2022212488.
10 Duan, W., Geng, M., Zhang, H. et al. (2023). Benzimidazole compound and medical use thereof. WO2023131333.
11 Yan, Q., J. Pan, and D. Sun. (2023). Process for preparation of ENPP1 inhibitor. WO2023197987.
12 Hawley, R. and K. Klumpp. (2020). Quinazoline derivatives as ectonucleotide pyrophosphatase phosphodiesterase 1 inhibitors and their preparation. WO2020140001.
13 Hawley, R. and K. Klumpp. (2020). Bicyclic heteroaryl derivatives as ectonucleotide pyrophosphatase phosphodiesterase 1 inhibitors and their preparation. WO2020210649.
14 Hawley, R. (2022). Preparation of bicyclic heteroaryl boronate derivatives as ectonucleotide pyrophosphatase phosphodiesterase 1 inhibitors. WO2022197734.
15 Deb, A., Jung, M., Chen, X. et al. (2022). Preparation of quinolines, triazines, serinamides and ureas as small molecule inhibitors of ENPP1. WO2022056068.
16 Deb, A., Jung, M., Chen, X. et al. (2023). Preparation of small molecule inhibitors of ENPP1. WO2023168240.
17 Gao, S., Li, J., Zhang, C. et al. (2023). Hydroxamic acid compound having enpp1 inhibitory activity and use thereof. WO2023036289.
18 Chang, L., Lee, S.Y., Leonczak, P. et al. (2014). Imidazopyridine- and purine-thioacetamide derivatives: potent inhibitors of nucleotide pyrophosphatase/phosphodiesterase 1 (NPP1). *Journal of Medicinal Chemistry* 57 (23): 10080–10100.
19 Gangar, M., Goyal, S., Raykar, D. et al. (2022). Design, synthesis and biological evaluation studies of novel small molecule ENPP1 inhibitors for cancer immunotherapy. *Bioorganic Chemistry* 119: 105549.
20 Ullah, S., EI-Gamal, M.I., EI-Gamal, R. et al. (2021). Synthesis, biological evaluation, and docking studies of novel pyrrolo[2,3-*b*]pyridine derivatives as both ectonucleotide pyrophosphatase/phosphodiesterase inhibitors and antiproliferative agents. *European Journal of Medicinal Chemistry* 217: 113339.
21 Lee, S.-Y., Fiene, A., Li, W. et al. (2015). Polyoxometalates – potent and selective ecto-nucleotidase inhibitors. *Biochemical Pharmacology* 93 (2): 171–181.

22 Iqbal, J., Levesque, S.A., Sevigny, J. et al. (2008). A highly sensitive CE-UV method with dynamic coating of silica-fused capillaries for monitoring of nucleotide pyrophosphatase/phosphodiesterase reactions. *Electrophoresis* 29 (17): 3685–3693.

23 Grobben, B., Claes, P., Roymans, D. et al. (2000). Ecto-nucleotide pyrophosphatase modulates the purinoceptor-mediated signal transduction and is inhibited by purinoceptor antagonists. 130 (1): 139–145.

24 Lopez, V., Schuh, H.M., Mirza, S. et al. (2023). Heparins are potent inhibitors of ectonucleotide pyrophosphatase/phospho-diesterase-1 (NPP1) – a promising target for the immunotherapy of cancer. *Frontiers in Immunology* 14: 1173634.

25 El-Gamal, M.I., Ullah, S., Zaraei, S.O. et al. (2019). Synthesis, biological evaluation, and docking studies of new raloxifene sulfonate or sulfamate derivatives as inhibitors of nucleotide pyrophosphatase/phosphodiesterase. *European Journal of Medicinal Chemistry* 181: 111560.

26 Anbar, H.S., EI-Gamam, R., Ullah, S. et al. (2020). Evaluation of sulfonate and sulfamate derivatives possessing benzofuran or benzothiophene nucleus as inhibitors of nucleotide pyrophosphatases/phosphodiesterases and anticancer agents. *Bioorganic Chemistry* 104: 104305.

27 Lee, S.-Y., Perotti, A., De Jonghe, S. et al. (2016). Thiazolo[3,2-a]benzimidazol-3(2H)-one derivatives: structure–activity relationships of selective nucleotide pyrophosphatase/phosphodiesterase1 (NPP1) inhibitors. *Bioorganic & Medicinal Chemistry* 24 (14): 3157–3165.

28 ClinicalTrials.gov 2024. Identifier for RBS2418: NCT05270213. https://clinicaltrials.gov/study/NCT05270213 (accessed 26 Aug 2024).

29 ClinicalTrials.gov 2024 Identifier for TXN10128: NCT05978492. https://clinicaltrials.gov/study/NCT05978492 (accessed 26 Aug 2024).

30 ClinicalTrials.gov 2024. identifier for SR-8541A: NCT06063681. https://clinicaltrials.gov/study/NCT06063681 (accessed 26 Aug 2024).

31 ClinicalTrials.gov 2024. Identifier for ZX-8177: CXHL2400346. https://www.cde.org.cn/main/xxgk/listpage/4b5255eb0a84820cef4ca3e8b6bbe20c (accessed 26 Aug 2024).

32 ClinicalTrials.gov 2024. Identifier for ZX-8177: CXHL2400347. https://www.cde.org.cn/main/xxgk/listpage/4b5255eb0a84820cef4ca3e8b6bbe20c (accessed 26 Aug 2024).

33 Csiki, I., Dong, A., Tuan, B.Y. et al. (2022). First-in-human experience using RBS2418, an oral ENPP1 inhibitor within an expanded access protocol in combination with pembrolizumab in a patient with metastatic adrenal cancer. *Journal of Clinical Oncology* 40 (16_suppl): e14550–e14550.

34 Kim, S., Ali, I., Yu, A. et al. (2021). Abstract LBA009: orally available ENPP1 inhibitor, TXN10128, restores STING activation in tumor microenvironment and confers anti-tumor responses in combination with immune checkpoint blockade. *Molecular Cancer Therapeutics* 20 (12_Supplement): LBA009.

35 Weston, A., Thode, T., NG, S. et al. (2023). 897-G SR-8541A, a small molecule inhibitor of ENPP1, enhances the effect of immune checkpoint inhibitors in a

colorectal cancer model. *Journal for ImmunoTherapy Of Canser* 11 (Suppl 2): A1826–A1826.

36 Weston, A.S., Thode, T., Shan, M. et al. (2024). Abstract CT161: first-in-human study of ENPP1 inhibitor, SR-8541A, for the treatment of solid tumors. *Cancer Research* 84 (7_Supplement): CT161.

37 Qin, X., Li, Y.Y., Sun, S. et al. (2023). Abstract 577: ENPP1 inhibitor ZX-8177 in combination with chemotherapy or radiation exhibits synergistic anti-tumor effects via STING-mediated response. *Cancer Research* 83 (7_Supplement): 577–577.

38 Chen, A.Y., Adamek, R.N., Dick, B.L. et al. (2019). Targeting metalloenzymes for therapeutic intervention. *Chemical Reviews* 119 (2): 1323–1455.

39 Xiao, Y.-C., Yu, J.L., Dai, Q.Q. et al. (2021). Targeting metalloenzymes by boron-containing metal-binding pharmacophores. *Journal of Medicinal Chemistry* 64 (24): 17706–17727.

14

Drug Discovery Targeting Oxygen-Sensing Hypoxia-Inducible Factor Prolyl Hydroxylases

Yue Wu and Xiaojin Zhang

China Pharmaceutical University, Jiangsu Key Laboratory of Drug Design and Optimization, and Department of Chemistry, 639 Longmian Dadao, Jiangning District, Nanjing, 211198, P.R. China

14.1 Introduction

14.1.1 Overview of the Oxygen-Sensing Pathway

Cellular oxygen homeostasis relies on a continuous oxygen supply, crucial for the survival of all aerobic organisms, including metazoans [1, 2]. Oxygen deficiency is a major contributor to cellular function. The mechanisms by which aerobic organisms adapt to changes in environmental oxygen levels have long fascinated physiologists [3]. In 2019, the Nobel Prize in Physiology or Medicine was awarded for the discovery of a mechanism that enables animal cells to sense and adjust to fluctuating oxygen availability. These findings significantly enhanced our understanding of the molecular pathways that regulate cellular responses to oxygen variations, with significant implications for various physiological and pathological conditions, including cancer, anemia, and ischemic diseases [4].

Decreased oxygen availability leads to cellular hypoxia, a condition where oxygen demand exceeds supply. Hypoxia can be continuous or intermittent and can present in either acute or chronic forms [5]. Ensuring proper oxygen levels throughout the body is vital for health, with the cardiovascular system being central to oxygen transport. Extended periods of inadequate oxygen supply can result in chronic hypoxia, which, although physiologically common at high altitudes, is also prevalent in diseases such as cardiovascular disorders, diabetes, and cancer [5, 6]. The evolution of effective oxygen-sensing mechanisms to mitigate hypoxia likely played a key role in the development of aerobic life.

The key cellular regulators of chronic oxygen homeostasis are hypoxia-inducible factors (HIFs), transcription factors sensitive to changes in oxygen tension [3, 5, 6]. HIF is a heterodimer composed of α and β subunits, mediating hypoxia responses at cellular and systemic levels. While HIF-β levels remain stable, HIF-α is upregulated in many cells and tissues under hypoxia [3, 5, 6]. This increase in HIF-α, and the subsequent enhancement of HIF-α,β transcriptional activity, is involved in both normal

Drug Discovery Targeting Metalloenzymes: Strategies and Applications, First Edition. Edited by Guo-Bo Li.

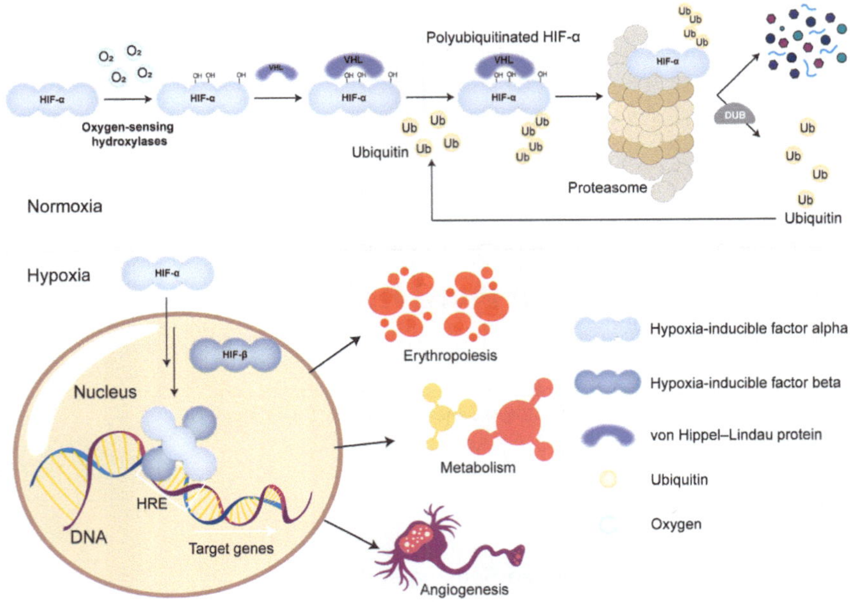

Figure 14.1 Overview of the oxygen-sensing pathway.

physiological adaptation and various pathologies, such as cardiovascular disease, cancer, metabolic disorders, and ischemia-related conditions [6].

Both HIF-α stability and transcriptional activities are regulated by oxygen and 2-oxoglutarate (2OG)-dependent hydroxylases [7–11], identified as key oxygen sensors in the HIF pathway during the early 2000s [9, 10]. HIF prolyl hydroxylases (HIF-PHDs) and factor inhibiting HIF (FIH) are crucial for cellular responses to hypoxia [8, 10], though they play distinct roles. Under hypoxic conditions, the hydroxylation of HIF-α by HIF-PHDs and FIH is inhibited due to limited oxygen, leading to enhanced HIF-α stability and transcriptional activity. This, in turn, activates HIF target genes [7, 10], including those encoding erythropoietin (EPO), glycolytic enzymes, and vascular endothelial growth factors (VEGFs) (Figure 14.1). While both enzymes regulate HIF-α transcription, FIH does so through a distinct mechanism from that of HIF-PHDs [7].

14.1.2 Role of Oxygen-Sensing Hydroxylases in Cellular Response

The oxygen-sensing hydroxylases, HIF-PHDs and FIH, are part of the 2OG-dependent oxygenase structural superfamily, one of the largest known families of non-heme, Fe(II)-dependent enzymes [12]. In human cells, there are three HIF-PHD isoforms (HIF-PHD1–3) [10, 13], as well as a single FIH isoform [14]. HIF-α exists in three isoforms (HIF-1–3α), with HIF-1α and HIF-2α being the most studied. Both are involved in the upregulation of specific gene sets in a context-dependent and sometimes overlapping manner [3, 6]. HIF-1α and HIF-2α have two transcriptional activation domains: the N-terminal activation domain

(NTAD) and the C-terminal activation domain (CTAD) [3, 5–7]. The HIF-PHDs predominantly regulate NTAD-mediated gene expressions, while FIH is more involved in CTAD-mediated regulation [3]. HIF-PHD2 is distinguished by a unique Myeloid-Nervy-DEAF1 zinc finger (MYND) finger domain, conserved across animals, which is absent in HIF-PHD1 and HIF-PHD3 [13, 15, 16], whereas FIH is found only sporadically in early animals [17].

Although HIF-PHDs and FIH both participate in HIF-mediated hypoxia sensing and response, they perform distinct roles and belong to different subfamilies of 2OG oxygenase, showcasing functional convergence toward related but separate functions. HIF-PHDs are part of the prolyl hydroxylase (PH) structural family VIII, typically monomeric, and include other prolyl hydroxylases and small molecule oxidant oxygenases [12, 18]. In contrast, FIH is a member of the Jumonji C (JmjC) structural family VI [19–22], which is often dimeric and includes protein hydroxylases and *N*-methyl lysine demethylases involved in histone demethylation via hydroxylation [18].

Under normoxic conditions, HIF-PHDs facilitate the C4 trans-hydroxylation of specific prolyl residues located in the oxygen-dependent degradation domain (ODD) of HIF-α. In HIF-1α, these residues are Pro402 and Pro564, while in HIF-2α, they are Pro490 and Pro531. This hydroxylation process relies on the cofactors 2OG and Fe(II). The modification of these proline residues in HIF-α significantly increases its affinity for von Hippel–Lindau (VHL) protein by more than 100-fold, promoting its interaction with the VHL ubiquitin ligase complex. This interaction results in the ubiquitination of HIF-α, marking it for recognition and subsequent degradation by the 26S proteasome [9]. In parallel, FIH catalyzes the C3 hydroxylation of a single asparaginyl residue within the CTAD of HIF-α – Asn803 in HIF-1α and Asn851 in HIF-2α. [14, 23–25]. This hydroxylation event inhibits the binding of HIF-α to the transcriptional coactivator p300/Cyclic AMP Response Element-Binding protein (CREB)-binding protein (p300/CBP), thereby modulating the transcriptional activity of HIF-α [10, 23] (Figure 14.2a).

The hydroxylation reactions catalyzed by HIF-PHDs and FIH are both sensitive to oxygen levels, but they exhibit different oxygen affinities. HIF-PHDs have a relatively low affinity for oxygen with an apparent K_m value of 229 ± 60 μM, which is slightly higher than the concentration of dissolved oxygen in the air (~200 μM). This makes HIF-PHDs inactive under mild hypoxic conditions. In contrast, FIH has a significantly higher affinity, with an apparent K_m value of 90 ± 20 μM, representing only 40% of the atmospheric oxygen concentration. This allows FIH to maintain its catalytic activity even under mild hypoxic conditions [26–29]. Under mild hypoxic conditions, the activity of HIF-PHDs is inhibited, preventing the C4 trans-hydroxylation of prolyl residues in HIF-α. However, FIH remains active and continues to catalyze the C3 hydroxylation of the asparaginyl residue in HIF-α. As a result, HIF-α can stabilize and translocate to the nucleus, but its transcriptional activity is partially suppressed due to FIH-mediated hydroxylation, which blocks its interaction with p300/CBP. Under these conditions, only ODD-mediated HIF transcriptional activity can be preserved in cells [23] (Figure 14.2b).

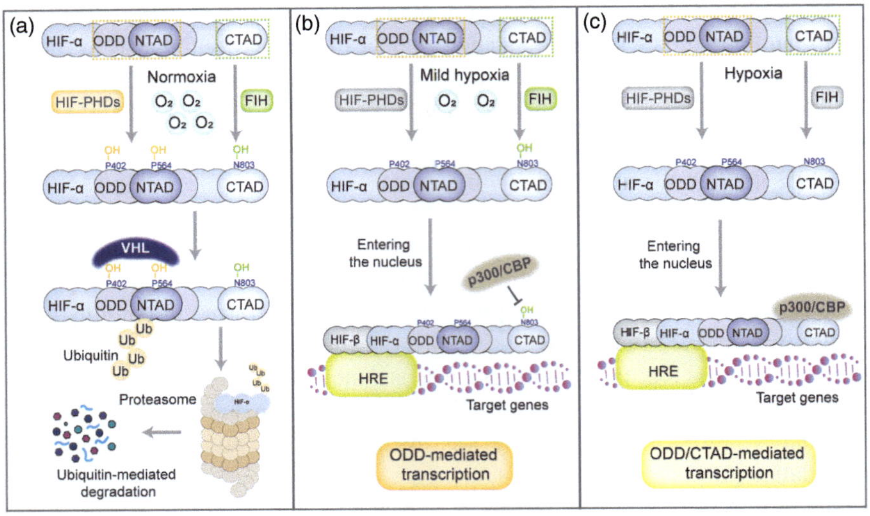

Figure 14.2 Overview of the roles of the oxygen-sensing hydrolases in cellular response under normoxia (a), mild hypoxia (b), and hypoxia (c) conditions.

Under hypoxic conditions, the hydroxylation of the oxygen-dependent enzymes HIF-PHDs and FIH becomes less efficient. As a result, HIF-α stabilizes and translocates into the nucleus. Within the nucleus, the HIFα-HIFβ-p300/CBP complex forms and binds to hypoxia-responsive elements (HREs) in the promoter regions of HIF target genes, which contain the consensus sequence 5′-(A/G)CGTG-3′. This binding initiates the transcriptional activation of these genes [2, 4, 7, 30, 31] (Figure 14.2c). The specificity of HIF-regulated transcription – whether in terms of tissues, cell type, or physiological context – largely depends on which HIF-α isoforms are predominant in a given tissue or disease state.

As 2OG-dependent hydroxylases, both FIH and HIF-PHDs [10, 13, 14, 32] utilize the same Fe(II) cofactor and require 2OG and dioxygen as cosubstrates, generating carbon dioxide and succinate as coproducts (Figure 14.2) [10, 13, 14, 32]. Their active sites, while related, exhibit significant differences in detail. Both enzymes employ a conserved two-histidine, one carboxylate (from aspartate) motif to coordinate the active site Fe(II), forming a "facial triad" that occupies three of the six possible coordination sites in an octahedral coordination geometry [21, 22, 33, 34]. Notably, although 2OG oxygenases use similar Fe(II) binding ligands, their catalytic kinetics and mechanistics can vary considerably [18, 26, 35]. Studies indicate that HIF-PHDs, particularly HIF-PHD2, exhibit high affinity for Fe(II) and 2OG, whereas FIH binds these cofactors less tightly [36]. Among human HIF hydroxylases, FIH and HIF-PHD2 are the most extensively studied. Both enzymes catalyze highly stereoselective reactions, incorporating an oxygen atom from atmospheric O_2 into their alcohol products [24, 27, 37]. HIF-PHD2 appears particularly well-suited for its role as a hypoxia sensor due to its efficient binding of Fe(II) and 2OG, as well as its limited ability to oxidize 2OG in the absence of substrate. Under isolated protein conditions, the reaction of O_2

with the HIF-PHD2.Fe(II).2OG.HIF-α complex is rate-limiting, aligning with its proposed function in hypoxia sensing [8, 10, 26, 38, 39]. Modeling studies suggest that the rate of O_2 transport to the HIF-PHD2 active site, followed by its binding to Fe(II) – likely involving the displacement of a metal-coordinated water molecule – plays a central role in the slow, dioxygen-regulated reaction of HIF-PHD2 [39, 40].

In line with cellular studies, the apparent K_m values for oxygen (K_m(app)(O_2)) are consistently lower for FIH compared to PHD2 when using HIF-1α and 2α OOD fragment-derived substrates [8, 26, 30]. Additionally, under pre-steady-state conditions, the O_2-initiated reaction of FIH occurs significantly faster than that of HIF-PHD2 [8, 38]. This faster reaction of FIH with O_2 aligns with crystallographic evidence, which shows that FIH, at least for some substrates, has a vacant coordination site adjacent to the oxidized substrate C—H bond, ready for O_2 binding. In contrast, such a site is not observed in HIF-PHD2. [21, 41]. However, it is important to note that FIH's kinetics in cells may be complicated by its interaction with other substrates and its dimeric structure, unlike the monomeric HIF-PHDs [21, 22]. The reported activities of both the HIF-PHDs and FIH are influenced by the length of the HIF-α fragments used as substrate. FIH, in particular, requires relatively longer peptides for efficient catalysis. Furthermore, studies indicate that the HIF-2α CTAD exhibits reduced activity compared to the HIF-1α CTAD when tested with isolated FIH, suggesting that FIH may be less effective in modifying HIF-2α than HIF-1α [30].

FIH and HIF-PHDs exhibit distinct sensitivities to peroxide in their hydroxylation of HIF-α, with FIH-catalyzed asparagine hydroxylation being significantly more susceptible to peroxide than HIF-PHD-catalyzed prolyl hydroxylation [42]. Peroxide rapidly inhibits FIH activity, resulting in reduced HIF-α asparagine hydroxylation and increased transcriptional activity. This suggests that FIH may function as a sensor for both peroxide and hypoxia. However, further research is needed to explore the sensitivity of other 2OG oxygenases to peroxide, as the current data may partially reflect the relative resistance of HIF-PHD catalysis to peroxide (Table 14.1).

14.2 Hypoxia-inducible Factor Prolyl Hydroxylases (HIF-PHDs)

14.2.1 Classification of HIF-PHDs

HIF-PHDs were initially discovered in 2001 through genomic database searches aimed at identifying sequences containing conserved cofactor-binding residues and the potential to form a jelly-roll fold [43]. In human cells, three HIF-PHD isoforms (or Egl nine homologs [EGLNs]) have been identified: HIF-PHD1–3. These isoforms exhibit high sequence homology in their C-terminal domains but differ significantly in their N-terminal domains (Figure 14.3). The C-terminal of all three isoforms contains a shared "finger-like" loop and a Fe(II)- and 2OG-dependent

Table 14.1 Comparison of selected properties of HIF-PHD2 and FIH.

Comparison		HIF-PHD2	FIH
Similarities		Both are Fe(II) and 2OG-dependent dioxygenases producing succinate and CO_2 as coproducts. Both are hypoxia sensors regulating HIF transcription. Both have the conserved 2OG oxygenase distorted core double-stranded β-helix (DSBH) fold and similar Fe(II) coordination chemistry, but there are key differences in their active sites, including in their 2OG and substrate binding modes. The HIF-PHD2 has a high affinity for Fe(II) and 2OG and FIH less so.	
Differences	Hydroxylation sites	Pro402 and 564 in HIF-1α Pro405 and 531 in HIF-2α (ODD)	Asn803 in HIF-1α Asn851 in HIF-2α (CTAD)
	HIF activity regulation	stability of HIF-α	HIF-α transactivational capacity
	Preferred oligomeric form	monomeric	dimeric
	Efficiency on HIF-1α and HIF-2α	Effective on both HIF-1α and HIF-2α (but PHD3 selectively hydroxylates C-terminal oxygen-dependent degradation domain [CODD])	Evidence for reduced relative effectiveness on HIF-2α
	FIH is active at lower O_2 levels	Inactive Km (O_2): 229 ± 60 μM, i.e. slightly above the atmospheric O_2 concentration (~ 200 μM)/slow reaction with O_2	Active K_m (O_2): 90 ± 20 μM
	Sensibility to peroxide	Less sensitive	Sensitive
	Oxidative metabolism regulation	HIF-PHD2 loss gives rise to the classical cellular response to hypoxia, i.e. increased glycolysis	FIH loss accelerates the rate of O_2 consumption
	Regulation of HIF target genes	Also important in NTAD-mediated expression, e.g. transferrin	Particularly important in CTAD mediated expression, (e.g. glut1, hk2, and ldha)/ regulates CBP/p300 mediated expression

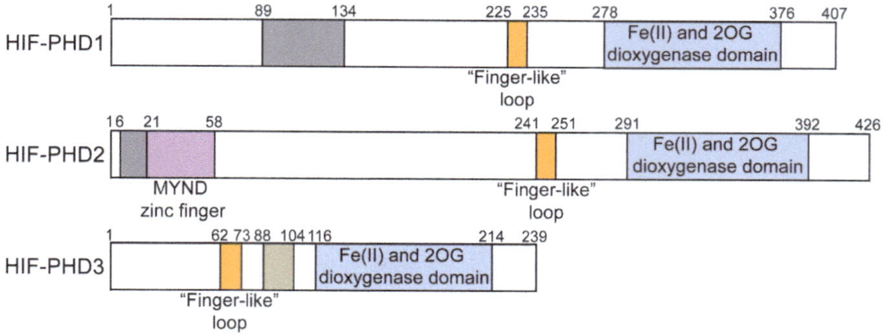

Figure 14.3 The domain features of HIF-PHDs.

dioxygenase domain. The dioxygenase domain is responsible for the catalytic activity, while the "finger-like" loop plays a crucial role in substrate specificity [44]. Unlike HIF-PHD1 and HIF-PHD3, HIF-PHD2 uniquely features a MYND-type zinc finger domain [11, 15, 42].

The three isoforms of HIF-PHDs exhibit distinct cellular distributions. Fluorescent imaging studies reveal that HIF-PHD1 is predominantly localized in the nucleus, while HIF-PHD2 is mainly found in the cytoplasm. HIF-PHD3, however, is detectable in both the nucleus and cytoplasm [45]. This variation in localization suggests differences in their abilities to hydroxylate proline residues on HIF-α. For HIF-1α, all three isoforms can hydroxylate Pro564, but only HIF-PHD1 and HIF-PHD2 are capable of hydroxylating Pro402. Notably, the K_m values of HIF-PHD1 and HIF-PHD2 for catalyzing the peptide fragment containing Pro402 are 20–50 times higher than their K_m values for the peptide fragment containing Pro564 [46]. Furthermore, studies revealed that HIF-PHD2 demonstrates significantly higher catalytic activity in proline hydroxylation compared to HIF-PHD1 and HIF-PHD3. Gene knockout experiments further confirm that HIF-PHD2 plays a central role in regulating HIF-α levels [47].

14.2.2 Catalytic Function of HIF-PHDs

Similar to most other 2OG-dependent hydroxylases, HIF-PHDs require O_2, Fe(II), and 2OG for the hydroxylation of proline residues. The catalytic process of HIF-PHDs begins with the complexation of Fe(II), followed by the ordered sequential binding of 2OG, oxygen, and HIF-α to the active site (Figure 14.4) [10, 43]. In the resting state, Fe(II) is coordinated by a 2-His-1-Asp triad (His379, His313, and Asp201), with the remaining three coordination sites occupied by labile water molecules [21, 41, 43]. This arrangement is crucial for stabilizing the complex in the absence of HIF-α [34]. 2OG binds in a bidentate manner through its C1 carboxylate and C2 ketone oxygen, forming an octahedral coordination structure [34, 43]. The C5 carboxylate group forms a strong ionic bond with the highly conserved Arg383 at the back of the catalytic sites. Subsequently, the HIF-α ODD binds in a way that positions the prolyl residue adjacent to the Fe(II),

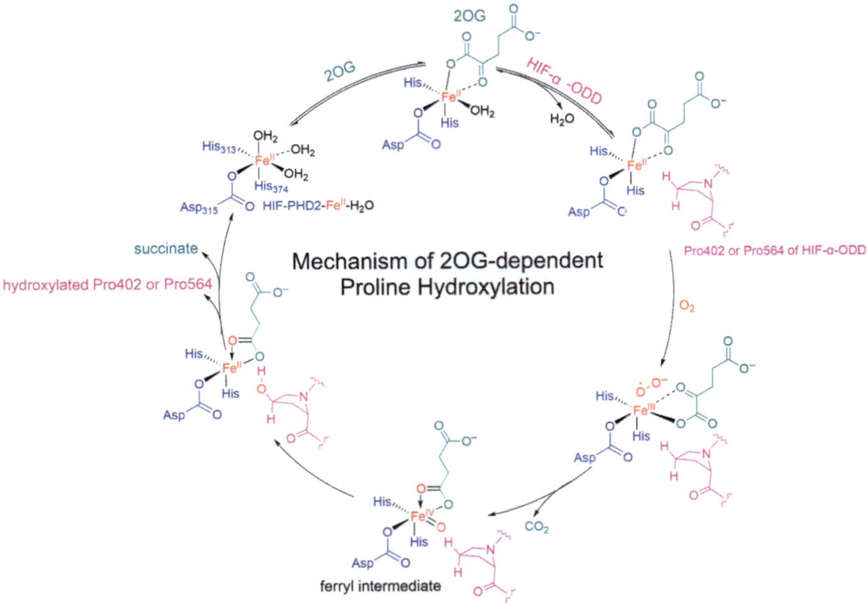

Figure 14.4 Outline mechanism for HIF-PHD2-catalyzed proline-residue hydroxylation.

generating a Fe(III)-linked superoxide. The distal oxygen of the superoxide then attacks the C2 carbonyl of 2OG, leading to oxidative decarboxylation. This reaction produces succinate, carbon dioxide (which likely exits the active site efficiently), and a Fe(IV) = O intermediate, the latter being the active oxidant [48]. The binding of substrate, such as prolyl in HIF-α ODD, is considered essential before the formation of the Fe(IV) = O intermediate. Without the substrate, the highly reactive metal-oxo species could autoxidize active site residues, resulting in enzyme inactivation. High-spin Fe(IV) = O complexes exhibit varying reactivities toward hydrocarbon oxidation and can adopt either octahedral or trigonal bipyramidal geometries [39]. It is plausible that a change in the geometry of the metal center during oxidation facilitates the reorganization of the catalytic site, allowing the HIF proline residue to move closer to the metal-oxo center for hydroxylation. An X-ray co-crystal structure of an ODD HIF fragment bound to the HIF-PHD2 catalytic domain shows Pro564 positioned away from the presumed apical metal-oxo center, suggesting that a conformational shift is necessary for hydroxylation at the pro(R) position of the C—H bond at C4 [41].

14.2.3 Structural Features of HIF-PHDs

Given the central role of HIF-PHD2 in regulating HIF-α levels, its structural features are described here as a representative of HIF-PHDs [28, 46, 49]. HIF-PHD2 is a 426-residue protein with a calculated molecular mass of 46 kDa [50]. Its core structure features a conserved double-stranded β-helix (DSBH) fold, comprised of eight β strands, which supports the binding of Fe(II) and 2OG. Three α-helices brace

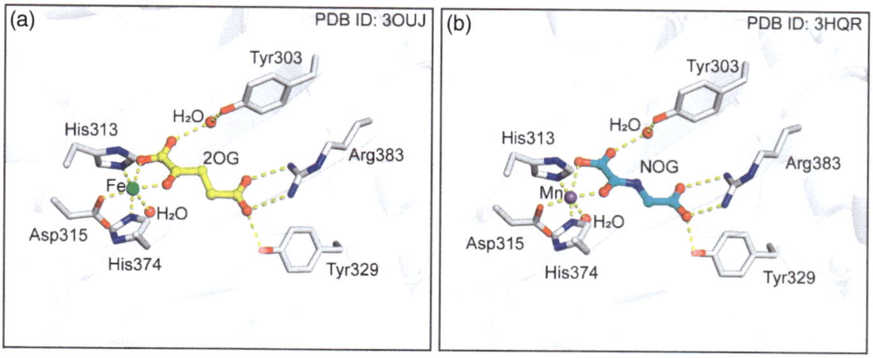

Figure 14.5 (a) View from a crystal structure of PHD2 complexed with the cosubstrate 2OG (PDB ID: 3OUJ *Source:* Adapted from [41]). (b) View from a crystal structure of PHD2 complexed with the cosubstrate 2OG analog NOG (PDB ID: 3HQR *Source:* Adapted from [41]).

the exterior of the protein, forming a scaffold that stabilizes the β sheets. The conserved iron-binding triad residues (His313,His374,Asp315) coordinate half of the ligand sphere around the bound Fe(II) [34].

The crystal structure of the endogenous cofactor 2OG bound to HIF-PHD2's catalytic domain has been resolved (PDB ID: 3OUJ [41]), confirming the hypothesized binding mode. In addition to the bidentate chelation of 2OG to the Fe(II) center *via* the C1 and C2 oxygen atoms, a salt bridge forms between the C5 carboxylate and Arg383, and a hydrogen bond is established between the C5 carboxylate and Tyr329. Further hydrogen bonding to Tyr303 is mediated through a structural water molecule in the active site (Figure 14.5a). A similar binding mode is observed in the crystal structure of HIF-PHD2 complexed with *N*-oxalylglycine (NOG, PDB ID: 3HQR [41]), a near-isosteric analog of 2OG (Figure 14.5b). These structural insights highlight the precise coordination and binding interactions essential for the catalytic activity of HIF-PHD2.

In 2009, Chowdhury et al. reported the crystal structure of the catalytic domain of HIF-PHD2 in complex with a peptide representing the ODD of HIF-1α (Figure 14.6a, PDB ID: 3HQR [41]). In this structure, 2OG and Fe(II) were replaced by NOG and Mn(II), respectively. Additionally, the Schofield group solved the crystal structure of HIF-PHD2 in complex with Fe(II) and the inhibitor *N*-[(4-Hydroxy-8-iodo-3-isoquinolinyl)carbonyl]glycine (**1**) (PDB ID: 2G19 [34]). Superimposing the structures of HIF-PHD2.Fe(II).**1** and HIF-PHD2.Mn(II).ODD revealed similar backbone conformations for the major (β1, β4, β5, β8, β10) and minor (β6, β7, β9) β sheets of DSBH, as well as for three of the four α helices (α1-α3) in HIF-PHD2. However, differences in the regions surrounding the active site suggest the presence of two mobile elements. The most significant difference involves residues 237–254 of HIF-PHD2, which adopt a finger-like "β2β3" conformation in HIF-PHD2.Fe(II).**1** structure but form a loop in the HIF-PHD2.Mn(II).ODD structure. This β2β3/loop encloses the Pro564 region of the HIF-α ODD peptide and the active site of HIF-PHD2. A smaller conformational

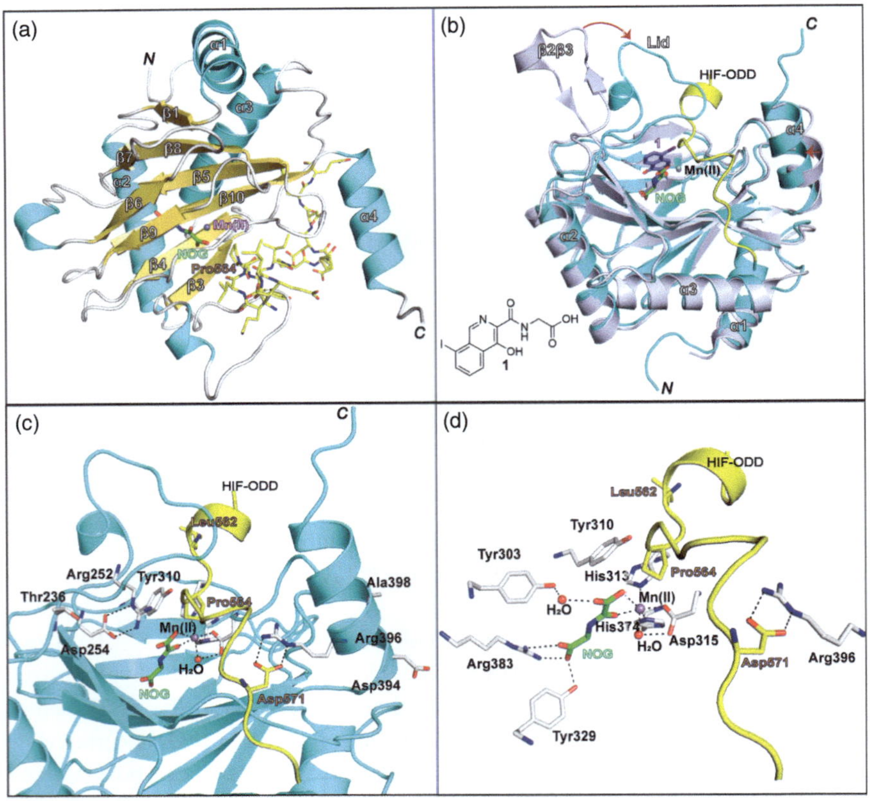

Figure 14.6 Crystallographic analysis of HIF-PHD2 complex structure. (a) Stereo view ribbons representation of HIF-PHD2.Mn(II).ODD complex structure. (b) Stereo view ribbons representation of HIF-PHD2.Mn(II).ODD complex structure (cyan, PDB ID: 3HQR *Source:* Modified from [41]) superimposed with HIF-PHD2.Fe(II).**1** (light blue, PDB ID: 2G19 *Source:* Modified from [34]), representing conformational differences in the β2β3/loop and *C*-terminal α4-helix. (c) The HIF-PHD2.Mn(II).ODD complex (PDB ID: 3HQR *Source:* Modified from [41]) structure with the ODD fragment as a yellow cartoon model. Pro564 is close to the catalytic center. (d) Zoomed-in view of the catalytic site of the HIF-PHD2.Mn(II).ODD complex.

change is also observed in the C-terminal helix α4 (Figure 14.6b). The loop conformation observed in the HIF-PHD2.Mn(II).ODD structure likely represents a catalytically productive complex. While the finger-like conformation (β2β3) in the HIF-PHD2.Fe(II).**1** structure may partly result from specific crystal contacts, it is plausible that this or a similar conformation could facilitate an "open" active site capable of binding HIF-ODD. After ODD binding, the same residues may adopt an extended loop and helix, as seen in the HIF-PHD2.Mn(II).ODD structure, effectively enclosing the conserved LXXLAP motif of ODD. The HIF-PHD2.Mn(II).ODD complex also shows that the Pro564 of HIF-1α, located at the apex of a shallow bend of ODD, Mn(II), and NOG, is embedded deep within the active site (Figure 14.6c,d). During hydroxylation, the 4*R* carbon–hydrogen bond of Pro564 is cleaved while retaining stereochemistry. These structural insights highlight the dynamic nature of HIF-PHD2's active site and its role in substrate binding and catalysis.

14.3 Targeting HIF-PHDs as a Promising Strategy for Anemia Treatment

Anemia is a condition characterized by a reduction in red blood cells (RBCs) or hemoglobin levels in circulation. It can result from chronic kidney disease (CKD), inflammatory disorders, cancer, genetic disorders, nutritional deficiencies, and certain medications [51, 52]. Nutritional deficiency anemia is especially prevalent in women, the elderly, and children, and is typically treated with iron and vitamin supplementation [52]. Thalassemia, a common genetic disorder, also contributes to anemia. CKD, inflammatory diseases, and chemotherapy can impair EPO synthesis and disrupt iron homeostasis. The primary treatment approach aims to stimulate erythropoiesis [53].

Erythropoiesis occurs in the bone marrow (Figure 14.7), where erythroid progenitors proliferate and differentiate into reticulocytes and RBCs. Myeloid stem cells give rise to RBCs, white blood cells, and platelets, first differentiating into burst-forming unit-erythroid (BFU-E) cells and then into colony-forming unit-erythroid (CFU-E) progenitors. CFU-Es mature into proerythroblasts, which undergo mitosis to form erythroblasts. These erythroblasts progress through basophilic, polychromatic, and orthochromatic stages. They then expel their nucleus to become reticulocytes, which enter the bloodstream. After shedding organelles like the Golgi apparatus, mitochondria, and the endoplasmic reticulum, reticulocytes mature into RBCs. EPO is crucial for the differentiation from BFU-E to erythroblast, while iron is required for RBC maturation from erythroblasts [54, 55].

Erythropoiesis-stimulating agents (ESAs), such as recombinant human erythropoietin (rhEPO), are the primary treatment for anemia [54]. However, the use of ESAs may lead to increased blood pressure and an increased risk of cardiovascular events. Thrombosis may occur when using ESAs. More importantly, the use of ESAs may cause functional iron deficiency because increased RBC production requires more iron to synthesize hemoglobin. Therefore, the use of ESAs needs to be accompanied by additional iron supplementation [53, 56].

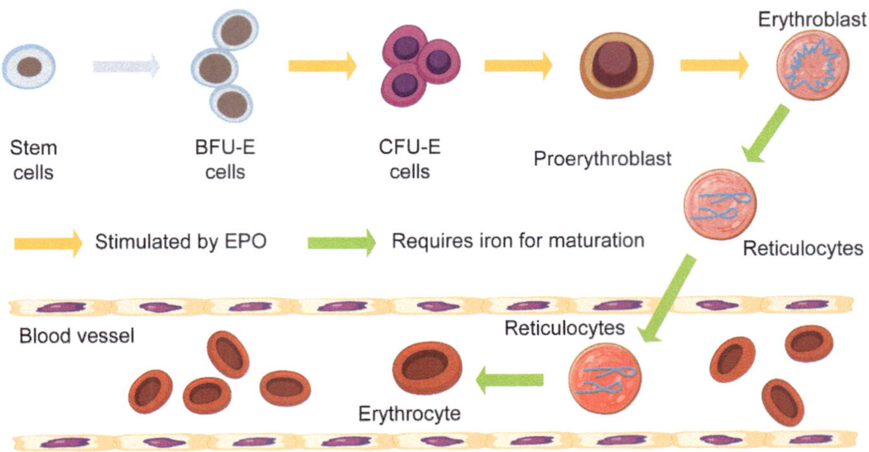

Figure 14.7 The process of erythropoiesis.

In both humans and rodents, renal fibroblasts primarily activate HIF-2α, rather than HIF-1α, in response to hypoxia, suggesting that HIF-2α plays a crucial role in normal EPO production [57]. Genetic studies further support the essential role of HIF-2α in erythropoiesis. Inhibition of HIF-PHDs predominantly stabilizes HIF-2α, stimulating EPO production [58]. Under normal conditions, HIF-PHD2 is the main HIF prolyl hydroxylase in cultured cells, and genetic studies show that deletion or knockdown of HIF-PHD2 sufficiently activates the HIF pathway. In humans, a mutation in one allele of HIF-PHD2 is enough to increase hematocrit, demonstrating that reduced HIF-PHD2 activity enhances EPO production [59]. These findings indicate that HIF-PHD2 inhibitors are a promising treatment for conditions like renal anemia, which involve abnormal EPO production [53].

To date, six HIF-PHD inhibitors have been approved, including Roxadustat [60], Vadadustat [61], Daprodustat [62], Enarodustat [63], Molidustat [64], and Desidustat [65] (Table 14.2). On 18 December 2018, Roxadustat, the first-in-class HIF-PHD inhibitor developed by FibroGen, was approved by the National Medical Products Administration (NMPA) in China. In February 2023, the U.S. Food and Drug Administration (FDA) approved Daprodustat, and in March 2024, Akebia received FDA approval for Vadadustat for treating anemia in adult dialysis patients with CKD.

Pharmacological inhibition of HIF-PHD2 stabilizes HIF-2α, which not only stimulates EPO production by renal interstitial cells but also downregulates hepcidin [66, 67]. These effects enhance erythropoiesis and iron homeostasis, helping to reverse anemia in patients with CKD. HIF-PHD inhibitors, such as Daprodustat, inhibit HIF-PHD activity under normal conditions, leading to HIF-2α stabilization. This, in turn, prompts renal interstitial cells to produce EPO. Additionally, HIF-2α inactivates hepcidin and upregulates key iron transporters, including ferroprotein (FPN), transferrin (Tf), the divalent metal transporter-1 (DMT1), and duodenal cytochrome b (DcytB), there by promoting iron absorption and transport [68] (Figure 14.8).

14.4 *In-vitro* Screening for HIF-PHD Inhibitors

Efficient *in vitro* screening assays are critical for developing HIF-PHD inhibitors. Various assays have been designed for 2OG oxygenases, including those that monitor 2OG consumption, HIF-1α hydroxylation, and affinity-based interactions [69, 70].

Assays monitoring 2OG consumption and HIF-1α hydroxylation are both based on enzymatic reaction, often tracking cosubstrate depletion (O_2, 2OG) and/or coproduct formation (succinate, CO_2), either directly (e.g. by Mass Spectrometry [MS]) or indirectly (e.g. by enzyme-coupled assays). While these assays can be useful, they may not always accurately reflect substrate oxidation, as 2OG turnover can occur nonenzymatically or be decoupled from substrate oxidation. Therefore, assays that directly monitor substrate depletion and product formation, ideally in a simultaneous manner, are developed, such as MS-based assays or, in some cases, antibody-based assays [71]. Examples of assays used in the discovery and development of HIF-PHD inhibitors are shown in Figure 14.9.

Table 14.2 Approved HIF-PHD inhibitors.

Drug	Structure	Originator	Approval
Roxadustat	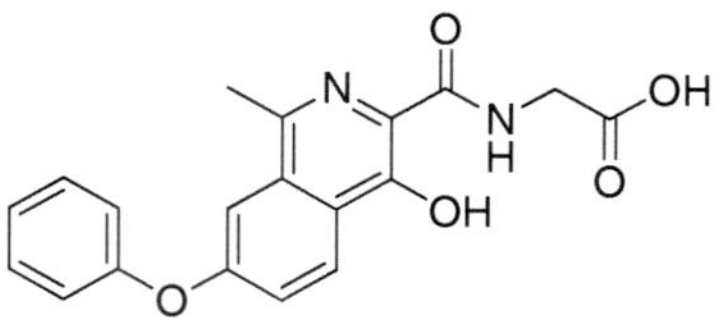	FibroGen	China (Dec, 2018), Japan (Nov, 2020), and EU (Aug, 2021)
Vadadustat	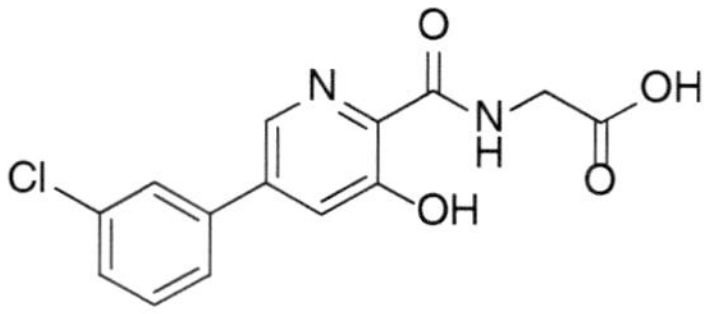	Akebia	Japan (Jun, 2020) and US (Mar, 2024)
Daprodustat	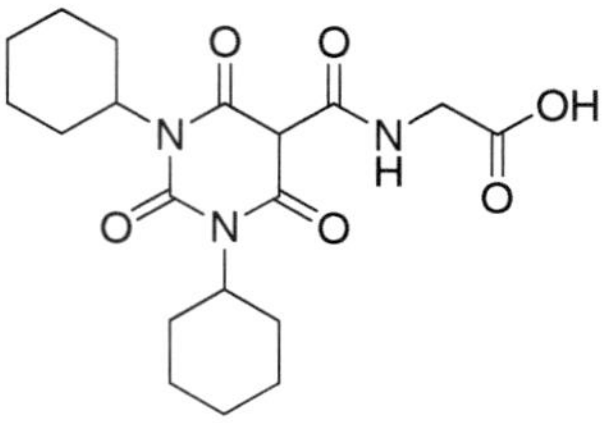	GlaxoSmithKline	Japan (Jun, 2020) and US (Feb, 2023)
Enarodustat	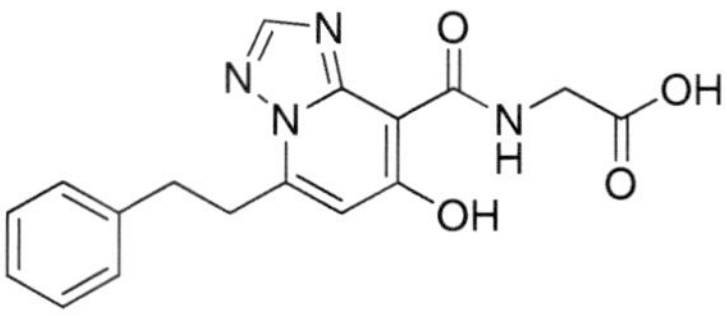	Japan Tobacco	Japan (Sep, 2020)
Molidustat	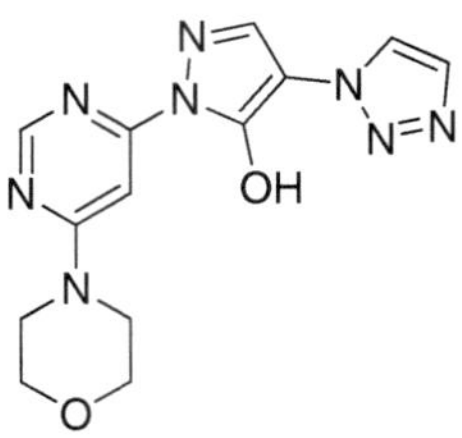	Bayer	Japan (Jan, 2021)
Desidustat	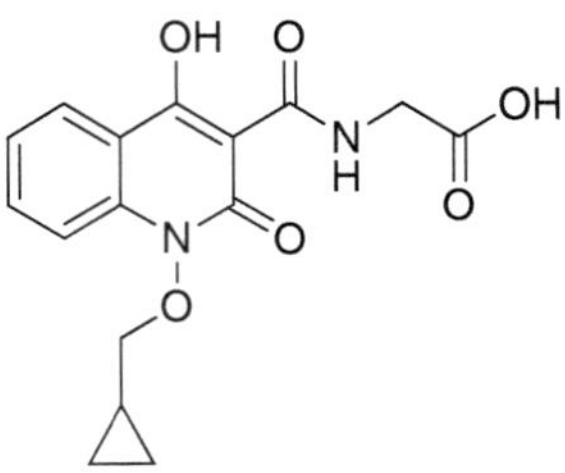	Zydus	India (Mar, 2022)

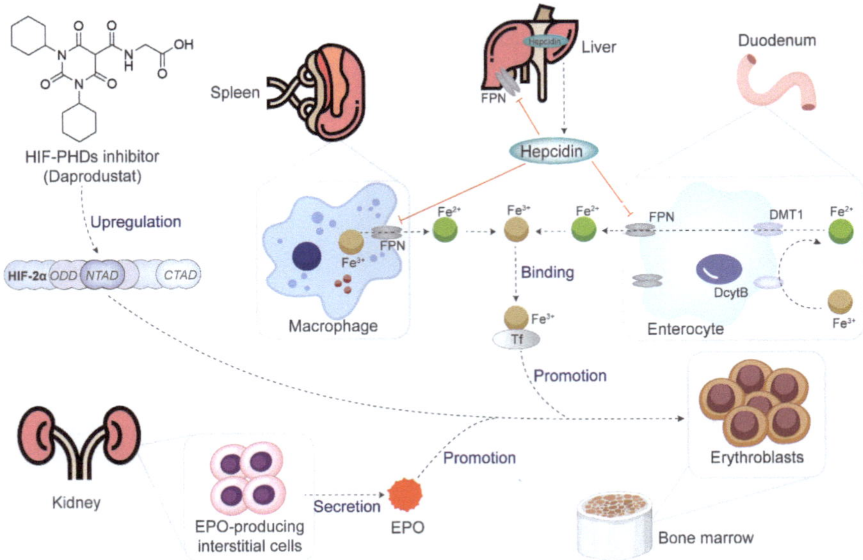

Figure 14.8 The process of erythropoiesis.

One method involves evaluating HIF-PHD2 inhibitors using a 2OG consumption-based assay (Figure 14.9a). In this assay, post-reaction derivatization of 2OG by *O*-phenylenediamine (OPD) produces a fluorescent product, 3-(2-carboxyethyl)-2(1*H*)-quinoxalinone, which is measured by excitation at 340 nm and emission at 420 nm [72]. For more detect monitoring of 2OG consumption, MS- and nuclear magnetic resonance (NMR)-based methods have also been employed [73–75]. For example, matrix-assisted laser desorption/ionization-time of flight-MS (matrix-assisted laser desorption/ionization time-of-flight mass [MALDI-TOF-MS]) and solid phase extraction coupled to MS methods have been used to monitor the 2OG consumption [74].

Furthermore, several assays based on the hydroxylation of HIF-1α were also reported. In the AlphaScreen assay (Figure 14.9b), the biotinylated HIF-1α ODD peptide can be conjugated by a streptavidin-labeled donor bead. When the hydroxylation reaction catalyzed by HIF-PHD2 occurs, the hydroxylated Pro564 can specifically bind to the Hyp564 antibody, which connects with the acceptor bead. Upon laser excitation, the photosensitizer in the donor beads generates excited singlet oxygen, which activates nearby acceptor bead fluorophores, causing emission at 520–620 nm. The HIF-PHD2 inhibitors suppress the hydroxylation of Pro564, leading to a lower signal [76].

Although enzymatic assays can evaluate compound inhibition of HIF-PHD2, they do not assess the binding affinity between small molecules and the protein. In 2015, the Zhang group developed an affinity-based fluorescence polarization (FP) assay (Figure 14.9c) using a fluorescein isothiocyanate (FITC)-labeled HIF-1α ODD peptide as a probe [77]. When bound to HIF-PHD2, the rotation of the probe slows down, causing polarized light emission. Competing inhibitors displace the probe,

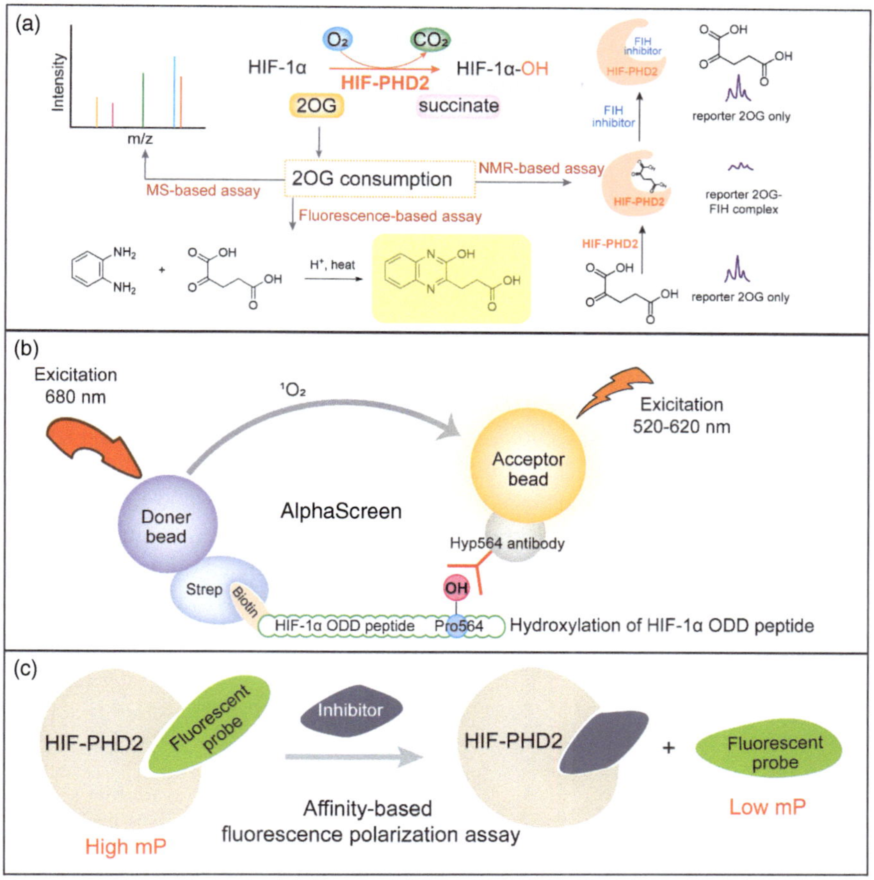

Figure 14.9 Reported *in vitro* screening methods for HIF-PHD2 inhibitors. (a) Assays detecting the consumption of 2OG; (b) AlphaScreen assay detecting the hydroxylation of HIF-1α; (c) Affinity-based fluorescence polarization (FP) assay.

increasing rotation and depolarizing the light, allowing for affinity estimation. However, this assay struggles with compounds of weak affinities, such as fragments or tricarboxylic acid (TCA) cycle-related compounds. In 2020, Zhang and the Schofield group reported a small-molecule probe-based FP assay [78], which can better identify weak binders and inhibitors like NOG that fail to bind in the HIF-1α peptide-based assay due to the interference with key active site regions [79].

14.5 Current Drug Discovery Targeting HIF-PHDs

HIF-PHD inhibitors activate HIF by preventing proline hydroxylation and proteasomal degradation. Recent advances show that these inhibitors offer a promising approach for treating CKD-induced anemia. Several HIF-PHD inhibitors have been approved or are in clinical trials, most of which are pan-HIF-PHD inhibitors, with the strongest activity against HIF-PHD2, though some exhibit better efficacy against HIF-PHD1. HIF-PHD2, a dioxygenase dependent on the cofactor 2OG, is stabilized by a salt bridge between the carboxylic acid fragment of 2OG and Arg383. To mimic 2OG, carboxylic acid motifs are key pharmacophores in HIF-PHD2 inhibitors, though some compounds, such as Molidustat, lacking a carboxylic acid group, also show high potency.

14.5.1 HIF-PHD2 Inhibitors with Carboxylic Acid Motif

The synthesis of 2OG analogs was initially targeted for designing HIF-PHD2 inhibitors (Figure 14.10), with most clinically advanced molecules being 2OG derivatives. *N*-oxalylglycine (**1**, NOG), the first reported 2OG mimetic [80], showed a stronger interaction with HIF-PHD2 with the IC_{50} value of approximately 12.3 μM (Figure 14.5b) [81]. FibroGen developed inhibitors with an isoquinoline skeleton, including **FG-2216** (**2**), the first small-molecule HIF-PHD2 inhibitor in clinical trials [82]. However, its clinical development was suspended in 2006 due to the death from fulminant hepatitis. Roxadustat (**3**), another FibroGen candidate [83, 84], became the first HIF-PHD2 inhibitor approved for CKD-related anemia in China [60] and later received European Medicines Agency (EMA) approval in 2021, and it was also marketed in Japan as Evrenzo.

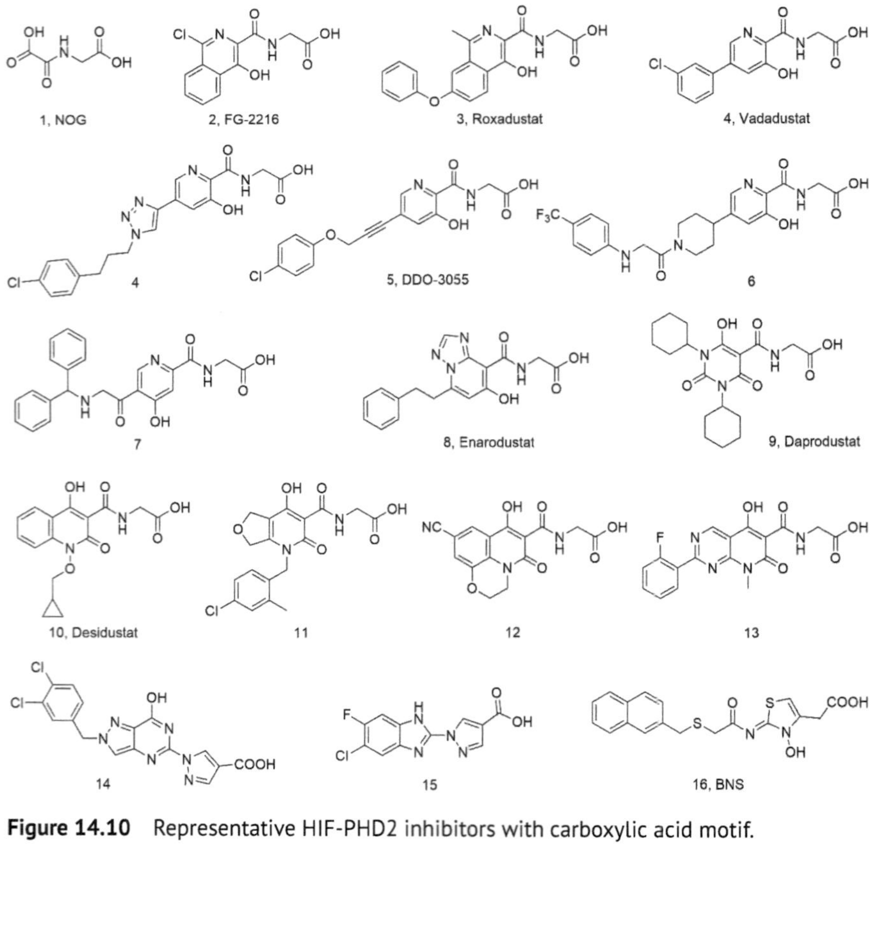

Figure 14.10 Representative HIF-PHD2 inhibitors with carboxylic acid motif.

Procter and Gamble developed monocyclic pyridines, including Vadadustat (**4**), which was licensed to Akebia Therapeutics [85]. Vadadustat was approved in Japan in 2020 for anemia in both dialysis and non-dialysis CKD patients [61] and received FDA approval in 2024. Notably, several pyridine-based inhibitors (**4–6**) reported by Zhang and You's group showed superior binding affinity to HIF-PHD2 compared to Roxadustat and Vadadustat [86–88]. In affinity-based FP assays, Roxadustat and Vadadustat show IC_{50} values of 115.2 nM and 256.9 nM, respectively, while **4–6** demonstrated IC_{50} values of 22.73 nM, 15.62 nM, and 22.53 nM, respectively.

Structurally, the HIF-PHD2 inhibitors mentioned above mimic 2OG, competitively occupying the catalytic pocket. In this pocket, the central metal Fe(II) is coordinated by a 2-His-1-Asp triad (His374, His313, and Asp315). Compounds **2–5** bind to the Fe(II) in a bidentate manner, forming an octahedral coordination. Additionally, the carboxyl group of compounds **2–5** forms an ionic hydrogen bond with Arg383, while the phenol interacts with Tyr303 (Figure 14.11a–e). The HIF peptide binds to the substrate binding pocket, composed of Trp258, Met299, Arg322, Trp389, and Phe391. Molecular docking suggests that Roxadustat, which occupies the catalytic pocket, does not bind the substrate binding pocket (PDB ID: 3HQR [41], Figure 14.11b,c), aligning with the co-crystal structure of Vadadustat with HIF-PHD2 (PDB ID: 5OX6 [75], Figure 14.11d). Interestingly, high-affinity HIF-PHD2 inhibitors like **DDO-3055** (**5**) can bind both the catalytic pocket and substrate binding pocket, interacting with Arg322 (Figure 14.11e), which contributes to their superior inhibitory activity.

Merck has reported bis-carboxamide derivatives as potent HIF-PHD2 inhibitors [90, 91], exemplified by compound **7**, which shows an IC_{50} value of 0.62 nM [92, 93]. A series of triazolopyridine derivatives [94] were disclosed by Japan Tobacco, leading to the discovery of the clinical candidate Enarodustat (**8**), which received regulatory approval in Japan in 2020 [63]. Enarodustat, featuring a 2-phenyl ethyl side chain, exhibited strong inhibitory activity against HIF-PHD2 with an IC_{50} value of 0.22 μM and effectively stimulated EPO release in Hep3B cells with an EC_{50} value of 5.7 μM. Additionally, Enarodustat significantly increased EPO levels in mice and rats. Enarodustat (1 and 3 mg/kg, oral) increased hemoglobin levels in a dose-dependent manner after one month in rats.

GlaxoSmithKline (GSK) reported a pyrimidine-trione class of inhibitors, exemplified by Daprodustat (**9**), which has been approved in several regions [95]. In Japan, it was approved in 2020 for CKD patients [62]. Daprodustat was approved by the FDA in February 2023, marking an important milestone for patients with CKD-related anemia, especially for those who prefer an oral treatment option over injectable therapies. Daprodustat, a potent HIF-PHD2 inhibitor with an IC_{50} of 22.2 nM, increased reticulocytes and hemoglobin in B6D2F1 mice in a dose-dependent manner after one week of treatment.

Cadila Healthcare disclosed a series of HIF-PHD2 inhibitors containing an *N*-alkoxyquinolone skeleton [96]. These compounds increased EPO and hemoglobin levels in mice after oral administration. Among them, Desidustat (**10**) was approved in India for CKD patients, regardless of dialysis status [65].

Merck reported a series of compounds with dihydrothienopyridone or dihydrofuropyridone skeletons as potent HIF-PHD2 inhibitors [97]. Extensive work has

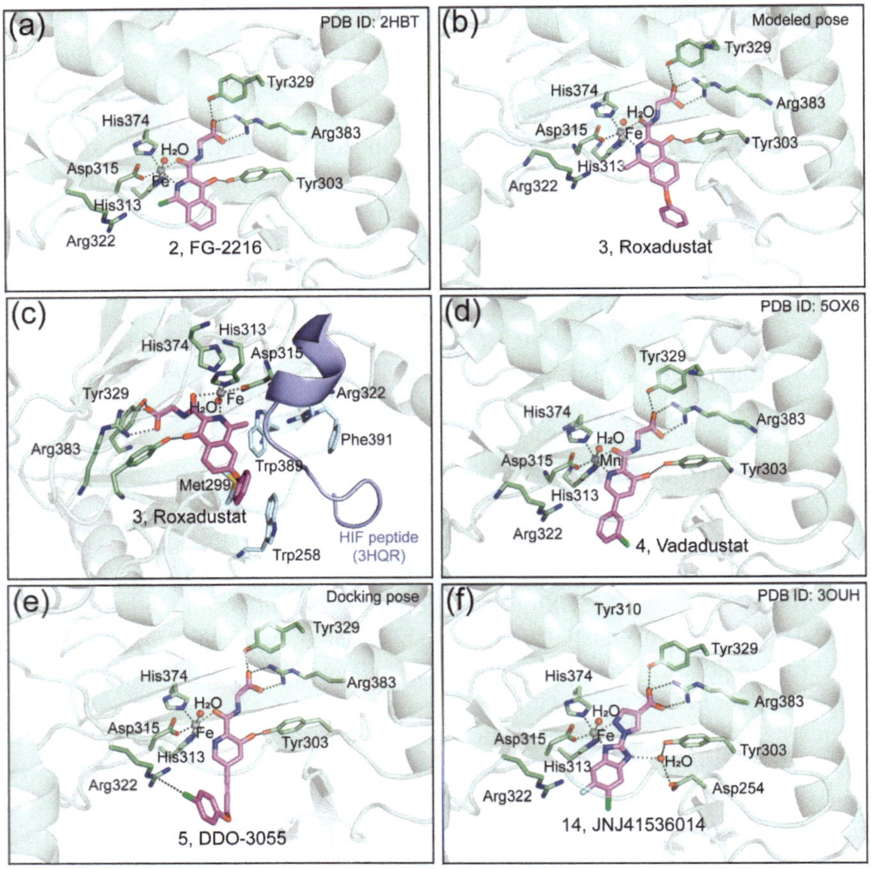

Figure 14.11 Crystallographic analysis of representative carboxylic acid HIF-PHD2 inhibitors with HIF-PHD2. (a) HIF-PHD2 complexed with Fe (II) and **FG-2216** (PDB ID: 2HBT *Source:* Modified from [34]); (b) Predicted binding pose of Roxadustat with HIF-PHD2; (c) Predicted binding pose of Roxadustat (violet) with the key residues (green) in HIF-PHD2 catalytic sites and superimposition with HIF peptide (purple) that was extracted from a HIF-PHD2-HIF-α peptide complex (PDB ID: 3HQR *Source:* Modified from [41]); (d) HIF-PHD2 complexed with Mn (II) and Vadadustat (PDB ID: 5OX6 *Source:* Ref. [75] / The Royal Society of Chemistry / CC BY 4.0.); (e) Predicted binding pose of **DDO-3055** with HIF-PHD2 occupying the HIF peptide binding site; (f) HIF-PHD2 complexed with Fe (II) and **JNJ41536014** (PDB ID: 3OUH *Source:* Ref. [89] / American Chemical Society).

focused on the pharmacokinetic (PK) profiles of these compounds. Compound **11** demonstrated significantly higher availability in the liver, with a liver/plasma drug concentration ratio exceeding 35. Merck also disclosed a series of quinolone-based compounds [98]. Among them, compound **12** with a morpholine-fused tricyclic skeleton exhibited an IC_{50} value of 1.8 nM to HIF-PHD2.

Mitsubishi Tanabe reported a series of pyrazolopyrimidine derivatives as potent HIF-PHD2 inhibitors [99]. Among them, compound **13**, featuring a bulky bis(4-chlorophenyl)methyl group, can effectively inhibit HIF-PHD2 ($IC_{50} = 0.02\ \mu M$) and then correlate with a 40-fold increase in EPO.

Janssen Pharmaceuticals reported a series of HIF-PHD2 inhibitors with a benzimidazole-2-pyrazole skeleton [89]. Among them, **JNJ41536014** (**14**) showed preferable inhibitory activity against HIF-PHD2 with a pIC_{50} value of 7.1. As shown in the co-crystal structure of **JNJ41536014** with HIF-PHD2 (PDB ID: 3OUH [89]), the iron atom is coordinated by the two sp^2 nitrogen atoms of the benzimidazole and pyrazole rings, while the carboxylic acid group interacts with Arg383. The benzimidazole NH group is near an ordered water molecule, indicating a potential water-bridged interaction with Tyr303 and Asp254 (Figure 14.11f).

14.5.2 Non-carboxylic Acid HIF-PHD2 Inhibitors

Most clinically advanced molecules share a common carboxylic acid motif to maintain the ionic hydrogen bond with Arg383. Interestingly, several HIF-PHD2 inhibitors have been reported that lack a carboxylic acid group. (Figure 14.12). Among them, Molidustat was approved in Japan in 2020, highlighting the potency of non-carboxylic acid HIF-PHD2 inhibitors.

Several triazole-based HIF-PHD2 inhibitors were reported. Notably, the Schofield research team identified compound **15** as a highly effective HIF-PHD2 inhibitor, demonstrating an IC50 value of 4.8 nM [100]. Structural analysis of the HIF-PHD2 complex with **15** (PDB ID: 5A3U [100]) reveals that the inhibitor's pyridine and pyrazolone rings chelate the catalytic metal through their nitrogen atoms. The triazole moiety occupies the 2OG C5 carboxylate binding pocket, establishing hydrogen bonding with Arg383. Additionally, the carboxylate side chain of compound 15 engages in electrostatic interactions with Arg322, a residue crucial for substrate binding (Figure 14.13a).

Bayer reported a series of HIF-PHD2 inhibitors featuring pyrazolone cores, where the 3-pyridyl group was replaced with five-membered nitrogen-containing heterocycles [104]. A prominent example from this series is Molidustat (**16**), which exhibits an IC_{50} of 280 nM and gained approval in Japan in 2020 for treating anemia in CKD patients. A concise structure–activity relationship (SAR) analysis was conducted, focusing on the pyrazole core, triazole ring, and pyrimidine ring. The study revealed that substituting the triazole ring with other heterocycles while retaining a nitrogen atom at the third position preserved inhibitory activity, highlighting the critical role of this heteroatom for efficacy [105]. As illustrated in Figure 14.13b, the triazole in Molidustat occupies the 2OG C5 carboxylate binding site of HIF-PHD2, consistent with its function as a carboxylate bioisostere. Unlike 2OG and its analogs, such as glycinamide-based inhibitors, the triazole in Molidustat interacts directly with only one guanidino group of Arg383, while the other interaction is mediated through a water molecule. The nitrogen atom of triazole forms a hydrogen bond with Tyr329 via a water bridge, and it engages in π–π stacking with Tyr303, which hydrogen bonds with the enolic form of the pyrazolone ring [64]. In addition, Taisho Pharmaceuticals disclosed a series of triazole-substituted heteroaryl amide compounds, with compound **17** demonstrating an IC_{50} of 61 nM [106]. Daiichi reported pyrazole-based HIF-PHD2 inhibitors [107]. Among them, compound **18** can cause a 40-fold increase in EPO levels. HIF-PHD2 inhibitors with a pyrazole central core

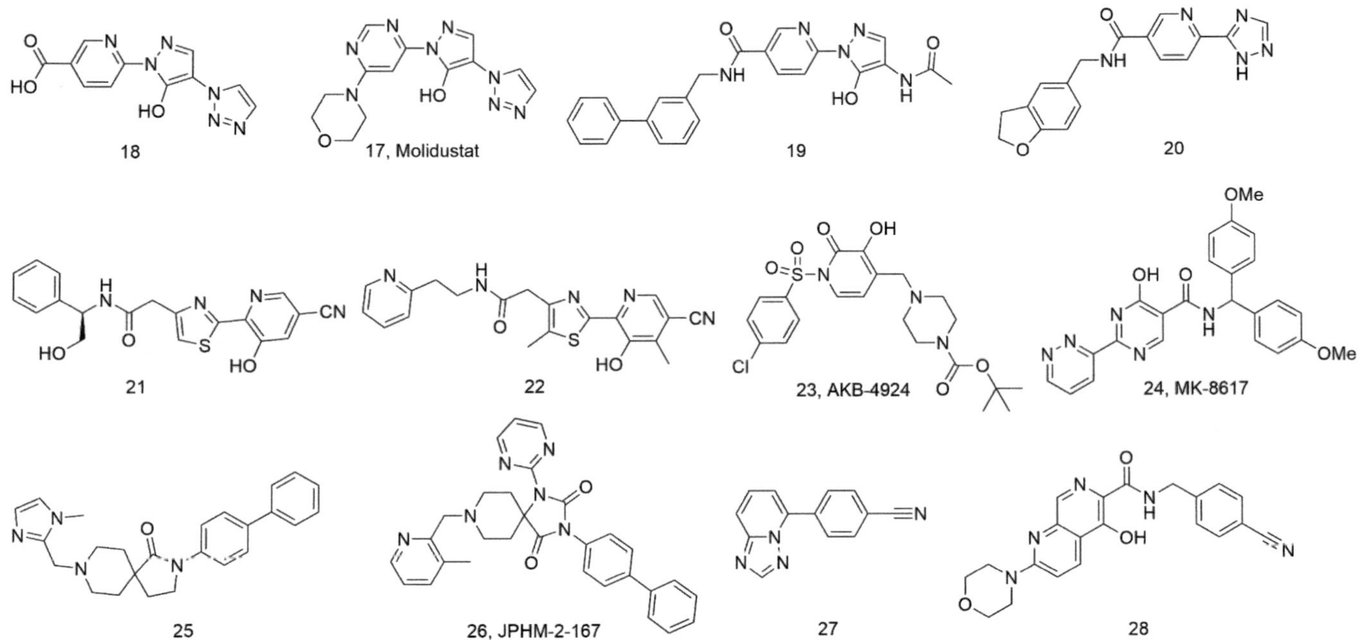

Figure 14.12 Representative non-carboxylic acid HIF-PHD2 inhibitors.

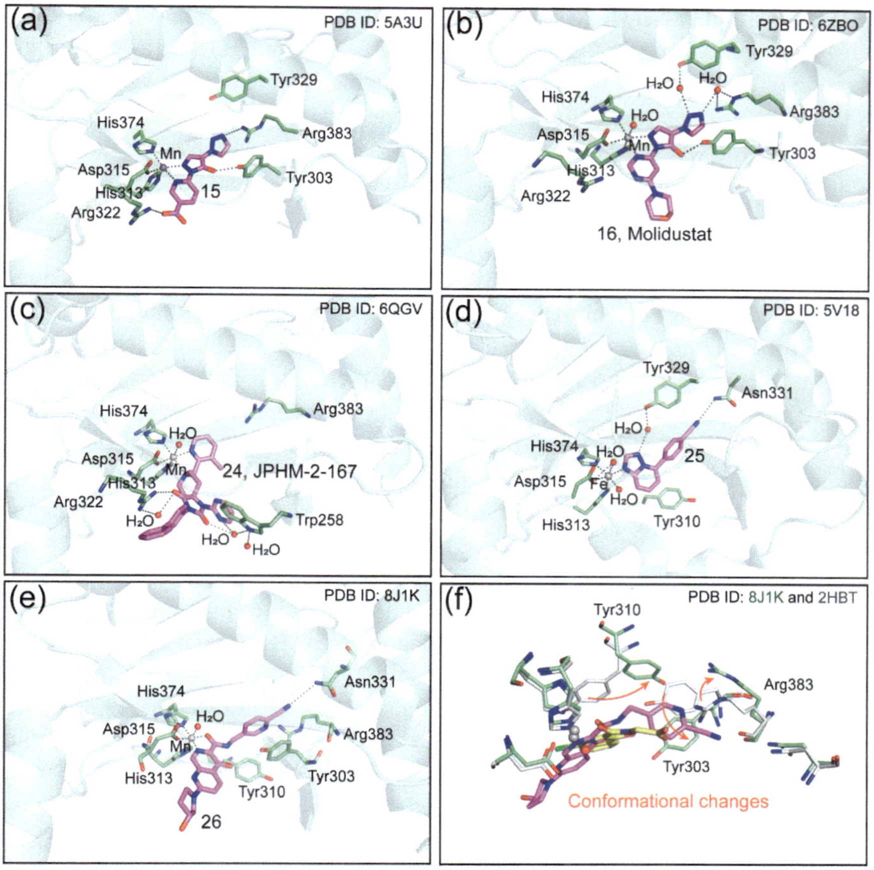

Figure 14.13 Crystallographic analysis of representative non-carboxylic acid HIF-PHD2 inhibitors with HIF-PHD2. (a) HIF-PHD2 complexed with Mn (II) and **18** (PDB ID: 5A3U *Source:* Modified from [100]); (b) HIF-PHD2 complexed with Mn (II) and Molidustat (PDB ID: 6ZBO *Source:* Ref. [64] / John Wiley & Sons / CC BY 4.0); (c) HIF-PHD2 complexed with Mn (II) and **JPHM-2-167** (PDB ID: 6QGV *Source:* Ref. [101] / The Royal Society of Chemistry / CC BY 4.0); (d) HIF-PHD2 complexed with Fe (II) and **27** (PDB ID: 5V18 *Source:* Ref. [102] / American Chemical Society); (e) HIF-PHD2 complexed with Mn (II) and **28** (PDB ID: 8J1K *Source:* Ref. [103] / American Chemical Society); (f) Conformational changes of Tyr303, Tyr310, and Arg383 in **28** (green, PDB ID: 8J1K [103]) and **FG-2216** (grey, PDB ID: 2HBT [34]) bounded systems.

were also reported by Takeda, exemplified by compound **19**, which showed high inhibitory activity against HIF-PHD2 with a pIC_{50} value of 8 [108].

A series of thiazole derivatives was reported by CystalGenomics [109]. The SAR study suggested that the presence of a cyano group is crucial for HIF-PHD2 inhibitory activity. This is attributed to the cyano group's interactions with Arg383 and Tyr329. Among these derivatives, compound **20** demonstrated the most potent HIF-PHD2 inhibition, exhibiting an IC_{50} value of 0.4 μM in an enzymatic assay. However, its poor permeability resulted in no significant influence on the EPO release in Hep3B cells. A subsequent optimized derivative, compound **21**, displayed reduced inhibitory activity (IC_{50} = 2.1 μM) but achieved a 40-fold increase in EPO secretion [110].

5-Aminocarbonyl-4-hydroxypyrimidine derivatives were identified by Merck as HIF-PHD2 inhibitors through high-throughput screening (HTS). Structure optimization of those hits led to **MK-8617** (**22**), which exhibited an IC_{50} value of 1 nM [111]. Merck also reported a novel spiroindolone series of HIF-PHD2 inhibitors by MS-based HTS. The optimized compound **23** with an essential 2-pyridyl methyl group showed the highest potency (IC_{50} = 0.7 nM) [112].

The Schofield group has conducted extensive SAR and crystallographic studies on HIF-PHD2 inhibitors containing a spiro[4.5]decanone scaffold [101]. **JPHM-2-167** (**24**) can significantly inhibit HIF-PHD2-induced hydroxylation of prolyl residues in both CODD and N-terminal oxygen-dependent degradation domain (NODD) of HIF-1α with the IC_{50} of 253 nM and 127 nM, respectively. The structure of HIF-PHD2 in complex with **JPHM-2-167** and Mn(II), a substitution for Fe(II), was reported (PDB ID: 6QGV [101]). As shown in Figure 14.13c, the 3-methyl pyridine moiety of **JPHM-2-167** occupies the 2OG binding pocket. The catalytic metal is chelated by the tertiary amine of the nitrogen of the 3-methyl pyridine and the piperidine ring in **JPHM-2-167**. Additionally, the terminal ring of the biphenyl substituent forms a cation–π interaction with Arg322, which also hydrogen bonds to the imidazolidine-2,4-dione moiety of **JPHM-2-167**.

Takeda disclosed a series of 1,2,4-triazolo-[1,5-*a*]pyridine compounds exhibiting a novel monodentate binding interaction, identified as HIF-PHD1 inhibitors with an IC_{50} value of 32 nM [102]. The structure of HIF-PHD2 in complex with **25** and Fe(II) (PDB ID: 5 V18 [102]) shows that **25** binds to HIF-PHD2 also in a monodentate manner. The benzonitrile group of **25** extends into the HIF-PHD2 protein, with the nitrile forming a hydrogen bond with the NH of Asn331 (Figure 14.13d).

Insilico Medicine utilized structure-based drug design (SBDD) and generative models to develop a series of HIF-PHD2 inhibitors featuring a benzonitrile moiety [103]. Through iterative optimization of potency and solubility, compound **26** was identified as a potent HIF-PHD2 inhibitor with an IC_{50} value of 2.5 nM. X-ray co-crystal structure (PDB ID: 8J1K [103]) shows that the binding mode of the core region of **26** binds similarly to other 2OG derivatives, despite lacking a carboxylic acid group. Notably, the cyan group of **26** displaces Arg383 and Tyr303, creating a larger inner subpocket, and forms a hydrogen bond with Asn331. Furthermore, the pyridine ring engages in π–π stacking with Tyr303 and is oriented perpendicular to Tyr310 (Figure 14.13e,f).

14.6 Clinical Opportunities and Challenges for HIF-PHD Inhibitors

In conclusion, targeting oxygen-sensing HIF-PHDs represents a promising frontier in anemia therapeutics. By stabilizing HIF-α, HIF-PHD inhibitors effectively stimulate endogenous EPO production, offering a novel and potentially superior alternative to traditional ESAs. These inhibitors not only enhance patient compliance through oral administration but also hold potential for broader therapeutic applications in ischemic and cardiovascular diseases. To date, there are six

HIF-PHD inhibitors approved for treating anemia associated with CKD. However, their clinical adoption hinges on overcoming several challenges, including managing long-term safety concerns, navigating regulatory complexities, and accounting for patient-specific responses. A significant concern is the range of potential side effects, particularly thromboembolic events. The FDA declined the marketing approval submission for Roxadustat due to thrombotic side effects, and although Daprodustat received FDA approval, it includes a black box warning. This underscores the critical importance of mitigating clinical side effects in the development of HIF-PHD inhibitors. As research advances, a deeper understanding of the HIF pathway's intricacies will be pivotal in optimizing these therapies, ensuring they deliver maximum benefit while minimizing risks.

Furthermore, HIF-PHD inhibitors have attracted considerable interest not only for their role in treating anemia but also for their broader therapeutic potential (Figure 14.14). Research has shown that HIF-2α activation can target the gene encoding alkaline ceramidase 2 (ACER2), which regulates ceramide catabolism. In adipocytes, HIF-2α activation upregulates ACER2 expression, resulting in reduced plasma cholesterol levels. Studies have demonstrated that Roxadustat-induced HIF-2α activation exerts protective effects against atherosclerosis, accompanied by decreased levels of adipose and plasma ceramide as well as plasma cholesterol, underscoring the promise of HIF-PHD inhibitors in managing atherosclerosis [113].

Additionally, the HIF-1α activation induced by HIF-PHD inhibitors increases Sirtuin 1-dependent deacetylation of the Sost promoter. This process reduces sclerostin

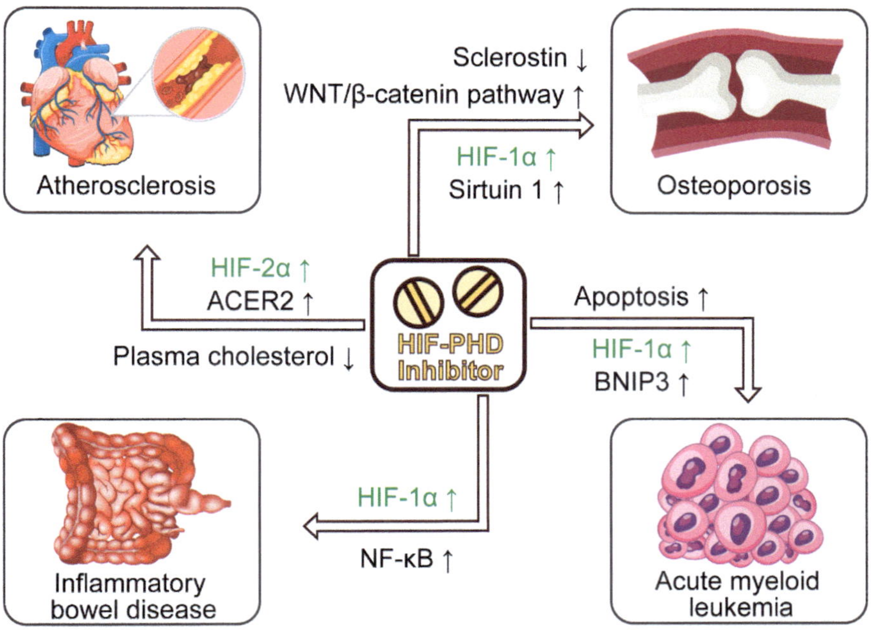

Figure 14.14 Clinical opportunities beyond anemia of HIF-PHD inhibitors.

expression and amplifies wingless-related integration (WNT)/β-catenin signaling. The oxygen-sensing function of HIF-PHDs in osteocytes negatively regulates bone mass by epigenetically controlling sclerostin expression. This mechanism suggests that HIF-PHD inhibitors could offer a promising therapeutic approach for treating osteoporosis [114].

Recent research indicated that clinically used HIF-PHD inhibitors stabilize HIF-1α in acute myeloid leukemia (AML) cells, exerting antileukemic effects in an HIF-1α-dependent manner. The HIF-1α stabilization upregulates the expression of BNIP3, which disrupts pro-leukemogenic pathways, reprograms metabolism, and induces apoptosis. Thus, HIF-PHD inhibition would be a promising approach for AML treatment [115].

Additionally, HIF-PHD inhibitors have demonstrated therapeutic potential in inflammatory bowel disease (IBD) by modulating the HIF pathway. HIF-PHD2 inhibition by small molecules stabilizes HIF-1α, which plays a critical role in enhancing the barrier function of the intestinal epithelium and reducing inflammation. HIF-1α activation promotes the expression of genes involved in maintaining intestinal barrier integrity, reducing epithelial permeability, and enhancing mucosal healing. Consequently, HIF-PHD inhibitors may help mitigate the chronic inflammation characteristic of IBD, offering a novel therapeutic approach for managing this debilitating condition [116]. Several clinical trials are underway to evaluate the effects of HIF-PHD inhibitors on IBD. Notably, **ISM5411**, an oral HIF-PHD inhibitor developed using Insilico Medicine's AI-driven pipeline, is undergoing Phase I clinical trials for IBD treatment.

Ultimately, HIF-PHD inhibitors could redefine the landscape of the treatment of anemia and beyond, ushering in a new era of targeted, efficient, and safer therapeutic strategies.

References

1 Konisti, S., Kiriakidis, S., and Paleolog, E.M. (2012). Hypoxia–a key regulator of angiogenesis and inflammation in rheumatoid arthritis. *Nature Reviews Rheumatology* 8: 153–162.

2 Taylor, C.T. and McElwain, J.C. (2010). Ancient atmospheres and the evolution of oxygen sensing via the hypoxia-inducible factor in metazoans. *Physiology* 25: 272–279.

3 Ivan, M. and Kaelin, W.G. (2017). The EGLN-HIF O_2–sensing system: multiple inputs and feedbacks. *Molecular Cell* 66: 772–779.

4 Mills, D.B., Francis, W.R., Vargas, S. et al. (2018). The last common ancestor of animals lacked the HIF pathway and respired in low-oxygen environments. *eLife* 7: e31176.

5 Semenza, G.L. (2009). Regulation of oxygen homeostasis by hypoxia-inducible factor 1. *Physiology* 24: 97–106.

6 Pugh, C.W. and Ratcliffe, P.J. (2017). New horizons in hypoxia signaling pathways. *Experimental Cell Research* 356: 116–121.

7 Strowitzki, M.J., Cummins, E.P., and Taylor, C.T. (2019). Protein hydroxylation by hypoxia-inducible factor (HIF) hydroxylases: unique or ubiquitous? *Cells* 8: e2404115.

8 Tarhonskaya, H., Hardy, A.P., Howe, E.A. et al. (2015). Kinetic investigations of the role of factor inhibiting hypoxia-inducible factor (FIH) as an oxygen sensor. *Journal of Biological Chemistry* 290: 19726–19742.

9 Kaelin, W.G. Jr., and Ratcliffe, P.J. (2008). Oxygen sensing by metazoans: the central role of the HIF hydroxylase pathway. *Molecular Cell* 30: 393–402.

10 Schofield, C.J. and Ratcliffe, P.J. (2004). Oxygen sensing by HIF hydroxylases. *Nature Reviews. Molecular: Cell Biology* 5: 343–354.

11 Cramer, T., Yamanishi, Y., Clausen, B.E. et al. (2003). HIF-1α is essential for myeloid cell-mediated inflammation. *Cell* 112: 645–657.

12 Aik, W.S., Chowdhury, R., Clifton, I.J. et al. (2015). CHAPTER 2. Introduction to structural studies on 2-oxoglutarate-dependent oxygenases and related enzymes. In: *2-Oxoglutarate-Dependent Oxygenases* (ed. C. Schofield and R. Hausinger), 59–94. The Royal Society of Chemistry.

13 Epstein, A.C.R., Gleadle, J.M., McNeill, L.A. et al. (2001). C. elegans EGL-9 and mammalian homologs define a family of dioxygenases that regulate HIF by prolyl hydroxylation. *Cell* 107: 43–54.

14 Hewitson, K.S., McNeill, L.A., Riordan, M.V. et al. (2002). Hypoxia-inducible factor (HIF) asparagine hydroxylase is identical to factor inhibiting HIF (FIH) and is related to the cupin structural family. *Journal of Biological Chemistry* 277: 26351–26355.

15 Lippl, K., Boleininger, A., McDonough, M.A. et al. (2018). Born to sense: biophysical analyses of the oxygen sensing prolyl hydroxylase from the simplest animal Trichoplax adhaerens. *Hypoxia* 6: 57–71.

16 Loenarz, C., Coleman, M.L., Boleininger, A. et al. (2011). The hypoxia-inducible transcription factor pathway regulates oxygen sensing in the simplest animal, Trichoplax adhaerens. *EMBO Reports* 12: 63–70.

17 Hampton-Smith, R.J., Davenport, B.A., Nagarajan, Y., and Peet, D.J. (2019). The conservation and functionality of the oxygen-sensing enzyme Factor Inhibiting HIF (FIH) in non-vertebrates. *PloS One* 14: e0216134.

18 Islam, M.S., Leissing, T.M., Chowdhury, R. et al. (2018). 2-Oxoglutarate-dependent oxygenases. *Annual Review of Biochemistry* 87: 585–620.

19 Markolovic, S., Leissing, T.M., Chowdhury, R. et al. (2016). Structure-function relationships of human JmjC oxygenases-demethylases versus hydroxylases. *Current Opinion in Structural Biology* 41: 62–72.

20 Liu, T., Abboud, M.I., Chowdhury, R. et al. (2020). Biochemical and biophysical analyses of hypoxia sensing prolyl hydroxylases from dictyostelium discoideum and Toxoplasma gondii. *Journal of Biological Chemistry* 295: 16545–16561.

21 Elkins, J.M., Hewitson, K.S., McNeill, L.A. et al. (2003). Structure of factor-inhibiting hypoxia-inducible factor (HIF) reveals mechanism of oxidative modification of HIF-1 alpha. *Journal of Biological Chemistry* 278: 1802–1806.

22 Dann, C.E. 3rd, Bruick, R.K., and Deisenhofer, J. (2002). Structure of factor-inhibiting hypoxia-inducible factor 1: an asparaginyl hydroxylase involved in the hypoxic response pathway. *Proceedings of the National Academy of Sciences of the United States of America* 99: 15351–15356.

23 Lando, D., Peet, D.J., Whelan, D.A. et al. (2002). Asparagine hydroxylation of the HIF transactivation domain a hypoxic switch. *Science* 295: 858–861.

24 McNeill, L.A., Hewitson, K.S., Claridge, T.D. et al. (2002). Hypoxia-inducible factor asparaginyl hydroxylase (FIH-1) catalyses hydroxylation at the beta-carbon of asparagine-803. *Biochemical Journal* 367: 571–575.

25 Wu, Y., Li, Z., McDonough, M.A. et al. (2021). Inhibition of the oxygen-sensing asparaginyl hydroxylase factor inhibiting hypoxia-inducible factor: a potential hypoxia response modulating strategy. *Journal of Medicinal Chemistry* 64: 7189–7209.

26 Koivunen, P., Hirsila, M., Gunzler, V. et al. (2004). Catalytic properties of the asparaginyl hydroxylase (FIH) in the oxygen sensing pathway are distinct from those of its prolyl 4-hydroxylases. *Journal of Biological Chemistry* 279: 9899–9904.

27 Light, K.M., Hangasky, J.A., Knapp, M.J., and Solomon, E.I. (2013). Spectroscopic studies of the mononuclear non-heme Fe(II) enzyme FIH: second-sphere contributions to reactivity. *Journal of the American Chemical Society* 135: 9665–9674.

28 Hirsila, M., Koivunen, P., Gunzler, V. et al. (2003). Characterization of the human prolyl 4-hydroxylases that modify the hypoxia-inducible factor. *Journal of Biological Chemistry* 278: 30772–30780.

29 Iyer, S.R., Chaplin, V.D., Knapp, M.J., and Solomon, E.I. (2018). O_2 activation by nonheme Fe(II) alpha-ketoglutarate-dependent enzyme variants: elucidating the role of the facial triad carboxylate in FIH. *Journal of the American Chemical Society* 140: 11777–11783.

30 Ehrismann, D., Flashman, E., Genn, D.N. et al. (2007). Studies on the activity of the hypoxia-inducible-factor hydroxylases using an oxygen consumption assay. *Biochemical Journal* 401: 227–234.

31 Wu, D., Potluri, N., Lu, J. et al. (2015). Structural integration in hypoxia-inducible factors. *Nature* 524: 303–308.

32 Chan, M.C., Ilott, N.E., Schodel, J. et al. (2016). Tuning the transcriptional response to hypoxia by inhibiting hypoxia-inducible factor (HIF) prolyl and asparaginyl hydroxylases. *Journal of Biological Chemistry* 291: 20661–20673.

33 Hegg, E.L. and Que, L. (1997). The 2-His-1-carboxylate facial triad–an emerging structural motif in mononuclear non-heme iron(II) enzymes. *European Journal of Biochemistry* 625–629.

34 McDonough, M.A., Li, V., Flashman, E. et al. (2006). Cellular oxygen sensing: crystal structure of hypoxia-inducible factor prolyl hydroxylase (PHD2). *Proceedings of the National Academy of Sciences of the United States of America* 103: 9814–9819.

35 Tian, Y.M., Yeoh, K.K., Lee, M.K. et al. (2011). Differential sensitivity of hypoxia inducible factor hydroxylation sites to hypoxia and hydroxylase inhibitors. *Journal of Biological Chemistry* 286: 13041–13051.

36 McNeill, L.A., Flashman, E., Buck, M.R. et al. (2005). Hypoxia-inducible factor prolyl hydroxylase 2 has a high affinity for ferrous iron and 2-oxoglutarate. *Molecular BioSystems* 1: 321–324.

37 Loenarz, C., Mecinović, J., Chowdhury, R. et al. (2009). Evidence for a stereo-electronic effect in human oxygen sensing. *Angewandte Chemie, International Edition in English* 48: 1784–1787.

38 Tarhonskaya, H., Chowdhury, R., Leung, I.K. et al. (2014). Investigating the contribution of the active site environment to the slow reaction of hypoxia-inducible factor prolyl hydroxylase domain 2 with oxygen. *Biochemical Journal* 463: 363–372.

39 Flashman, E., Hoffart, L.M., Hamed, R.B. et al. (2010). Evidence for the slow reaction of hypoxia-inducible factor prolyl hydroxylase 2 with oxygen. *FEBS Journal* 277: 4089–4099.

40 Domene, C., Jorgensen, C., and Schofield, C.J. (2020). Mechanism of molecular oxygen diffusion in a hypoxia-sensing prolyl hydroxylase using multiscale simulation. *Journal of the American Chemical Society* 142: 2253–2263.

41 Chowdhury, R., McDonough, M.A., Mecinovic, J. et al. (2009). Structural basis for binding of hypoxia-inducible factor to the oxygen-sensing prolyl hydroxylases. *Structure* 17: 981–989.

42 Masson, N., Singleton, R.S., Sekirnik, R. et al. (2012). The FIH hydroxylase is a cellular peroxide sensor that modulates HIF transcriptional activity. *EMBO Reports* 13: 251–257.

43 Rabinowitz, M.H. (2013). Inhibition of hypoxia-inducible factor prolyl hydroxylase domain oxygen sensors: tricking the body into mounting orchestrated survival and repair responses. *Journal of Medicinal Chemistry* 56: 9369–9402.

44 Flashman, E., Bagg, E.A.L., Chowdhury, R. et al. (2008). Kinetic rationale for selectivity toward *N*- and *C*-terminal oxygen-dependent degradation domain substrates mediated by a loop region of hypoxia-inducible factor prolyl hydroxylases. *Journal of Biological Chemistry* 283: 3808–3815.

45 Huang, J., Zhao, Q., Mooney, S.M., and Lee, F.S. (2002). Sequence determinants in hypoxia-inducible factor-1alpha for hydroxylation by the prolyl hydroxylases PHD1, PHD2, and PHD3. *Journal of Biological Chemistry* 277: 39792–39800.

46 Appelhoff, R.J., Tian, Y.M., Raval, R.R. et al. (2004). Differential function of the prolyl hydroxylases PHD1, PHD2, and PHD3 in the regulation of hypoxia-inducible factor. *Journal of Biological Chemistry* 279: 38458–38465.

47 Takeda, K., Aguila, H.L., Parikh, N.S. et al. (2008). Regulation of adult erythropoiesis by prolyl hydroxylase domain proteins. *Blood* 111: 3229–3235.

48 England, J., Guo, Y., Van Heuvelen, K.M. et al. (2011). A more reactive trigonal-bipyramidal high-spin oxoiron(IV) complex with a cis-labile site. *Journal of the American Chemical Society* 133: 11880–11883.

49 Hsieh, M.M., Linde, N.S., Wynter, A. et al. (2007). HIF prolyl hydroxylase inhibition results in endogenous erythropoietin induction, erythrocytosis, and modest fetal hemoglobin expression in rhesus macaques. *Blood* 110: 2140–2147.
50 Bruick, R.K. and McKnight, S.L. (2022). A conserved family of prolyl-4-hydroxylases that modify HIF. *Science* 294: 1337–1340.
51 Kalantar-Zadeh, K., Jafar, T.H., Nitsch, D. et al. (2021). Chronic kidney disease. *Lancet* 398: 786–802.
52 Babitt, J.L. and Lin, H.Y. (2012). Mechanisms of anemia in CKD. *Journal of the American Society of Nephrology* 23: 1631–1634.
53 Sankaran, V.G. and Weiss, M.J. (2015). Anemia: progress in molecular mechanisms and therapies. *Nature Medicine* 21: 221–230.
54 Mikhail, A., Covic, A., and Goldsmith, D. (2008). Stimulating erythropoiesis: future perspectives. *Kidney and Blood Pressure Research* 31: 234–246.
55 Jelkmann, W. (2011). Regulation of erythropoietin production. *Journal of Physiology* 589: 1251–1258.
56 Bunn, H.F. (2007). New agents that stimulate erythropoiesis. *Blood* 109: 868–873.
57 Lappin, T.R. and Lee, F.S. (2019). Update on mutations in the HIF: EPO pathway and their role in erythrocytosis. *Blood Reviews* 37: 100590.
58 Wang, G.L. and Semenza, G.L. (1993). Desferrioxamine induces erythropoietin gene expression and hypoxia- inducible factor 1 DNA-binding activity: implications for models of hypoxia signal transduction. *Blood* 82: 3610–3615.
59 Su, K., Li, Z., Yu, Y., and Zhang, X. (2020). The prolyl hydroxylase inhibitor roxadustat: paradigm in drug discovery and prospects for clinical application beyond anemia. *Drug Discovery Today* 25: 1262–1269.
60 Dhillon, S. (2019). Roxadustat: first global approval. *Drugs* 79: 563–572.
61 Markham, A. (2020). Vadadustat: first approval. *Drugs* 80: 1365–1371.
62 Dhillon, S. (2020). Daprodustat: first approval. *Drugs* 80: 1491–1497.
63 Markham, A. (2021). Enarodustat: first approval. *Drugs* 81: 169–174.
64 Figg, W.D. Jr., McDonough, M.A., Chowdhury, R. et al. (2021). Structural basis of prolyl hydroxylase domain inhibition by molidustat. *Chem MedChem* 16: 2082–2088.
65 Dhillon, S. (2022). Desidustat: first approval. *Drugs* 82: 1207–1212.
66 Li, Z., You, Q., and Zhang, X. (2019). Small-molecule modulators of the hypoxia-inducible factor pathway: development and therapeutic applications. *Journal of Medicinal Chemistry* 62: 5725–5749.
67 Yu, Y., Yang, F., Yu, Q. et al. (2021). Discovery of a potent and orally bioavailable hypoxia-inducible factor 2alpha (HIF-2alpha) agonist and its synergistic therapy with prolyl hydroxylase inhibitors for the treatment of renal anemia. *Journal of Medicinal Chemistry* 64: 17384–17402.
68 Shah, Y.M. and Xie, L. (2014). Hypoxia-inducible factors link iron homeostasis and erythropoiesis. *Gastroenterology* 146: 630–642.
69 Rose, N.R., McDonough, M.A., King, O.N.F. et al. (2011). Inhibition of 2-oxoglutarate dependent oxygenases. *Chemical Society Reviews* 49: 4364–4397.

70 Khan, A., Schofield, C.J., and Claridge, T.D.W. (2020). Reducing agent-mediated nonenzymatic conversion of 2-oxoglutarate to succinate: implications for oxygenase assays. *Chembiochem* 21: 2898–2902.

71 Woon, E.C., Demetriades, M., Bagg, E.A. et al. (2012). Dynamic combinatorial mass spectrometry leads to inhibitors of a 2-oxoglutarate-dependent nucleic acid demethylase. *Journal of Medicinal Chemistry* 55: 2173–2184.

72 McNeill, L.A., Bethge, L., Hewitson, K.S., and Schofield, C.J. (2005). A fluorescence-based assay for 2-oxoglutarate-dependent oxygenases. *Analytical Biochemistry* 336: 125–131.

73 Leung, I.K., Demetriades, M., Hardy, A.P. et al. (2013). Reporter ligand NMR screening method for 2-oxoglutarate oxygenase inhibitors. *Journal of Medicinal Chemistry* 56: 547–555.

74 Holt-Martyn, J.P., Chowdhury, R., Tumber, A. et al. (2020). Structure-activity relationship and crystallographic studies on 4-hydroxypyrimidine HIF prolyl hydroxylase domain inhibitors. *Chemistry and Medicine Chemistry* 15: 270–273.

75 Yeh, T.L., Leissing, T.M., Abboud, M.I. et al. (2017). Molecular and cellular mechanisms of HIF prolyl hydroxylase inhibitors in clinical trials. *Chemical Science* 8: 7651–7668.

76 Chowdhury, R., Candela-Lena, J.I., Chan, M.C. et al. (2013). Selective small molecule probes for the hypoxia inducible factor (HIF) prolyl hydroxylases. *ACS Chemical Biology* 7: 13312.

77 Lei, Y., Hu, T., Wu, X. et al. (2015). Affinity-based fluorescence polarization assay for high-throughput screening of prolyl hydroxylase 2 inhibitors. *ACS Medicinal Chemistry Letters* 6: 1236–1240.

78 Li, Z., Zhen, S., Su, K. et al. (2020). A small-molecule probe for monitoring binding to prolyl hydroxylase domain 2 by fluorescence polarisation. *Chemical Communications* 56: 14199–14202.

79 Li, Z., Wu, Y., Zhen, S. et al. (2022). In situ inhibitor synthesis and screening by fluorescence polarization: an efficient approach for accelerating drug discovery. *Angewandte Chemie International Edition* 61: e202211510.

80 Baader, E., Tschank, G., Baringhaus, K.H. et al. (1994). Inhibition of prolyl 4-hydroxylase by oxalyl amino acid derivatives in vitro, in isolated microsomes and in embryonic chicken tissues. *Biochemical Journal* 300: 525–530.

81 Corner, T.P., Teo, R.Z.R., Wu, Y. et al. (2023). Structure-guided optimisation of N-hydroxythiazole-derived inhibitors of factor inhibiting hypoxia-inducible factor-α. *Chemical Science* 14: 12098–12120.

82 Chai, D., Fitch, D. M. 2009. Prolyl hydroxylase inhibitors. WO2009134850A1.

83 Guenzler-Pukall, V., Wang, Q., Langsetmo, P. I., Guo, G. 2009. Methods for reducing blood pressure. WO2009058403A1.

84 Long, W., Zhang, J., Hu, Y., Wang, Y. 2013. Polymorphic forms of compounds as prolyl hydroxylase inhibitor, and uses thereof. WO2013013609A1.

85 Kawamoto, R. M. 2008. Prolyl hydroxylase inhibitors and method of use. WO2008002576A2.

86 Wu, Y., Jiang, Z., Li, Z. et al. (2018). Click chemistry-based discovery of [3-hydroxy-5-(1*H*-1,2,3-triazol-4-yl)picolinoyl]glycines as orally active hypoxia-inducing factor prolyl hydroxylase inhibitors with favorable safety profiles for the treatment of anemia. *Journal of Medicinal Chemistry* 61: 5332–5349.

87 Zhang, X., Lei, Y., Hu, T. et al. (2020). Discovery of clinical candidate (5-(3-(4-chlorophenoxy)prop-1-yn-1-yl)-3-hydroxypicolinoyl)glycine, an orally bioavailable prolyl hydroxylase inhibitor for the treatment of anemia. *Journal of Medicinal Chemistry* 63: 10045–10060.

88 Wu, Y., Zhang, L., Sun, Z. et al. (2023). Preferred conformation-guided discovery of potent and orally active HIF prolyl hydroxylase 2 inhibitors for the treatment of anemia. *Journal of Medicinal Chemistry* 66: 8545–8563.

89 Rosen, M.D., Venkatesan, H., Peltier, H.M. et al. (2010). Benzimidazole-2-pyrazole HIF prolyl 4-hydroxylase inhibitors as oral erythropoietin secretagogues. *ACS Medicinal Chemistry Letters* 1: 526–529.

90 Zhou, C., Zou, W., Hua, Y., Dang, Q. 2013. Substituted pyrimidines. WO2013040789A1.

91 Dang, Q., Zhou, C., Zou, W., Hua, Y. 2013. Substituted pyrimidines. WO2013043621A1.

92 Ujjainwalla, F., Tan, J. Q., Dang, Q. et al. 2016. Substituted pyridine inhibitors of HIF prolyl hydroxylase. WO2016054806A1.

93 Ujjainwalla, F., Tan, J. Q., Dang, Q. et al. 2016. Substituted pyridine inhibitors of HIF prolyl hydroxylase. WO2016057743A1.

94 Ogoshi, Y., Matsui, T., Mitani, I. et al. (2017). Discovery of JTZ-951: a HIF prolyl hydroxylase inhibitor for the treatment of renal anemia. *ACS Medicinal Chemistry Letters* 8: 1320–1325.

95 Ariazi, J.L., Duffy, K.J., Adams, D.F. et al. (2017). Discovery and pre-clinical characterization of GSK1278863 (Daprodustat), a small molecule hypoxia inducible factor–prolyl hydroxylase inhibitor for anemia. *Journal of Pharmacology and Experimental Therapeutics* 363: 336–347.

96 Desai, R. C., Pandya, V., Patel, P. R. 2014. Novel quinolone derivatives. WO2014102818A1.

97 Cai, J., Crespo, A., Du, X. et al. 2016. Inhibitors of HIF prolyl hydroxylase WO2016049100A1.

98 Cai, J., Colandrea, V., Crespo, A., et al. 2016. Inhibitors of HIF prolyl hydroxylase. WO2016049099A1.

99 Nakajima, T., Goi, T., Kawata, A. et al. 2014. Pyrazolopyrimidine compound. WO2014030716A1.

100 Rocha, S., Chan, M.C., Atasoylu, O. et al. (2015). Potent and selective triazole-based inhibitors of the hypoxia-inducible factor prolyl-hydroxylases with activity in the murine brain. *PloS One* 10.

101 Holt-Martyn, J.P., Tumber, A., Rahman, M.Z. et al. (2019). Studies on spiro[4.5]decanone prolyl hydroxylase domain inhibitors. *Medicinal Chemistry Communications* 10: 500–504.

102 Ahmed, S., Ayscough, A., Barker, G.R. et al. (2017). 1,2,4-Triazolo-[1,5-a] pyridine HIF prolylhydroxylase domain-1 (PHD-1) inhibitors with a novel monodentate binding interaction. *Journal of Medicinal Chemistry* 60: 5663–5672.

103 Xu, J., Ding, X., Fu, Y. et al. (2024). Discovery of novel and potent prolyl hydroxylase domain-containing protein (PHD) inhibitors for the treatment of anemia. *Journal of Medicinal Chemistry* 67: 1393–1405.

104 Thede, K., Flamme, I., Oehme, F. et al. Jeske, M. 2010. Substituted dihydropyrazolones for treating cardiovascular and hematological diseases. US20100305085A1.

105 Beck, H., Jeske, M., Thede, K. et al. (2018). Discovery of Molidustat (BAY 85-3934): a small-molecule oral HIF-prolyl hydroxylase (HIF-PH) inhibitor for the treatment of renal anemia. *Chemistry and Medicine Chemistry* 13: 988–1003.

106 Suga, Y. Shimizu, Y. Kawabe, K. et al. 2015. Heteroaryl compound substituted by triazolyl. WO2015163472A1.

107 Sakamoto, A. Tanaka, N. Fukuda, T. 2015. 4-Alkanoylamino-3-pyrazolone derivative. US2015011552A1.

108 Brown, J. W. Davis, M. Ivetac, A. et al. 2014. 6-(5-Hydroxy-1H-pyrazol-1-yl) nicotinamide derivatives and their use as PHD inhibitors. WO2014160810A1.

109 Hong, Y. R. Shin, D. Ro, S. et al. 2010. Phenol derivatives and methods of use thereof. WO2010018458A2

110 Hong, Y.R., Kim, H.T., Ro, S. et al. (2014). Discovery of novel 2-[2-(3-hydroxy-pyridin-2-yl)-thiazol-4-yl]-acetamide derivatives as HIF prolyl 4-hydroxylase inhibitors; SAR, synthesis and modeling evaluation. *Bioorganic and Medicinal Chemistry Letters* 24: 3142–3145.

111 Debenham, J.S., Madsen-Duggan, C., Clements, M.J. et al. (2016). Discovery of *N*-[bis(4-methoxyphenyl)methyl]-4-hydroxy-2-(pyridazin-3-yl)pyrimidine-5-carboxamide (MK-8617), an orally active pan-inhibitor of hypoxia-inducible factor prolyl hydroxylase 1-3 (HIF PHD1-3) for the treatment of anemia. *Journal of Medicinal Chemistry* 59: 11039–11049.

112 Vachal, P., Miao, S., Pierce, J.M. et al. (2012). 1,3,8-Triazaspiro[4.5]decane-2,4-diones as efficacious pan-inhibitors of hypoxia-inducible factor prolyl hydroxylase 1-3 (HIF PHD1-3) for the treatment of anemia. *Journal of Medicinal Chemistry* 55: 2945–2959.

113 Zhang, X., Zhang, Y., Wang, P. et al. (2019). Adipocyte hypoxia-inducible factor 2alpha suppresses atherosclerosis by promoting adipose ceramide catabolism. *Cell Metabolism* 30: 937–951.

114 Stegen, S., Stockmans, I., Moermans, K. et al. (2018). Osteocytic oxygen sensing controls bone mass through epigenetic regulation of sclerostin. *Nature Communications* 9: 2557.

115 Lawson, H., Holt-Martyn, J.P., Dembitz, V. et al. (2024). The selective prolyl hydroxylase inhibitor IOX5 stabilizes HIF-1α and compromises development and progression of acute myeloid leukemia. *Nature Cancer*. https://doi.org/10.1038/s43018-024-00761-w.

116 Tambuwala, M.M., Cummins, E.P., Lenihan, C.R. et al. (2010). Loss of prolyl hydroxylase-1 protects against colitis through reduced epithelial cell apoptosis and increased barrier function. *Gastroenterology* 139: 2093–2101.

15

Hijacking Histone Demethylase KDM5B for Novel Therapeutics

Wen-Long Wang[1], *Guan-Jun Yang*[2], *and Bin Yu*[1]

[1]*Zhengzhou University, College of Chemistry, State Key Laboratory of Antiviral Drugs, Pingyuan Laboratory, Science Road #100, Zhengzhou 450001, China*
[2]*School of Marine Sciences, Ningbo University, State Key Laboratory for Managing Biotic and Chemical Threats to the Quality and Safety of Agro-products, No.818 Fenghua Road, Ningbo 315211, China*

15.1 Introduction

Methylation and demethylation of histone lysines impact human genes' transcriptional regulation [1–3]. Demethylases that target *N*-methyl-lysine on histones, known as KDMs, have become a focus in drug discovery following the identification oflysine-specific demethylase 1 (LSD1) [4]. Reported KDMs include the flavin adenine dinucleotide (FAD)–dependent KDM1 subfamily and the Jumonji C (JmjC) domain-containing Jumonji domain (JMJD) family (KDM2–KDM7) [5, 6]. Lysine-specific demethylase 5B (KDM5B) is part of the JMJD subfamily (JmjC-KDMs) that can remove H3K4me2/3 methyl groups [7]. H3K4 dimethylation and trimethylation mark the transcription start sites [8], suggesting that H3K4me2/3 demethylation catalyzed by KM5B leads to transcriptional repression [9–11]. Moreover, KDM5B has been linked to repairing DNA [12–14], resistance to drugs [15–19], stemness [20], and immunotherapy of cancers [21, 22]. KDM5B was initially found in breast cancer cells that abundantly express c-ErbB2 [23]. Later, overexpression of KDM5B was found in various cancers, including esophageal cancer, prostate cancer, gastric cancer, hepatocellular carcinoma (HCC), lung cancer, melanoma, and leukemia [21, 24–37]. As an oncogene, KDM5B plays a key role in various cancers. Hijacking KDM5B could cure cancer effectively [38–42]. While there are some highly potent KDM5B inhibitors, only a limited number of them are currently being investigated. **GS-5801,** developed by Gilead Sciences, is a liver-targeted prodrug. This compound, by demethylating H3K4me3, has demonstrated efficacy in reducing viral antigens and RNA levels [43]. **GS-5801** was discontinued in a phase 1 clinical trial for chronic hepatitis B virus (HBV) treatment in the United States and New Zealand on 6 October 2018 (Trial numbers: ACTRN12616001260415p and ACTRN12616001375448p).

Drug Discovery Targeting Metalloenzymes: Strategies and Applications, First Edition. Edited by Guo-Bo Li.

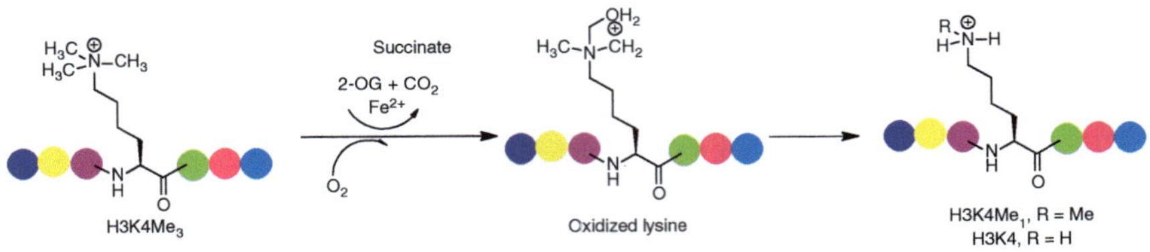

Figure 15.1 KDM5B-mediated demethylation process.

15.2 Structure of KDM5B and Its Catalytic Mechanisms

Human KDM5B consists of 1544 amino acids [23, 44] and includes JmjC, AT-rich interactive domain (ARID), Jumonji N (JmjN), PHD, PLU1 motif, and the C_5HC_2 zinc finger domains [9, 23]. JmjN and JmjC are necessary for demethylation [37]. While for catalytic activity, the ARID domain is unnecessary, which helps substrate recognition [45]. The PHD1 domain can regulate catalytic activity allosterically [46]. However, PHD2 and PHD3 do not recognize H3K4 methylation states. KDM5B-mediated demethylation relies on α-ketoglutarate, Fe^{2+}, and O_2. KDM5B facilitates 2-oxogluterate (2-OG) and Fe^{2+} oxidation to produce the demethylated lysine and formaldehyde [6, 47] (Figure 15.1).

15.3 KDM5B Biological Functions

15.3.1 KDM5B's Transcriptional Regulation

KDM5B was first discovered in human breast cancer cells [23, 48], and its demethylation role was identified before 2007 [49–51]. KDM5B, through a demethylation that differs from LSD1 and LSD2, can remove tri- and di-methyl marks from H3K4 [52, 53]. As a transcriptional repressor [51], KDM5B also interacts with BF-1 and PAX9 (two transcription factors) [54] and CAV1 and BRCA1 (tumor suppressor genes). KDM5B-mediated transcriptional repression is associated with proliferation, cell-cycle regulation, mitosis, and embryonic stem cell (ESC) self-renewal [8, 20]. Bente Madsen et al. showed KDM5B's roles in meiotic transcription [48]. Scibetta Angelo et al. found that elevated levels of KDM5B control the cell cycle at the M phase [55]. KDM5B was essential for the neural self-renewal and differentiation of ESCs [8, 20]. The genome analysis of Ewing's sarcoma (ES) cells revealed that KDM5B was concentrated on active gene promoters and enhancers marked with H3K4 methylation, playing a role in regulating ESC pluripotency [56]. Studies demonstrated that KDM5B significantly impacted key developmental genes [8, 57–59].

15.3.2 KDM5B in Cancer

15.3.2.1 KDM5B in Breast Cancer

KDM5B plays a crucial role in breast cancer progression by repressing transcription [60, 61]. It is overexpressed in ER^+ MCF-7 cells, and its expression promotes cell proliferation by aiding G1 progression [51]. Studies have shown that reducing

KDM5B levels in MCF-7 cells through shRNAi inhibited tumor growth *in vivo* [62]. High levels of KDM5B were linked to poor prognosis in breast tumors that are hormone receptor-positive [63]. By regulating MALAT1 and hsa-miR-448, KDM5B was also linked to aggressive breast cancers [64]. Additionally, KDM5B suppressed CCL14 expression, thereby inhibiting breast cancer angiogenesis and metastasis *in vivo* [65]. Knocking down KDM5B upregulated BRCA1, CAV1, and HOXA5, three tumor suppressor genes [66]. Therefore, targeting KDM5B with drugs could effectively treat breast cancer.

15.3.2.2 KDM5B in Melanoma

Roesch Alexander et al. showed that in malignant melanomas, KDM5B was downregulated, which is opposite to that observed in breast cancer [67]. In melanoma cells, they later discovered the KDM5B's tumor-suppressive functions [25, 68]. In 2010, it was reported that KDM5B expression in melanoma subpopulations was dynamically and heterogeneously regulated [24]. Isolated KDM5B-positive melanomas were highly proliferative, but knocking down KDM5B initially accelerated tumor growth before leading to exhaustion [24]. Roesch revealed challenges in determining the role of KDM5B. A study involving 121 consecutive uveal melanoma patients reported high expression of KDM5B through immunohistochemical assays, with higher levels correlating with lower survival rates [69]. Another study demonstrated that increased expression of KDM5B was a potential biomarker for melanoma [70]. In a 3D model, blocking KDM5B decreased invasion and colony formation, indicating that targeting KDM5B could provide a novel approach to regulate cell behavior in melanoma [71].

15.3.2.3 KDM5B in HCC

High levels of KDM5B expression were detected in HCC, with a positive link to metastasis [26]. KDM5B overexpression in these cells promoted proliferation, migration, invasion, and the epithelial–mesenchymal transition (EMT) process [26]. In HCC patients, elevated KDM5B levels were linked to a poor prognosis [27]. Knocking down KDM5B induced G1/S cell-cycle arrest and notably inhibited HCC proliferation [27]. Another study revealed significant overexpression of KDM5B in HCC cases with HBV infection [72]. In summary, KDM5B is an oncogene and prognostic indicator for HCC [73].

15.3.2.4 KDM5B in Lung Cancer

KDM5B was overexpressed in tissues of lung cancer [33]. P53 was associated with cell proliferation, survival, and invasion in cancers [74, 75]. Targeting KDM5B through RNA interference significantly reduced the proliferation, possibly involving p53 [32]. However, knocking down sirtuin 1 (SIRT1) and KDM5B markedly inhibited migration of A549 cells without affecting proliferation [33]. Studies on non-small cell lung cancers (NSCLCs) showed that through activating c-Met signaling, high levels of KDM5B increased tumor aggressiveness and worsened the NSCLC patients' prognosis [76].

15.3.2.5 KDM5B in Prostate Cancer

Overexpressed KDM5B in metastatic prostate tissues was linked to PCa cell invasion and metastasis [34]. Androgen receptor (AR) and androgens were linked to prostate cancer, and KDM5B can regulate AR's transcription [37, 77]. By repressing KDM5B expression, overexpressed miR-29a inhibited prostate cancer cells' proliferation and induced their apoptosis [36]. Simultaneously, inactivated Skp2 decreased the levels of H3K4me3 [78]. Lu et al. reported that SKP2 regulates KDM5B through the ubiquitination pathway, leading to aberrant alterations in H3K4me3 levels during tumorigenesis and castration-resistant prostate cancer (CRPC) development [78].

15.3.2.6 KDM5B in Leukemia

KDM5B overexpression inhibited the growth of leukemia [40, 41]. The depletion of KDM5B in HL-60 and Jeko-1 cell lines cleaved apoptotic proteins C-myc, Bcl-2, and procaspase-3, leading to decreased cell viability and increased apoptosis [79]. In mixed-lineage leukemia (MLL)-rearranged acute myelocytic leukemia (AML) cells, KDM5B was found to negatively regulate leukemogenesis by modulating H3K4 methylation levels [42]. Additionally, IKZF1 acts as a tumor suppressor associated with B-cell precursor acute lymphoblastic leukemia (B-ALL), and is targeted by casein kinase II (CK2), an oncogenic kinase commonly elevated in ALL [38, 41]. Wang et al. revealed that IKZF1 and HDAC1 regulate the transcription of KDM5B, identifying it as a potential drug target for treating B-ALL, noting that CK2 inhibition led to downregulation of KDM5B expression [41].

15.3.2.7 KDM5B in Other Cancers

KDM5B overexpression in esophageal cancers is associated with decreased overall survival [29]. It has also been linked to cancer stem cells in the esophagus, and knocking it down reduces the proliferation and invasion of esophageal cancer cells [28]. In gastric cancer samples, KDM5B is upregulated compared to normal tissues, and silencing it promotes cell growth and metastasis [30]. Quantitative RT-PCR shows KDM5B overexpression in bladder cancer tissues, and siRNA inhibition significantly suppresses proliferation abilities [32, 80]. In colon cancer, KDM5B was overexpressed, while silencing it in human oral squamous cell carcinoma inhibited invasion and migration, reducing the activities of cancer stem cells and enhancing the tumor-inhibiting effects of radiotherapy [81, 82]. Wang et al. showed that KDM5B was expressed at higher levels in epithelial ovarian cancer compared to benign ovarian tumors and normal ovaries [83]. In glioma cells, upregulated expression of KDM5B led to increased proliferation by regulating p21 gene expression [84]. Cui et al. reported KDM5B was upregulated in head and neck carcinoma [85].

15.3.3 KDM5B in Cancer Immunotherapy

Immunogenic cancer-testis antigens (CTAs) are encoded by genes that are typically expressed in placenta or male germ cells [86]. When CTAs are abnormally expressed in somatic cells, they can trigger an immune response. Targeting CTAs has become a promising approach for cancer immunotherapy. Rao and colleagues discovered that in lung cancer cells, reducing KDM5B could boost decitabine (DAC)-induced CTA activation, improving cancer immunotherapy effectiveness [21]. The stimulator of interferon genes (STING) pathway helps fight infections and cancers [87]. In 2019, Wu et al. demonstrated that STING expression is inhibited by KDM5B-C, and they showed that in breast cancer cells, suppressing KDM5B could reactivate the STING pathway [22]. In breast cancer cells, reactivating STING through inhibition of KDM5B led to a strong interferon response [22]. These findings suggest the use of KDM5 inhibitors for cancer immunotherapies.

15.3.4 KDM5B in Drug Resistance

Treatment resistance has long been a significant issue in metastatic melanoma, with numerous reports linking KDM5B to drug resistance. Roesch et al. [88] found that depleting KDM5B could enhance the sensitivity of drug-tolerant melanoma cells to common chemotherapeutics by disrupting continuous tumor maintenance. Ahn et al. [89] further showed that KDM5B regulated melanoma cells that are drug-tolerant. Tumor heterogeneity poses a significant challenge for cancer therapy, particularly due to subpopulations exhibiting progenitor cell traits or stem cell traits. Liu et al. [90] also demonstrated that KDM5B regulates the transition of drug-sensitive subpopulations in melanoma-propagating cells.

Kuo et al. [91] were the first to show how KDM5B contributed to drug resistance in neuroblastoma (NB) cells. Previous studies have revealed that the XRCC1, a DNA repair protein, can prevent cell death induced by cisplatin through apoptosis [92]. Xu and colleagues [19] discovered that drug-resistant cells exhibit decreased methylation of H3K4 but increased expression of KDM5B. Elevated levels of KDM5B reduced H3K4 methylation, leading to cisplatin resistance by involving XRCC1-mediated DNA repair mechanisms. In estrogen receptor-positive (ER^+) breast tumors, high levels of KDM5B were linked to treatment resistance and a poor prognosis [15]. Drug-tolerant HER2-positive ($HER2^+$) breast cancers responded well to KDM5 inhibition. Endometrial cancers often showed elevated levels of KDM5B, which correlates with reduced sensitivity to paclitaxel treatment [93]. Knocking down KDM5B in two resistant endometrial cancer cells restored sensitivity to paclitaxel (PTX) [93]. Leadem et al. [16] demonstrated that combining KDM5 inhibitor with 5-aza-2′-deoxycytidine significantly enhanced the effectiveness of DAC treatment. This synergistic effect between the two agents suggests a promising approach for overcoming drug resistance issues.

15.4 KDM5B Inhibitors

KDM5B is part of the 2-OG oxygenase family [94]. Reported inhibitors of KDM5B are reversible or covalent inhibitors that act as Fe^{2+} chelators and compete with 2-OG. Other reported 2-OG oxygenases [95, 96] have conserved binding sites for Fe^{2+} and 2-OG [96, 97]. While some potent KDM5B inhibitors have been identified, there are only a few in clinical use [6, 18, 98–102]. Existing KDM5B inhibitors still face challenges such as poor selectivity and pharmacokinetic (PK) parameters.

15.4.1 Reversible Inhibitors

15.4.1.1 2-OG Analogs

NOG (*N*-oxalylglycine, compound **1**, Figure 15.2) is bound to Fe^{2+} through the amide group and its C-1 carboxylate oxygen. It was found to be a broad-spectrum inhibitor of 2-OG oxygenases by binding to the 2-OG site [103–105]. It was later found to inhibit KDM5B *in vitro* (IC_{50} = 24.5 μM) [5, 106]. However, **NOG** was not selective and inhibited JmjC-KDMs nonspecifically. The crystal KDM5B/**NOG** structure showed that the metal coordinated with the two carbonyl oxygens on the oxalyl group in a bidentate way (PDB ID: 5A1F) [5]. Similarly, 2-hydroxyglutarates **R-2HG** and **S-2HG** (compounds **2** and **3** in Figure 15.2) inhibited 2-OG oxygenases. Both compounds were weak KDM5B inhibitors (IC_{50} = 3600 and1600 μM, respectively) [107]. Laukka et al. noted that, as the 2-OG derivative, citrate (compound **4** in Figure 15.2) weakly inhibited KDM5B with an IC_{50} of 800 μM [108]. Succinate (**5**) and oxaloacetate (**6**) (Figure 15.2) deactivated KDM5B (IC_{50} = 1400 and 900 μM, respectively). Most reported derivatives for KDM5B had low cellular permeability and selectivity. Prodrugs were then developed to improve permeability and efficacy (e.g. **NOG** [109]).

15.4.1.2 Isonicotinic Acids

Initially, 2,4-pyridinedicarboxylic acid (**2,4-PDCA**, **7**, Figure 15.3) inhibited 2-OG oxygenase, KDM4E, and KDM6 [94, 110]. Kristensen et al. identified it as an KDM5B inhibitor *in vitro* [44] due to sequence homology with KDM4-6 [111]. The IC_{50} value was determined to be 3 μM using the formaldehyde dehydrogenase (FDH)-coupled assay [44]. However, **2,4-PDCA** was not selective against other KDM5 enzymes and showed low permeability [112]. The crystal **2,4-PDCA**/KDM5B structure analysis revealed a bidentate binding mode (PDB ID: 5A3W), in which

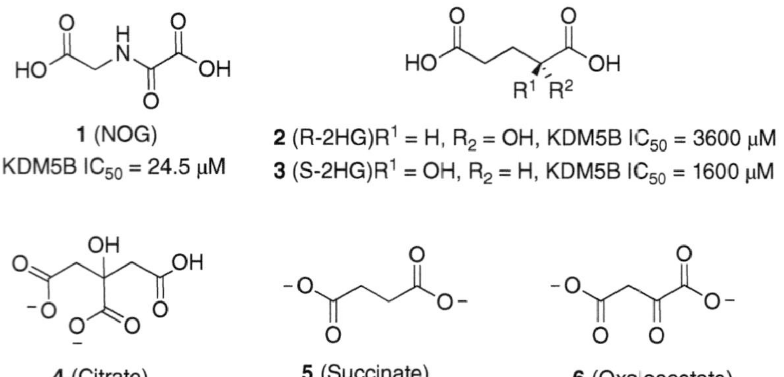

1 (NOG)
KDM5B IC_{50} = 24.5 μM

2 (R-2HG)R^1 = H, R_2 = OH, KDM5B IC_{50} = 3600 μM
3 (S-2HG)R^1 = OH, R_2 = H, KDM5B IC_{50} = 1600 μM

4 (Citrate)
KDM5B IC_{50} = 800 μM

5 (Succinate)
KDM5B IC_{50} = 1400 μM

6 (Oxaloacetate)
KDM5B IC_{50} = 900 μM

Figure 15.2 Structures of 2-OG derivatives (**1–6**).

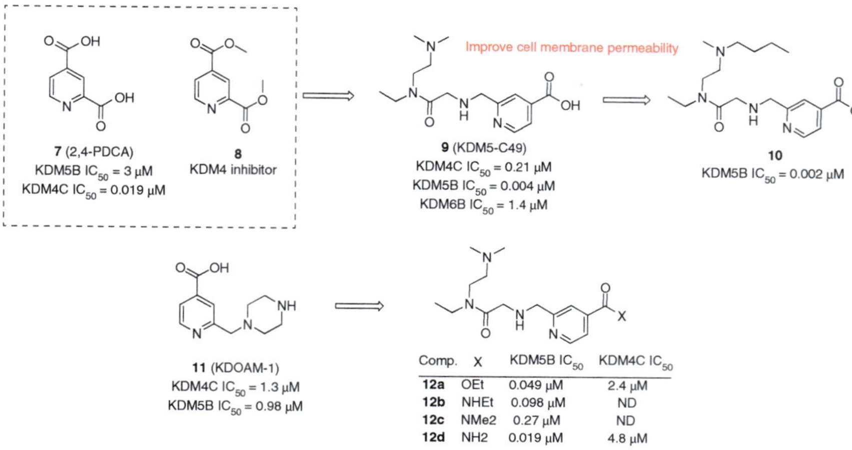

Comp.	X	KDM5B IC_{50}	KDM4C IC_{50}
12a	OEt	0.049 μM	2.4 μM
12b	NHEt	0.098 μM	ND
12c	NMe2	0.27 μM	ND
12d	NH2	0.019 μM	4.8 μM

Figure 15.3 Optimizations of isonicotinic acid derivatives (**7–12d**).

the carbonyl oxygen and the pyridine nitrogen chelated Fe^{2+} [5]. Additionally, Mackeen et al. [112] reported that the **2,4-PDCA** prodrug (**8**, Figure 15.3) was a cell-permeable KDM4 inhibitor.

Further modifications of **2,4-PDCA** gave more potent and selective KDM5B inhibitors (e.g. **KDOAM-25** [101] and **KDM5-C49** [5]). **KDM5-C49** (**9**, Figure 15.3) potently inhibited KDM5B (IC_{50} =0.004 μM) [5]. It also showed inhibitory activity against other JmjC-KDMs, including KDM5A, KDM5C-D, and KDM6B. Notably, there was significant selectivity observed between KDM5B and KDM6B for **KDM5-C49**. The crystal structure analysis revealed that the binding site for 2-OG was occupied by the compound. The aminomethyl nitrogen and the pyridine nitrogen chelated with the metal ion in a bidentate manner. Additionally, polar interactions were observed between residues Arg^{98}, Tyr^{425}, Glu^{501}, Asn^{509}, Lys^{517}, while hydrophobic interactions involved Trp^{487}, Val^{99}, and Phe^{496}. In 2024, Suzuki et al. [113] optimized compound **9** by introducing the *n*-butyl to enhance its cellular permeability and activity. Compound **10** exhibited a similar IC_{50} value against KDM5B in enzymatic assays compared to compound **9** (IC_{50} =0.002 μM), but its prodrug demonstrated six times higher membrane permeability in parallel artificial membrane permeability assay (PAMPA) than that of compound **9**'s prodrug.

Tumber et al. [101] discovered KDM5B inhibitors **12a–d** based on compound **11** (IC_{50} =1.3 μM for KDM4C; IC_{50} =0.98 μM for KDM5C; Figure 15.3). These inhibitors exhibited IC_{50} values of 0.049, 0.098, 0.27, and 0.019 μM, respectively. Among them, compound **12a** (also known as **GS-5801**), acting as a **KDM5-C49** (**GS-080**) prodrug, displayed strong inhibition of KDM5B *in vitro*. Compounds **12b–d**, in which carboxyl groups were replaced with amide groups, exhibited slightly lower KDM5B inhibition but higher cell permeability than **KDM5-C49**. Compound **12d** exhibited the highest KDM5B inhibition (IC_{50} =0.019 μM) and selectivity over KDM4C. It also moderately inhibited MM1S cell proliferation (IC_{50} =30 μM) and caused G1 phase cell-cycle arrest. Johansson et al. [5] reported the co-crystal structure of compound **12d** in complex with KDM5B (PBD: A53N), revealing a pose identical to that observed for the structure reported for **KDM5-C49**.

15.4.1.3 Bipyridines

Chang et al. [114] demonstrated the utility of 4,4-dicarboxy-2,2-bipyridine for the development of KDM4E inhibitors. They optimized compound **13** (KDM4E IC_{50} = 6.4 μM, Figure 15.4) to yield the potent compound **14** (Figure 15.4, KDM4E IC_{50} = 0.11 μM) through the carboxyl moiety modification. The pyridinyl nitrogen in compound **14** chelates with the catalytic metal. Nie et al. introduced compound **15** by adding a pyrazolylpyridine core, building on the similarities between KDM4A and KDM5B (KDM5B IC_{50} = 4.4 μM, Figure 15.4); here, to reduce its metal chelation affinity, the pyrazole ring was used to replace the pyridine. The structure–activity relationships (SARs) indicated that substituents attached to the phenyl ring enhanced KDM5B inhibition; Notably, compounds bearing the 4-Me substituent and 3-OH exhibited superior potency (compound **16**, IC_{50} = 0.067 μM).

Nie et al. [115] developed the benzyloxypyrazolylpyridine compound (**17**, Figure 15.4). Compound **17** showed significantly improved KDM5B inhibition compared to compound **16** (IC_{50} = 0.001 μM). Substitutions on the phenyl ring demonstrated similar potency against KDM5B. Compound **17**, containing 2-Me and 4-Cl on the phenyl ring, was potent and able to penetrate cells (IC_{50} = 0.002 μM) (Figure 15.4). Compound **18** accumulated H3K4me3 in ZR-75-1 cells (H3K4me3 EC_{50} = 0.09 μM). Additionally, compound **18** demonstrated efficacy in the MCF-7 xenograft model. Bavetsias et al. [98] identified compound **19**, showing micromolar potency against KDM5B. The nitrogen atoms of pyridine and thiazole could coordinate bidentately with the active site metal. Substituting the –COOH group with amide notably decreased effectiveness against KDM5B. The carboxylic acid appears crucial for binding strength and could be linked to limited cellular permeability.

15.4.1.4 Pyrimidinones

Westaway et al. [102] identified **GSK-467** as a pan-KDM5 inhibitor to enhance cell penetration. In a separate study, **GSK-467** was shown to strongly inhibit KDM5B in an *alpha* screen assay (IC_{50} = 0.026 μM) [5]. The compound **21**/KDM5B structure (PBD ID: 5FUN) revealed that **GSK467** bound to the pocket that 2-OG occupies. The pyrido-nitrogen monodentate coordinated with the metal, while the oxygen atom of pyrimidine-4(3*H*)-one reacted with Lys517 through a hydrogen bond. Furthermore, hydrophobic interactions were observed with Trp519, Phe496, and Tyr488.

Alterations at the C8 position of compound **22** (KDM5B IC_{50} = 1.3 μM, Figure 15.5) resulted in the creation of compounds **23** and **24** [99]. The SAR analysis of the phenyl ring substituents increased inhibition potency toward KDM5B, with the exception of the 3-OMe substitution. Electron-withdrawing groups were more effective than electron-donating ones. Compound **23**, with a phenyl ring substituted by 4-Cl, exhibited strong KDM5B inhibition (IC_{50} = 0.014 μM). A different group of compounds with different substitutions on the benzyl ring showed strong KDM5B inhibition. Compound **24** was highly active against both KDM4B and

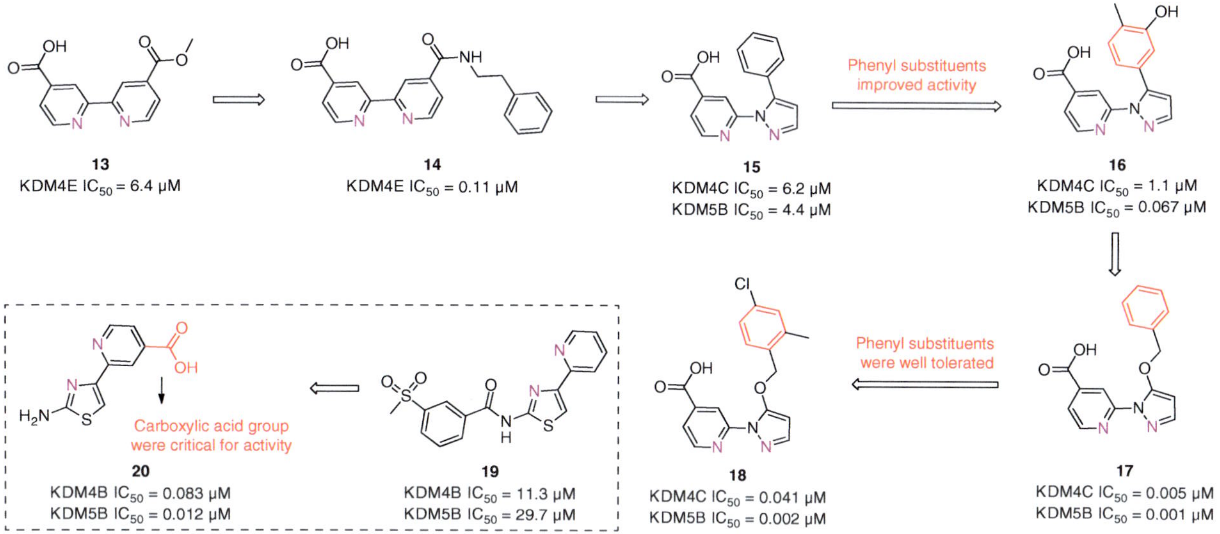

Figure 15.4 Hit-to-lead optimizations of bipyridine and pyrazolylpyridine derivatives (**13–20**).

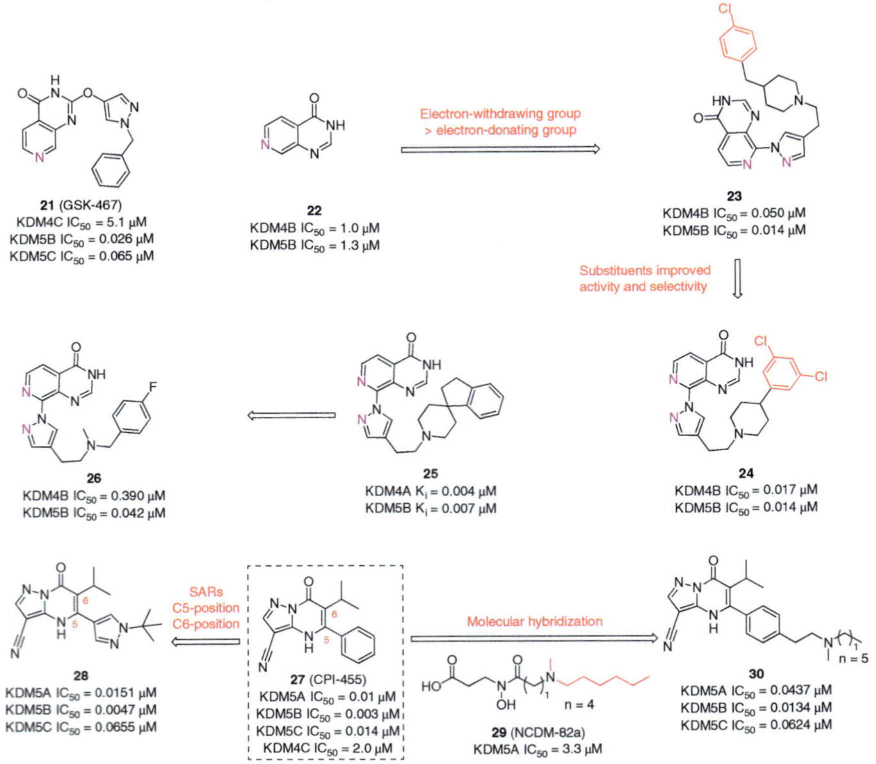

Figure 15.5 Pyrimidinone-containing KDM5 inhibitors(**21–30**).

KDM5B (IC_{50} =0.017 and 0.014 μM, respectively), indicating the importance of the substituents on the benzyl group for the activity. Both electron-donating and electron-withdrawing groups improved inhibitory potency against KDM5B. To enhance selectivity, Le et al. [116] introduced compound **25** (K_i =0.007 and 0.004 μM for KDM5B and KDM4A, respectively, Figure 15.5) as a potent dual inhibitor targeting the KDM4/5 subfamilies with cell-penetrating properties using structure-based drug design. Compound **26** (Figure 15.5) showed strong inhibition of KDM5B (IC_{50} =0.042 μM). The compound **26**/KDM5B complex structure (PBD ID: 5FPL) indicated the binding of the pyridyl and pyrazole nitrogen atoms to Fe^{2+}. A hydrogen bond interaction between the pyridopyrimidinone CONH group and residues K517/Y425 was also found [98].

Vinogradova et al. [18] reported **CPI-455** as a strong KDM5B inhibitor (IC_{50} = 3 nM) using high-throughput screening. While it showed decreased effectiveness in PC9 cells (H3K4Me3 EC_{50} =5.2 μM), in HeLa cells, **CPI-455** raised overall H3K4me3 levels [99]. In cancer cells, the demethylation function of KDM5 is essential for drug tolerance. **CPI-455** inhibited drug-tolerant states in different cancer cell models, like erlotinib-resistant cell lines. **CPI-455** lowered plasma clearance and exhibited high oral bioavailability (C_{max} =192 μM) when given orally at 100 mg/kg. Liang et al. [117] modified the C5 and C6 positions of

CPI-455. Compound **28** (Figure 15.5) was developed with similar activity (KDM5B IC_{50} = 0.0047 μM) but increased activity in PC9 cells (H3K4Me3 EC_{50} = 0.34 μM). Miyake and colleagues [118] created compound **30** by combining fragments from **CPI-455** and **NCDM-82a** to compete with 2-OG [100]. Compound **30** increased levels of H3K4Me in A549 and showed stronger growth inhibition (GI_{50} = 29.6 μM) than **CPI-455**.

15.4.1.5 Pyrazoles

A pyrazole-based KDM5B inhibitor **31** was found using structure-based virtual screening (IC_{50} = 9.32 μM, Figure 15.6) [119]. Further optimizations gave more potent compound **32** (IC_{50} = 0.0244 μM) [119]. SAR analysis at the pyrazole N-1 position revealed that the phenyl ring modifications were essential for inhibiting the activity. Electron-donating substituents were preferred over electron-withdrawing ones for higher potency. Compound **32** effectively suppressed KDM5B in MKN45 cells, leading to a significant increase in H3K4me2/3 accumulation. Compound **32** inhibited the proliferation of MKN45 cells, wound healing, and migration. The selectivity over other KDMs was also evaluated. These findings demonstrate that compound **32** exhibits selectivity toward KDM5A/B/C over KDM4A/C and KDM6B.

Compound **33** [120] (Figure 15.6) potently inhibited all KDM5 isoforms (KDM5A/B/C, IC_{50} = 0.045/0.056/0.055 μM). Our group analyzed the X-ray co-crystal structure of compound **35** bound to KDM5 (PDB code: 5V9T) and modified it by adding a urea linker in the cyclopropyl moiety, resulting in **TK-129** [121] (compound **34**, Figure 15.6). **TK-129** showed better inhibition of KDM5B (IC_{50} = 0.044 μM) compared to KDM5A/C (IC_{50} = 0.079 and 0.353 μM, respectively). *In vitro* studies demonstrated that **TK-129** decreased Ang II-induced activation and had favorable pharmacokinetic properties (F = 42.37%). Additionally, *in vivo* experiments indicated that **TK-129** effectively reduced myocardial remodeling and fibrosis.

15.4.1.6 Other KDM5B Inhibitors

PBIT (compound **35**, Figure 15.7) was found to be a weak inhibitor of KDM5B (KDM5B IC_{50} = 3 μM) in a high-throughput screening [122, 123]. **Ebselen** (compound **36**, Figure 15.7) also showed activity at the micromolar level [123]. **Catechols** are iron chelators that can inhibit different 2-OG oxygenases [124]. In line with this, **caffeic acid** (compound **37**, Figure 15.7) and **Esculetin** (compound **38**, Figure 15.7) exhibited low-micromolar IC_{50} values against KDM5B [125]. In 2023, Wu et al. [126] reported that pyrazole-[3,4-*b*]pyridine derivatives act as KDM5B inhibitors. The most potent derivative (compound **39**, Figure 15.7) inhibited KDM5B(IC_{50} = 0.025 μM) and displayed strong antitumor effects on different prostate cancer cells PC-3 and LNCaP (IC_{50} = 2.18 μM and 4.34 μM, respectively).

JSK-J1 (compound **40**) and **JSK-J4** (compound **42,** the ethyl ester prodrug of **41**) were identified as potent inhibitors of KDM6B by Kruidenier et al. [127]. Heinemann et al. [128] found that **JSK-J1** and **JSK-J4** were also inhibitors of KDM5

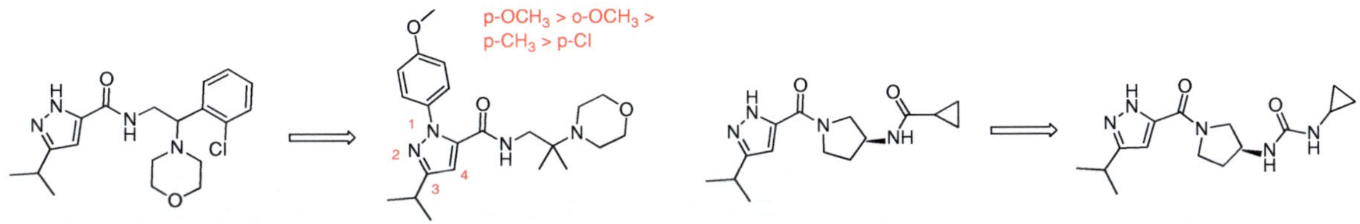

31
KDM5B IC_{50} = 9.32 μM

32
KDM4A IC_{50} = 0.954 μM
KDM4C IC_{50} = 1.112 μM
KDM5A IC_{50} = 0.025 μM
KDM5B IC_{50} = 0.024 μM
KDM5C IC_{50} = 0.025 μM
KDM6A IC_{50} > 1 μM

33
KDM5A IC_{50} = 0.045 μM
KDM5B IC_{50} = 0.056 μM
KDM5C IC_{50} = 0.055 μM

34
KDM5A IC_{50} = 0.079 μM
KDM5B IC_{50} = 0.044 μM
KDM5C IC_{50} = 0.353 μM

Figure 15.6 Chemical structures of derivatives containing pyrazole (**31–34**).

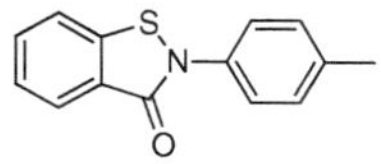

35 (PBIT)
KDM5B IC_{50} = 3 μM

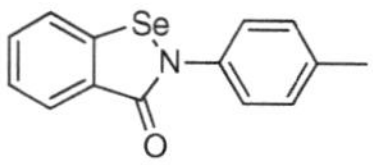

36 (Ebselen)
KDM5B IC_{50} = 5 μM

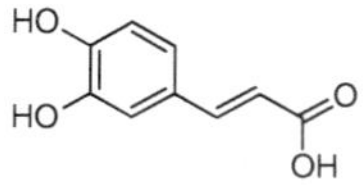

37 (Caffeic acid)
KDM5B IC_{50} = 2.88 μM

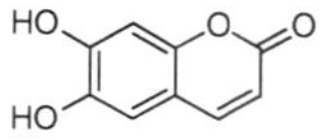

38 (Esculetin)
KDM5B IC_{50} = 4.60 μM

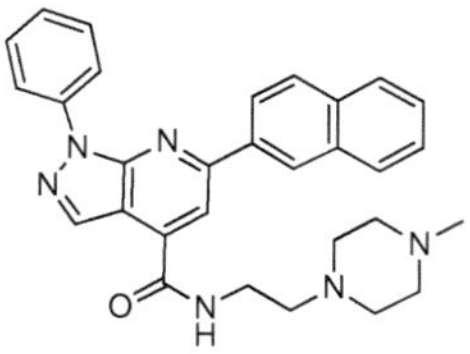

39
KDM5B IC_{50} = 0.025 μM

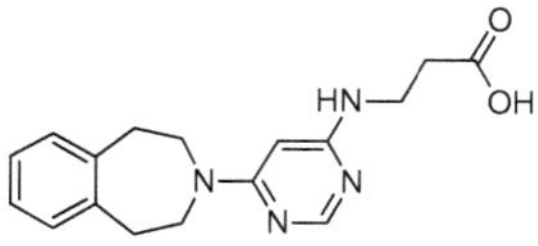

40 (JSK-J1)
KDM5B IC_{50} = 1.7 μM
KDM6B IC_{50} = 0.06 μM

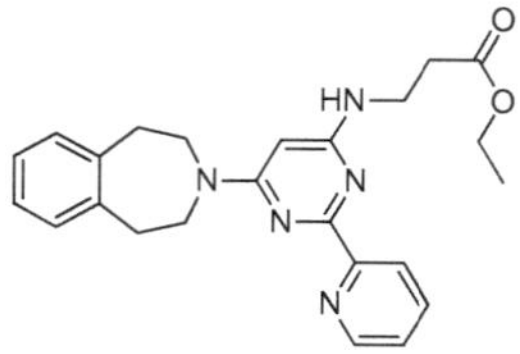

41 (JSK-J4)
KDM5B IC_{50} = 9.7 μM

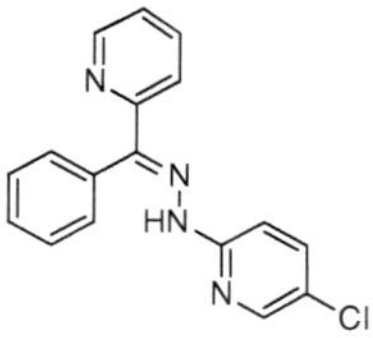

42 (JIB-04)
KDM5B IC_{50} = 5 μM
KDM5C IC_{50} = 42 μM

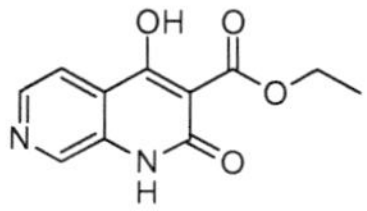

43
KDM5A IC_{50} = 0.06 μM
KDM5B IC_{50} = 0.02 μM
KDM5C IC_{50} = 0.08 μM

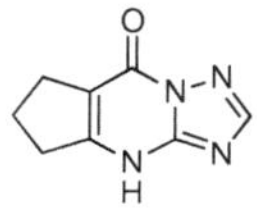

44
KDM5B IC_{50} = 0.203 μM

Figure 15.7 Other KDM5B inhibitors (**35–44**).

(IC_{50} = 1.7 and 9.7 μM, respectively). **JIB-04** (compound **43**, *E*-isomer, Figure 15.7) broadly inhibited JmjC-KDMs [129]. While **JIB-04** does not compete with 2-OG, its inhibitory activity may be attributed to Fe^{2+} chelation [129]. Horton et al. [45] showed that **JIB-04** inactivated KDM5B (IC_{50} = 5 μM) and suppressed MCF-7 and MDA-MB-231 cell growth (GI_{50} = 0.3 and 0.022 μM, respectively). Compound **43** was identified as a selective KDM5 inhibitor competitive with 2-OG over KDM4C and KDM2B subfamilies [130]. Despite its potency against KDM5 subfamilies, compound **43** did not exhibit cellular efficacy on global H3K4me3 levels at 30 μM. After screening our in-house library, we discovered compound **44** inhibited KDM5B potently (IC_{50} = 0.203 μM) [131].

15.4.2 Covalent KDM5B Inhibitors

Covalent inhibitors, like omeprazole [132] and afatinib [133], have been successfully applied in clinical practice. These inhibitors offer potential advantages in terms of cellular efficiency. In 2018, Horton et al. [134] introduced the first covalent KDM5 inhibitor (compound **45**, Figure 15.8), which competed with 2-OG inhibitor and covalently bound to Cys^{481} of KDM5A through an acrylic amide group. Compound **45** also potently inhibited KDM5B (IC_{50} = 0.22 μM) in an alpha assay, which is approximately seven times more potent than its effect on KDM4A (Figure 15.8).

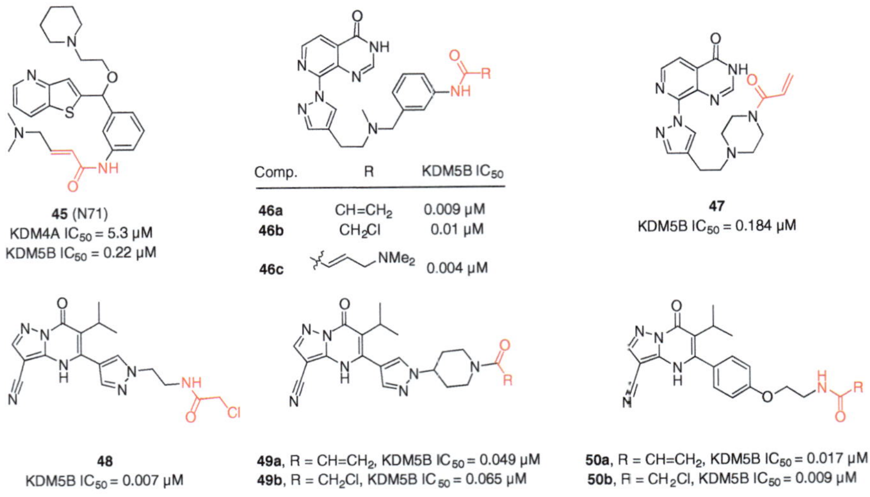

Figure 15.8 Covalent KDM5 inhibitors (**45–50b**).

Vazquez-Rodriguez et al. [135] reported **CPI-455**-derived pyridopyrimidinone (compound **21**) and compound **27**. JmjC-KDMs sequence alignments revealed C497 and C480 unique to the KDM5 subfamilies, suggesting their potential as nucleophiles for covalent modifications within the KDM5 family. To enhance this reactivity, compounds **45–50** were synthesized by introducing covalent electrophilic moieties like acrylamide and chloroacetyl into compounds **21** and **27**. These new compounds exhibited strong inhibition against KDM5B *in vitro*, with mass spectrometry (MS) confirming their covalent binding. For instance, compound **47** specifically targeted C480 in KDM5B, while also showing some interaction with C497. Notably, three key compounds – **46a**, **48**, and **49b** – displayed potent activity against KDM5B (IC_{50} = 0.009, 0.007, and 0.065 μM respectively). Cellular assays using NanoBRET revealed good activity levels for these same compounds, with IC_{50} values of approximately 10.6 μM for compound **46a**, 0.53 μM for compound **48**, and 0.30 μM for compound **49b**. Immunoprecipitation, along with sequencing assays, demonstrated that compounds **46a**, **48**, and **49b** induced an accumulation of H3K4me3 marks at transcriptional start sites.

15.5 KDM5B Degraders

KDM5B is important in tumor development through its demethylase and nonenzymatic functions [136–138]. However, its use of KDM5B inhibitors in clinic is limited as they only silence genes by removing methyl groups. Proteolysis-targeting chimeras (PROTAC) uses the cell's ubiquitin–proteosome system (UPS) machinery to break down the target protein [139, 140]. PROTAC molecules offer increased selectivity and efficacy in degrading proteins compared to traditional small molecule inhibitors [141].

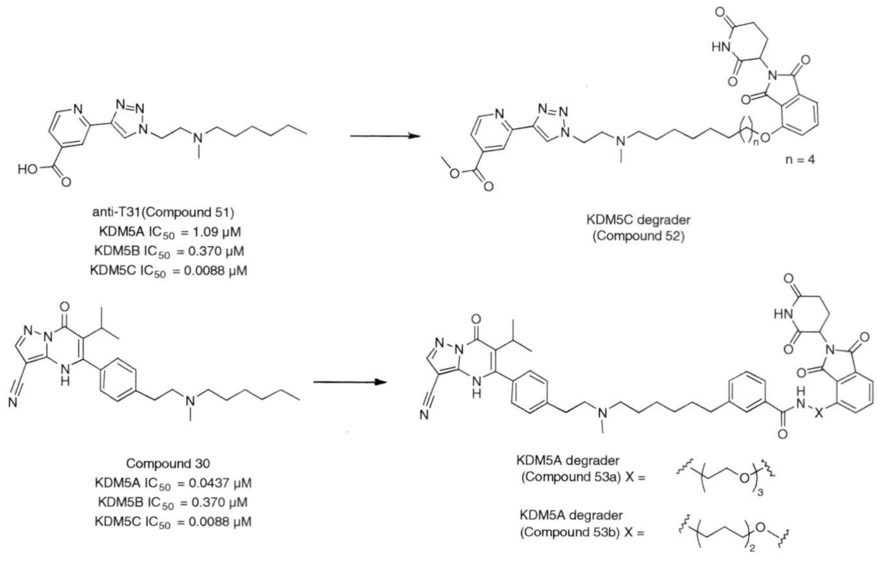

Figure 15.9 KDM5 degraders (**51–53b**).

Building on the **anti-T31** (compound **51**, Figure 15.9), a strong KDM5C inhibitor [142], Suzuki et al. [143] developed the first KDM5 degrader (**52**). This degrader can hinder the "scaffolding function," effectively restraining PC-3 cell growth with superior potency compared to the KDM5C inhibitor. They later utilized compound **30** to develop KDM5A degraders (compounds **53a** and **53b**) for treating neurodegenerative disorders [144]. These degraders were found to significantly enhance neurite outgrowth in N2a cells. However, while these PROTACs can degrade KDM5 protein, they require high concentrations to be effective, and their ability to degrade KDM5B was not assessed.

In 2024, the Chen group reported the first KDM5B degrader **GT-653** (compound **54**, Figure 15.10) based on CPI-455 [145]. The cereblon (CRBN) ligand was selected as the E3 ubiquitin ligase ligand. The linker was placed in benzene, which is identified as solvent-exposed by simulating its binding mode with KDM5B protein (PDB ID: 5A3N). Similar to compounds **53a** and **53e**, an excessively long or short linker can hinder the formation of the ternary complex of "KDM5B-PROTACs-CRBN." The linker length, as seen in compound **53b**, is appropriate. In comparison to compound **53d**, compound **53c** demonstrated enhanced KDM5B degradation by replacing an amine group with an ether bond in the CRBN-linker connection. Notably, relocating the amide bond caused a significant degradation rate to increase from 6.31% to 68.35%. This enhancement is due to how the repositioned amide bond impacted KDM5B binding to PROTACs. Furthermore, **GT-653** exclusively degraded KDM5B without affecting KDM5A and KDM5C, suggesting potential challenges in forming ternary complexes involving CRBN with KDM5A or KDM5C.

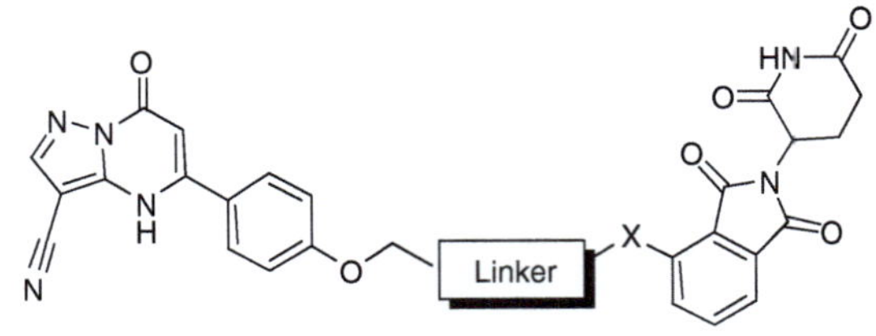

Comp. (10 μM)	Linker	X	Degradation (% Control)
53a	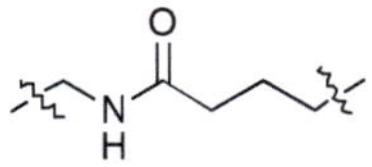	N	0
53b	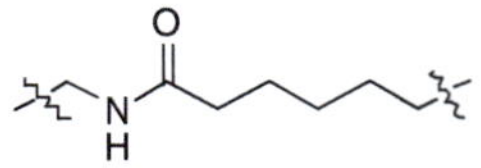	N	10.75
53c	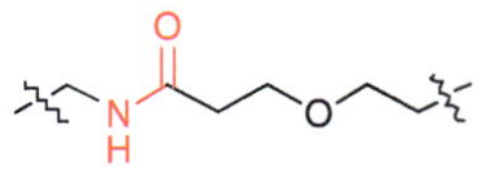	O	6.31
53d	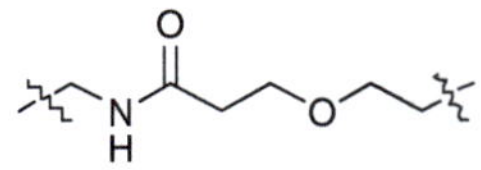	N	5.27
53e	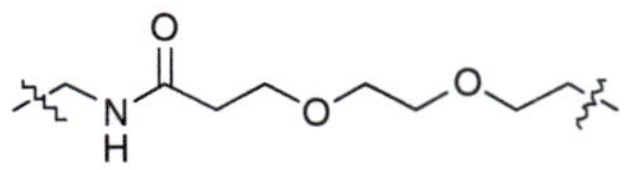	N	0
GT-653 (54)	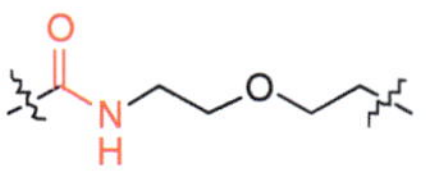	O	68.35

Figure 15.10 KDM5B degraders (**53a–53e, 54**).

15.6 Conclusion

Recent studies have revealed links between KDM5B, drug resistance, and cancer immunotherapy, highlighting promising avenues for exploration. This chapter summarized diverse biological functions of KDM5B and compounds that target it, including inhibitors and degraders. Current inhibitors of KDM5B, like 2-OG-competitive inhibitors and Fe^{2+} chelators, struggle with cell penetration and selectivity. Future KDM5B inhibitor development should prioritize enhancing selectivity and potency. Comprehensive studies on KDM5B structures and functions are essential for optimizing its effectiveness in cancer treatment. Therefore, there is value in developing new inhibitors along with associated screening methods and crystal structures to uncover additional binding modes like allosteric sites or noncatalytic domains of KDM5B. Despite identifying numerous inhibitor chemotypes, none have received Food and Drug Administration (FDA) approval yet. For example, Gilead Sciences discontinued **GS-5801** for treating chronic HBV. Reported KDM5A degraders exhibit good selectivity among different isoforms but require high concentrations to degrade specifically targeted proteins like KDM5B. Hence, identifying more E3 ubiquitin ligases and their corresponding ligands is essential for establishing SARs that could lead to potential clinical candidates.

Glossary

2 OG 2-oxoglutarate
FAD Flavin adenine dinucleotide
JARID Jumonji and ARID-domain-containing protein
JmjC Jumonji C domain
NSCLC Non-small cell lung cancer
AML Acute myelocytic leukemia
PROTAC Proteolysis-targeting chimera
UPS Ubiquitin–proteosome system
CRBN Cereblon

Acknowledgment

We acknowledge the financial support from the National Natural Science Foundation of China (Nos. 22277110 and 82473761), Natural Science Foundation of Henan Province (Nos. 242301420005 and 252300421243), and Key Research Project for Basic Research in Henan Province Universities (No. 25ZX001).

References

1 Martin, C. and Zhang, Y. (2005). The diverse functions of histone lysine methylation. *Nature Reviews Molecular Cell Biology* 6: 838–849.
2 Shi, Y., Lan, F., Matson, C. et al. (2004). Histone demethylation mediated by the nuclear amine oxidase homolog LSD1. *Cell* 119: 941–953.
3 Tsukada, Y.-i., Fang, J., Erdjument-Bromage, H. et al. (2006). Histone demethylation by a family of JmjC domain-containing proteins. *Nature* 439: 811–816.
4 Falkenberg, K.J. and Johnstone, R.W. (2014). Histone deacetylases and their inhibitors in cancer, neurological diseases and immune disorders. *Nature Reviews Drug Discovery* 13: 673–691.
5 Johansson, C., Velupillai, S., Tumber, A. et al. (2016). Structural analysis of human KDM5B guides histone demethylase inhibitor development. *Nature Chemical Biology* 12: 539–545.
6 McAllister, T.E., England, K.S., Hopkinson, R.J. et al. (2016). Recent progress in histone demethylase inhibitors. *Journal of Medicinal Chemistry* 59: 1308–1329.
7 Kooistra, S.M. and Helin, K. (2012). Molecular mechanisms and potential functions of histone demethylases. *Nature Reviews Molecular Cell Biology* 13: 297–311.
8 Schmitz, S.U., Albert, M., Malatesta, M. et al. (2011). Jarid1b targets genes regulating development and is involved in neural differentiation. *The EMBO Journal* 30: 4586–4600.
9 Barski, A., Cuddapah, S., Cui, K. et al. (2007). High-resolution profiling of histone methylations in the human genome. *Cell* 129: 823–837.

10 Bernstein, B.E., Mikkelsen, T.S., Xie, X. et al. (2006). A bivalent chromatin structure marks key developmental genes in embryonic stem cells. *Cell* 125: 315–326.

11 Mikkelsen, T.S., Ku, M., Jaffe, D.B. et al. (2007). Genome-wide maps of chromatin state in pluripotent and lineage-committed cells. *Nature* 448: 553–560.

12 Hendriks, I.A., Treffers, L.W., Verlaan-de, V.M. et al. (2015). SUMO-2 orchestrates chromatin modifiers in response to DNA damage. *Cell Reports* 10: 1778–1791.

13 Khoury-Haddad, H., Nadar-Ponniah, P.T., Awwad, S., and Ayoub, N. (2015). The emerging role of lysine demethylases in DNA damage response: dissecting the recruitment mode of KDM4D/JMJD2D to DNA damage sites. *Cell Cycle* 14: 950–958.

14 Mocavini, I., Pippa, S., Licursi, V. et al. (2019). JARID 1B expression and its function in DNA damage repair are tightly regulated by mi RNAs in breast cancer. *Cancer Science* 110: 1232–1243.

15 Hinohara, K., Wu, H.-J., Vigneau, S. et al. (2018). KDM5 histone demethylase activity links cellular transcriptomic heterogeneity to therapeutic resistance. *Cancer Cell* 34: 939–953.

16 Leadem, B.R., Kagiampakis, I., Wilson, C. et al. (2018). A KDM5 inhibitor increases global H3K4 trimethylation occupancy and enhances the biological efficacy of 5-Aza-2′-deoxycytidine. *Cancer Research* 78: 1127–1139.

17 Roesch, A., Vultur, A., Bogeski, I. et al. (2013). Overcoming intrinsic multidrug resistance in melanoma by blocking the mitochondrial respiratory chain of slow-cycling JARID1Bhigh cells. *Cancer Cell* 23: 811–825.

18 Vinogradova, M., Gehling, V.S., Gustafson, A. et al. (2016). An inhibitor of KDM5 demethylases reduces survival of drug-tolerant cancer cells. *Nature Chemical Biology* 12: 531–538.

19 Xu, W., Zhou, B., Zhao, X. et al. (2018). KDM5B demethylates H3K4 to recruit XRCC1 and promote chemoresistance. *International Journal of Biological Sciences* 14: 1122–1132.

20 Xie, L., Pelz, C., Wang, W. et al. (2011). KDM5B regulates embryonic stem cell self-renewal and represses cryptic intragenic transcription. *The EMBO Journal* 30: 1473–1484.

21 Rao, M., Chinnasamy, N., Hong, J.A. et al. (2011). Inhibition of histone lysine methylation enhances cancer–testis antigen expression in lung cancer cells: implications for adoptive immunotherapy of cancer. *Cancer Research* 71: 4192–4204.

22 Wu, L., Cao, J., Cai, W.L. et al. (2018). KDM5 histone demethylases repress immune response via suppression of STING. *PLoS Biology* 16: e2006134.

23 Lu, P.J., Sundquist, K., Baeckstrom, D. et al. (1999). A novel gene (PLU-1) containing highly conserved putative DNA/chromatin binding motifs is specifically up-regulated in breast cancer. *Journal of Biological Chemistry* 274: 15633–15645.

24 Roesch, A., Fukunaga-Kalabis, M., Schmidt, E.C. et al. (2010). A temporarily distinct subpopulation of slow-cycling melanoma cells is required for continuous tumor growth. *Cell* 141: 583–594.

25 Roesch, A., Mueller, A.M., Stempfl, T. et al. (2008). RBP2-H1/JARID1B is a transcriptional regulator with a tumor suppressive potential in melanoma cells. *International Journal of Cancer* 122: 1047–1057.

26 Tang, B., Qi, G.Y., Tang, F. et al. (2015). JARID1B promotes metastasis and epithelial-mesenchymal transition via PTEN/AKT signaling in hepatocellular carcinoma cells. *Oncotarget* 6: 12723–12739.

27 Wang, D., Han, S., Peng, R. et al. (2016). Depletion of histone demethylase KDM5B inhibits cell proliferation of hepatocellular carcinoma by regulation of cell cycle checkpoint proteins p15 and p27. *Journal of Experimental and Clinical Cancer Research* 35: 1–13.

28 Kano, Y., Konno, M., Ohta, K. et al. (2013). Jumonji/Arid1b (Jarid1b) protein modulates human esophageal cancer cell growth. *Molecular and Clinical Oncology* 1: 753–757.

29 Sun, L.L., Sun, X.X., Xu, X.E. et al. (2013). Overexpression of Jumonji AT-rich interactive domain 1B and PHD finger protein 2 is involved in the progression of esophageal squamous cell carcinoma. *Acta Histochemica* 115: 56–62.

30 Wang, Z.R., Tang, F., Qi, G.Y. et al. (2015). KDM5B is overexpressed in gastric cancer and is required for gastric cancer cell proliferation and metastasis. *American Journal of Cancer Research* 5: 87–100.

31 Han, L., Liang, X.H., Chen, L.X. et al. (2013). SIRT1 is highly expressed in brain metastasis tissues of non-small cell lung cancer (NSCLC) and in positive regulation of NSCLC cell migration. *International Journal of Clinical and Experimental Pathology* 6: 2357–2365.

32 Hayami, S., Yoshimatsu, M., Veerakumarasivam, A. et al. (2010). Overexpression of the JmjC histone demethylase KDM5B in human carcinogenesis: involvement in the proliferation of cancer cells through the E2F/RB pathway. *Molecular Cancer* 9: 1–14.

33 Shen, X.D., Zhuang, Z.X., Zhang, Y.S. et al. (2015). JARID1B modulates lung cancer cell proliferation and invasion by regulating p53 expression. *Tumor Biology* 36: 7133–7142.

34 Crea, F., Sun, L., Mai, A. et al. (2012). The emerging role of histone lysine demethylases in prostate cancer. *Molecular Cancer* 11: 1–10.

35 Ke, X.S., Qu, Y., Rostad, K. et al. (2009). Genome-wide profiling of histone H_3 lysine 4 and lysine 27 trimethylation reveals an epigenetic signature in prostate carcinogenesis. *Cancer Research* 69: e4687.

36 Li, J.L., Wan, X.C., Qiang, W. et al. (2015). MiR-29a suppresses prostate cell proliferation and induces apoptosis via protein regulation. *International Journal of Clinical and Experimental Medicine* 8: 5329–5339.

37 Xiang, Y., Zhu, Z., Han, G. et al. (2007). JARID1B is a histone H3 lysine 4 demethylase up-regulated in prostate cancer. *Proceedings of the National Academy of Sciences* 104: 19226–19231.

38 Gowda, C., Song, C., Kapadia, M. et al. (2017). Regulation of cellular proliferation in acute lymphoblastic leukemia by casein kinase II (CK2) and Ikaros. *Advances in Biological Regulation* 63: 71–80.

39 Huang, Y.Q., Zou, Y., Zheng, R.J., and Ma, X.D. (2018). Down-regulation of JARID1B expression inhibits cell proliferation, induces apoptosis and blocks cell cycle in human acute lymphoblastic leukemia cells. *European Review for Medical and Pharmacological Sciences* 22: 1366–1373.

40 Shokri, G., Doudi, S., Fathi-Roudsari, M. et al. (2018). Targeting histone demethylases KDM5A and KDM5B in AML cancer cells: a comparative view. *Leukemia Research* 68: 105–111.

41 Wang, H., Song, C., Ding, Y. et al. (2016). Transcriptional regulation of JARID1B/KDM5B histone demethylase by ikaros, histone deacetylase 1 (HDAC1), and casein kinase 2 (CK2) in B-cell acute lymphoblastic leukemia. *Journal of Biological Chemistry* 291: 4004–4018.

42 Wong, S.H.K., Goode, D.L., Iwasaki, M. et al. (2015). The H3K4-methyl epigenome regulates leukemia stem cell oncogenic potential. *Cancer Cell* 28: 198–209.

43 Gilmore, S., Tam, D., Dick, R. et al. (2017). Antiviral activity of GS-5801, a liver-targeted prodrug of a lysine demethylase 5 inhibitor, in a hepatitis B virus primary human hepatocyte infection model. *Journal of Hepatology* 66: S690–S691.

44 Kristensen, L.H., Nielsen, A.L., Helgstrand, C. et al. (2012). Studies of H3K4me3 demethylation by KDM5B/Jarid1B/PLU1 reveals strong substrate recognition in vitro and identifies 2,4-pyridine-dicarboxylic acid as an in vitro and in cell inhibitor. *The FEBS Journal* 279: 1905–1914.

45 Horton, J.R., Engstrom, A., Zoeller, E.L. et al. (2016). Characterization of a linked Jumonji domain of the KDM5/JARID1 family of histone H3 lysine 4 demethylases. *Journal of Biological Chemistry* 291: 2631–2646.

46 Longbotham, J.E., Chio, C.M., Dharmarajan, V. et al. (2019). Histone H3 binding to the PHD1 domain of histone demethylase KDM5A enables active site remodeling. *Nature Communications* 10: 94.

47 Walport, L.J., Hopkinson, R.J., and Schofield, C.J. (2012). Mechanisms of human histone and nucleic acid demethylases. *Current Opinion in Chemical Biology* 16: 525–534.

48 Madsen, B., Tarsounas, M., Burchell, J.M. et al. (2003). PLU-1, a transcriptional repressor and putative testis-cancer antigen, has a specific expression and localisation pattern during meiosis. *Chromosoma* 112: 124–132.

49 Christensen, J., Agger, K., Cloos, P.A.C. et al. (2007). RBP2 belongs to a family of demethylases, specific for tri- and dimethylated lysine 4 on histone 3. *Cell* 128: 1063–1076.

50 Iwase, S., Lan, F., Bayliss, P. et al. (2007). The X-linked mental retardation gene SMCX/JARID1C defines a family of histone H3 lysine 4 demethylases. *Cell* 128: 1077–1088.

51 Yamane, K., Tateishi, K., Klose, R.J. et al. (2007). PLU-1 is an H3K4 demethylase involved in transcriptional repression and breast cancer cell proliferation. *Molecular Cell* 25: 801–812.

52 Anand, R. and Marmorstein, R. (2007). Structure and mechanism of lysine-specific demethylase enzymes. *Journal of Biological Chemistry* 282: 35425–35429.

53 Nottke, A., Colaiácovo, M.P., and Shi, Y. (2009). Developmental roles of the histone lysine demethylases. *Development* 136: 879–889.

54 Tan, K., Shaw, A.L., Madsen, B. et al. (2003). Human PLU-1 has transcriptional repression properties and interacts with the developmental transcription factors BF-1 and PAX9. *Journal of Biological Chemistry* 278: 20507–20513.

55 Scibetta, A.G., Santangelo, S., Coleman, J. et al. (2007). Functional analysis of the transcription repressor PLU-1/JARID1B. *Molecular and Cellular Biology* 27: 7220–7235.

56 Kidder, B.L., Hu, G.Q., and Zhao, K. (2014). KDM5B focuses H3K4 methylation near promoters and enhancers during embryonic stem cell self-renewal and differentiation. *Genome Biology* 15: 1–19.

57 Albert, M., Schmitz, S.U., Kooistra, S.M. et al. (2013). The histone demethylase Jarid1b ensures faithful mouse development by protecting developmental genes from aberrant H3K4me3. *PLoS Genetics* 9: e1003461.

58 Cellot, S., Hope, K.J., Chagraoui, J. et al. (2013). RNAi screen identifies Jarid1b as a major regulator of mouse HSC activity. *Blood* 122: 1545–1555.

59 Huang, J.J., Zhang, H.Y., Wang, X.L. et al. (2015). Impairment of preimplantation porcine embryo development by histone demethylase knockdown through disturbance of bivalent H3K4me3-H3K27me3 modifications. *Biology of Reproduction* 92: 72–72.

60 Barrett, A., Santangelo, S., Tan, K. et al. (2007). Breast cancer associated transcriptional repressor PLU-1/JARID1B interacts directly with histone deacetylases. *International Journal of Cancer* 121: 265–275.

61 Klein, B.J., Piao, L.H., Xi, Y.X. et al. (2014). The histone-H3K4-specific demethylase KDM5B binds to its substrate and product through distinct PHD fingers. *Cell Reports* 6: 325–335.

62 Catchpole, S., Spencer-Dene, B., Hall, D. et al. (2011). PLU-1/JARID1B/KDM5B is required for embryonic survival and contributes to cell proliferation in the mammary gland and in ER breast cancer cells. *International Journal of Oncology* 38: 1267–1277.

63 Yamamoto, S., Wu, Z., Russnes, H.G. et al. (2014). JARID1B is a luminal lineage-driving oncogene in breast cancer. *Cancer Cell* 25: 762–777.

64 Bamodu, O.A., Huang, W.C., Lee, W.H. et al. (2016). Aberrant KDM5B expression promotes aggressive breast cancer through MALAT1 overexpression and downregulation of Hsa-miR-448. *BMC Cancer* 16: 1–18.

65 Li, Q., Shi, L., Gui, B. et al. (2011). Binding of the JmjC demethylase JARID1B to LSD1/NuRD suppresses angiogenesis and metastasis in breast cancer cells by repressing chemokine CCL14. *Cancer Research* 71: 6899–6908.

66 Rasmussen, P.B. and Staller, P. (2014). The KDM5 family of histone demethylases as targets in oncology drug discovery. *Epigenomics* 6: 277–286.

67 Roesch, A., Becker, B., Meyer, S. et al. (2005). Retinoblastoma-binding protein 2-homolog 1: a retinoblastoma-binding protein downregulated in malignant melanomas. *Modern Pathology* 18: 1249–1257.

68 Roesch, A., Becker, B., Schneider-Brachert, W. et al. (2006). Re-expression of the retinoblastoma-binding protein 2-homolog 1 reveals tumor-suppressive functions in highly metastatic melanoma cells. *Journal of Investigative Dermatology* 126: 1850–1859.

69 Radberger, P., Radberger, A., Bykov, V.J.N. et al. (2012). JARID1B protein expression and prognostic implications in uveal melanoma. *Investigative Ophthalmology and Visual Science* 53: 4442–4449.

70 Kuzbicki, L., Lange, D., Straczynska-Niemiec, A., and Chwirot, B.W. (2013). JARID1B expression in human melanoma and benign melanocytic skin lesions. *Melanoma Research* 23: 8–12.

71 Vogel, F.C.E., Bordag, N., Zügner, E. et al. (2019). Targeting the H3K4 demethylase KDM5B reprograms the metabolome and phenotype of melanoma cells. *Journal of Investigative Dermatology* 139: 2506–2516.

72 Wang, X.Y., Oishi, N., Shimakami, T. et al. (2017). Hepatitis B virus X protein induces hepatic stem cell-like features in hepatocellular carcinoma by activating KDM5B. *World Journal of Gastroenterology* 23: 3252–3261.

73 Bayo, J., Fiore, E.J., Dominguez, L.M. et al. (2019). A comprehensive study of epigenetic alterations in hepatocellular carcinoma identifies potential therapeutic targets. *Journal of Hepatology* 71: 78–90.

74 Yang, P., Du, C.W., Kwan, M. et al. (2013). The impact of p53 in predicting clinical outcome of breast cancer patients with visceral metastasis. *Scientific Reports* 3: 2246.

75 Zhou, C., Chen, H., and Wang, A. (2013). P53 codon 72 polymorphism and lung cancer risk: evidence from 27,958 subjects. *Tumor Biology* 34: 2961–2969.

76 Kuo, K.T., Huang, W.C., Bamodu, O.A. et al. (2018). Histone demethylase JARID1B/KDM5B promotes aggressiveness of non-small cell lung cancer and serves as a good prognostic predictor. *Clinical Epigenetics* 10: 1–12.

77 Nilsson, E.M., Laursen, K.B., Whitchurch, J. et al. (2015). MiR137 is an androgen regulated repressor of an extended network of transcriptional coregulators. *Oncotarget* 6: 35710–35725.

78 Lu, W.F., Liu, S.J., Li, B. et al. (2015). SKP2 inactivation suppresses prostate tumorigenesis by mediating JARID1B ubiquitination. *Oncotarget* 6: 771–788.

79 Su, H.Y., Ma, X.D., Huang, Y.Q. et al. (2015). JARID1B deletion induced apoptosis in Jeko-1 and HL-60 cell lines. *International Journal of Clinical and Experimental Pathology* 8: 171–183.

80 Li, X., Su, Y.P., Pan, J.H. et al. (2013). Connexin 26 is down-regulated by KDM5B in the progression of bladder cancer. *International Journal of Molecular Sciences* 14: 7866–7879.

81 Lin, C.-S., Lin, Y.-C., Adebayo, B.O. et al. (2015). Silencing JARID1B suppresses oncogenicity, stemness and increases radiation sensitivity in human oral carcinoma. *Cancer Letters* 368: 36–45.

82 Tarnowski, M., Czerewaty, M., Deskur, A. et al. (2016). Expression of cancer testis antigens in colorectal cancer: new prognostic and therapeutic implications. *Disease Markers* 2016: 1987505.

83 Wang, L.S., Mao, Y.F., Du, G.Q. et al. (2015). Overexpression of JARID1B is associated with poor prognosis and chemotherapy resistance in epithelial ovarian cancer. *Tumor Biology* 36: 2465–2472.

84 Dai, B., Hu, Z.Q., Huang, H. et al. (2014). Overexpressed KDM5B is associated with the progression of glioma and promotes glioma cell growth via downregulating p21. *Biochemical and Biophysical Research Communications* 454: 221–227.

85 Cui, Z.B., Song, L.W., Hou, Z.Y. et al. (2015). PLU-1/JARID1B overexpression predicts proliferation properties in head and neck squamous cell carcinoma. *Oncology Reports* 33: 2454–2460.

86 Hong, J.A., Kang, Y., Abdullaev, Z. et al. (2005). Reciprocal binding of CTCF and BORIS to the NY-ESO-1 promoter coincides with derepression of this cancer-testis gene in lung cancer cells. *Cancer Research* 65: 7763–7774.

87 Flood, B.A., Higgs, E.F., Li, S.Y. et al. (2019). STING pathway agonism as a cancer therapeutic. *Immunological Reviews* 290: 24–38.

88 Roesch, A., Vultur, A., Bogeski, I. et al. (2013). Overcoming intrinsic multidrug resistance in melanoma by blocking the mitochondrial respiratory chain of slow-cycling JARID1B cells. *Cancer Cell* 23: 811–825.

89 Ahn, A., Chatterjee, A., and Eccles, M.R. (2017). The slow cycling phenotype: a growing problem for treatment resistance in melanoma. *Molecular Cancer Therapeutics* 16: 1002–1009.

90 Liu, X.N., Zhang, S.M., McGeary, M.K. et al. (2019). KDM5B promotes drug resistance by regulating melanoma-propagating cell subpopulations. *Molecular Cancer Therapeutics* 18: 706–717.

91 Kuo, Y.T., Liu, Y.L., Adebayo, B.O. et al. (2015). JARID1B expression plays a critical role in chemoresistance and stem cell-like phenotype of neuroblastoma cells. *Plos One* 10: 1–14.

92 Xu, W., Wang, S., Chen, Q. et al. (2014). TXNL1-XRCC1 pathway regulates cisplatin-induced cell death and contributes to resistance in human gastric cancer. *Cell Death and Disease* 5: 1055.

93 Li, L.J., Shou, H.F., Wang, Q.Q., and Liu, S.X. (2019). Investigation of the potential theranostic role of KDM5B/miR-29c signaling axis in paclitaxel resistant endometrial carcinoma. *Gene* 694: 76–82.

94 Rose, N.R., McDonough, M.A., King, O.N.F. et al. (2011). Inhibition of 2-oxoglutarate dependent oxygenases. *Chemical Society Reviews* 40: 4364–4397.

95 Clifton, I.J., McDonough, M.A., Ehrismann, D. et al. (2006). Structural studies on 2-oxoglutarate oxygenases and related double-stranded β-helix fold proteins. *Journal of Inorganic Biochemistry* 100: 644–669.

96 McDonough, M.A., Loenarz, C., Chowdhury, R. et al. (2010). Structural studies on human 2-oxoglutarate dependent oxygenases. *Current Opinion in Structural Biology* 20: 659–672.
97 Aik, W., McDonough, M.A., Thalhammer, A. et al. (2012). Role of the jelly-roll fold in substrate binding by 2-oxoglutarate oxygenases. *Current Opinion in Structural Biology* 22: 691–700.
98 Bavetsias, V., Lanigan, R.M., Ruda, G.F. et al. (2016). 8-Substituted pyrido [3, 4-d] pyrimidin-4 (3 H)-one derivatives as potent, cell permeable, KDM4 (JMJD2) and KDM5 (JARID1) histone lysine demethylase inhibitors. *Journal of Medicinal Chemistry* 59: 1388–1409.
99 Gehling, V.S., Bellon, S.F., Harmange, J.C. et al. (2016). Identification of potent, selective KDM5 inhibitors. *Bioorganic and Medicinal Chemistry Letters* 26: 4350–4354.
100 Itoh, Y., Sawada, H., Suzuki, M. et al. (2015). Identification of Jumonji AT-rich interactive domain 1A inhibitors and their effect on cancer cells. *Acs Medicinal Chemistry Letters* 6: 665–670.
101 Tumber, A., Nuzzi, A., Hookway, E.S. et al. (2017). Potent and selective KDM5 inhibitor stops cellular demethylation of H3K4me3 at transcription start sites and proliferation of MM1S myeloma cells. *Cell Chemical Biology* 24: 371–380.
102 Westaway, S.M., Preston, A.G.S., Barker, M.D. et al. (2016). Cell penetrant inhibitors of the KDM4 and KDM5 families of histone lysine demethylases. 2. Pyrido[3,4-d]pyrimidin-4(3)-one derivatives. *Journal of Medicinal Chemistry* 59: 1370–1387.
103 Elvidge, G.P., Glenny, L., Appelhoff, R.J. et al. (2006). Concordant regulation of gene expression by hypoxia and 2-oxoglutarate-dependent dioxygenase inhibition : the role of HIF-1α, HIF-2α, and other pathways. *Journal of Biological Chemistry* 281: 15215–15226.
104 Mole, D.R., Schlemminger, I., McNeill, L.A. et al. (2003). 2-Ooxoglutarate analogue inhibitors of HIF prolyl hydroxylase. *Bioorganic and Medicinal Chemistry Letters* 13: 2677–2680.
105 Schofield, C.J. and Ratcliffe, P.J. (2004). Oxygen sensing by HIF hydroxylases. *Nature Reviews Molecular Cell Biology* 5: 343–354.
106 Hopkinson, R.J., Tumber, A., Yapp, C. et al. (2013). 5-Carboxy-8-hydroxyquinoline is a broad spectrum 2-oxoglutarate oxygenase inhibitor which causes iron translocation. *Chemical Science* 4: 3110–3117.
107 Xu, W., Yang, H., Liu, Y. et al. (2011). Oncometabolite 2-hydroxyglutarate is a competitive inhibitor of α-ketoglutarate-dependent dioxygenases. *Cancer Cell* 19: 17–30.
108 Laukka, T., Myllykoski, M., Looper, R.E., and Koivunen, P. (2018). Cancer-associated 2-oxoglutarate analogues modify histone methylation by inhibiting histone lysine demethylases. *Journal of Molecular Biology* 430: 3081–3092.
109 Hamada, S., Kim, T.-D., Suzuki, T. et al. (2009). Synthesis and activity of N-oxalylglycine and its derivatives as Jumonji C-domain-containing histone

lysine demethylase inhibitors. *Bioorganic and Medicinal Chemistry Letters* 19: 2852–2855.

110 Rose, N.R., Ng, S.S., Mecinovic, J. et al. (2008). Inhibitor scaffolds for 2-oxoglutarate-dependent histone lysine demethylases. *Journal of Medicinal Chemistry* 51: 7053–7056.

111 Klose, R.J., Kallin, E.M., and Zhang, Y. (2006). JmjC-domain-containing proteins and histone demethylation. *Nature Reviews Genetics* 7: 715–727.

112 Mackeen, M.M., Kramer, H.B., Chang, K.H. et al. (2010). Small-molecule-based inhibition of histone demethylation in cells assessed by quantitative mass spectrometry. *Journal of Proteome Research* 9: 4082–4092.

113 Terao, M., Yamashita, Y., Takada, Y. et al. (2024). Structural optimization of a lysine demethylase 5 inhibitor for improvement of its cellular activity. *Bioorganic and Medicinal Chemistry* 98: 117579.

114 Chang, K.H., King, O.N.F., Tumber, A. et al. (2011). Inhibition of histone demethylases by 4-carboxy-2,2′-bipyridyl compounds. *ChemMedChem* 6: 759–764.

115 Nie, Z., Shi, L.H., Lai, C. et al. (2018). Structure-based design and discovery of potent and selective KDM5 inhibitors. *Bioorganic and Medicinal Chemistry Letters* 28: 1490–1494.

116 Le Bihan, Y.-V., Lanigan, R.M., Atrash, B. et al. (2019). C8-substituted pyrido [3, 4-d] pyrimidin-4 (3H)-ones: studies towards the identification of potent, cell penetrant Jumonji C domain containing histone lysine demethylase 4 subfamily (KDM4) inhibitors, compound profiling in cell-based target engagement assays. *European Journal of Medicinal Chemistry* 177: 316–337.

117 Liang, J., Zhang, B., Labadie, S. et al. (2016). Lead optimization of a pyrazolo [1, 5-a] pyrimidin-7 (4H)-one scaffold to identify potent, selective and orally bioavailable KDM5 inhibitors suitable for in vivo biological studies. *Bioorganic and Medicinal Chemistry Letters* 26: 4036–4041.

118 Miyake, Y., Itoh, Y., Hatanaka, A. et al. (2019). Identification of novel lysine demethylase 5-selective inhibitors by inhibitor-based fragment merging strategy. *Bioorganic and Medicinal Chemistry* 27: 1119–1129.

119 Zhao, B., Liang, Q.Q., Ren, H.M. et al. (2020). Discovery of pyrazole derivatives as cellular active inhibitors of histone lysine specific demethylase 5B (KDM5B/JARID1B). *European Journal of Medicinal Chemistry* 192: 112161.

120 Liang, J., Labadie, S., Zhang, B.R. et al. (2017). From a novel HTS hit to potent, selective, and orally bioavailable KDM5 inhibitors. *Bioorganic and Medicinal Chemistry Letters* 27: 2974–2981.

121 Tang, K., Qi, Y.R., Li, Y.L. et al. (2022). Discovery of novel pyrazole-based KDM5B inhibitor TK-129 and its protective effects on myocardial remodeling and fibrosis. *Journal of Medicinal Chemistry* 65: 12979–13000.

122 Sekirnik, R., Rose, N.R., Thalhammer, A. et al. (2009). Inhibition of the histone lysine demethylase JMJD2A by ejection of structural Zn(II). *Chemical Communications* 6376–6378.

123 Thinnes, C.C., England, K.S., Kawamura, A. et al. (2014). Targeting histone lysine demethylases - progress, challenges, and the future. *Biochimica Et Biophysica Acta-Gene Regulatory Mechanisms* 1839: 1416–1432.

124 Sakurai, M., Rose, N.R., Schultz, L. et al. (2010). A miniaturized screen for inhibitors of Jumonji histone demethylases. *Molecular Biosystems* 6: 357–364.

125 Sayegh, J., Cao, J., Zou, M.R. et al. (2013). Identification of small molecule inhibitors of Jumonji AT-rich interactive domain 1B (JARID1B) histone demethylase by a sensitive high throughput screen. *Journal of Biological Chemistry* 288: 9408–9417.

126 Cao, Y.Q., Yang, P., Yang, Y.X. et al. (2023). Discovery of a novel 1H-pyrazole-[3,4-b] pyridine-based lysine demethylase 5B inhibitor with potential anti-prostate cancer activity that perturbs the phosphoinositide 3-kinase/AKT pathway. *European Journal of Medicinal Chemistry* 251: 115250.

127 Kruidenier, L., Chung, C.W., Cheng, Z.J. et al. (2012). A selective jumonji H3K27 demethylase inhibitor modulates the proinflammatory macrophage response. *Nature* 488: 404–408.

128 Heinemann, B., Nielsen, J.M., Hudlebusch, H.R. et al. (2014). Inhibition of demethylases by GSK-J1/J4. *Nature* 514: E1–E2.

129 Wang, L., Chang, J.J., Varghese, D. et al. (2013). A small molecule modulates Jumonji histone demethylase activity and selectively inhibits cancer growth. *Nature Communications* 4: 2035.

130 Labadie, S.S., Dragovich, P.S., Cummings, R.T. et al. (2016). Design and evaluation of 1,7-naphthyridones as novel KDM5 inhibitors. *Bioorganic and Medicinal Chemistry Letters* 26: 4492–4496.

131 Liu, H.-M., Yu, B., Wang, S. (2019). KDM5B inhibitor for treating pulmonary carcinoma and its preparation method. CN109293663A.

132 Potashman, M.H. and Duggan, M.E. (2009). Covalent modifiers: an orthogonal approach to drug design. *Journal of Medicinal Chemistry* 52: 1231–1246.

133 Watanuki, Z., Kosai, H., Osanai, N. et al. (2014). Synergistic cytotoxicity of afatinib and cetuximab against EGFR T790M involves Rab11-dependent EGFR recycling. *Biochemical and Biophysical Research Communications* 455: 269–276.

134 Horton, J.R., Woodcock, C.B., Chen, Q. et al. (2018). Structure-based engineering of irreversible inhibitors against histone lysine demethylase KDM5A. *Journal of Medicinal Chemistry* 61: 10588–10601.

135 Vazquez-Rodriguez, S., Wright, M., Rogers, C.M. et al. (2019). Design, synthesis and characterization of covalent KDM5 inhibitors. *Angewandte Chemie-International Edition* 58: 515–519.

136 Liu, X. and Secombe, J. (2015). The histone demethylase KDM5 activates gene expression by recognizing chromatin context through its PHD reader motif. *Cell Reports* 13: 2219–2231.

137 Ohguchi, Y. and Ohguchi, H. (2022). Diverse functions of KDM5 in cancer: transcriptional repressor or activator? *Cancers* 14: 3270.

138 Zhang, S.M., Cai, W.L., Liu, X.N. et al. (2021). KDM5B promotes immune evasion by recruiting SETDB1 to silence retroelements. *Nature* 598: 682–687.

139 Sakamoto, K.M. (2005). Chimeric molecules to target proteins for ubiquitination and degradation. *Methods in Enzymology* 399: 833–847.

140 Schneekloth, J.S., Fonseca, F.N., Koldobskiy, M. et al. (2004). Chemical genetic control of protein levels: selective in vivo targeted degradation. *Journal of the American Chemical Society* 126: 3748–3754.

141 Li, K. and Crews, C.M. (2022). PROTACs: past, present and future. *Chemical Society Reviews* 51: 5214–5236.

142 Miyake, Y., Itoh, Y., Suzuma, Y. et al. (2020). Metalloprotein-catalyzed click reaction for in situ generation of a potent inhibitor. *Acs Catalysis* 10: 5383–5392.

143 Iida, T., Itoh, Y., Takahashi, Y. et al. (2021). Design, synthesis, and biological evaluation of lysine demethylase 5 C degraders. *ChemMedChem* 16: 1609–1618.

144 Iida, T., Itoh, Y., Takahashi, Y. et al. (2024). Identification of proteolysis targeting chimeras (PROTACs) for lysine demethylase 5 and their neurite outgrowth-promoting activity. *Chemical and Pharmaceutical Bulletin* 72: 638–647.

145 Guan, T., Zhang, Y.S., Li, S. et al. (2024). Discovery of an efficacious KDM5B PROTAC degrader GT-653 up-regulating IFN response genes in prostate cancer. *European Journal of Medicinal Chemistry* 272: 116494.

16

Advances and Future Directions in Small-Molecule LpxC Inhibitors Targeting Gram-Negative Bacteria

Yue Liu and You-Cai Xiao

Sichuan University, Key Laboratory of Drug-Targeting and Drug Delivery System of the Ministry of Education and Sichuan Research Center for Drug Precision Industrial Technology, West China School of Pharmacy, No. 17, Section 3, Southern Renmin Rd. Chengdu 610041, P.R. China

16.1 Introduction

Due to the misuse of antibiotics, the issue of bacterial resistance is becoming increasingly serious. Multidrug-resistant Gram-negative bacteria (MDRGN) pose a significant threat to public health [1]. However, the variety of available antimicrobial agents is limited, hence, there is an urgent need in the clinic for antimicrobial drugs with entirely new targets or mechanisms to combat the growing bacterial resistance.

Gram-negative bacteria have an outer membrane that serves as a natural barrier, preventing cationic and hydrophobic molecules from entering the cell. The outer membrane is composed of proteins, phospholipids, and lipopolysaccharides (LPS), with the lipopolysaccharides forming the outer monolayer of the outer membrane in most Gram-negative bacteria. Lipid A is the hydrophobic part of the lipopolysaccharide, anchoring the LPS in the outer monolayer. Bacteria lacking lipid A are mostly nonviable, and mutants with reduced lipid A biosynthesis grow slowly and are sensitive to a variety of antibiotics [2, 3]. Additionally, lipid A is also the primary source of toxicity of LPS and can cause life-threatening septic shock [4, 5]. Therefore, inhibiting the biosynthesis of lipid A is expected to be used in the treatment of bacterial infections caused by Gram-negative bacteria.

In the biosynthesis of lipid A, nine enzymes are involved in catalysis, among which the deacetylation reaction catalyzed by LpxC is the first key step in the synthesis (Figure 16.1) [2]. Moreover, LpxC is highly conserved in Gram-negative bacteria and has no homology with mammalian proteins [6, 7]. Therefore, LpxC can serve as an ideal antibacterial drug target enzyme. Inhibiting LpxC indirectly disrupts the synthesis of LPS, ultimately leading to bacterial cell death.

In 1996, Merck & Co. first described LpxC inhibitors [8]. To date, only two inhibitors (ACHN-975 and RC-01) have progressed to clinical trials, but both were terminated during Phase I, and no drugs have been marketed yet [9]. In 2023, LPC-233 has shown good safety and antibacterial properties and is actively

Drug Discovery Targeting Metalloenzymes: Strategies and Applications, First Edition. Edited by Guo-Bo Li.

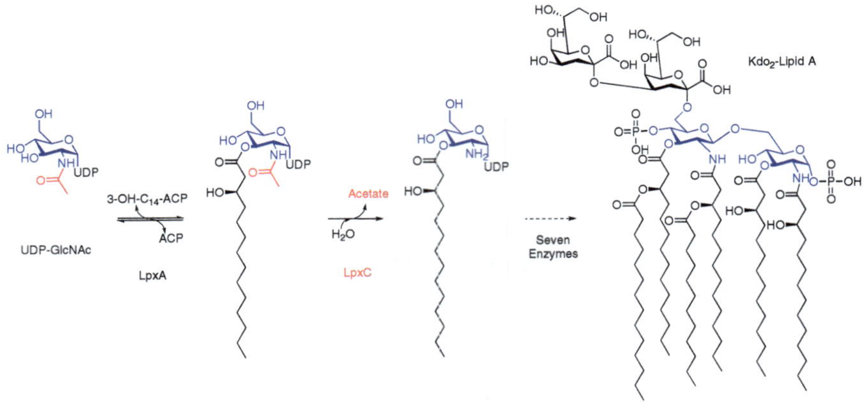

Figure 16.1 Reaction catalyzed by LpxC and structure of *E. coli* Lipid A.

advancing to Phase I clinical trials [10]. This article will mainly summarize the various LpxC inhibitors that have been reported to date.

16.2 LpxC Structure and Function

16.2.1 LpxC Structure

LpxC is a metalloenzyme that chelates with zinc ions and is highly conserved in Gram-negative bacteria [7]. X-ray crystal structures reveal that LpxC contains two structural domains, Domain I and Domain II, which are classic $\alpha + \beta$ protein folds. Each domain is composed of five β-sheet structures and two main α-helix structures, with the β-sheets sandwiching the α-helices to form a typical "β-α-α-β" sandwich structure. The amino acid sequences of the two domains are slightly different, but their two-dimensional topological structures remain the same. The connection between the two domains is the active site of the entire enzyme.

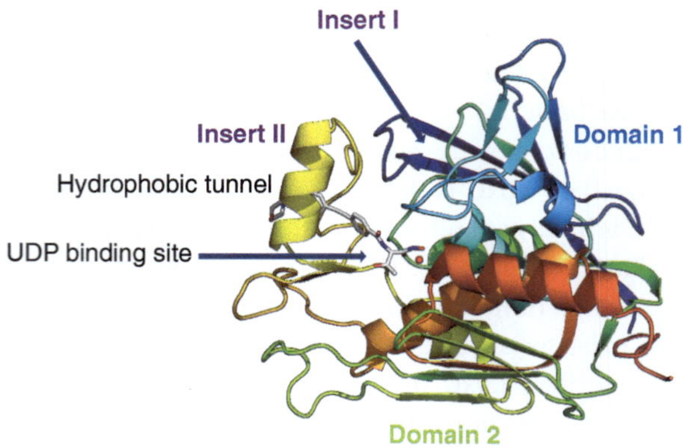

Figure 16.2 LpxC structure (*P. aeruginosa*, PDB: 5U39).

In addition, each domain contains an insertion region (Insert I and Insert II) with different β-sheets. Insert I, composed of three β-sheets, defines the active site of LpxC; Insert II is a narrow, closed hydrophobic channel (β-α-β structure) linked to zinc ions through some conserved hydrophobic amino acid residues. The zinc ions can form metal ion bonds with certain chelating groups to exert their function. The hydrophobic channel can be occupied by hydrophobic long chains, such as myristic acid or the hydrophobic long-chain groups of inhibitors, which can enhance the recognition ability of the inhibitor with the LpxC enzyme, allowing the zinc ions at the active center of LpxC to effectively coordinate with the chelating groups of the inhibitor (such as hydroxamates). The binding of LpxC to the uridine diphosphate (UDP)-glucose part of the substrate reveals another nucleotide binding site within the active region, which is also important for promoting the recognition and binding of the substrate and enzyme. The inhibition of LpxC activity mainly occurs in the hydrophobic channel and the Zn^{2+} active site, and inhibitors can suppress the activity of LpxC by binding to these two sites (Figure 16.2).

16.2.2 LpxC Catalytic Mechanism

The McClerren and Hernick research groups have proposed two similar mechanisms for LpxC catalysis, suggesting that the catalytic function of LpxC is achieved through an acid–base pair, but they have different views on the roles of histidine and asparagine in the active site. McClerren and colleagues [11] believe that in the deacetylation reaction, E78 acts as a catalytic base, abstracting a proton from a water molecule bound to the zinc ion, thereby activating the oxygen atom of the water molecule to undergo a nucleophilic attack on the carbonyl carbon of the acetyl group in the substrate, forming a tetrahedral intermediate anion, and finally the terminal amine of glucosamine abstracts a proton from E78 to release acetic acid and form glucosamine. In this process, H265 (253 of AaLpxC) neither donates nor abstracts a proton, but merely serves to stabilize the tetrahedral intermediate (Figure 16.3a). However, Hernick and others [12] argue that the terminal amine of glucosamine receives a proton from H265, not E78, and that it is not H265 but T191 that stabilizes the tetrahedral intermediate (Figure 16.3b). In addition, some studies [13] have reported that the phosphate group is involved in the catalytic action of the zinc ion, and there are also quantum mechanical model studies showing that hydroxamates form a pentacoordinate intermediate with the zinc ion, which has a strong binding force.

16.3 Hydroxamate LpxC Inhibitors

16.3.1 *N*-Arylacyl-L-Amino Acids

In 2007, Zhou et al. [14–16] reported a new class of LpxC inhibitors bearing the *N*-arylacyl-L-amino acids scaffold. The representative compound **1** (CHIR-090) shares a similar, although previously unrecognized, chemical scaffold with

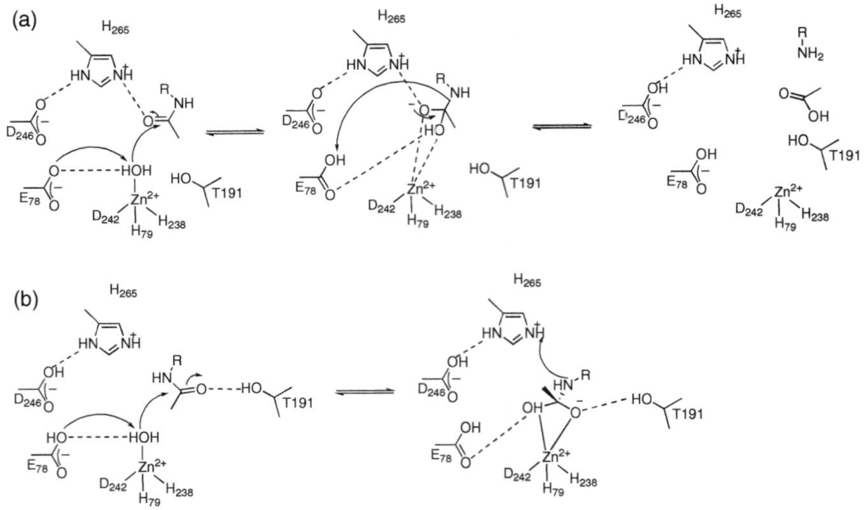

Figure 16.3 LpxC catalytic mechanism. (a) Catalytic mechanism proposed by McClerren; (b) Catalytic mechanism proposed by Hernick.

other small-molecule LpxC inhibitors. Its antimicrobial activity is comparable to that of tobramycin and ciprofloxacin, and it exhibits significant antibiotic activity against both *Escherichia coli* and *Pseudomonas aeruginosa*. The structure of these compounds can be divided into five parts (Figure 16.4a): P1 is the zinc ion chelating group; the different substituents in region P2 have varying impacts on antimicrobial activity; P3 is the linker connecting the hydrophobic group and the chelating group; P4 is the hydrophobic segment that occupies the hydrophobic VI pocket of the LpxC enzyme; P5 is the terminal group (solvent-exposed region), which generally has little effect on antimicrobial activity but mainly improves the physicochemical or metabolic properties of the molecule. In 2007, Zhou's group reported the binding mode of the *A. aeolicus* LpxC-CHIR-090 complex (Figure 16.4b). CHIR-090 exploited several conserved and essential features of LpxC to form a tight-binding complex. First, the hydroxamate moiety could coordinate the catalytic zinc ion, which is further strengthened by the coordination with H74, H226, and D230. Second, several hydrogen bonds are formed between the ligand (P2 and P3) and E73, T179, and K227. Third, the threonyl methyl group of CHIR-090 forms vdW contacts with the aromatic ring of F180. In addition, the biphenyl acetylene (P4) inserts into the LpxC hydrophobic passage near the active site, including I18, I186, I189, G198, L200, T203, and V205 (Figure 16.4c).

In 2011, Zhou et al. [17] reported a series of compounds, such as compound **2** (LPC-009), which use linear diacetylene group as a hydrophobic scaffold (Figure 16.5a). Some LpxC enzymes develop resistance due to the narrow exit of the hydrophobic channel by a single Ser-to-Gly mutation. The diacetylene group has a narrower skeleton and can pivot, adapting to different LpxCs and overcoming resistance. This compound shows a general enhancement of potency (2–64 fold) over CHIR-090 against a variety of clinically important Gram-negative pathogens, including *E. coli, P. aeruginosa, K. pneumoniae,* and others. Compound binding

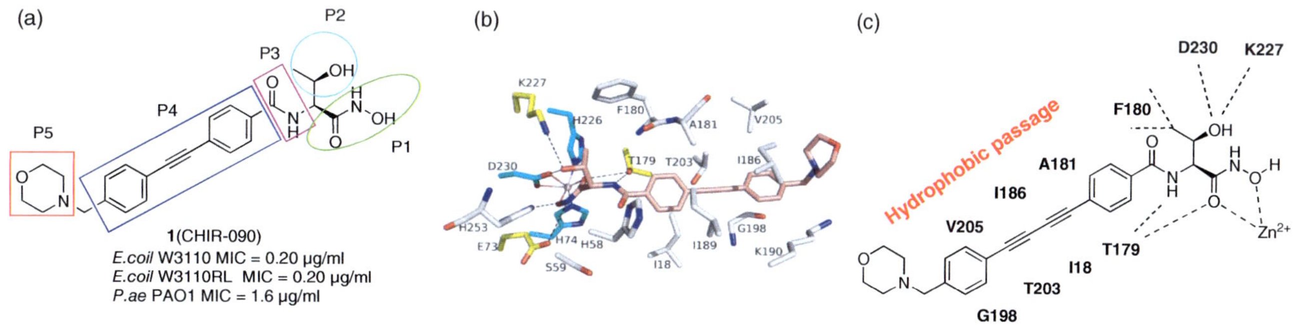

Figure 16.4 (a): Chemical structure of **1** (CHIR-090); (b): The binding mode of **1** with *A. aeolicus* LpxC (PDB: 2JT2); (c) Molecular interaction map between **1** and *A. aeolicus* LpxC.

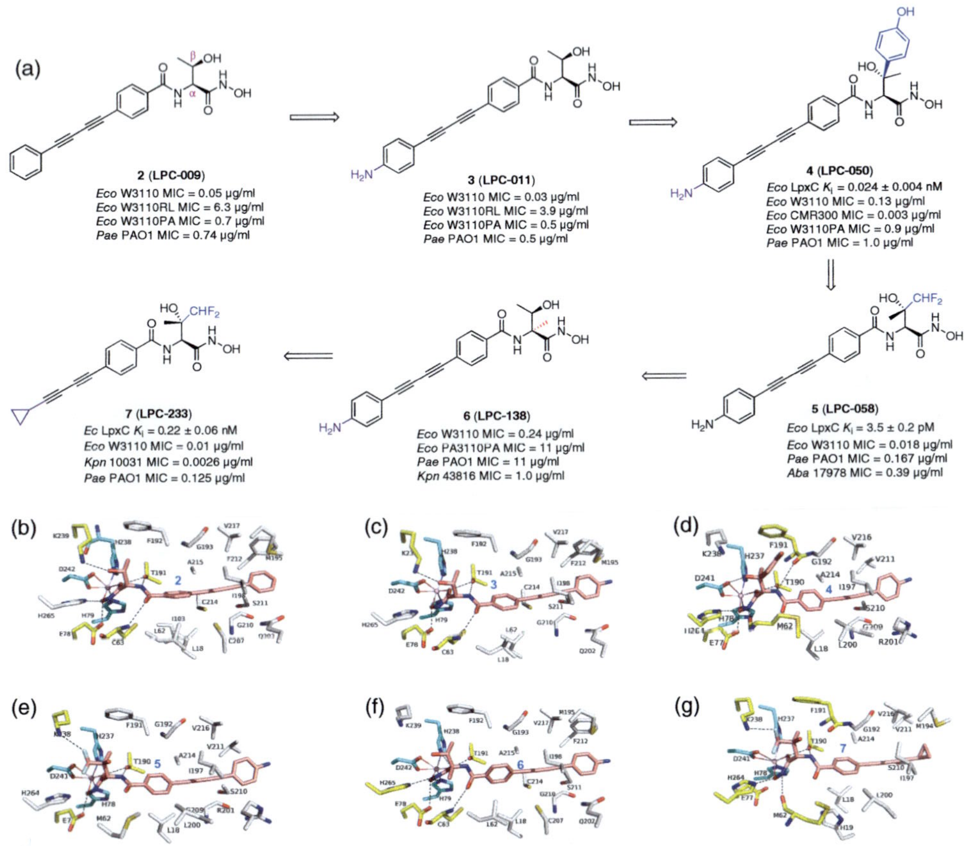
(a)
2 (LPC-009)
Eco W3110 MIC = 0.05 μg/ml
Eco W3110RL MIC = 6.3 μg/ml
Eco W3110PA MIC = 0.7 μg/ml
Pae PAO1 MIC = 0.74 μg/ml
3 (LPC-011)
Eco W3110 MIC = 0.03 μg/ml
Eco W3110RL MIC = 3.9 μg/ml
Eco W3110PA MIC = 0.5 μg/ml
Pae PAO1 MIC = 0.5 μg/ml
4 (LPC-050)
Eco LpxC K_i = 0.024 ± 0.004 nM
Eco W3110 MIC = 0.13 μg/ml
Eco CMR300 MIC = 0.003 μg/ml
Eco W3110PA MIC = 0.9 μg/ml
Pae PAO1 MIC = 1.0 μg/ml
5 (LPC-058)
Eco LpxC K_i = 3.5 ± 0.2 pM
Eco W3110 MIC = 0.018 μg/ml
Pae PAO1 MIC = 0.167 μg/ml
Aba 17978 MIC = 0.39 μg/ml
6 (LPC-138)
Eco W3110 MIC = 0.24 μg/ml
Eco PA3110PA MIC = 11 μg/ml
Pae PAO1 MIC = 11 μg/ml
Kpn 43816 MIC = 1.0 μg/ml
7 (LPC-233)
Ec LpxC K_i = 0.22 ± 0.06 nM
Eco W3110 MIC = 0.01 μg/ml
Kpn 10031 MIC = 0.0026 μg/ml
Pae PAO1 MIC = 0.125 μg/ml
(b)
(c)
(d)
(e)
(f)
(g)

Figure 16.5 (a): Linear diacetylene scaffold based LpxC inhibitors **2–7** developed by Zhou; (b): Crystal structure of the *E. Coli* LpxC and compound **2** (PDB code: 3P3G); (c): Crystal structure of the *E. Coli* LpxC and compound **3** (PDB code: 3PS1); (d): Crystal structure of the *P. aeruginosa* LpxC and compound **4** (PDB code: 4LCH); (e): Crystal structure of the *P. aeruginosa* LpxC and compound **5** (PDB code: 5DDR); (f): Crystal structure of the *E. Coli* LpxC and compound **6** (PDB code: 4MQY); (g): Crystal structure of the *P. aeruginosa* LpxC and compound **7** (PDB code: 8E4A).

is captured in complexes with representative *E. Coli* LpxC, which is similar to CHIR-090 (Figure 16.5b).

To improve the solubility of LPC-009 in aqueous solution, the same group [18] investigated various substituents on the terminal phenyl ring of LPC-009 and their differential antibiotic activities. The representative compound **3** (LPC-011) with *para*-amino-substituent showed increased solubility and antibiotic activities compared to LPC-009 (Figure 16.5a). Co-crystal structure of the *E. Coli* LpxC and compound **3** confirmed that the terminal amino group is exposed to the solvent (Figure 16.5c). In addition, the author demonstrated that the *S*-configuration at the Cα position is essential for antibiotic activity, while the configuration at the Cβ position has a limited impact on the overall antibiotic activity. The same strategy has been used by researchers from Achaogen, leading to the clinical compound ACHN-975. But it was terminated in Phase I clinical trials due to causing inflammation at the injection site.

In 2013, Zhou et al. [19] added an additional aryl group at the β-position of compound **3** (LPC-011), expanding the inhibitor-binding surface in LpxC and enhancing the potency against LpxC in enzymatic assays. The representative compound **4** (LPC-050) demonstrates antibiotic activity comparable to that of compound **1** (Figure 16.5a). This indicates that the Cβ position of the succinyl group is an effective structural position for enhancing the binding affinity of LpxC inhibitors with the enzyme and emphasizes the importance of maintaining a balanced hydrophobicity and hydrophilicity profile in developing effective LpxC-targeting antibiotics. Crystal structure of the *P. aeruginosa* LpxC and compound **4** also indicates that the hydrogen bond between the inhibitor Cβ-hydroxyl group and K238 of LpxC remains intact, and the inhibitor Cβ-methyl group similarly makes a favorable vdW contact with the side chain of F191 of LpxC. In addition, the phenol ring of **4** points toward F191, forming a favorable T-shaped π–π interaction (Figure 16.5d).

In 2016, the same group [20, 21] developed compound **5** (LPC-058), which has broad-spectrum antimicrobial activity through the study of inhibitor envelope and was the first LpxC inhibitor to show effective antibiotic activity against the *A. baumannii* ATCC 17978 strain (Figure 16.5a). Addition of the difluoromethyl moiety strengthens electrostatic interactions with amino acids and enhances membrane permeability [22]. Co-crystal structure confirmed that one of the fluoro could form a strong H-bond interaction with K238 (Figure 16.5e).

In 2014, Zhou et al. [23] clarified that the conformational plasticity of the βa-βb loop of Insert I of *E. Coli* LpxC allows it to accommodate inhibitors with divergent chemical scaffolds at the active site, including compounds that contain *R*-substituted bulky moieties at the Cα-position next to the hydroxamate group and compounds with double substitutions at the Cα position. In contrast, the Insert I of *P. aeruginosa* LpxC appears to have a more rigid βa-βb loop, which does not undergo significant conformational changes upon inhibitor binding, leading to a severe penalty of the binding energy. Therefore, more flexible inhibitors are needed to overcome the conformational heterogeneity of Insert I and Insert II of LpxC, and this feature can also be exploited to design specific inhibitors. The introduction of a methyl group at the α-position of compound **6** (LPC-138) increases steric hindrance, preventing the degradation of the hydroxamate group (Figure 16.5a).

In 2023, Zhou et al. [10] reported a slow, tight-binding LpxC inhibitor, compound **7** (LPC-233), which increases its half-life through a two-step process (Figure 16.5). After binding to LpxC, the shape of the enzyme–inhibitor complex changes to some extent, forming a more stable complex that prolongs the time of action in the body. This compound is a rapidly bactericidal antibiotic, unaffected by existing resistance mechanisms and has an extremely low incidence of bacterial resistance mutations. It also shows broad activity against clinically isolated Gram-negative bacteria *in vitro*. In animal experiments, it has been effective through various routes of administration, such as oral, intravenous, and intraperitoneal injection, and has oral bioavailability, making it a promising treatment for stubborn urinary tract infections (UTI). LPC-233 is highly specific to LpxC, highly plasma-bound, but its affinity for LpxC competitively releases it from plasma proteins, only slightly affecting the MIC values of LPC-233. Due to the absence of an amine group in the head and high plasma binding, which limits the free amount, no adverse cardiovascular toxicity has been detected for LPC-233. Structural analysis of LPC-233 in complex with *P. aeruginosa* LpxC shows that the zinc ion chelates with the hydroxamate that forms hydrogen bonds with E77 and H264, the fluorine atom engages in electrostatic interactions with K238, the succinyl methyl makes vdW interactions with the hydrophobic cluster's F191 in the active site, and the hydroxyl group is exposed to the solvent (Figure 16.5g). The phenyl diacetylene cyclopropane occupies the hydrophobic channel, and the terminal cyclopropane interacts with residues (M194, I197, V211, and V216) at the exit of the hydrophobic channel, conforming to the L-shaped channel. The cyclopropane also ensures the specificity of the LpxC inhibitor by reducing the linearity and planarity of the tail group.

In 2011, Mansoor et al. [24] replaced the P3 region with benzolactam and urea derivatives. The benzolactam class (such as compound **8**) had LpxC inhibitory effects but lacked cellular efficacy, highlighting the importance of the hydrogen bonding interaction between the peptide amide NH and Thr-179 in terms of biochemical and cellular efficacy (Figure 16.6). Some urea derivatives (such as compound **9**) exhibited whole-cell activity and broad-spectrum antibacterial activity (Figure 16.6). It was demonstrated that enzyme efficacy could be achieved by forming a tight complex between the LpxC inhibitor and the enzyme by utilizing several conserved basic features of LpxC (catalytic zinc binding, peptide linker binding, and maintaining hydrophobic contacts within the hydrophobic channel), but cellular efficacy requires finding the right balance between polarity and hydrophobicity.

In 2012, Warmus et al. [25] used biphenyl as a hydrophobic pocket binding element to avoid the potential toxicity of the acetylene moiety and optimized based

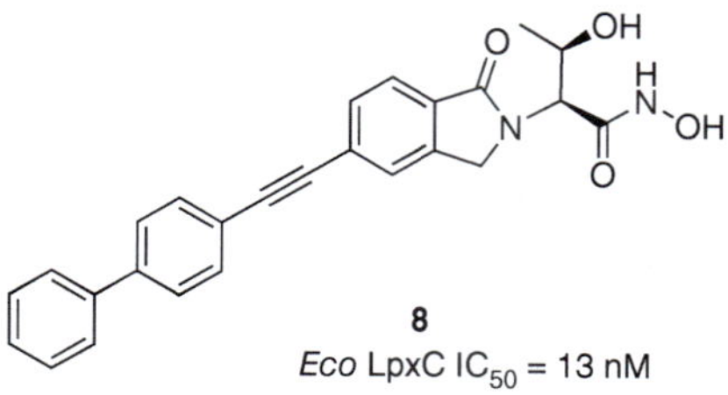

8
Eco LpxC IC_{50} = 13 nM

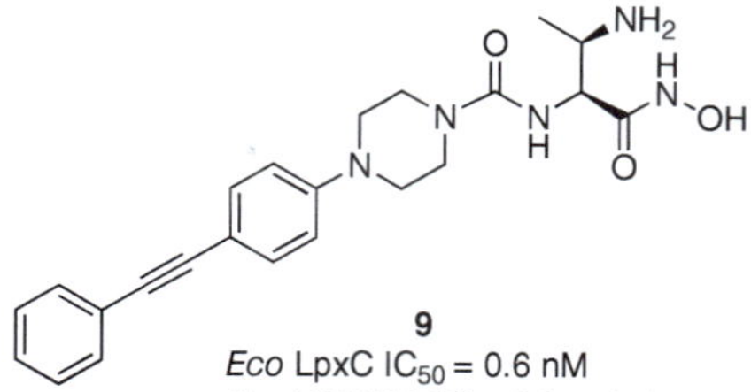

9
Eco LpxC IC_{50} = 0.6 nM
Eco HS294 MIC = 0.8 μg/ml
Eco ATCC25922 MIC = 12.5 μg/ml
Eco ATCC27853 MIC = 6.25 μg/ml

Figure 16.6 Benzolactam and urea-derived LpxC inhibitors.

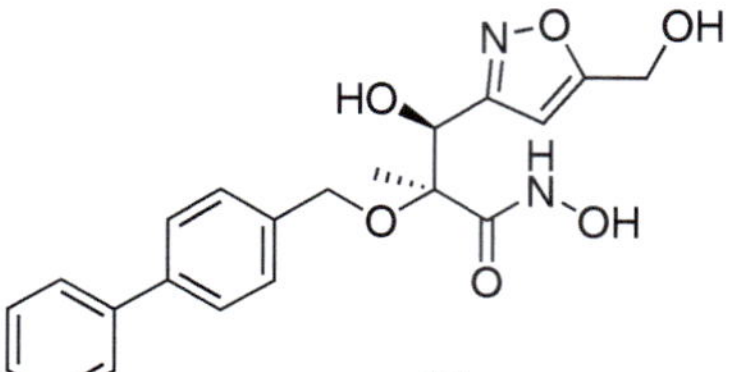

10
Pae LpxC IC_{50} = 0.6 nM
Pae PAO280 MIC = 0.015 μg/ml

Figure 16.7 The biphenyl scaffold-based LpxC inhibitors.

on compound **8**. By introducing an α-Me to increase steric hindrance and prevent hydrolysis of the hydroxamate, incorporating an isoxazole to bind with the sugar pocket, and adding a hydroxyl group to reduce LogD to the optimal range (1–2.2), the resulting compound **10** was the first LpxC inhibitor to show activity against wild-type *P. aeruginosa* (Figure 16.7).

In 2013, Hale et al. [26] reported a series of products with different amino acid substitutions, evaluating the potential for improved potency at both enzymatic and cellular levels by building into the UDP pocket, among which the glutamine analogs were the most effective (Figure 16.8, such as compound **11**). The author provides the first wild-type structure of *P. aeruginosa* LpxC with **11**. Compound **11** shows a similar

(a)

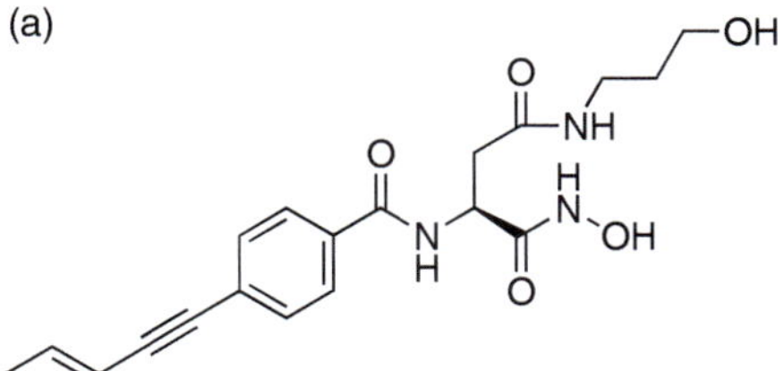

11
Pae LpxC IC_{50} = 5.3 nM
Eco LpxC IC_{50} = 1.3 nM

(b)

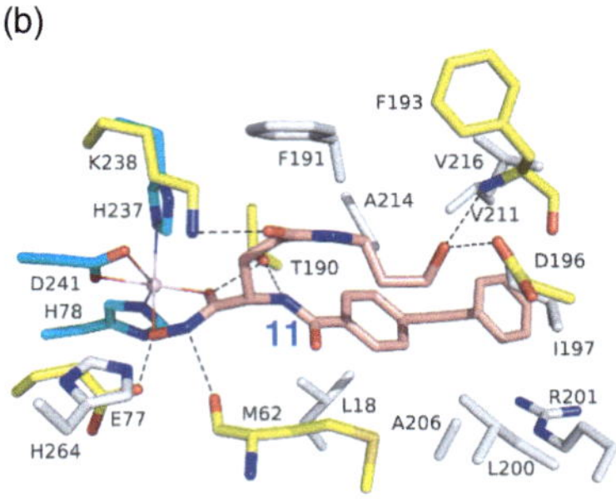

Figure 16.8 (a) LpxC inhibitor **11** with substituents anchoring to the UDP pocket; (b) Crystal structure of the *P. aeruginosa* LpxC and compound **11** (PDB code: 4J3D).

binding mode with LpxC compared with CHIR-090. Furthermore, the crystal structure shows the hydroxypropyl group attached to the amide form hydrogen bonds with the Asp196 side chain and Phe193 backbone amine, which might explain the improvement in the *P. aeruginosa* LpxC IC50 over the compound that cannot form this hydrogen bond.

In 2017, Zhang et al. [27] developed potent bicyclic LpxC inhibitors, among which compound **12** showed broad-spectrum inhibitory effects against Gram-negative bacteria (Figure 16.9). Moreover, compound **12** exhibits robust efficacy in multiple bacterial infection models in animals. However, its progression as a clinical candidate was hindered by acute intravenous (IV) tolerability issues observed in rats. These acute toxic effects are believed to be mediated by its potent binding to sodium channels.

In the same year, Piizzi et al. [28] demonstrated that the geometry and polarity of the propargyl ether group are relatively small and nonlinear, which is conducive to the specific inhibition of *Pseudomonas aeruginosa* LpxC, and is the most suitable for the hydrophobic tunnel (Figure 16.10). For example, compound **13** showed reduced cytotoxicity to mammalian cell lines, improved solubility and plasma protein binding, while maintaining effective anti-*Pseudomonas aeruginosa* activity both *in vitro* and *in vivo*.

16.3.2 Alkyl Sulfone

In 2012, Brown et al. [29] reported a new class of alkyl sulfone-hydroxamate inhibitors, with the representative compound **14**, which showed strong selective

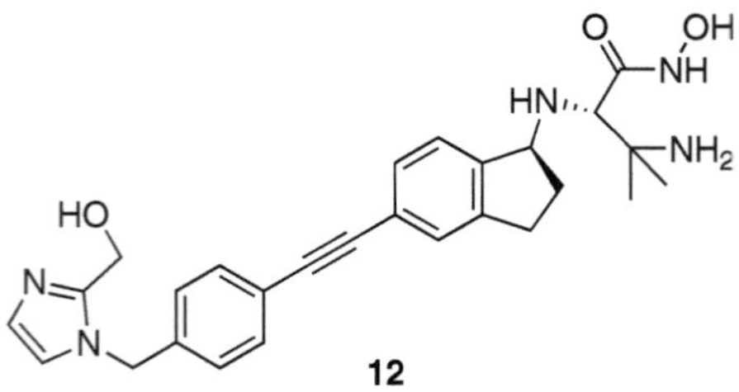

12

Eco ATCC25922 MIC = 0.5 μg/ml
Kpn 847 MIC = 4 μg/ml
Pae ATCC27853 MIC = 1 μg/ml

Figure 16.9 Bicyclic LpxC inhibitor.

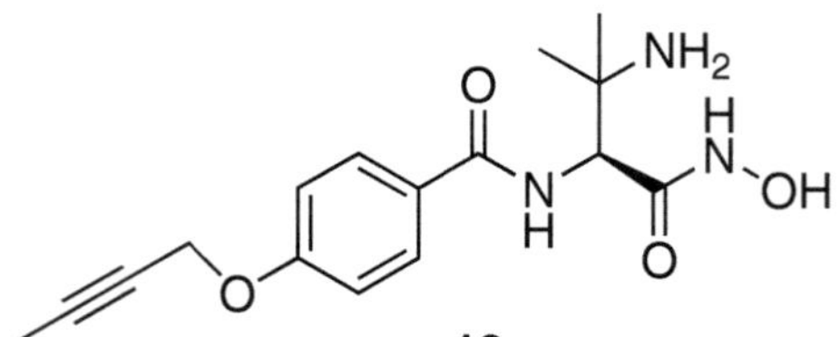

13

Pae LpxC IC_{50} = 1.5 nM
Pae WT MIC = 1.0 μg/ml
Pae MDR MIC = 2 μg/ml

Figure 16.10 Propargyl ether-based LpxC inhibitor.

enzyme inhibition and broad-spectrum whole-cell activity, and exhibited antibacterial activity in a mouse infection model (Figure 16.11). The crystal structure (compound **15** with *P. aeruginosa* LpxC, Figure 16.11b) revealed that the hydroxamate headgroup binds to the zinc atom in the active site; the alkyl sulfone headgroup forms hydrogen bond interactions with the Lys238 residue in the active site, and the methyl group attached to the sulfone close to Phe191 is located in a smaller hydrophobic space that cannot accommodate larger substituents; the methyl group at the quaternary carbon center may interact with the nearby Met62 through vdW forces, locking the molecule in an effective *R* configuration; the hydrophobic tail interacts with the hydrophobic tunnel in the enzyme. However, this compound has issues such as high clearance rate, high plasma protein binding, and low solubility.

In the same year, Montgomery et al. [30] carried out structural modifications and improvements on compound **14**, resulting in a series of pyridone alkyl sulfone compounds represented by **16**. By replacing the benzene ring with the polar group pyridone, they were able to improve solubility and the free fraction. Additionally, this study found that introducing methoxy, fluorine, or chlorine on the pyridone benzene ring, or adding a third ring (such as an aryl heterocycle) in the para position could enhance their activity, leading to the discovery of many effective derivatives represented by **16.** The co-crystal structure of **16** in *P. aeruginosa* LpxC enzyme revealed a similar binding mode that was seen for hydroxamate methylsulfone headgroup containing biphenyl compounds (Figure 16.11c). Interestingly, the pyridone oxygen oriented toward methionine 62 in a relatively hydrophobic pocket rather than binding in the opposite orientation to interact with threonine 190.

In 2018, Lee et al. [31] employed a computational scaffold hopping strategy, resulting in two types of oxazolidinone and isoxazoline inhibitors with potent antibacterial activity, represented by compounds **18** and **19** (Figure 16.12). The study found that compounds with shorter hydrophobic tails exhibited strong MIC against *P. aeruginosa*, and an increase in hydrophobic groups enhanced activity against *E. coli* and *K. pneumoniae*. Compounds with longer hydrophobic tails tolerated polar groups at the tail end and showed good antibacterial activity. Among them, compound **18** was proven to be effective against *P. aeruginosa*. The co-crystal structure revealed that the oxazolidinone connects the sulfone/hydroxamate part of the inhibitor with a hydrophobic phenyl group while maintaining a low-energy conformation, and the carbonyl oxygen of the oxazolidinone forms a favorable polar interaction with His 19 in the majority of the hydrophobic binding pockets (Figure 16.12b).

In 2019, Cohen et al. [32] demonstrated that hydroxamic acid is not the cause of cardiovascular toxicity in LpxC inhibitors. They developed a phosphate prodrug, compound **20**, which increases solubility and rapidly converts to the active drug, compound **21**, upon intravenous administration (Figure 16.13). However, the prodrug still possesses a therapeutic window insufficient to support further clinical development.

In the same year, Renslo et al. [33], inspired by the artemisinin (TRX) framework, coupled the cage-like iron carrier TRX with **22** (PF-5081090), taking advantage of the bacteria's uptake of Fe^{2+} during infection to achieve enrichment of antibiotics at the site of infection, reduce off-target effects, and improve efficacy and tolerability

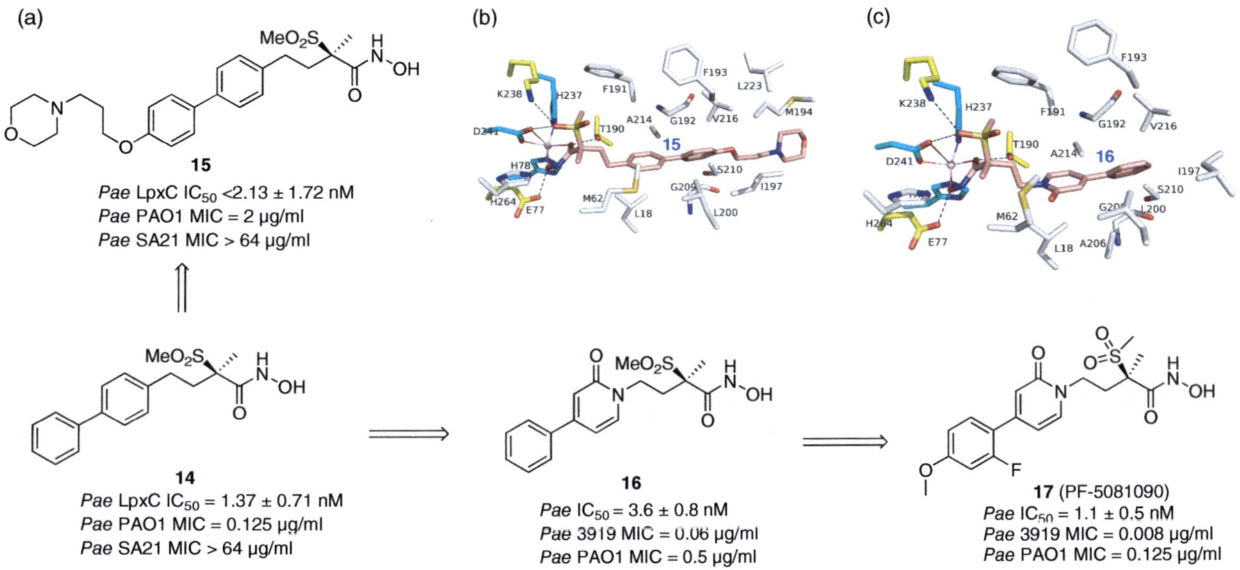

Figure 16.11 (a): Alkyl sulfone-hydroxamate based LpxC inhibitors **14–17**; (b): Crystal structure of the *P. aeruginosa* LpxC and compound **15** (PDB code: 3U1Y); (c): Crystal structure of the *P. aeruginosa* LpxC and compound **16** (PDB code: 3UHM).

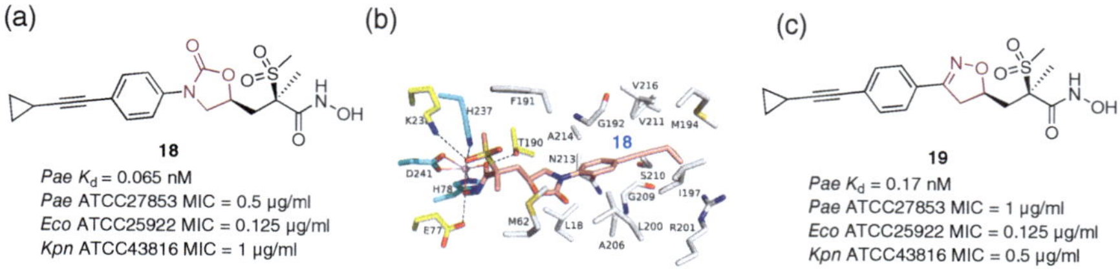

Figure 16.12 (a): Oxazolidinone-based LpxC inhibitor **18**; (b): Crystal structure of the *P. aeruginosa* LpxC and compound **18** (PDB code: 6MAE); (c): Isooxazoline-based LpxC inhibitor **19.**

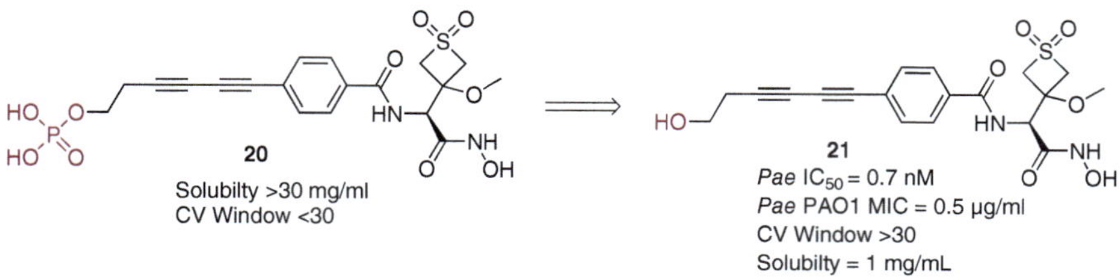

Figure 16.13 Phosphate prodrug designed for LpxC inhibitor.

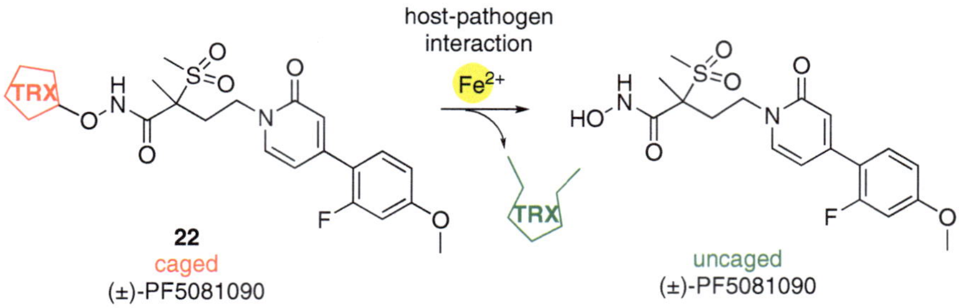

Figure 16.14 Iron (II)-caged LpxC inhibitor.

(Figure 16.14). Experiments showed that this ferrous cage-like LpxC inhibitor was effective in an acute *Pseudomonas aeruginosa* mouse lung infection model, but it showed little activity in cell culture experiments.

In 2020, Researchers from Idorsia Pharmaceuticals [34] reported LpxC inhibitors based on a bicyclic core, which mainly include (i) isoindolin-1-ones, (ii) 1,2-dihydro-3*H*-pyrrolo [1,2-*c*]imidazole-3-ones, and (iii) 4,5-dihydro-6*H*-thieno [2,3-*c*]pyrrol-6-ones (Figure 16.15). Among them, the pyrroloimidazolone series (core II), such as compounds **23** and **24**, was given priority due to their better scalability. However, these inhibitors required high doses to achieve *in vivo* efficacy and had low solubility within the pH range for intravenous administration. Through optimization, compounds **25** and **26** were obtained, which significantly improved antibacterial activity and metabolic stability, had lower clearance rates, and exhibited suitable physicochemical properties, making them suitable for the development of high-dose intravenous formulations [35].

Common LpxC inhibitors include a configurationally stable α-stereocenter, and most inhibitors have a hydrogen (H) at the α-position. However, the sulfonyl group's

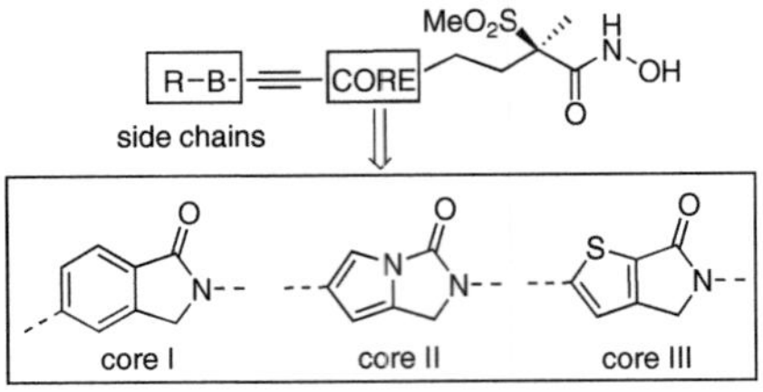

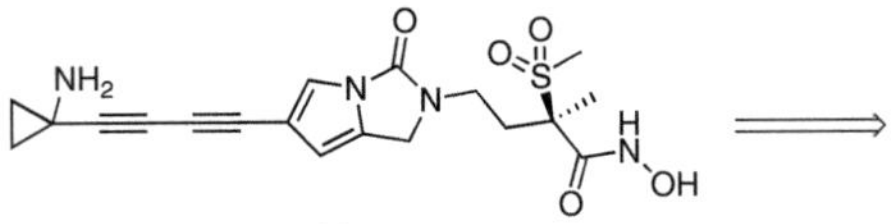

23

Eco ATCC25922 MIC = 0.25 µg/ml
Kpn T6474 MIC = 0.25 µg/ml
Pae ATCC27853 MIC = 0.5 µg/ml
Pae PAO1 MIC = 0.5 µg/ml

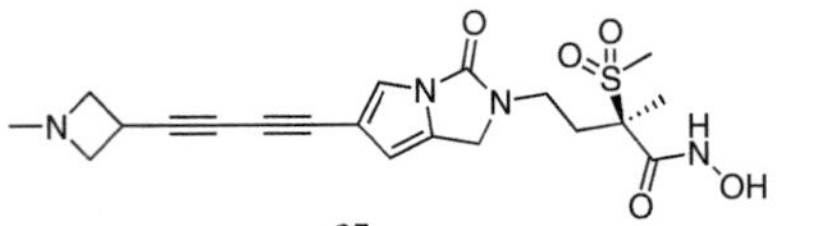

25

Eco ATCC25922 MIC = 0.5 µg/ml
Kpn T6474 MIC = 0.5 µg/ml
Pae ATCC27853 MIC = 0.5 µg/ml

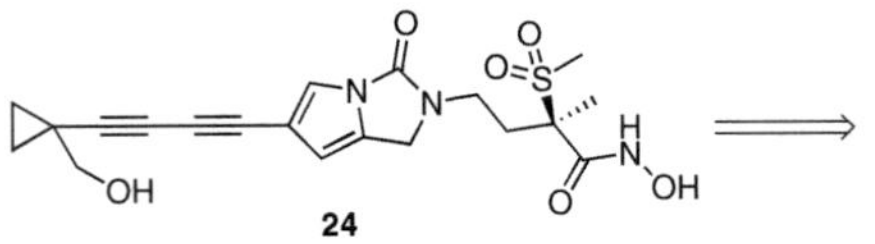

24

Eco ATCC25922 MIC = 0.25 µg/ml
Kpn T6474 MIC = 1 µg/ml
Pae ATCC27853 MIC = 0.5 µg/ml
Pae PAO1 MIC = 1 µg/ml

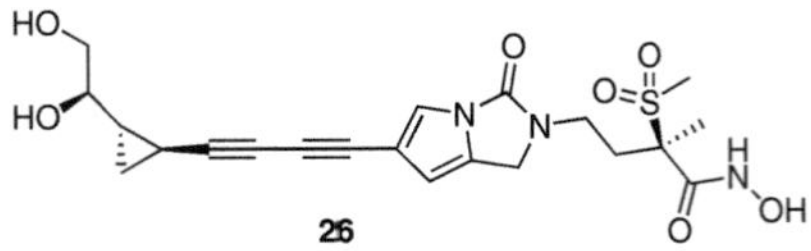

26

Eco ATCC25922 MIC = 0.5 µg/ml
Kpn T6474 MIC = 1 µg/ml
Pae ATCC27853 MIC = 1 µg/ml

Figure 16.15 Pyrroloimidazolone-based bicyclic LpxC inhibitors.

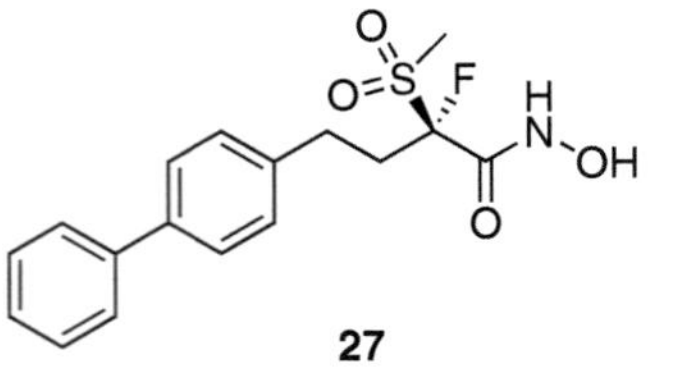

27

Pae HER 1018 MIC = 12.5 µg/ml
Kpn BAA 2146 MIC = 25 µg/ml
Aba ATCC19606 MIC >50 µg/ml

Figure 16.16 Fluorinated LpxC inhibitor.

electron-withdrawing effect can make the α-H acidic, leading to a reduction in activity with racemic products. Therefore, alkyl sulfone class inhibitors use a methyl group to stabilize the α-stereocenter. Brenner-Moyer et al. [35] replaced the α-methyl of compound **14** with a fluorine atom (Figure 16.16); the small size of the F atom more closely resembles that of a hydrogen atom, which might be more conducive to the adjacent groups approaching the target residues, thereby enhancing activity. However, experiments showed that the fluorine-substituted compounds had stable configurations, but their activity was not significantly improved. Replacing Me (or H) at the α-stereocenter of these LpxC inhibitors with F may not offer a significant advantage.

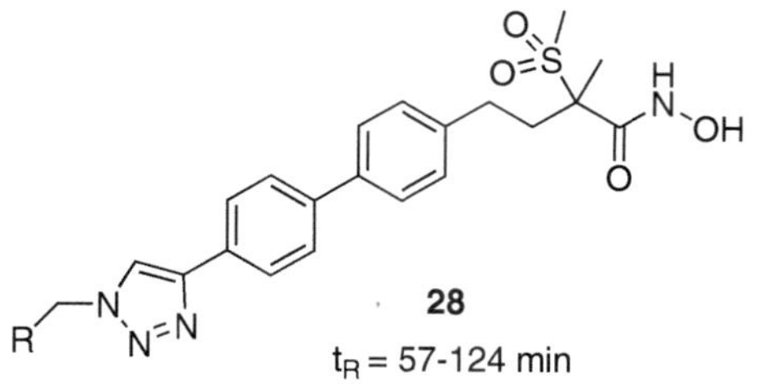

28

t_R = 57-124 min

Figure 16.17 Triazole-based LpxC inhibitor with longer residence times.

In 2022, Basak et al. [37] proposed a model in which the Insert II helix moves from an open conformation found in complexes of the enzyme with substrate or short residence time compounds to a closed conformation for long residence time inhibitors. An increase in residence time can extend the post-antibiotic effect (PAE), thereby reducing the frequency of administration and increasing the therapeutic window. The study found that the triazole-based compounds **28** have longer residence times and better potency (smaller K_i values) than the non-triazole-based compounds, and the triazole substituent is well tolerated (Figure 16.17).

16.3.3 Others

16.3.3.1 Aryloxazoline

In 1996, Onishi et al. [8] first reported the aryloxazoline class of LpxC inhibitors and synthesized a series of analogs. The structure of these compounds can be divided into three parts: the aryl fragment, the heterocycle fragment, and the chelating group. The representative compounds **29–31** have shown potent antibacterial activities toward *E. Coli* strains (Figure 16.18). In 1999, Chen et al. [38] found that the chelating activity of hydroxamic acid was optimal, and the activity increased when the aryl fragment was connected to hydrophobic groups with electron-donating substituents (tri-substituted at the three, four, and five positions). Hydrophilic or heterocyclic groups were detrimental to the activity, which was related to membrane permeability. Subsequently, Klline, Pirrung et al. [39, 40] studied oxazoline, oxazine, and thiazole derivatives to broaden the antibacterial spectrum. Aryloxazoline inhibitors have issues such as the production of toxic amine compounds from the degradation of hydroxamic acid and poor bacteriostatic activity against *P. aeruginosa*.

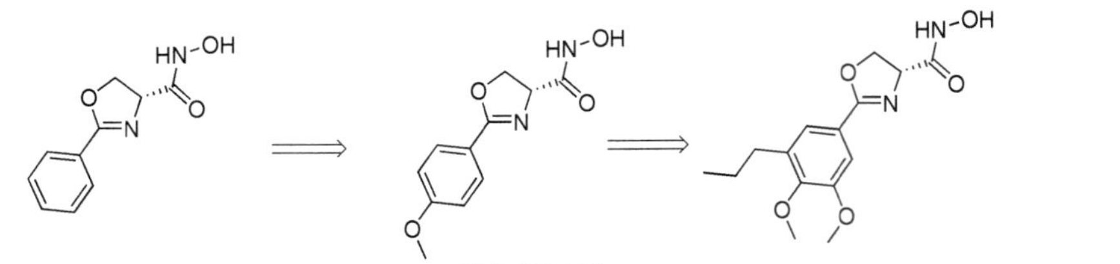

29 (L-573,655)
Eco LpxC IC_{50} = 3 μM/ml
Eco envA$^+$ MIC = 200–400 μM/ml
Eco envA1 MIC = 3–6 μM/ml

30 (L-159,692)
Eco LpxC IC_{50} = 0.6 μM/ml
Eco envA$^+$ MIC = 25–40 μM/ml
Eco envA1 MIC = 0.25 μM/ml

31 (L-161,240)
Eco LpxC IC_{50} = 3 μM/ml
Eco envA$^+$ MIC = 1–3 μM/ml
Eco envA1 MIC = 0.008–0.016 μM/ml

Figure 16.18 Aryloxazoline-based LpxC inhibitor.

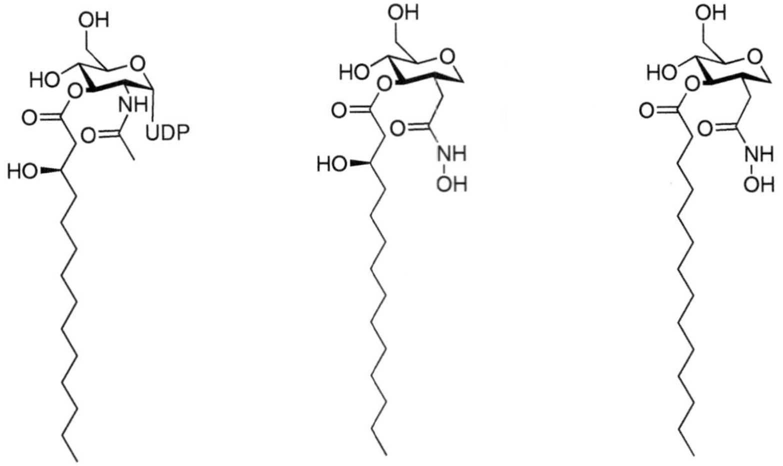

LpxC natural substrate

32 (TU-517)
Aae LpxC IC_{50}=18.1 ± 3.6 μM
Eco LpxC IC_{50} = 2.0 ± 1.3 μM
Eco LpxC K_i = 190 ± 50 nM

33 (TU-514)
Aae LpxC IC_{50} = 7.0 ± 0.5 μM
Eco LpxC IC_{50} = 7.2 ± 1.9 μM
Eco LpxC K_i = 650 ± 280 nM

Figure 16.19 LpxC substrate analogs.

16.3.3.2 LpxC Substrate Analogs

Based on the research of aryloxazoline inhibitors, it was found that the hydroxamic acid group plays an important role. In 2000, Jackman et al. [41] synthesized a series of LpxC substrate analogs containing the hydroxamic acid group, with representative compounds being **32** (TU-517) and **33** (TU-514) (Figure 16.19). TU-514 can efficiently inhibit a variety of LpxCs, including those from *E. coli* and *A. aeolicus in vitro*. However, it has almost no antibacterial activity *in vivo*, possibly because it cannot penetrate the outer membrane of Gram-negative bacteria or is metabolized and expelled by the cells. Modifications to the hydrophobic region and pyran ring of TU-514 still resulted in poor activity [42]. In addition, shortening the alkyl chain significantly reduced the activity against *E. coli* LpxC and *A. aeolicus* LpxC.

16.3.3.3 Sulfonamide–Hydroxamate Derivative

In 2002, Clements et al. [43] screened a library of metalloenzymatic inhibitors and identified a series of sulfonamide–hydroxamate derivative compounds, with representative compounds being **34** and **35**, which exhibited broad-spectrum bacteriostatic activity but were inactive against *Pseudomonas aeruginosa* (Figure 16.20).

16.3.3.4 *C*-Furanoside Derivatives

In 2012, Oddo et al. [44] synthesized a series of *C*-furanoside LpxC inhibitors, where conformational restriction maintains the hydroxylated group in a specific relative position to the lipophilic side chain. Modifications to the hydrophobic fragment revealed that longer, rigid linear structures, such as diphenylbutadiyne, exhibited better activity [45–48]. Subsequent research identified (2*S*, 3*S*, 4*R*, 5*S*)-furanoside **36** as the stereoisomer with the highest inhibitory activity against LpxC [49, 50]

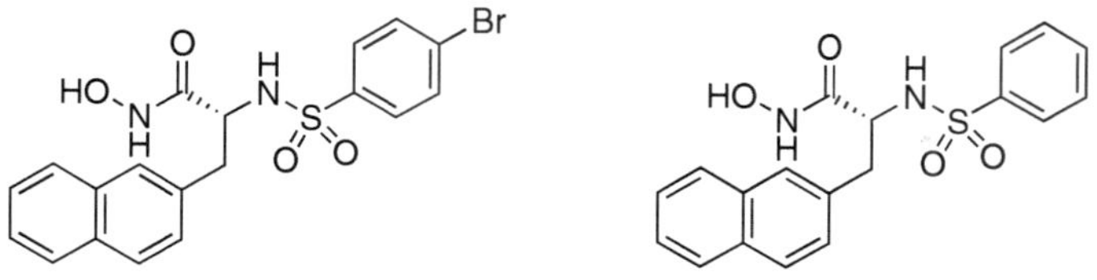

34 (BB-78484)
Eco ATCC 25922 MIC = 1 μg/ml
Kpn ATCC 13883 MIC = 2 μg/ml
Pae ATCC 27853 MIC >32 μg/ml

35 (BB-78485)
Eco ATCC 25922 MIC = 0.25 μg/ml
Kpn ATCC 13883 MIC = 1 μg/ml
Pae ATCC 27853 MIC = 4 μg/ml

Figure 16.20 Sulfonamide–hydroxamate derivative-based LpxC inhibitors.

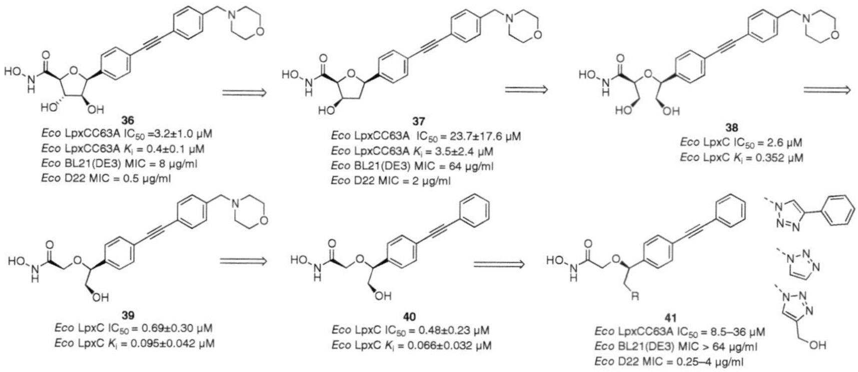

Figure 16.21 *C*-furanoside-based LpxC inhibitors.

(Figure 16.21). In 2021, Dreger et al. [51] synthesized a series of monohydroxytetrahydrofuran compounds to investigate the impact of the hydroxyl group on the furan on antibacterial activity and LpxC inhibitory activity. They found that compound **37** (2*S*, 3*R*, 5*R*) was the most effective LpxC inhibitor among them (Figure 16.21). Molecular docking suggested that LpxC prefers tetrahydrofuran derivatives lacking a hydroxyl group at the fourth position, possibly because the 4-hydroxyl group replaces an energetically stable water molecule from its position, thereby reducing the translational and rotational freedom of the protein and ligand during complex formation, and causing an unfavorable entropic effect.

In 2013, Jana et al. [48] reported the glycoside ring-opening derivative **38**, which showed better activity than the conformationally restricted ones (Figure 16.21). In 2014, Löppenberg et al. [45] reported compounds **39** and **40**, whose activity did not improve, but emphasized the importance of the lipophilic long chain, the position of the hydroxymethyl group on the benzyl group, and the S configuration of the stereocenter (Figure 16.21). In 2020, Katharina et al. [52] replaced the hydroxyl group with a triazole group (**41**) to enhance the bacteriostatic activity of the compound. Molecular docking showed that the aromatic interaction between the triazole ring of the compound and F192 is very important for the activity of the inhibitor, and the interaction between the basic fragment of the substituent on the triazole ring and K239 also enhances the activity.

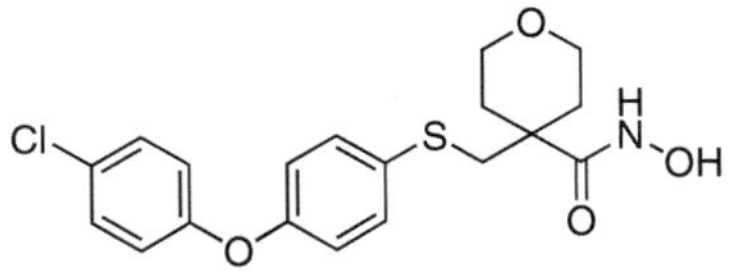

42

Pae LpxC IC_{50} = 7.4 ± 2.6 nM
Pae ARC546 MIC = 6.25 μM
Pae ARC545 MIC = 50 μM
Eco ARC524 MIC = 50 μM
Eco ARC523 MIC > 200 μM

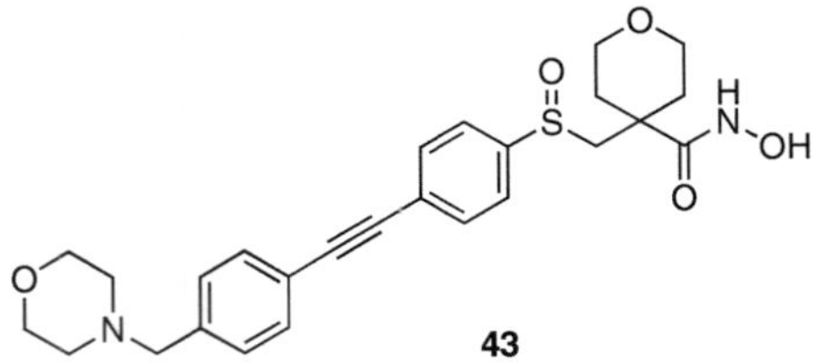

43

Pae LpxC IC_{50} = 3.1 ± 2.9 nM
Pae ARC546 MIC < 0.2 μM
Pae ARC545 MIC = 25 μM
Eco ARC524 MIC < 0.2 μM
Eco ARC523 MIC = 1.56 μM

Figure 16.22 Tetrahydrofuran-based LpxC inhibitor.

16.3.3.5 Tetrahydrofuran Derivatives

In 2014, Murphy-Benenato et al. [53] screened AstraZeneca's compound collection and identified compound **42**, a derivative of a known inhibitor (RS-130830) of matrix metalloprotease MMP-2, -8, -9 (Figure 16.22). The oxygen of the tetrahydropyran forms a hydrogen bond interaction with Lys238, and the tetrahydrofuran carbon framework engages in vdW interactions with the hydrophobic phenylalanine of the UDP pocket. Moreover, the cyclic core inhibits the metabolism of the hydroxamate ester, thus retaining the tetrahydrofuran ring for optimization to improve selectivity. Among them, compound **43** showed the highest cellular activity but still had inhibitory effects on MMPs, so future designs will focus on replacing the tetrahydrofuran core (Figure 16.22).

16.3.3.6 Oxazolidinone

In 2016, Kurasaki et al. [54] employed a scaffold hopping approach to restrict the conformation of the threonine part and discovered a series of new oxazolidinone inhibitors, among which the most active compound **44** had a relatively low efflux rate and exhibited nanomolar concentration inhibition against *E. coli* LpxC enzyme (Figure 16.23). It showed significant antibacterial activity against both

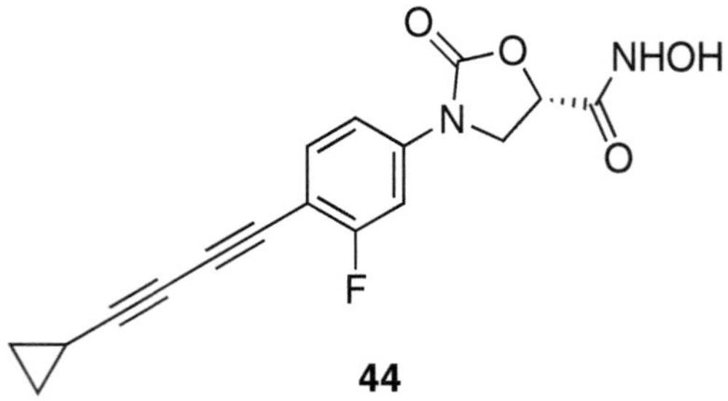

44

Eco LpxC IC_{50} = 6 nM
Eco TG1 MIC = 0.016 μg/ml
Eco KAM3 MIC = 0.004 μg/ml
Kpn ATCC 13883 MIC = 0.063 μg/ml

Figure 16.23 Oxazolidinone-based LpxC inhibitor.

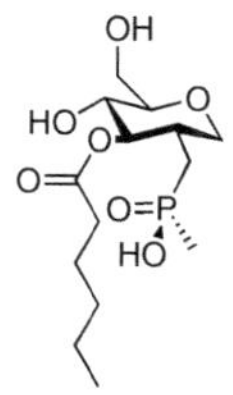

45 (6SHT55)
Aae LpxC IC_{50} = 192±38 μM
Eco LpxC IC_{50} = 115±33 μM

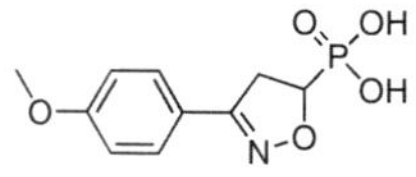

46
Eco LpxC IC_{50} = 4±2 μM

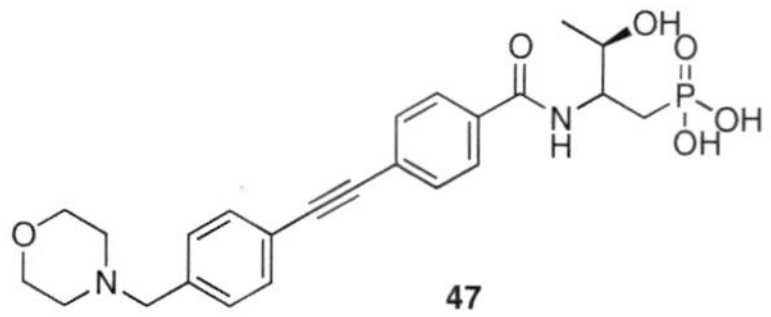

47
Eco LpxC IC_{50} = 4.5 nM
Pae LpxC IC_{50} = 9.5 nM
Eco ACTT 25922 MIC = 0.28 μg/ml
Pae ACTT BAA-47 MIC = 2.06 μg/ml
Aba ACTT 19606 MIC = 0.16 μg/ml
Kpn ATCC 700603 MIC = 0.86 μg/ml

Figure 16.24 Phosphate-based LpxC inhitiors.

E. coli and *K. pneumoniae*, but had little effect on *P. aeruginosa* and *A. baumannii*. Molecular docking with *E. coli* LpxC revealed that the oxygen atom at position 1 of the oxazolidinone of compound 60 made dual contacts with the main chain NH and side chain thiol of C63, and the fluorine atom on the phenyl group interacted with the thiol group of C207, providing new insights for the rational design of novel LpxC inhibitors.

16.4 Non-Hydroxamate Inhibitors

16.4.1 Phosphate Derivatives

Research has found thatmany zinc ion metalloenzymes, such as thermophilic protease, carboxypeptidase A, and collagenase, can be inhibited by compounds containing phosphate (salt) groups. In 2000, Jackman et al. [41] introduced a phosphate into the substrate analog inhibitor to obtain compound **45** (6SHT55), which has relatively weak inhibitory effects on *E. coli* and *A. aeolicus* LpxC (Figure 16.24). In 2002, Pirrung et al. [55] found that the preference for zinc coordination by various groups was as follows: hydroxamate ≈ phosphonate ≈ thioacetoxyacetyl > thiolacetyl > phosphinate > carboxylate, sulfonamide, and hydrazide. In 2016, Wang Yucheng et al. [56] replaced the hydroxamate group in CHIR-090 with a phosphate group to obtain compound **47** (Figure 16.24). This compound shows broad-spectrum antibacterial activities against various strains.

16.4.2 Aliphatic Carboxylic Acids and Amphoteric Benzoic Acids

In 2007, Shin et al. [57] reported a class of amphiphilic molecules targeting the hydrophobic channel. These compounds (**48** and **49**), which contain long hydrophobic fatty alkyl chains linked to carboxylic and benzoic acid derivatives, showed too weak antibacterial activity to merit further research (Figure 16.25).

16.4.3 Uracil Nucleoside Derivatives

In 2009, Brab et al. [58] targeted the UDP-binding site and screened a uridine-based library for new LpxC inhibitors. The representative compound **50** is a pH-dependent

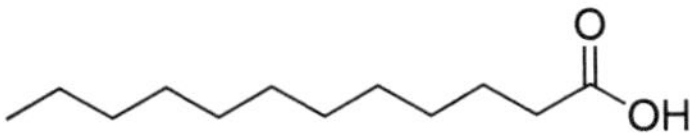

48
Aae LpxC K_d = 0.9 μM

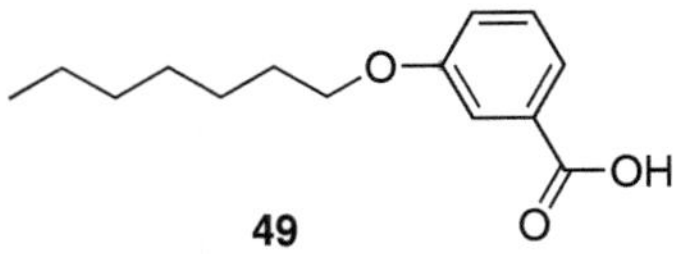

49
Aae LpxC K_d = 2.0 μM

Figure 16.25 Carboxylic acid–based inhibitors.

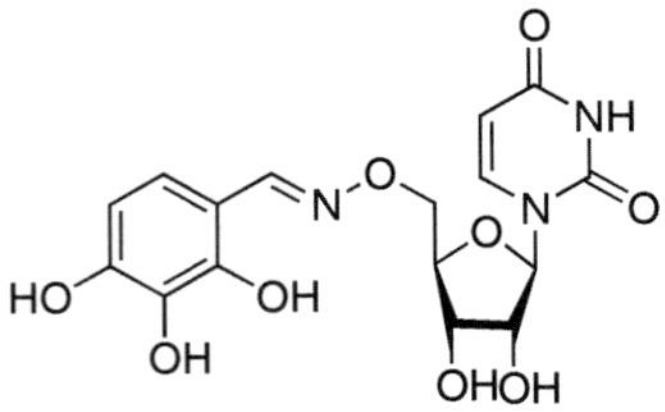

50
Eco LpxC IC_{50} = 27±5 μM

Figure 16.26 Uracil nucleoside derived LpxC inhibitor.

two-step *E. coli* inhibitor that does not contain a zinc ion chelating group or a hydrophobic side chain, and it exerts its inhibitory effect by competitively binding to the enzyme in the first step of the reaction (Figure 16.26). The study found that the hydroxyl groups at positions 3 and 4 may be essential for activity. These compounds lack antibiotic activity, but they provide a new scaffold for the optimization of existing LpxC inhibitors.

16.4.4 Novel *N*-Hydroxy Formamides

In 2020, Furuya et al. [59] replaced the hydroxamic acid with *N*-hydroxyformamide and used interactions in and around the sugar pocket to improve activity, probably developing a series of potent LpxC inhibitors. Among them, compound **51** had acceptable pharmacokinetics (PK) and *in vitro* safety data, but still had the side effect of lowering blood pressure (Figure 16.27). The toxicity related to LpxC inhibitors is likely driven by the entire pharmacophore, not just the terminal hydroxamic acid. For example, a basic amine group near the aromatic ring is a common ion channel pharmacophore [60].

16.4.5 Novel Hydroxyimidazole Derivatives

In 2020, Yamada et al. [61] identified the lead compound **52** with the most promising development prospects (Figure 16.28a). In 2021, Ushiyama et al. [62] reported compound **53**, which has a low risk of cardiovascular side effects (Figure 16.28b). This class of LpxC inhibitors uses hydroxyimidazole to replace the hydroxamic acid for zinc ion binding, improves interactions with the substrate-binding cleft,

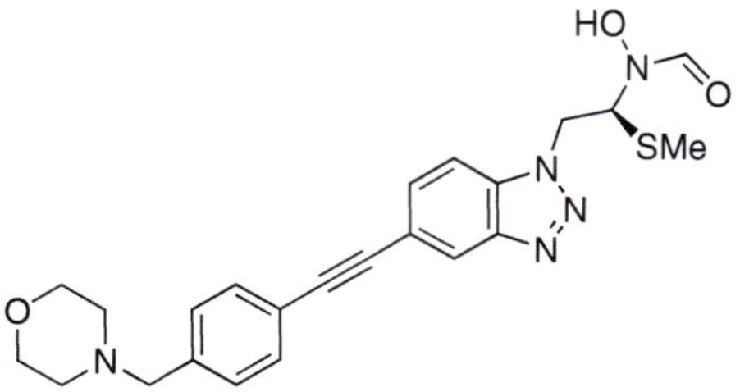

51
Pae IC_{50} <1 nM
Eco IC_{50} <10 nM
Pae PAO1 MIC = 4 μg/ml
Eco ATCC25922 MIC = 0.13 μg/ml
Kpn ATCC700603 MIC = 4 μg/ml

Figure 16.27 *N*-Hydroxyformamide-based LpxC inhibitor.

(a)

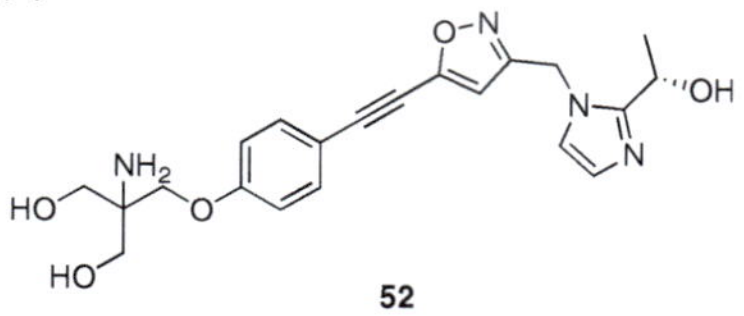

52
Pae LpxC IC_{50} = 20.0 nM
Eco ATCC25922 MIC = 16 μg/ml
Pae ATCC27853 MIC = 4 μg/ml
Kpn ATCC13883 MIC = 64 μg/ml

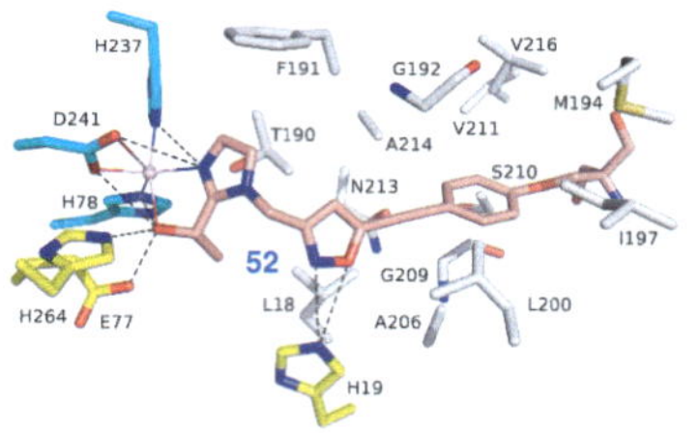

(b)

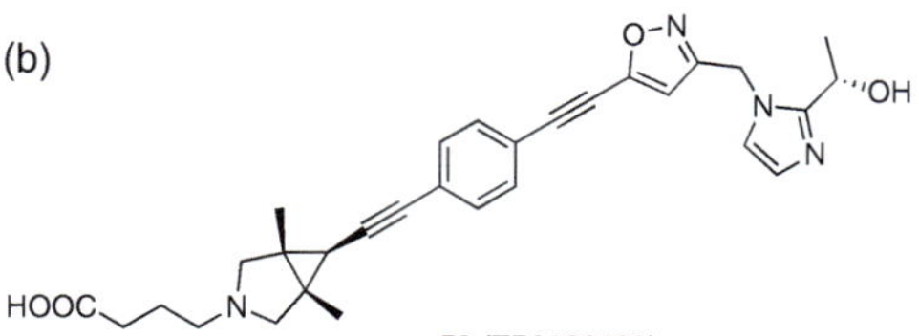

53 (TP0586532)
Pae LpxC IC_{50} = 0.10 μM
Eco ATCC25922 MIC = 2 μg/ml
Kpn ATCC13883 MIC = 4 μg/ml

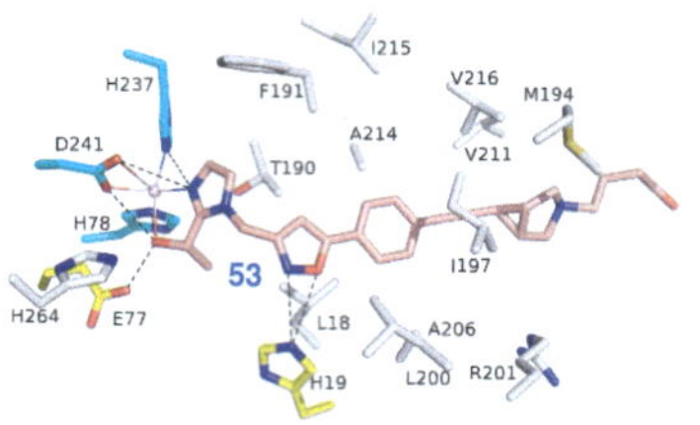

Figure 16.28 (a): Hydroxyimidazole-based LpxC inhibitor **52** and co-crystal structure with *P. aeruginosa* LpxC (PDB code: 7CI9); (b): Hydroxyimidazole-based LpxC inhibitor **53** and co-crystal structure with *P. aeruginosa* LpxC (PDB code: 7DEN).

enhances chemical activity, and simultaneously reduces binding to human proteins, offering significant development potential. The co-crystal structure of **52** and **53** with *P. aeruginosa* LpxC revealed that the compound forms a bidentate complex with trigonal bipyramidal geometry to the zinc through the hydroxyl oxygen atom and an imidazole nitrogen. In addition, several hydrogen bonds are formed between the imidazole and isoxazole of the ligand and E77, H264, and H19.

16.5 Summary and Outlook

Antimicrobial resistance (AMR) represents one of the most pressing global health challenges of the twenty-first century. The relentless evolution of resistant bacterial strains necessitates the development of novel antibacterial agents that target previously untapped or underutilized pathways. Among these, LpxC inhibitors have emerged as a promising class of compounds with significant potential in combating Gram-negative bacterial infections. This essay explores the application and potential of LpxC inhibitors in antibacterial drug research, focusing on their unique mechanism of action, challenges in development, and prospects for future applications.

LpxC inhibitors offer several advantages over conventional antibiotics. First, their unique target significantly reduces the likelihood of cross-resistance with existing drugs, such as β-lactams or fluoroquinolones. Second, Gram-negative bacteria, known for their formidable defense mechanisms, including efflux pumps and porin mutations, are particularly vulnerable to outer membrane disruptions caused by LpxC inhibition. Furthermore, LpxC inhibitors exhibit broad-spectrum activity against many Gram-negative pathogens, including *E. coli, K. pneumoniae, P. aeruginosa*, and *A. baumannii*. Many of these organisms are listed by the World Health Organization (WHO) as critical priorities for new antibiotic development due to their resistance to multiple drug classes.

Several LpxC inhibitors have been identified and studied, with varying degrees of success. Early compounds, such as CHIR-090, demonstrated potent antibacterial activity but suffered from issues such as poor pharmacokinetics and toxicity *in vivo*. Subsequent efforts have focused on improving these properties through structure-based drug design and optimization of pharmacological profiles. One promising candidate, LPC-233, has shown strong *in vitro* and *in vivo* efficacy against multidrug-resistant Gram-negative pathogens. It demonstrates favorable pharmacokinetic properties, including good oral bioavailability and minimal toxicity in preclinical studies. Similarly, PF-5081090, another LpxC inhibitor, exhibits potent activity against *P. aeruginosa* and has been highlighted for its therapeutic potential in cystic fibrosis–related infections.

The current challenges in developing LpxC inhibitors can be summarized as follows: (i) metabolite toxicity: Functional groups such as hydroxamic acid and acetylene are potential sources of toxicity. To address this, one strategy is to design new zinc-chelating groups or modify the hydroxamic acid structure, such as by increasing steric hindrance or using cyclization to reduce its metabolic degradation. Among alternative chelators, imidazole groups have shown significant promise; (ii) off-target effects: The human body contains numerous zinc-dependent enzymes, making selectivity a critical concern. LpxC has three primary binding sites: the Zn^{2+} ion, the hydrophobic tunnel, and the UDP binding site. Most existing inhibitors target the first two sites, but incorporating interactions with all three sites could enhance selectivity and reduce off-target effects. However, this approach may also increase the complexity of synthesis; (iii) solubility: Many LpxC inhibitors suffer from poor solubility, limiting their clinical applicability. Salt formation or structural modifications to improve solubility can be explored to overcome this issue; (iv) membrane permeability: Some LpxC inhibitors demonstrate strong enzyme inhibition but poor cellular activity, likely due to insufficient membrane permeability or active efflux by bacterial pumps. Achieving a balance between hydrophilicity and lipophilicity is critical for optimizing permeability. For instance, studies have shown that the outer membrane of *Pseudomonas aeruginosa* can be penetrated by basic compounds, suggesting that incorporating basic groups into LpxC inhibitors may reduce expulsion by efflux pumps. Addressing these challenges is essential to developing effective, safe, and clinically viable LpxC inhibitors for treating Gram-negative bacterial infections. By focusing on structural optimization, improving selectivity, and addressing pharmacokinetic and pharmacodynamic properties, LpxC inhibitors have the potential to become a powerful tool in combating AMR.

In summary, LpxC inhibitors represent a compelling frontier in antibacterial drug research. Their unique mechanism of action, targeting the biosynthesis of lipid A, offers significant advantages over conventional antibiotics, particularly against multidrug-resistant Gram-negative pathogens. While challenges related to toxicity, resistance, and pharmacokinetics remain, advances in medicinal chemistry and drug delivery technologies continue to address these obstacles.

References

1 World Health Organization (2017). Global priority list of antibiotic-resistant bacteria to guide research, discovery, and development of new antibiotics [Z].https://www.who.int/news/item/27-02-2017-who-publishes-list-of-bacteria-for-which-new-antibiotics-are-urgently-needed/ accessed 19 October 2024.

2 Raetz, C.R. and Whitfield, C. (2002). Lipopolysaccharide endotoxins. *Annual Review of Biochemistry* 71: 635–700.

3 Sorensen, P.G., Lutkenhaus, J., Young, K. et al. (1996). Regulation of UDP-3-O-[R-3-hydroxymyristoyl]-N-acetylglucosamine deacetylase in *Escherichia coli*: the second enzymatic step of lipid a biosynthesis. *Journal of Biological Chemistry* 271 (42): 25898–25905.

4 Miller, S.I., Ernst, R.K., and Bader, M.W. (2005). LPS, TLR4 and infectious disease diversity. *Nature Reviews Microbiology* 3 (1): 36–46.

5 Wyckoff, T.J., Raetz, C.R., and Jackman, J.E. (1998). Antibacterial and anti-inflammatory agents that target endotoxin. *Trends in Microbiology* 6 (4): 154–159.

6 Langklotz, S., Baumann, U., and Narberhaus, F. (2012). Structure and function of the bacterial AAA protease FtsH. *Biochimica et Biophysica Acta* 1823 (1): 40–48.

7 Barb, A.W. and Zhou, P. (2008). Mechanism and inhibition of LpxC: an essential zinc-dependent deacetylase of bacterial lipid A synthesis. *Current Pharmaceutical Biotechnology* 9 (1): 9–15.

8 Onishi, H.R., Pelak, B.A., Gerckens, L.S. et al. (1996). Antibacterial agents that inhibit lipid A biosynthesis. *Science* 274 (5289): 980–982.

9 Niu, Z., Lei, P., Wang, Y. et al. (2023). Small molecule LpxC inhibitors against gram-negative bacteria: Advances and future perspectives. *European Journal of Medicinal Chemistry* 253: 115326.

10 Zhao, J., Cochrane, C.S., Najeeb, J. et al. (2023). Preclinical safety and efficacy characterization of an LpxC inhibitor against Gram-negative pathogens. *Science Translational Medicine* 15 (708): eadf5668.

11 Mcclerren, A.L., Zhou, P., Guan, Z. et al. (2005). Kinetic analysis of the zinc-dependent deacetylase in the lipid A biosynthetic pathway. *Biochemistry* 44 (4): 1106–1113.

12 Hernick, M., Gennadios, H.A., Whittington, D.A. et al. (2005). UDP-3-O-((R)-3-hydroxymyristoyl)-N-acetylglucosamine deacetylase functions through a general acid-base catalyst pair mechanism. *The Journal of Biological Chemistry* 280 (17): 16969–16978.

13 Hernick, M. and Fierke, C.A. (2005). Zinc hydrolases: the mechanisms of zinc-dependent deacetylases. *Archives of Biochemistry and Biophysics* 433 (1): 71–84.

14 Andersen, N.H., Bowman, J., Erwin, A. et al. (2004). *Antibacterial Agents, World Intellectual Property Organization, Patent WO 2004/062601 A2*, 324. Emeryville, CA: Chiron.

15 Mcclerren, A.L., Endsley, S., Bowman, J.L. et al. (2005). A slow, tight-binding inhibitor of the zinc-dependent deacetylase LpxC of lipid A biosynthesis with antibiotic activity comparable to ciprofloxacin. *Biochemistry* 44 (50): 16574–16583.

16 Barb, A.W., Mcclerren, A.L., Snehelatha, K. et al. (2007). Inhibition of lipid A biosynthesis as the primary mechanism of CHIR-090 antibiotic activity in *Escherichia coli*. *Biochemistry* 46 (12): 3793–3802.

17 Lee, C.J., Liang, X., Chen, X. et al. (2011). Species-specific and inhibitor-dependent conformations of LpxC: implications for antibiotic design. *Chemistry & Biology* 18 (1): 38–47.

18 Liang, X., Lee, C.J., Chen, X. et al. (2011). Syntheses, structures and antibiotic activities of LpxC inhibitors based on the diacetylene scaffold. *Bioorganic & Medicinal Chemistry* 19 (2): 852–860.

19 Liang, X., Lee, C.J., Zhao, J. et al. (2013). Synthesis, structure, and antibiotic activity of aryl-substituted LpxC inhibitors. *Journal of Medicinal Chemistry* 56 (17): 6954–6966.

20 Lee, C.-J., Liang, X., Wu, Q. et al. (2016). Drug design from the cryptic inhibitor envelope. *Nature Communications* 7 (1): 10638.

21 Liang, X., Gopalaswamy, R., Navas, F. 3rd, et al. (2016). A Scalable synthesis of the difluoromethyl-allo-threonyl hydroxamate-based LpxC inhibitor LPC-058. *The Journal of Organic Chemistry* 81 (10): 4393–4398.

22 Titecat, M., Liang, X., Lee, C.J. et al. (2016). High susceptibility of MDR and XDR gram-negative pathogens to biphenyl-diacetylene-based difluoromethyl-allo-threonyl-hydroxamate LpxC inhibitors. *The Journal of Antimicrobial Chemotherapy* 71 (10): 2874–2882.

23 Lee, C.J., Liang, X., Gopalaswamy, R. et al. (2014). Structural basis of the promiscuous inhibitor susceptibility of Escherichia coli LpxC. *ACS Chemical Biology* 9 (1): 237–246.

24 Mansoor, U.F., Vitharana, D., Reddy, P.A. et al. (2011). Design and synthesis of potent gram-negative specific LpxC inhibitors. *Bioorganic & Medicinal Chemistry Letters* 21 (4): 1155–1161.

25 Warmus, J.S., Quinn, C.L., Taylor, C. et al. (2012). Structure based design of an *in vivo* active hydroxamic acid inhibitor of *P. aeruginosa* LpxC. *Bioorganic & Medicinal Chemistry Letters* 22 (7): 2536–2543.

26 Hale, M.R., Hill, P., Lahiri, S. et al. (2013). Exploring the UDP pocket of LpxC through amino acid analogs. *Bioorganic & Medicinal Chemistry Letters* 23 (8): 2362–2367.

27 Zhang, J., Chan, A., Lippa, B. et al. (2017). Structure-based discovery of LpxC inhibitors. *Bioorganic & Medicinal Chemistry Letters* 27 (8): 1670–1680.

28 Piizzi, G., Parker, D.T., Peng, Y. et al. (2017). Design, synthesis, and properties of a potent inhibitor of *Pseudomonas aeruginosa* deacetylase LpxC. *Journal of Medicinal Chemistry* 60 (12): 5002–5014.

29 Brown, M.F., Reilly, U., Abramite, J.A. et al. (2012). Potent inhibitors of LpxC for the treatment of Gram-negative infections. *Journal of Medicinal Chemistry* 55 (2): 914–923.

30 Montgomery, J.I., Brown, M.F., Reilly, U. et al. (2012). Pyridone methylsulfone hydroxamate LpxC inhibitors for the treatment of serious Gram-negative infections. *Journal of Medicinal Chemistry* 55 (4): 1662–1670.

31 Lee, P.S., Lapointe, G., Madera, A.M. et al. (2018). Application of virtual screening to the identification of new LpxC inhibitor chemotypes, oxazolidinone and isoxazoline. *Journal of Medicinal Chemistry* 61 (20): 9360–9370.

32 Cohen, F., Aggen, J.B., Andrews, L.D. et al. (2019). Optimization of LpxC inhibitors for antibacterial activity and cardiovascular safety. *ChemMedChem* 14 (16): 1560–1572.

33 Blank, B.R., Talukder, P., Muir, R.K. et al. (2019). Targeting mobilization of ferrous iron in *Pseudomonas aeruginosa* infection with an Iron(II)-Caged LpxC inhibitor. *ACS Infectious Diseases* 5 (8): 1366–1375.

34 Surivet, J.-P., Panchaud, P., Specklin, J.-L. et al. (2020). Discovery of novel inhibitors of LpxC displaying potent in vitro activity against gram-negative bacteria. *Journal of Medicinal Chemistry* 63 (1): 66–87.

35 Panchaud, P., Surivet, J.P., Diethelm, S. et al. (2020). Optimization of LpxC inhibitor lead compounds focusing on efficacy and formulation for high dose intravenous administration. *Journal of Medicinal Chemistry* 63 (1): 88–102.

36 Rodríguez-Alvarado, M., Russo, R., Connell, N.D. et al. (2020). Design, organocatalytic synthesis, and bioactivity evaluation of enantiopure fluorinated LpxC inhibitors. *Organic & Biomolecular Chemistry* 18 (30): 5867–5878.

37 Basak, S., Li, Y., Tao, S. et al. (2022). Structure–kinetic relationship studies for the development of long residence time LpxC inhibitors. *Journal of Medicinal Chemistry* 65 (17): 11854–11875.

38 Chen, M.-H., Steiner, M.G., De Laszlo, S.E. et al. (1999). Carbohydroxamido-oxazolidines: antibacterial agents that target lipid A biosynthesis. *Bioorganic & Medicinal Chemistry Letters* 9 (3): 313–318.

39 Kline, T., Andersen, N.H., Harwood, E.A. et al. (2002). Potent, novel in vitro inhibitors of the *pseudomonas aeruginosa* deacetylase LpxC. *Journal of Medicinal Chemistry* 45 (14): 3112–3129.

40 Pirrung, M.C., Tumey, L.N., Mcclerren, A.L. et al. (2003). High-throughput catch-and-release synthesis of oxazoline hydroxamates. Structure-activity relationships in novel inhibitors of *Escherichia coli* LpxC: *in vitro* enzyme inhibition and antibacterial properties. *Journal of the American Chemical Society* 125 (6): 1575–1586.

41 Jackman, J.E., Fierke, C.A., Tumey, L.N. et al. (2000). Antibacterial agents that target lipid A biosynthesis in gram-negative bacteria. Inhibition of diverse UDP-3-O-(r-3-hydroxymyristoyl)-N-acetylglucosamine deacetylases by substrate analogs containing zinc binding motifs. *The Journal of Biological Chemistry* 275 (15): 11002–11009.

42 Li, X., Mcclerren, A.L., Raetz, C.R.H. et al. (2005). Mapping the active site of the bacterial enzyme Lpxc using novel carbohydrate-based hydroxamic acid inhibitors. *Journal of Carbohydrate Chemistry* 24: 583–609.

43 Clements John, M., Coignard, F., Johnson, I. et al. (2002). Antibacterial activities and characterization of novel inhibitors of LpxC. *Antimicrobial Agents and Chemotherapy* 46 (6): 1793–1799.

44 Oddo, A. and Holl, R. (2012). Design and stereoselective synthesis of a C-aryl furanoside as a conformationally constrained CHIR-090 analogue. *Carbohydrate Research* 359: 59–64.

45 Jana, S.K., Löppenberg, M., Daniliuc, C.G. et al. (2013). Development of novel LpxC inhibitors: chiral-pool synthesis of C-triazolyl glycosides. *Tetrahedron* 69: 9434–9442.

46 Jana, S.K., Löppenberg, M., Daniliuc, C.G. et al. (2014). C-Triazolyl β-d-furanosides as LpxC inhibitors: stereoselective synthesis and biological evaluation. *Tetrahedron* 70 (37): 6569–6577.

47 Jana, S.K., Löppenberg, M., Daniliuc, C.G. et al. (2015). Synthesis and biological evaluation of C-ethynyl furanosides as LpxC inhibitors. *Tetrahedron* 71 (6): 956–966.

48 Löppenberg, M., Müller, H., Pulina, C. et al. (2013). Synthesis and biological evaluation of flexible and conformationally constrained LpxC inhibitors. *Organic & Biomolecular Chemistry* 11 (36): 6056–6070.

49 Dreger, A., Kharwb, O., Agoglitta, O. et al. (2019). Chiral pool synthesis, biological evaluation and molecular docking studies of c-furanosidic LpxC inhibitors. *ChemMedChem* 14 (8): 871–886.

50 Dreger, A., Hoff, K., Agoglitta, O. et al. (2021). Antibacterial activity of xylose-derived LpxC inhibitors – synthesis, biological evaluation and molecular docking studies. *Bioorganic Chemistry* 107: 104603.

51 Dreger, A., Hoff, K., Agoglitta, O. et al. (2021). Synthesis, biological evaluation, and molecular docking studies of deoxygenated C-glycosides as LpxC inhibitors. *Bioorganic Chemistry* 117: 105403.

52 Hoff, K., Mielniczuk, S., Agoglitta, O. et al. (2020). Synthesis and biological evaluation of triazolyl-substituted benzyloxyacetohydroxamic acids as LpxC inhibitors. *Bioorganic & Medicinal Chemistry* 28 (13): 115529.

53 Murphy-Benenato, K.E., Olivier, N., Choy, A. et al. (2014). Synthesis, structure, and SAR of tetrahydropyran-based LpxC inhibitors. *ACS Medicinal Chemistry Letters* 5 (11): 1213–1218.

54 Kurasaki, H., Tsuda, K., Shinoyama, M. et al. (2016). LpxC inhibitors: design, synthesis, and biological evaluation of oxazolidinones as gram-negative antibacterial agents. *ACS Medicinal Chemistry Letters* 7 (6): 623–628.

55 Pirrung, M.C., Tumey, L.N., Raetz, C.R.H. et al. (2002). Inhibition of the antibacterial target UDP-(3-O-acyl)-N-acetylglucosamine deacetylase (LpxC): isoxazoline zinc amidase inhibitors bearing diverse metal binding groups. *Journal of Medicinal Chemistry* 45 (19): 4359–4370.

56 Yucheng, W., Guoning, Z., Juxian, W. et al. (2018). New zinc ion chelator and its preparation and application in anti-Gram-negative bacterial infection [P]. Chinese patent CN105669750B.

57 Shin, H., Gennadios, H.A., Whittington, D.A. et al. (2007). Amphipathic benzoic acid derivatives: synthesis and binding in the hydrophobic tunnel of the zinc deacetylase LpxC. *Bioorganic & Medicinal Chemistry* 15 (7): 2617–2623.

58 Barb, A.W., Leavy, T.M., Robins, L.I. et al. (2009). Uridine-based inhibitors as new leads for antibiotics targeting *Escherichia coli* LpxC. *Biochemistry* 48 (14): 3068–3077.

59 Furuya, T., Shapiro, A.B., Comita-Prevoir, J. et al. (2020). N-Hydroxyformamide LpxC inhibitors, their *in vivo* efficacy in a mouse *Escherichia coli* infection model, and their safety in a rat hemodynamic assay. *Bioorganic & Medicinal Chemistry* 28 (24): 115826.

60 Cavalli, A., Poluzzi, E., De Ponti, F. et al. (2002). Toward a pharmacophore for drugs inducing the long QT syndrome: insights from a CoMFA study of HERG K(+) channel blockers. *Journal of Medicinal Chemistry* 45 (18): 3844–3853.

61 Yamada, Y., Takashima, H., Walmsley, D.L. et al. (2020). Fragment-based discovery of novel non-hydroxamate Lpxc inhibitors with antibacterial activity. *Journal of Medicinal Chemistry* 63 (23): 14805–14820.

62 Ushiyama, F., Takashima, H., Matsuda, Y. et al. (2021). Lead optimization of 2-hydroxymethyl imidazoles as non-hydroxamate LpxC inhibitors: Discovery of TP0586532. *Bioorganic & Medicinal Chemistry* 30: 115964.

17

Substrate and Inhibitor Discovery of Human Glutaminyl Cyclases

Jun Mou[1], Xiang-Min Dong[1], Jing-Wei Wu[1], Ling-Ling Yang[2], and Guo-Bo Li[1]

[1]*Sichuan University, Department of Medicinal Chemistry, West China School of Pharmacy, No.17, Section 3, Renmin South Road, Chengdu 610041, Sichuan, P.R. China*
[2]*Xihua University, College of Food and Bioengineering, No.999, Jinzhou Road, Jinniu District, Chengdu 610039, China*

17.1 Introduction

Post-translational modifications (PTMs) expand the functional diversity of the proteome by modulating protein stability, conformation, and interaction networks [1–3]. N-terminal pyroglutamation (pyroglutamate, pE) is a distinctive PTM that critically influences protein stability, bioactivity, and receptor affinity. Formation of the N-terminal pE residue is catalyzed by zinc-dependent glutaminyl cyclases, and in humans these occur as two isoforms, the secretory form (sQC) and the Golgi-resident form (gQC). The zinc-coordinating residues and the catalytic triad in the active pockets of sQC and gQC are highly conserved, giving rise to similar catalytic mechanisms. However, their differing subcellular localizations (sQC in secretory vesicles, gQC in the Golgi) and subtle active-site structural differences result in distinct substrate repertoires and divergent physiological roles.

pE formation contributes to normal peptide maturation (for example, thyrotropin-releasing hormone and other neuroendocrine peptides) but also to disease. Pyroglutamylated Aβ (pE-Aβ) is especially aggregation-prone and neurotoxic and is a key component of Alzheimer's disease (AD) plaques; N-terminal pE on CD47 strengthens SIRPα binding and promotes cancer immune evasion; pE-modified BTN family members can alter Vγ9Vδ2 T cell recognition and cytotoxicity, impacting antitumor immunity. These links make sQC/gQC attractive therapeutic targets, yet important challenges remain. The substrate repertoire is incompletely defined, and drug discovery has been hampered by a shortage of clinical candidates, limited target selectivity among preclinical inhibitors, suboptimal pharmacokinetics and safety concerns. Therefore, in the following sections, we summarize the structural and catalytic characteristics, substrates, associated diseases, and reported inhibitors of sQC/gQC, along with their respective inhibition mechanisms.

J.M., X.-M.D. and J.-W.W. are co-first authors.

Drug Discovery Targeting Metalloenzymes: Strategies and Applications, First Edition. Edited by Guo-Bo Li.

17.2 Structural and Catalytic Features of sQC and gQC

17.2.1 sQC/gQC Structures

sQC/gQC are structurally similar to the M28 peptidase family, which includes aminopeptidases and carboxypeptidases characterized by co-catalytic zinc ions. The primary distinction between sQC/gQC and other M28 peptidases lies in the loops surrounding the active-site pockets. Furthermore, unlike M28 enzymes that possess two co-catalytic zinc ions, sQC/gQC contain only a single catalytically active zinc ion, structurally equivalent to the higher affinity Zn1 found in M28 enzymes. This difference arises from a slight rotation in the side chains of residues His_{140} and Asp_{159}, which forms a unique hydrogen bond network in sQC/gQC, thereby preventing the coordination of Zn2 (Figure 17.1a) [4].

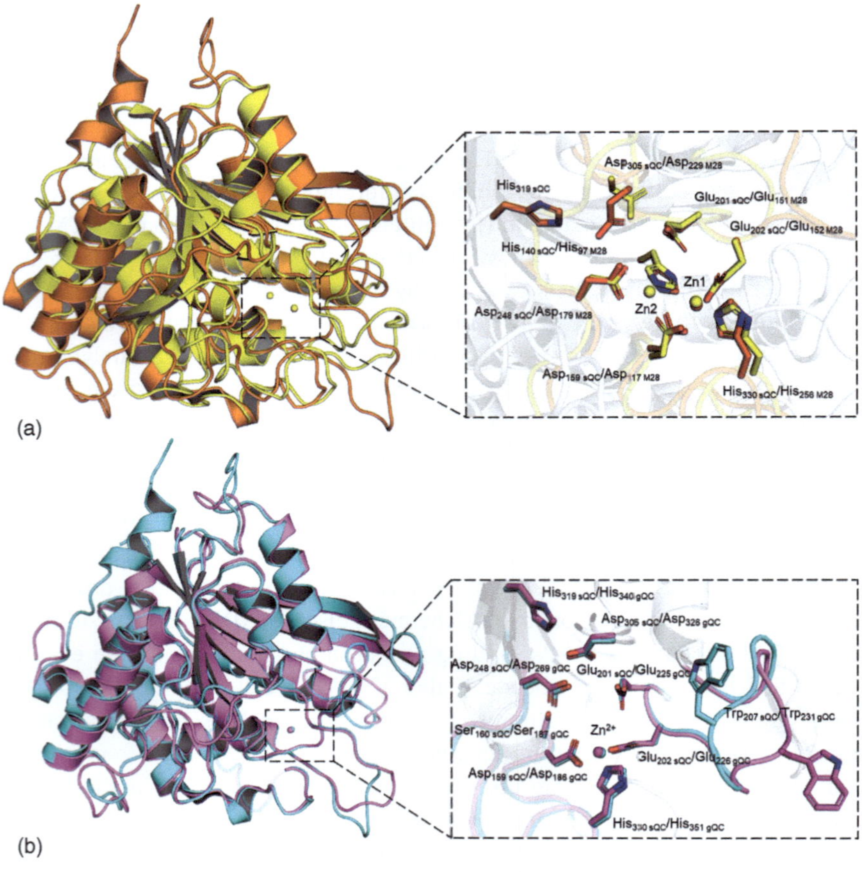

Figure 17.1 Comparison of the M28 enzyme and hQC structures. (a) Superimposition of the structures of sQC (orange) and M28 (yellow) enzyme. The hydrogen bond network formed by the trad of Glu_{201}–Asp_{305}–Asp_{248} hinders the combination of the Zn2. (b) Superimposition of the structures of sQC (cyan) and gQC (violet). The conformational differences between Trp_{207} in sQC and Trp_{231} in gQC result in variations in the size of their binding sites, which in turn affect substrate specificity.

sQC is encoded by the QPCT gene located at 2p22.2, while gQC is encoded by the QPCTL gene located at 19p13.32 [5, 6]. sQC contains an N-terminal signaling sequence that facilitates secretion, leading to its predominant expression in the endocrine and central nervous systems, where it regulates various neurotransmitters and hormones. In contrast, gQC has an N-terminal anchoring sequence that targets it to the Golgi apparatus, where it primarily functions in modifying intracellular proteins, especially those in the secretory pathway. Despite their distinct localizations, sQC and gQC share approximately 45% sequence identity, a similar mixed α/β architecture, and catalyze the same enzymatic reaction [7, 8].

Both isoforms include a signal peptide composed of 27–28 amino acid residues with a positively charged N-terminus, a central hydrophobic region with 10 residues, and a C-terminus containing critical nonpolar residues. Their structures resemble an open sandwich topology, featuring two α-helices on one side, six α-helices on the opposite side, and a central six-stranded β-sheet [9].

The structural differences between sQC and gQC are primarily attributed to variations in the flexibility of their loops, particularly loop2, located at the active site. In gQC, the substrate-binding site is significantly extended due to a 15 Å shift in the position of the indole ring of Trp_{231} on loop2 compared to Trp_{207} in sQC (Figure 17.1b).

The catalytic domain of sQC/gQC features a hydrophobic entrance and a relatively narrow binding pocket. In the apo structure, a catalytic zinc ion resides at the bottom of the active pocket, coordinated by three conserved residues – Asp, Glu, and His (Asp_{159}, Glu_{202}, and His_{330} in sQC; Asp_{186}, Glu_{226}, and His_{351} in gQC) – and a water molecule. Upon substrate entry into the binding pocket, the substrate replaces the water molecule, binding to the zinc ion while maintaining a tetrahedral structure. Additional conserved residues, including Glu_{201}, Trp_{207}, Asp_{248}, Asp_{305}, Phe_{325}, and Trp_{329} in sQC and Glu_{225}, Trp_{231}, Asp_{269}, Asp_{326}, Phe_{346}, and Trp_{350} in gQC, are situated near the zinc-binding site, suggesting potential involvement in interactions with the catalytic center (Figure 17.1b).

In sQC, the active site exists in two conformations: open and closed. The primary difference between these conformations is the orientation of the indole ring of Trp_{207}, which may switch between the two conformations during catalysis. In contrast, gQC features a more open and negatively charged active site, with the indole ring of Trp_{231} consistently oriented outward, forming a hydrogen bond with Pro_{256} [8]. This structural difference may underlie the varying substrate specificities of sQC and gQC.

17.2.2 Proposed sQC/gQC Catalytic Mechanisms

The physiological function of sQC and gQC is to catalyze the pyroglutamylation of N-terminal glutamine or glutamate in different proteins or peptides, leading to various physiological or pathological effects.

sQC/gQC are zinc-dependent enzymes, with the catalytic zinc ion located in the active pocket, where it coordinates with the substrate and polarizes it. Additionally, a unique hydrogen bond network, formed by the triads Glu_{201}–Asp_{248}–Asp_{305} in

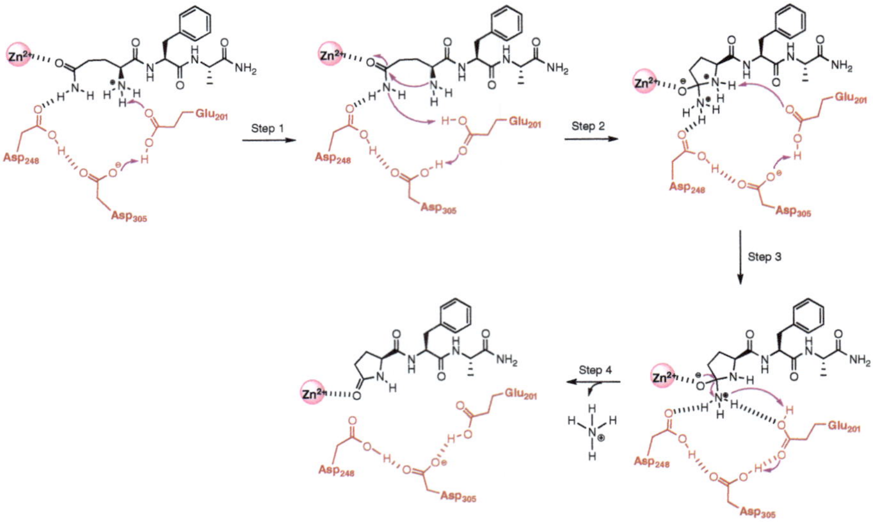

Figure 17.2 . sQC-catalyzed pyroglutamate modification mechanism for peptides containing N-terminal glutamate. The reactions are divided into four steps. During the reactions, the zinc ion polarizes the amide group through coordination and stabilizes the reaction intermediate, while the triad participates in the proton transfer process.

sQC and Glu_{225}–Asp_{326}–Asp_{269} in gQC, plays a pivotal role in the catalytic process [4, 10, 11]. When the substrate enters the sQC/gQC catalytic site, it displaces the water molecule bound to the metal and coordinates with the zinc ion via its side chain carbonyl group. The pyroglutamylation of the substrate is accompanied by the transfer of a proton from the substrate's α-amino group to the leaving amino or hydroxyl group. Figure 17.2 shows a possible catalytic mechanism for sQC/gQC. The zinc ion polarizes the γ-amino group and the acyl carbon through coordination with the acyl oxygen. Glu_{201} acts as a general base, abstracting a proton from the α-amino group, exposing a lone electron pair on the α-amino group. The α-amino group then attacks the polarized acyl carbon, forming a tetrahedral intermediate. The zinc ion stabilizes the negatively charged oxygen in the intermediate. Glu_{201} transfers the abstracted proton to the γ-amino group. Then, the γ-amino group departs, resulting in the formation of pyroglutamate.

17.3 Pathological and Therapeutic Perspective of sQC/gQC

Aberrant pE modifications are associated with the pathogenesis of several human diseases. Dysregulated pE modifications have been implicated in the pathogenesis of neurodegenerative disorders, including Alzheimer's disease (AD) and Parkinson's disease (PD) (Figure 17.3). In AD, the pE modifications on protein are a crucial

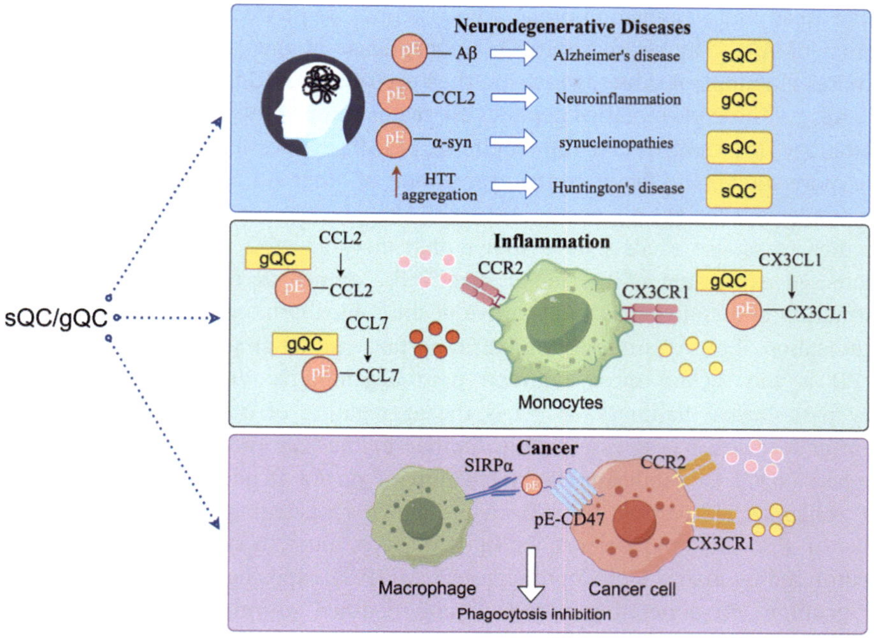

Figure 17.3 The role of sQC/gQC in disease pathogenesis.

event in the initiation and the progress of the disease, as the protein demonstrates increased neurotoxicity and a propensity to aggregate. Likewise, the pE modifications of α-synuclein serve as seeds for oligomer formation, contributing to enhanced aggregation, compromised degradation of α-synuclein, and an increased risk of PD. Recently, emerging studies have shown that excessive pE modifications on proteins are associated with cancer immunity. For example, the CD47 pE modifications affect the CD47-SIRPα interaction enabling the malignant cells to evade phagocytosis by macrophages (Figure 17.3) [12, 13].

17.3.1 Neurodegenerative Diseases

pE modification, catalyzed by sQC/gQC, has been implicated in the development of several neurodegenerative diseases, including AD, PD, Huntington's disease (HD), etc. These disorders are marked by the aggregation and accumulation of abnormal proteins. pE-modified peptides exhibit altered biochemical properties, such as increased hydrophobicity and stability, which promote protein aggregation and hinder proteolytic degradation [14]. These properties make pE-modified peptides significant contributors to neurodegenerative pathogenesis.

AD, a leading cause of cognitive decline in the elderly, is characterized by the accumulation of amyloid-beta (Aβ) in senile plaques. In early AD, these plaques primarily contain the non-toxic $A\beta_{1\text{-}40}$ peptide. As the disease progresses, the more toxic and aggregation-prone A$\beta_{1\text{-}42}$ peptide is produced. Enzymatic truncation of A$\beta_{1\text{-}42}$ by secretase and aminopeptidase at the 3rd or 11th positions exposes glutamate residues, which are then cyclized by sQC to form pE-A$\beta_{3\text{-}40}$ and pE-A$\beta_{3\text{-}42}$. These pE-modified peptides are major components of Aβ plaques in AD pathology [15]. Compared to full-length Aβ, pE-Aβ peptides aggregate more readily, are more stable, and facilitate the aggregation of other Aβ species, forming toxic low-molecular-weight oligomers [16]. gQC also plays a role in AD pathogenesis. Studies in mouse models have shown that elevated gQC levels correlate with increased expression of the chemokine CCL2, which accelerates Aβ oligomer formation and contributes to cognitive decline. Furthermore, gQC enhances the aggregation of pE-Aβ, underscoring its importance in AD progression.

PD is the second most common neurodegenerative disorder after AD. A key pathological hallmark of PD is the aggregation of α-synuclein, a process central to disease progression [17]. Similar to the role of secretory glutaminyl cyclase (sQC) in catalyzing the formation of pE-Aβ peptides, which promote Aβ oligomer formation in AD, truncated α-synuclein plays a comparable role in PD. This process occurs in two steps. First, α-synuclein is partially hydrolyzed by matrix metalloproteinase-3 (MMP-3), exposing a glutamate residue at position 79, generating pyroglutamate-modified α-synuclein (pE-79-α-syn). Subsequently, sQC catalyzes the cyclization of this glutamate residue, producing pyroglutamate-modified α-synuclein (pE-79-α-syn) [14, 17]. Compared to full-length α-synuclein, pE-79-a-syn exhibits enhanced neurotoxicity and aggregation rate, potentially acting as a seed for protein aggregation in synucleinopathies, contributing to disease pathogenesis.

HD is a hereditary neurodegenerative disorder characterized by progressive motor dysfunction, cognitive impairment, and psychiatric symptoms. It results from an expanded CAG trinucleotide repeat in the HTT gene, leading to the production of a mutant huntingtin protein with an abnormally long polyglutamine tract. sQC may contribute to HD pathogenesis through mechanisms similar to those observed in AD, potentially promoting huntingtin aggregation and neurotoxicity. Additionally, sQC-mediated neuroinflammatory pathways may intersect with dysregulated inflammation in HD, exacerbating neuronal damage. Further research is needed to clarify these mechanisms [18].

17.3.2 Inflammation

QC-mediated pE-modification also plays a key role in inflammatory processes by altering chemokine activity and stability. CCL2, a chemokine produced by microglial cells, astrocytes, and immune cells, recruits monocytes and microglia to sites of inflammation by binding to its receptor CCR2 [19]. Disruptions in CCL2 levels are associated with pathological changes in inflammatory diseases such as atherosclerosis, fibrosis, and AD. The intact N-terminus is essential for CCL2 to function properly. Any truncation or elongation of this region leads to a loss of function. *In vivo*, the N-terminus of CCL2 is typically cyclized into pE-CCL2 by sQC. Compared to CCL2, pE-CCL2 exhibits higher functional activity and an extended half-life, resulting in an exaggerated inflammatory response. *In vivo*, CCL2 is rapidly degraded by enzymes such as dipeptidyl peptidase 4 (DPP4), aminopeptidase P (ApP), and matrix metalloproteinase-1 (MMP-1). Given its susceptibility to enzymatic breakdown, modulating the formation of pyroglutamate at the N-terminus of CCL2 by inhibiting sQC activity presents a viable strategy for reducing receptor activation. This approach could potentially serve as an effective therapeutic intervention for inflammatory diseases by limiting the pro-inflammatory signaling associated with CCL2 [20].

CX3CL1, another chemokine involved in monocyte recruitment, also requires pE-modification at its N-terminus by QC for full activation. This modification is essential for the CX3CL1/CX3CR1 signaling axis and downstream activation of pathways such as ERK1/2, p38, and Akt. Given its role in inflammation, targeting QC to reduce pE-CX3CL1 levels offers a potential avenue for treating chronic and acute inflammatory diseases [21].

17.3.3 Cancer and Other Diseases

QC activity has also been implicated in cancer progression and other diseases by modulating protein stability and signaling pathways. In tissues from Sunitinib-nonresponsive renal cell carcinoma (RCC), reduced methylation levels in the sQC promoter region have been observed. Hypomethylation facilitates NF-κB binding and subsequently leads to the overexpression of sQC. Furthermore, the upregulation of sQC contributes to the modification of HRAS, which prevents its ubiquitination and subsequent degradation. Stabilized HRAS results in the activation of the ERK signaling pathway, ultimately promoting tumor progression in RCC. These findings highlight the critical role of sQC in tumor progression and the therapeutic challenges associated with RCC [22]. In addition to RCC, high sQC expression is observed in melanoma, potentially interfering with immune-targeted therapies by stabilizing tumor antigens with N-terminal glutamine residues [23]. In thyroid cancer, sQC expression is upregulated, correlating with increased levels of pE-CCL2. CCL2 is secreted predominantly in the pE-CCL2 form. This enhances monocyte recruitment and activates the CCL2-CCR2 signaling pathway, driving cancer progression. In contrast, gQC expression remains unchanged in thyroid cancer [24].

CD47 is a transmembrane protein widely expressed on the surface of various cell types, including immune cells, endothelial cells, and cancer cells. Its primary function is to act as a “don’t eat me” signal by binding to signal regulatory protein alpha (SIRPα) on macrophages and other phagocytic cells. This interaction inhibits the process of phagocytosis, thereby allowing cells to evade immune surveillance. The 19th glutamine at the N-terminus of CD47 is modified to pE by gQC, which is essential for its binding to SIRPα. The crystal structure of the CD47-SIRPα complex shows that pE is key to the binding interface. Knockout of gQC significantly reduces SIRPα's binding affinity to CD47, while sQC absence has no effect. These findings underscore gQC's critical role in cancer progression by modulating the CD47-SIRPα signaling axis [13].

Bone mineral density (BMD) is a crucial measure of bone strength and an indicator of osteoporosis risk. The study on the association between multiple nucleotide variations in the pituitary sQC and low radial BMD in adult women suggests that variations in the sQC gene may influence bone health. Genetic variations in sQC primarily contribute to osteoporosis susceptibility by affecting the regulation of peptide hormones, such as gonadotropin-releasing hormone (GnRH) and thyrotropin-releasing hormone (TRH) [25].

17.4 sQC/gQC Inhibitor Discovery

Given the pivotal role of N-terminal protein pE modifications catalyzed by sQC/gQC in pathological mechanisms, inhibiting sQC/gQC activity may offer a promising therapeutic opportunity for pE-related diseases. Hence, there has been a significant effort focused on the discovery and development of novel and effective sQC/gQC inhibitors, including some derived from natural products. Based on their metal-binding group (MBG), sQC/gQC inhibitors are primarily categorized into imidazole, benzimidazole, and triazole derivatives. The following sections review sQC/gQC inhibitor design strategies, chemical classes, and the molecular basis of inhibitor–target binding.

17.4.1 Imidazole Derivatives

In 2003, Vivoryon was the first to disclose that human sQC/gQC are metal-dependent enzymes and identified the imidazole as a weak competitive sQC/gQC inhibitor acting as a zinc chelating agent [26]. Subsequently, the focus shifted to exploring a set of five- and six-membered heterocycles, which were found to be less potent than imidazole. Modifications at the N1 position of the imidazole moiety significantly affected the inhibitory potency. Compared to imidazole, methylation and benzylation at the N1 position resulted in a 3- and 14-fold potency increase, respectively. However, methylation at the 2-position of 1-benzylimidazole is detrimental to the sQC/gQC inhibitory effect. Based on these results, structure-based screening of alkyl-imidazoles identified two moderately active derivatives, compounds 1 and 2, with K_i values of 1.2 μM and 818 nM, respectively (Figure 17.4). To further improve inhibitory potency, a ligand-based optimization approach was employed for the imidazol-1-yl-alkyl thiourea scaffold. As a result, structure–activity relationship (SAR) studies identified thiourea derivative **3** (also known as **PBD150**, K_i value of 60 nM for sQC) and the thioamide derivative **4** (K_i value of 90 nM for sQC) as the two most active inhibitors in the series (Figure 17.4) [27]. Crystal complex analysis shows that compound **3** coordinates the catalytic zinc ion via its imidazole ring,

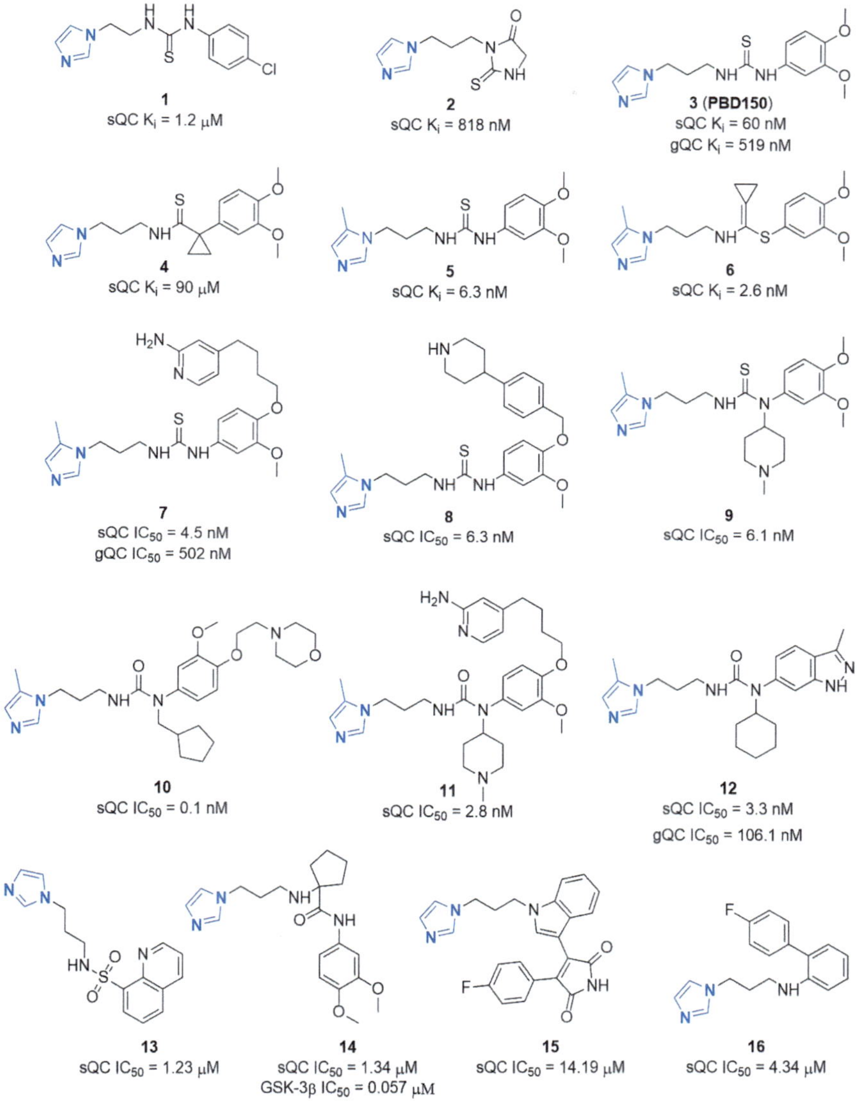

Figure 17.4 Representative sQC/gQC inhibitors **1–16** with imidazole and 5-methylimidazole moieties.

its urea group hydrogen-bonds with Gln_{304}, and its aryl substituents pack against Ile_{303}, Phe_{325} and Trp_{329}, including a π–π interaction with Phe_{325} (Figure 17.5).

By modifying the thiourea moiety of **PDB 150** to various bioisosteres, new classes of inhibitors were identified. A homology model of sQC was used to investigate how the MBG interacts with the sQC active site. In compounds **5** and **6**, the imidazole moiety of **PBD150** was replaced with 5-methylimidazole which significantly improved potency (Figure 17.4). Furthermore, the methyl-substituted imidazole derivatives **5** and **6** were shown shown to prevent pE-$A\beta_{3\text{-}40/42}$ formation in a cellular model [28].

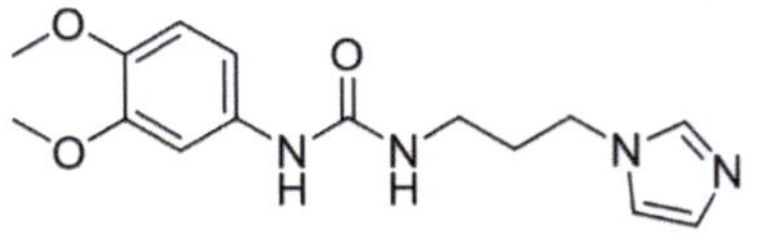

3 (PBD150)

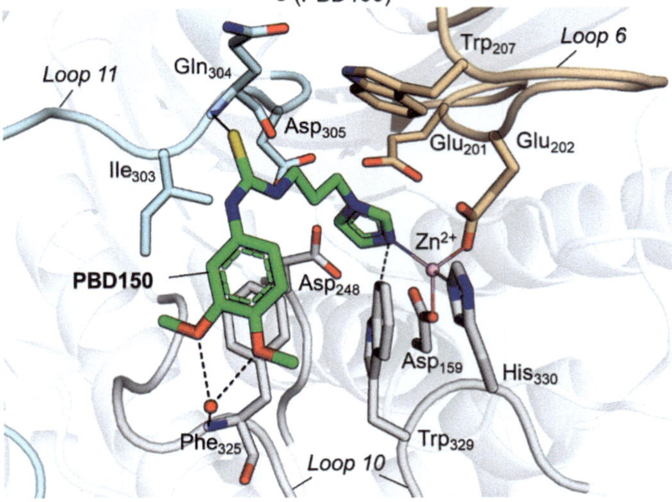

Figure 17.5 View of a crystal structure of the sQC:**PBD150** (3PBB). *Source:* Adapted from Huang et al. [8].

Over the past decades, Jeewoo and colleagues have devoted considerable effort to developing sQC/gQC inhibitors derived from 5-methylimidazole. In 2013, they summarized three pharmacophores of sQC/gQC inhibitors based on previously reported compounds: the A-region, which is the zinc-binding part (such as imidazole) that binds to zinc ions at the active site; the B-region, a hydrophobic residue containing a hydrogen bond donor (such as propyl urea) that mimics the amide nitrogen of Gln; and the C-region, an aromatic ring that simulates the Phe side chain [29]. In 2017, aiming to identify an additional pharmacophore termed the D-region, they reported a series of 5-methylimidazole derivatives guided by a proposed binding mode of the N-terminal tripeptide (Glu-Phe-Arg) of $A\beta_{3\text{-}42}$. Compared with **PBD150**, these derivatives displayed markedly enhanced inhibitory activity against sQC/gQC, with potencies increased by roughly 5- to 40-fold. Specifically, the D-region was found to strengthen ligand–protein interactions by mimicking the guanidinium group of Arg and forming additional contacts with the enzyme active site. Within this series, compound **7** proved most active, with IC_{50} value of 4.5 nM for sQC. Subsequent *in vivo* studies showed that compound **7** reduced brain levels of pE-Aβ and total Aβ and, thanks to its favorable blood–brain barrier (BBB) permeability, ultimately restored cognitive function in mouse models of AD. Aβ-lowering effect was attributed to a strong interaction between the introduced D-region pharmacophore and the carboxylate of Glu_{327} in the sQC binding site [30]. Similar to compound **7**, compound **8** was a D-region-modified analogue that exhibited potent sQC inhibitory activity *in vitro* (Figure 17.4); in acute AD mice, treatment with compound **8** could reduced the formation of =pE-A$\beta_{3\text{-}40}$ by 30% [31].

The crystal structure of the sQC:**PBD150** showed **PBD150** adopting a bent conformation at the sQC active site (Figure 17.5), leading to the investigation of N-substituted thiourea, urea, and α-substituted amide analogues inspired by this conformation. To induce the formation of Z-E conformers, various alkyl, aromatic, and heteroaromatic groups were added as conformational blockers. Comprehensive SAR analyses revealed that conformational restriction significantly enhanced sQC inhibition, with increases of up to 100-fold for ureas, 20-fold for thioureas, and 8-fold for amides. Therefore, this conformational restriction in the library is central to the enhanced potency. The most promising compound **9** (IC_{50} value of 6.1 nM for sQC, Figure 17.4) exhibited excellent efficacy, good BBB penetration, and low cytotoxicity. Further assessments corroborated that inhibitor **9** significantly reduces the generation of pE-A$\beta_{3\text{-}42}$ and total Aβ, and restored cognitive functions in AD mice [32].

Related studies have revealed potent sQC/gQC inhibitor with favorable drug-like properties, developed using pharmacophore-based and structure-based approaches. For example, compounds **10** and **11** exhibit low-nanomolar inhibition of sQC (Figure 17.4); importantly, compound **11** demonstrates superior *in vivo* efficacy, selectivity, and a more druggable profile than compound **10**. Therefore, compound **11** was tested in 5XFAD transgenic mice to assess its *in vivo* efficacy. Treatment with compound **11** significantly lowered pE-Aβ and total Aβ levels in the brain and improved alternation behavior in the Y-maze test [33]. In the following research, the researchers expanded the library of thiourea analogues using a bioisosteric replacement strategy and obtained compound **12**, which displayed high potency and favorable drug-like properties (Figure 17.4) [34].

Haiqiang Wu's team employed structure-guided design, replacing the thiourea motif with a diphenyl fragment to increase molecular rigidity and hydrophobicity, and synthesized a series of diphenyl-conjugated imidazole derivatives (DPCIs). Among these, derivative **13** showed good sQC inhibitory activity; in cultured cells, compound **13** strongly inhibited sQC activity without affecting its expression and markedly reduced the production of pE-A$\beta_{3\text{-}42}$. In addition, **13** scored well in BBB penetration assays and improved behavioral performance in an AD mouse model (Figure 17.4) [35]. Given recent findings that abnormal upregulation of sQC and glycogen synthase kinase-3β (GSK-3β) both contribute to AD pathogenesis, the team further adopted a multitarget-directed ligand (MTDL) strategy to design and synthesize a series of dual sQC/GSK-3β inhibitors featuring maleimide and imidazole motifs. These compounds exhibited potent GSK-3β inhibitory activity while retaining good sQC inhibition; for example, compound **14** showed IC_{50} values of 1.34 μM and 0.057 nM against sQC and GSK-3β, respectively (Figure 17.4). In a 3 × Tg-AD mouse model, compound **14** ameliorated cognitive deficits and reduced the anxiety-like behavior by concurrently lowering the activity of sQC and GSK-3β, reducing Tau hyperphosphorylation, and decreasing the accumulation of and pE-Aβ [36].

To identify novel scaffolds, the team performed virtual screening of approximately 3 million compounds from the Chimdi and Enamine databases using a combination of ligand-based and receptor–ligand pharmacophore models, which yielded compounds **15** and **16** as gQC hits (Figure 17.4) [37].

17.4.2 Benzimidazole Derivatives

Benzimidazol was also demonstrated act as a metal-binding motif for sQC/gQC binding. In 2013, Vivoryon first performed three-dimensional flexible alignments of known sQC/gQC inhibitors and their natural substrates to derive shared pharmacophore features, and then used that pharmacophore model to virtually screen a compound library. This process culminated in the identification of benzimidazolyl-1,3,4-oxadiazole hits with single-digit micromolar potency, which emerged as a promising chemotype for further optimization. Compound **17**, with a K_i value of 23 nM for sQC, proved to be the most potent inhibitor, exhibiting more than a twofold improvement in activity compared with **PBD150** (Figure 17.6) [38].

Vivoryon has secured a patent portfolio covering multiple structurally diverse sQC/gQC inhibitors, including a class of benzimidazole-based molecules exemplified by compound **18 (PQ529)** (Figure 17.6) [39]. A 2013 study reported that **PQ529** significantly delayed the onset of clinical arthritis symptoms [40]. A 2021 study demonstrated that **the compound** exerted good anti-renal inflammatory effects by inhibiting gQC and thereby suppressing CCL2/CCR2 [41]. Together, these findings suggest that **PQ529** may be a promising candidate for treating inflammation-related diseases.

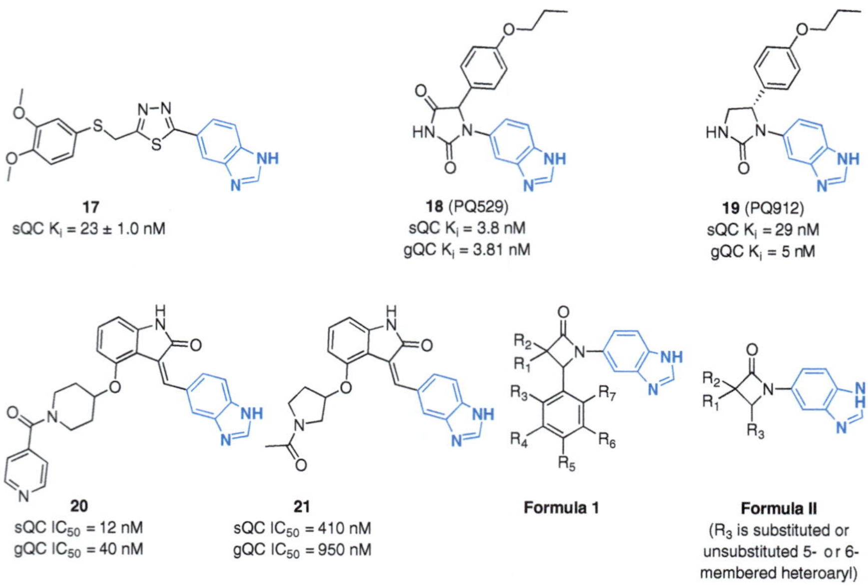

Figure 17.6 Representative sQC/gQC inhibitors **17–21**, **Formula I** and **Formula II** with benzimidazole motif.

Another representative of this series, compound **19** (**PQ912**, Figure 17.6), was the first sQC/gQC inhibitor to enter clinical trials [42, 43]. Fortunately, our group solved the X-ray crystal structure of the sQC:**PQ912** complex, which showed that the N3 atom of **PQ912** coordinates the active-site zinc ion in an atypical tetrahedral geometry. The N1 atom of the benzimidazole forms a weak hydrogen bond with the side chain of Asp_{248}, directed toward the catalytically significant central triad (Glu_{201}–Asp_{248}–Asp_{305}). The benzimidazole is tightly encased and stabilized by the indole groups of Trp_{207} and Trp_{329} through both face-to-face and edge-to-face π-π stacking interactions. In addition, the imidazolidin-2-one of **PQ912** forms a water-bridged hydrogen bond with Gln_{304}, while the propoxyphenyl is snugly accommodated in a hydrophobic pocket formed by Ile_{303}, Phe_{325}, and Trp_{329} (Figure 17.7a) [44].

Based on the sQC:**PQ912** crystal structure, our group designed and synthesized a series of novel benzimidazole derivatives. SAR studies identified several compounds with nanomolar inhibition against sQC/gQC. In particular, compound **20** demonstrated potency comparable to **PQ912**, with IC_{50} values of 0.012 μM and 0.040 μM against sQC/gQC, respectively. In MPTP-treated PD mouse models, compound **20** reversed the loss of dopaminergic neurons, reduced Iba1-positive microglia, and lowered levels of α-synuclein and CCL2, effects that together ameliorated MPTP-induced motor deficits across multiple behavioral tests [44]. We also solved the X-ray crystal structure of sQC:**21**. Similar to **PQ912**, the benzimidazole of compound **21** coordinates the active-site zinc ion, forms a hydrogen bond with Asp_{248}, and engages in π–π stacking with Trp_{207}. Furthermore, the 1-acetylpyrrolidin-3-yl substituent of compound **21** is well accommodated in a shallow groove formed by Tyr_{299}, Ile_{303}, Ser_{323}, and Phe_{325}, where it forms additional hydrogen bonds with Tyr_{299} and Ser_{323}. These interactions likely account for its strong inhibitory activity against both sQC/gQC (Figure 17.7b).

Fosun Pharma and Insilico Medicine have collaboratively developed **SM004-1057D**, a gQC inhibitor based on Formula I/II that is currently under investigation for applications in immuno-oncology, with its specific structure yet to be disclosed [45].

17.4.3 N-methyl Triazole Derivatives

The triazine ring reported by the Italian company Siena is a common and typical MBG in the design of sQC/gQC inhibitors. Compound **22** (**SEN177**, Figure 17.8), which incorporates this scaffold, exhibited activity comparable to **PQ912**, with IC_{50} values of 53 nM and 13 nM against sQC/gQC, respectively. In a HD model, **SEN177** effectively ameliorated disease phenotypes and reduced HTT aggregation at both cellular and animal experiments [46]. Moreover, the compound disrupts the CD47-SIRPα interaction by inhibiting gQC activity, thereby promoting the phagocytosis by immune cells and increasing immune-mediated cytotoxicity against tumors. Based on these findings, Valerius and co-workers described a combined immunotherapy approach employing **SEN177** together with an EGFR antibody [12, 47]. The X-ray cocrystal structure shows that **SEN177** replaces the zinc-binding

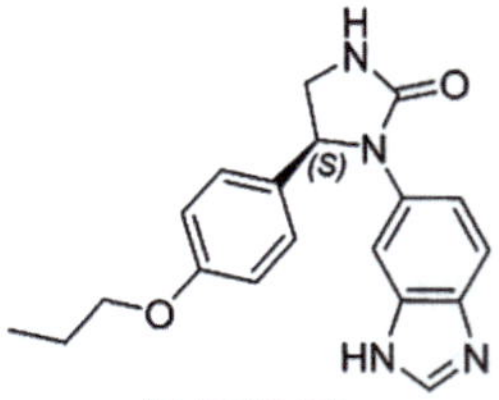

19 (PQ912)

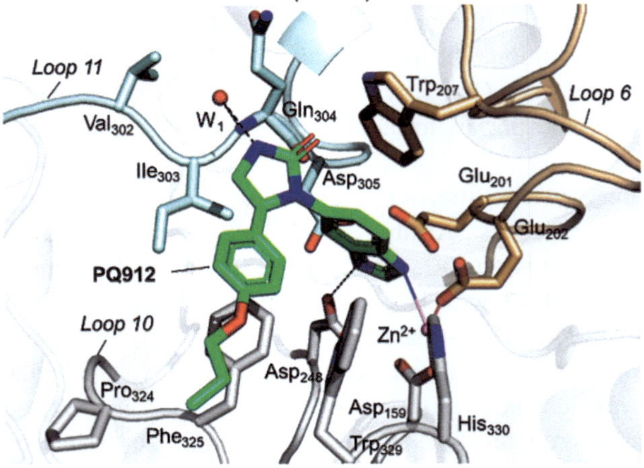

(a)

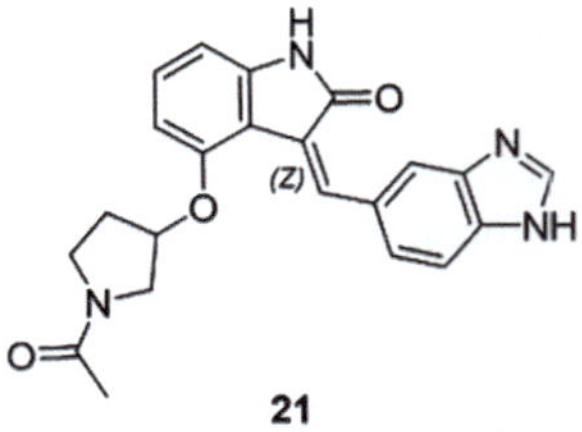

21

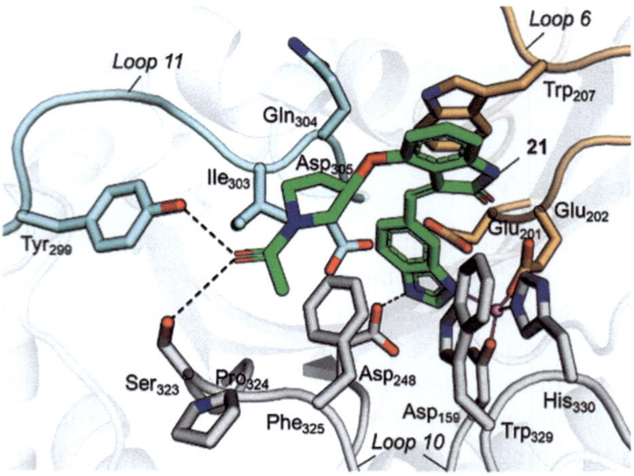

(b)

Figure 17.7 Crystallographic analysis of representative benzimidazole inhibitors **19** and **21** with sQC. (a) Crystal structures of sQC:**PQ912** (PDB code 8XGB) [44]. (b) Crystal structures of sQC:**21** (PDB code 8XGY). *Source:* [44] / American Chemical Society.

Figure 17.8 Representative N-methyl triazole-based sQC/gQC inhibitors **22–23**.

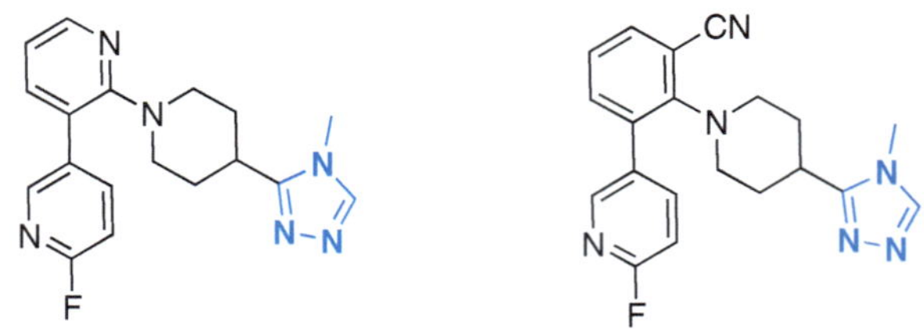

22 (SEN177)
sQC IC_{50} = 53 nM
gQC IC_{50} = 13 nM

23 (QP5020)
gQC IC_{50} = 15 nM

water molecule in the native enzyme chelates the zinc ion *via* the the triazole N1, forming a classic tetrahedral coordination geometry. The triazole fits into the hydrophobic pocket consisting of Trp_{207}, Phe_{325}, and Trp_{329}, with its N2 atom forming a weak hydrogen bond to the backbone nitrogen of Trp_{329}. Simultaneously, the pyridine nitrogen of **SEN177** establishes a water-bridging hydrogen bond to Gln_{304}, while the pyridine ring engages in π-π stacking with the side chain of Trp_{207}. An additional hydrogen bond is observed between the fluorine atom on the fluoropyridine and the N-H of His_{330} [46]. These multiple key interactions may explain why **SEN177** has excellent inhibition (Figure 17.9).

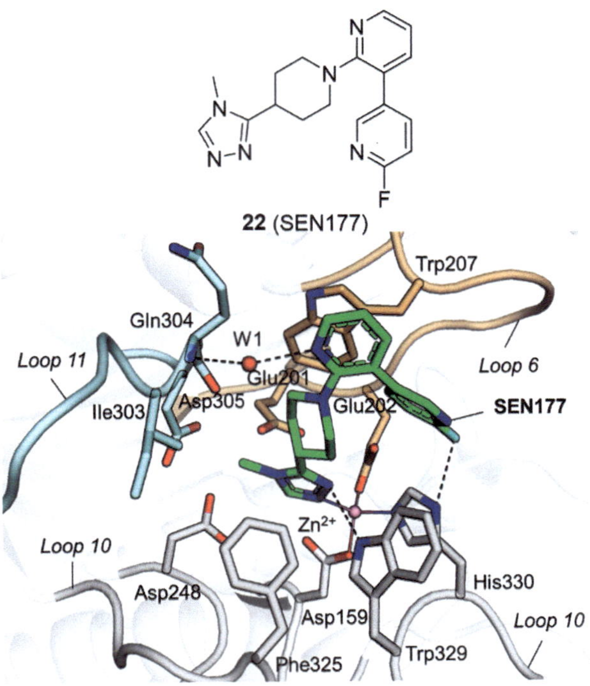

Figure 17.9 Crystal structures for sQC in complex with the inhibitor **22** (PDB code 6GBX). *Source:* [48] / Springer Nature / CC BY 4.0.

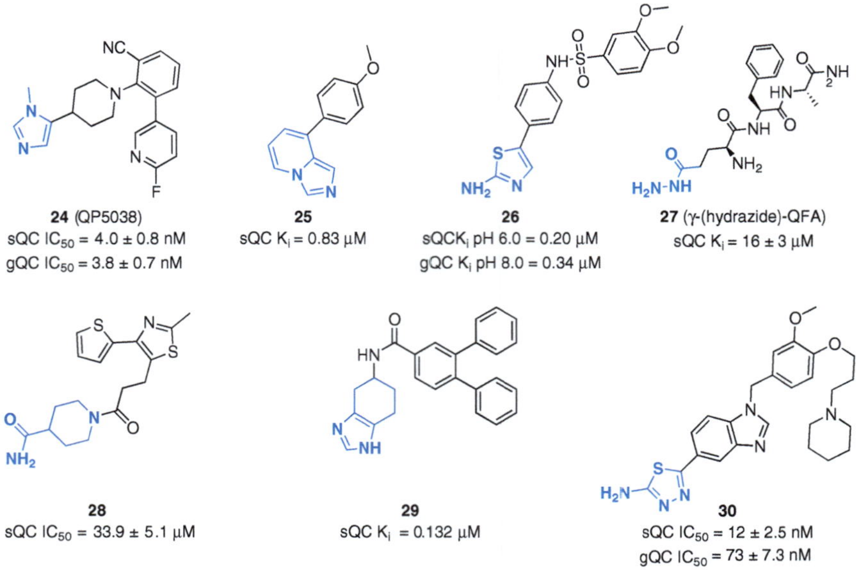

Figure 17.10 Representative compounds **24–30** with other scaffolds.

Leveraging the high conservation of the active sites between sQC and gQC, Wang and colleagues performed structure-based drug design using the sQC:SEN177 co-crystal structure. They replaced the pyridine ring nitrogen atom in **SEN177** with a cyano group, yielding compound **23** (**QP5020**). This modification was designed to enable the introduced cyano group to displace a water molecule in the gQC active site and form a direct hydrogen bond with the key residue Glu_{325}. The experimental results confirmed this rational design, as compound **23** exhibited a significant 8.7-fold increase in potency against gQC compared to the lead compound **SEN177** (Figure 17.8). Subsequent structural optimization by the team produced compound **24** (**QP5038**), which demonstrated nanomolar inhibitory activity, with IC_{50} values of 4.0 nM and 3.8 nM to sQC/gQC, respectively, and demonstrated promising antitumor efficacy*in vivo* studies (Figure 17.10) [48].

17.4.4 Others

In 2008, Vivoryon disclosed a novel class of inhibitors featuring an imidazo[1,5-*a*] pyridine MBG. Among them, the representative compound **25** showed micromolar inhibitory potency against sQC/gQC (Figure 17.10) [49].

In 2018, Vivoryon reported another series of compounds using 2-amino-1,3-thiazole as the MBG. The representative compound **26** exhibited micromolar inhibitory activity against sQC (Figure 17.10) [50].

Based on the analysis of the conformations and interactions of the substrate/product neurotensin within the active site of sQC, Tittmann team proposed a reaction pathway involving a tetrahedral transition state. And they hypothesized that molecules mimicking this transition state could serve as effective inhibitors. Subsequent experimental validation through sparse-matrix screening and kinetic isothermal titration calorimetry confirmed this hypothesis, revealing that the hydrazide group as a MBG exhibited the highest inhibitory activity among the tested compounds, significantly outperforming classical coordinating groups. The crystal structure of the sQC:**γ-(hydrazide)-QFA** complex demonstrated that the hydrazide forms a bidentate coordination with the catalytic zinc ion through its O and N2 atoms, resulting in a distorted five-membered chelate complex. This coordination geometry is stabilized by an extensive network of specific interactions with active site residues. The hydrazide O atom was observed to hydrogen-bond with the indole N-H group of Trp_{329}, while the N1 and N2 atoms interacted with both zinc-coordinating residues (His_{330}, Glu_{202}, and Asp_{159}) and key catalytic triad residues (Glu_{201} and Asp_{248}). Additional stabilization was provided by hydrogen bonding between the inhibitor's N-terminal α-amino group and Glu_{202}, as well as between the main chain atoms of the inhibitor and Gln_{304} (Figure 17.11a) [51]. These significant findings elucidate the structural basis of the hydrazide group as a highly effective MBG, providing a new strategic direction for the rational design of potent and highly selective sQC/gQC inhibitors.

Guided by pharmacophore-assisted high-throughput virtual screening, the Zhang group developed a series of piperidine-4-carboxamide derivatives. Among these, compound 28 demonstrated moderate inhibitory activity against sQC (IC_{50} = 33.9 μM, Figure 17.10). Crystal structure analysis revealed that compound **28** is anchored in the catalytic site by chelation of the active-site zinc ion *via* its amide moiety, which serves as a MBG. However, the compound does not form interactions with key hydrophobic residues (Ile_{303}, Phe_{325}, and Trp_{329}), which likely explains why its inhibitory potency remains at the micromolar level (Figure 17.11b) [52].

Some bacterial QCs, like *porphyromonas gingivalis* QC (PgQC), share structural and enzymatic similarity with hQC. Consequently, inhibitors developed against bacterial QC may also inhibit hQC. For instance, a compound **29**, which was originally synthesized as a PgQC inhibitor, exhibited good inhibitory activity against hQC with a K_i value of 0.132 μM (Figure 17.10) [53].

Through compound library screening, the Kang research team identified a hit compound containing a 2-amino-1,3,4-thiadiazole MBG. Subsequent structure-based optimization yielded lead compound **30**, which exhibited nanomolar-level inhibitory activity (Figure 17.10). In functional studies employing co-culture systems of A549 and H1975 lung cancer cells with THP-1 and U937 macrophages, treatment with compound **30** resulted in a dose-dependent enhancement of phagocytic activity in both macrophage types. This observed effect correlated with the inhibition of CD47-SIRPα interactions, indicating that the compound's immunomodulatory activity is achieved through blockade of this key immune checkpoint pathway, thereby demonstrating considerable therapeutic potential [54].

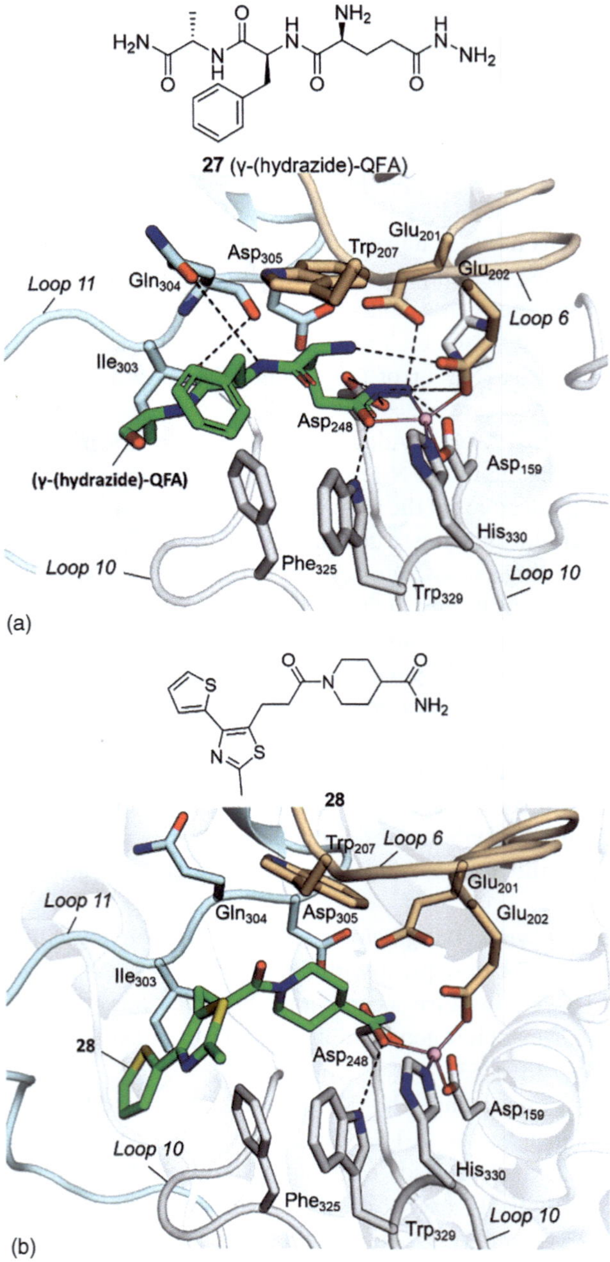

Figure 17.11 Crystallographic analysis of sQC:**27** and sQC:**28** complexes. (a) View of a crystal structure of the sQC:**27** (PDB code 6YI1). *Source:* Modified from [51]. (b) View of a crystal structure of the sQC:**28** (PDB code 7COZ) Adapted from [52].

17.4.5 Naturally Sourced Inhibitors

Natural products provide an important source for developing novel sQC/gQC inhibitors, with oleuropein aglycone (**31**, OLE, Figure 17.12) derived from extra virgin olive oil demonstrating significant therapeutic potential. Studies reveal that OLE not only effectively reduces cerebral $A\beta_{42}$ deposition in young and middle-aged TgCRND8 mouse models but also significantly alleviates pathological progression associated with increased pE-$A\beta_{3\text{-}42}$ levels during late disease stages. At the molecular level, OLE suppresses pE-$A\beta_{3\text{-}42}$ generation through downregulation of sQC expression, thereby interfering with the aggregation of both $A\beta_{42}$ and pE-$A\beta_{3\text{-}42}$. Furthermore, in advanced disease stages, OLE activates neuronal autophagy, enhances histone H3/H4 acetylation, and reduces histone deacetylase 2 expression, ultimately leading to improved synaptic function. These findings collectively demonstrate that OLE represents a natural compound with substantial potential for both preventing and treating AD through these multifaceted mechanisms [55, 56].

The Wessjohann team pioneered the application of reverse metabolomics integrated with natural product isolation techniques to identify three novel sulfolipids (compound **32**–**34**, Figure 17.12) from microalgae. These compounds demonstrated 76% inhibition of sQC at a concentration of 0.025 mg/ml. This study validates sulfolipids as promising scaffolds for novel sQC inhibitors and further expands the range of natural product–derived sQC inhibitor structures [56].

Haiqiang Wu's team chemically modified an apigenin scaffold to produce a series of analogues and clarified SAR, as exemplified by compound **35** (Figure 17.12). Activity data indicate that the C7-OH is essential for inhibitory potency, the C5-OH contributes to enhanced activity, and a 4-ethoxyphenyl substituent exerts only a modest effect. Overall, the study highlights the effectiveness of scaffold-based modification

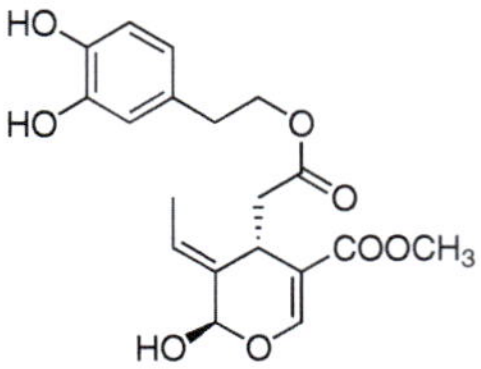

31 (Oleuropein aglycone, OLE)
Reduce sQC expression

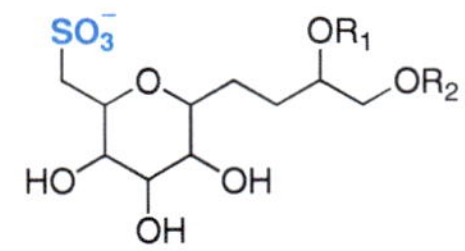

32 $R_1 = C_{15}H_{31}CO$ $R_2 = C_{17}H_{29}CO$
33 $R_1 = C_{15}H_{31}CO$ $R_2 = C_{17}H_{31}CO$
34 $R_1 = C_{15}H_{31}CO$ $R_2 = C_{15}H_{31}CO$
sQC Inhibition = 76% (0.025 mg/ml)

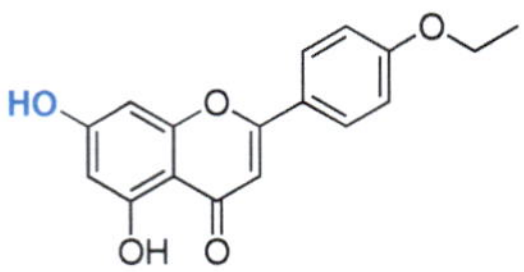

35
sQC IC_{50} = 14.2 γℵ1.1 μM

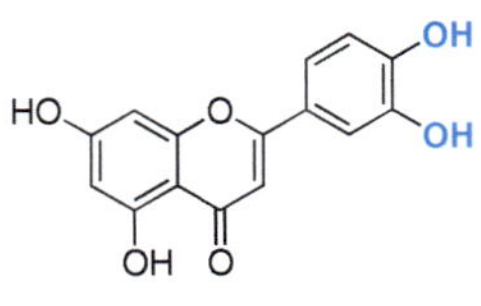

36 (Luteolin)
gQC K_D = 9.4 μM

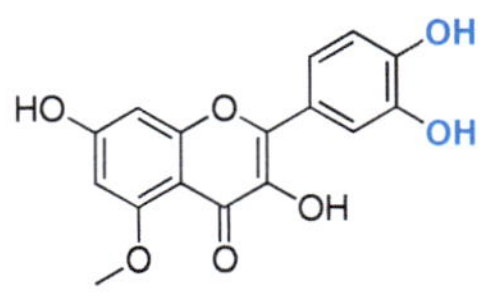

37 (Azaleatin)
sQC IC_{50} = 1.1 μM
K_D = 0.4 γℵ0.1 nM

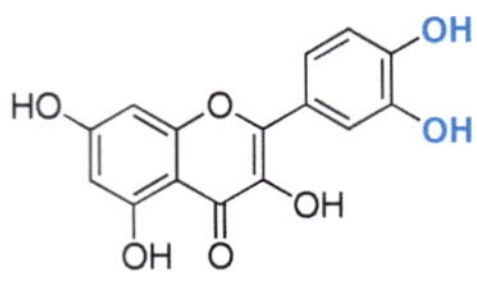

38 (Quercetin)
sQC IC_{50} = 4.3 μM
K_D = 5.3 γℵ0.5 nM

Figure 17.12 Naturally Sourced Chemicals **31**–**38**.

of natural products and provides a valuable reference for drug development efforts grounded in natural-product scaffolds [57].

Ge *et al.* employed fluorescence-activated cell sorting to identify luteolin (compound **36**) as a gQC inhibitor and validated its direct binding to gQC by pull-down assays and isothermal titration calorimetry (Figure 17.12). Mechanistic studies showed that luteolin inhibits gQC activity, thereby disrupting interactions between CD47-SIRPα and enhancing macrophage mediated phagocytosis of multiple myeloma H929 cells. By targeting gQC rather than CD47 directly, luteolin may avoid the anemia and other clinical side effects associated with antibody therapies against CD47, indicating promising translational potential [58].

Tseng group integrated receptor–ligand pharmacophore modeling with the Phar-MERGE and Phar-SEN screening methods to systematically screen natural product and traditional Chinese medicine compound libraries, identifying 35 compounds with sQC inhibitory activity. Among these, azaleatin (compound **37**) and quercetin (compound **38**) showed moderate inhibitory potency, with IC_{50} values of 1.1 μM and 4.3 μM, respectively (Figure 17.12) [59]. The study validates the computational screening strategy for discovering sQC inhibitors and broadens the natural-product chemical space available for their development.

17.5 Discovery Story of the Drug Candidate PQ912 and ISM8207

PQ912 and **ISM8207** are representative sQC/gQC inhibitors, and their discovery histories reflect two distinct research approaches, with **PQ912** developed through rational drug design and **ISM8207** identified by AI-driven screening. **PQ912** was the first sQC/gQC inhibitor to enter clinical trials and was developed to slow AD progression by preventing the formation of pE-Aβ. Mechanistic studies showing that sQC/gQC convert N-terminal glutamate residues of Aβ into pyroglutamate, yielding pE-Aβ species that are more prone to aggregation, more neurotoxic, accumulate in AD brains and drive cognitive decline [60–62].

In preclinical models **PQ912** strongly inhibited sQC/gQC with K_i values of 20-65 nM, and chronic treatment of AD transgenic mice markedly reduced pE-Aβ levels and improved spatial learning and memory [43]. The clinical development of **PQ912** (varoglutamstat) advanced systematically from Phase I to Phase IIb. Phase I studies in healthy volunteers confirmed an acceptable safety profile and defined pharmacokinetics, demonstrating dose-dependent central penetration and sQC inhibition in the cerebrospinal fluid [63]. However, the high-dose regimen led to increased gastrointestinal and skin adverse events along with higher discontinuation rates, indicating the necessity for dose optimization or slower titration. A subsequent randomized, double-blind, placebo-controlled Phase IIa trial in biomarker-confirmed early AD patients using 800 mg twice daily for 12 weeks achieved high target occupancy in CSF, estimated at over 90%, and yielded consistent exploratory signals. These included reduced EEG theta power, improved performance on the One Back working memory test, and favorable changes in synaptic and inflammatory biomarkers such as neurogranin and YKL-40. However, the high-dose regimen was associated with increased gastrointestinal and skin adverse events and higher discontinuation rates, underscoring the need for dose optimization or slower titration [64]. Based on these findings, the multicenter Phase IIb VIVIAD trial was launched to assess cognitive and biomarker outcomes in a larger, longer-term study [65]. Results announced in 2024 showed that the trial did not meet its primary cognitive endpoint, prompting the company to adjust its AD development strategy and shift focus toward renal indications. This journey underscores that while sQC inhibition is pharmacologically feasible and modulates biomarkers, translating these mechanistic effects into clear clinical benefit remains challenging, potentially requiring earlier intervention, precision dosing, stricter patient stratification, or combination therapies.

Developed by Insilico Medicine through its generative AI platform Pharma.AI, **ISM8207** (structure undisclosed) is a small-molecule inhibitor targeting gQC to prevent the N-terminal pE modification of CD47. This modification is critical for enhancing CD47 binding to the SIRPα receptor on macrophages, a mechanism exploited by tumors for immune evasion. Preclinical studies demonstrate that **ISM8207** effectively disrupts the CD47-SIRPα signaling axis and promotes macrophage-mediated phagocytosis of tumor cells. By targeting gQC rather than CD47, it may avoid the hematological toxicities, such as hemolytic anemia and thrombocytopenia, often associated with direct anti-CD47 antibody therapies. Furthermore, **ISM8207** exhibits favorable pharmacokinetics and tolerability profiles across both hematologic and solid tumor models. Following NMPA approval in 2023, the compound entered clinical trials and completed its first-in-human dosing in 2024, marking a significant milestone in the translation of AI-driven drug discovery into clinical evaluation (CTR20240727).

17.6 Concluding Remarks and Future Perspectives

In conclusion, neurodegenerative diseases, cancer, and inflammation significantly impact public health, highlighting the need for targeted therapies. Evidence shows that sQC/gQC play a key role in these diseases. In neurodegeneration, sQC/gQC promote protein aggregation by catalyzing pE-modified proteins like pE-α-synuclein and pE-Aβ. In cancer, gQC-driven pE-CD47 aids immune evasion by enhancing CD47-SIRPa interaction, while in inflammation, gQC-catalyzed pE-CCL2 activates inflammatory pathways. Additionally, elevated sQC/gQC in senescent cells hampers the clearance of apoptotic cells, worsening disease [66]. Given the varied substrates of sQC/gQC, challenges remain in improving tissue selectivity and BBB penetration for new inhibitors. SAR analysis will be crucial in this regard. Multi-target strategies addressing synergistic pathways offer promise for treating complex diseases like neurodegeneration and cancer. Despite setbacks, such as the **PQ912** Phase IIb trial failure, ongoing research into new inhibitors and their new indications brings hope for effective treatments in the near future.

Glossary

Human glutaminyl cyclase (hQC) is an enzyme that transforms N-terminal glutamine residues into pyroglutamate in peptides and proteins. It has two isoforms: secretory (sQC) and Golgi-resident (gQC).

Posttranslational Modifications (PTMs) are covalent and enzymatic changes to proteins during or after synthesis, affecting their properties and functions. For example, PE modification, phosphorylation, ubiquitination, and glycosylation.

Pyroglutamation (pE) is the conversion of N-terminal glutamine or glutamic acid in proteins into pyroglutamate through cyclization, a form of posttranslational modification (PTM).

Aminoacyl transferase is an enzyme involved in attaching amino acids to tRNA, a key step in protein synthesis.

Catalytic triad is an enzyme active site structure comprising three amino acid residues that collaborate to boost catalytic efficiency.

Dehydrogenation is a chemical reaction where hydrogen atoms are removed from a molecule, typically facilitated by en zymes like dehydrogenases.

β-Amyloid protein (Aβ) also called "amyloid β peptide", is produced from the hydrolysis of amyloid precursor protein (APP).

A metal-binding group (MBG) refers to specific atoms or functional groups within a compound that can form coordination bonds with metal ions via lone pair electrons, such as carboxyl groups, amino groups, and hydroxyl groups.

Bioisosteres are substances where groups or substituents with similar physical and chemical properties result in comparable or different biological activities.

BBB penetration refers to the ability of drugs or substances to cross the blood-brain barrier and enter the brain. The BBB is a barrier formed by tightly connected endothelial cells that protect the brain from harmful substances.

The Multi-Target-Directed Ligand (MTDL) strategy involves using a single molecule to affect multiple biological targets, making it suitable for treating complex diseases like neurodegenerative disorders and cancer.

References

1 Macek, B., Forchhammer, K., Hardouin, J. et al. (2019). Protein post-translational modifications in bacteria. *Nature Reviews Microbiology* 17: 651–664.

2 Agatemor, C., Middleton, S.A.D., and Toledo, D. (2022). How pervasive are post-translational and -transcriptional modifications? *Trends in Cell Biology* 32: 475–478.

3 Lee, J.M., Hammarén, H.M., Savitski, M.M., and Baek, S.H. (2023). Control of protein stability by post-translational modifications. *Nature Communications* 14: 201.

4 Huang, K.F., Huang, J.S., Wu, M.L. et al. (2021). A unique Carboxylic-Acid Hydrogen-Bond Network (CAHBN) confers glutaminyl cyclase activity on M28 family enzymes. *Journal of Molecular Cell Biology* 433: 166960.

5 Song, I., Chuang, C.Z., and Bateman, R.C. (1994). Molecular cloning, sequence analysis and expression of human pituitary glutaminyl cyclase. *Journal of Molecular Endocrinology* 13: 77–86.

6 Cynis, H., Rahfeld, J.U., Stephan, A. et al. (2008). Isolation of an isoenzyme of human glutaminyl cyclase: retention in the Golgi complex suggests involvement in the protein maturation machinery. *Journal of Molecular Cell Biology* 379: 966–980.

7 Seifert, F., Schulz, K., Koch, B. et al. (2009). Glutaminyl cyclases display significant catalytic proficiency for glutamyl substrates. *Biochemistry* 48: 11831–11833.

8 Huang, K.F., Liaw, S.S., Huang, W.L. et al. (2011). Structures of human Golgi-resident glutaminyl cyclase and its complexes with inhibitors reveal a large loop movement upon inhibitor binding. *Journal of Biological Chemistry* 286: 12439–12449.

9 Huang, K.F., Liu, Y.L., and Wang, A.H. (2005). Cloning, expression, characterization, and crystallization of a glutaminyl cyclase from human bone marrow: a single zinc metalloenzyme. *Protein Expression and Purification* 43: 65–72.

10 Huang, K.F., Liu, Y.L., Cheng, W.J. et al. (2005). Crystal structures of human glutaminyl cyclase, an enzyme responsible for protein N-terminal pyroglutamate formation. *Proceedings of the National Academy of Sciences of the United States of America* 102: 13117–13122.

11 Huang, K.F., Wang, Y.R., Chang, E.C. et al. (2008). A conserved hydrogen-bond network in the catalytic centre of animal glutaminyl cyclases is critical for catalysis. *Biochemical Journal* 411: 181–190.

12 Logtenberg, M.E.W., Jansen, J.H.M., Raaben, M. et al. (2019). Glutaminyl cyclase is an enzymatic modifier of the CD47- SIRPα axis and a target for cancer immunotherapy. *Nature Medicine* 25: 612–619.

13 Wu, Z., Weng, L., Zhang, T. et al. (2019). Identification of Glutaminyl Cyclase isoenzyme isoQC as a regulator of SIRPα-CD47 axis. *Cell Research* 29: 502–505.

14 Coimbra, J.R.M., Moreira, P.I., Santos, A.E., and Salvador, J.A.R. (2023). Therapeutic potential of glutaminyl cyclases: current status and emerging trends. *Drug Discovery Today* 28: 103644.

15 Zhang, Y., Wang, Y., Zhao, Z. et al. (2022). Glutaminyl cyclases, the potential targets of cancer and neurodegenerative diseases. *European Journal of Pharmacology* 931: 175178.

16 Gunn, A.P., Wong, B.X., Johanssen, T. et al. (2016). Amyloid-β peptide Aβ3pE-42 induces lipid peroxidation, membrane permeabilization, and calcium influx in neurons. *Journal of Biological Chemistry* 291: 6134–6145.

17 Hartlage-Rübsamen, M., Bluhm, A., Moceri, S. et al. (2021). A glutaminyl cyclase-catalyzed α-synuclein modification identified in human synucleinopathies. *Acta Neuropathologica* 142: 399–421.

18 Jimenez-Sanchez, M., Lam, W., Hannus, M. et al. (2015). siRNA screen identifies QPCT as a druggable target for Huntington's disease. *Nature Chemical Biology* 11: 347–354.

19 Deshmane, S.L., Kremlev, S., Amini, S., and Sawaya, B.E. (2009). Monocyte chemoattractant protein-1 (MCP-1): an overview. *Journal of Interferon & Cytokine Research* 29: 313–326.

20 Cynis, H., Hoffmann, T., Friedrich, D. et al. (2011). The isoenzyme of glutaminyl cyclase is an important regulator of monocyte infiltration under inflammatory conditions. *EMBO Molecular Medicine* 3: 545–558.

21 Kehlen, A., Haegele, M., Böhme, L. et al. (2017). N-terminal pyroglutamate formation in CX3CL1 is essential for its full biologic activity. *Bioscience Reports* 37: BSR20170712.

22 Zhao, T., Bao, Y., Gan, X. et al. (2019). DNA methylation-regulated QPCT promotes sunitinib resistance by increasing HRAS stability in renal cell carcinoma. *Theranostics* 9: 6175–6190.

23 Gillis, J.S. (2006). Microarray evidence of glutaminyl cyclase gene expression in melanoma: implications for tumor antigen specific immunotherapy. *Journal of Translational Medicine* 4: 27.

24 Kehlen, A., Haegele, M., Menge, K. et al. (2013). Role of glutaminyl cyclases in thyroid carcinomas. *Endocrine-Related Cancer* 20: 79–90.

25 Ezura, Y., Kajita, M., Ishida, R. et al. (2004). Association of multiple nucleotide variations in the pituitary glutaminyl cyclase gene (QPCT) with low radial BMD in adult women. *Journal of Bone and Mineral Research* 19: 1296–1301.

26 Schilling, S., Niestroj, A.J., Rahfeld, J.U. et al. (2003). Identification of human glutaminyl cyclase as a metalloenzyme. Potent inhibition by imidazole derivatives and heterocyclic chelators. *Journal of Biological Chemistry* 278: 49773–49779.

27 Buchholz, M., Heiser, U., Schilling, S. et al. (2006). The first potent inhibitors for human glutaminyl cyclase: synthesis and structure-activity relationship. *Journal of Medicinal Chemistry* 49: 664–677.

28 Buchholz, M., Hamann, A., Aust, S. et al. (2009). Inhibitors for human glutaminyl cyclase by structure based design and bioisosteric replacement. *Journal of Medicinal Chemistry* 52: 7069–7080.

29 Tran, P.T., Hoang, V.H., Thorat, S.A. et al. (2013). Structure-activity relationship of human glutaminyl cyclase inhibitors having an N-(5-methyl-1H-imidazol-1-yl) propyl thiourea template. *Bioorganic & Medicinal Chemistry* 21: 3821–3830.

30 Hoang, V.H., Tran, P.T., Cui, M. et al. (2017). Discovery of potent human glutaminyl cyclase inhibitors as anti-Alzheimer's agents based on rational design. *Journal of Medicinal Chemistry* 60: 2573–2590.

31 Ngo, V.T.H., Hoang, V.H., Tran, P.T. et al. (2018). Structure-activity relationship investigation of Phe-Arg mimetic region of human glutaminyl cyclase inhibitors. *Bioorganic & Medicinal Chemistry* 26: 3133–3144.

32 Hoang, V.H., Ngo, V.T.H., Cui, M. et al. (2019). Discovery of conformationally restricted human glutaminyl cyclase inhibitors as potent anti-Alzheimer's agents by structure-based design. *Journal of Medicinal Chemistry* 62: 8011–8027.

33 Van Manh, N., Hoang, V.H., Ngo, V.T.H. et al. (2021). Discovery of highly potent human glutaminyl cyclase (QC) inhibitors as anti-Alzheimer's agents by the combination of pharmacophore-based and structure-based design. *European Journal of Medicinal Chemistry* 226: 113819.

34 Van Manh, N., Hoang, V.H., Ngo, V.T.H. et al. (2022). Discovery of potent indazole-based human glutaminyl cyclase (QC) inhibitors as anti-Alzheimer's disease agents. *European Journal of Medicinal Chemistry* 244: 114837.

35 Li, M., Dong, Y., Yu, X. et al. (2017). Synthesis and evaluation of diphenyl conjugated imidazole derivatives as potential glutaminyl cyclase inhibitors for treatment of Alzheimer's disease. *Journal of Medicinal Chemistry* 60: 6664–6677.

36 Xie, Y., Chen, C., Lin, S. et al. (2023). Design, synthesis and anti-AD effects of dual inhibitor targeting glutaminyl cyclase/GSK-3β. *European Journal of Medicinal Chemistry* 248: 115089.

37 Zhou, Q., Cai, J., Qin, F. et al. (2024). Discovery of potential scaffolds for glutaminyl cyclase inhibitors: virtual screening, synthesis, and evaluation. *Bioorganic & Medicinal Chemistry* 97: 117542.

38 Ramsbeck, D., Buchholz, M., Koch, B. et al. (2013). Structure-activity relationships of benzimidazole-based glutaminyl cyclase inhibitors featuring a heteroaryl scaffold. *Journal of Medicinal Chemistry* 56: 6613–6625.

39 Coimbra, J.R.M. and Salvador, J.A.R. (2021). A patent review of glutaminyl cyclase inhibitors (2004-present). *Expert Opinion on Therapeutic Patents* 31: 809–836.

40 Hellvard, A., Maresz, K., Schilling, S. et al. (2013). Glutaminyl cyclases as novel targets for the treatment of septic arthritis. *Infectious Diseases Society of America* 207: 768–777.

41 Kanemitsu, N., Kiyonaga, F., Mizukami, K. et al. (2021). Chronic treatment with the (iso-)glutaminyl cyclase inhibitor PQ529 is a novel and effective approach for glomerulonephritis in chronic kidney disease. *Naunyn-Schmiedeberg's Archives of Pharmacology* 394: 751–761.

42 Heiser, U., Sommer, R., Ramsbeck, D., Meyer, A., Hoffmann, T., Boehme, L. and Demuth, H.-U. (2011) Preparation of Heterocyclic Imidazole Derivatives as Therapeutic Inhibitors of Glutaminyl Cyclase. WO2011029920.

43 Hoffmann, T., Meyer, A., Heiser, U. et al. (2017). Glutaminyl cyclase inhibitor PQ912 improves cognition in mouse models of Alzheimer's disease-studies on relation to effective target occupancy. *Journal of Pharmacology and Experimental Therapeutics* 362: 119–130.

44 Mou, J., Ning, X.L., Wang, X.Y. et al. (2024). X-ray structure-guided discovery of a potent benzimidazole glutaminyl cyclase inhibitor that shows activity in a Parkinson's disease mouse model. *Journal of Medicinal Chemistry* 67: 8730–8756.

45 Cheng, X., Liu, Y., Qin, L., Ren, F. and Wu, J. (2022) Beta-lactam Derivatives for the Treatment of Diseases. WO2022268179.

46 Pozzi, C., Di Pisa, F., Benvenuti, M., and Mangani, S. (2018). The structure of the human glutaminyl cyclase-SEN177 complex indicates routes for developing new potent inhibitors as possible agents for the treatment of neurological disorders. *Journal of Biological Inorganic Chemistry* 23: 1219–1226.

47 Baumann, N., Rösner, T., Jansen, J.H.M. et al. (2021). Enhancement of epidermal growth factor receptor antibody tumor immunotherapy by glutaminyl cyclase inhibition to interfere with CD47/signal regulatory protein alpha interactions. *Cancer Science* 112: 3029–3040.

48 Yu, L., Zhao, P., Sun, Y. et al. (2023). Development of a potent benzonitrile-based inhibitor of glutaminyl-peptide cyclotransferase-like protein (QPCTL) with antitumor efficacy. *Signal Transduction and Targeted Therapy* 8: 454.

49 Buchholz, M., Heiser, U., Niestroj, A. J. and Ramsbeck, D. (2008) Preparation of Imidazo[1,5-a]pyridine Derivatives as Inhibitors of Glutaminyl Cyclase. WO2008110523.

50 Heiser, U., Hoffmann, T., Lues, I. and Meyer, A. (2018) Preparation of Novel Heterocyclic Derivatives as Inhibitors of Glutaminyl Cyclase. WO2018178384.

51 Kupski, O., Funk, L.M., Sautner, V. et al. (2020). Hydrazidesare potent transition-state analogues for glutaminyl cyclase implicated in the pathogenesis of Alzheimer's disease. *Biochemistry* 59: 2585–2591.

52 Dileep, K.V., Sakai, N., Ihara, K. et al. (2021). Piperidine-4-carboxamide as a new scaffold for designing secretory glutaminyl cyclase inhibitors. *International Journal of Biological Macromolecules* 170: 415–423.

53 Ramsbeck, D., Taudte, N., Jänckel, N. et al. (2021). Tetrahydroimidazo[4,5-c]pyridine-based inhibitors of porphyromonas gingivalis glutaminyl cyclase. *Pharmaceuticals* 14: 1206.

54 Park, E., Song, K.H., Kim, D. et al. (2022). 2-Amino-1,3,4-thiadiazoles as glutaminyl cyclases inhibitors increase phagocytosis through modification of CD47-SIRPα checkpoint. *ACS Medicinal Chemistry Letters* 13: 1459–1467.

55 Luccarini, I., Grossi, C., Rigacci, S. et al. (2015). Oleuropein aglycone protects against pyroglutamylated-3 amyloid-ß toxicity: biochemical, epigenetic and functional correlates. *Neurobiology of Aging* 36: 648–663.

56 Hielscher-Michael, S., Griehl, C., Buchholz, M. et al. (2016). Natural products from microalgae with potential against Alzheimer's disease: sulfolipids are potent glutaminyl cyclase inhibitors. *Marine Drugs* 14: 203.

57 Li, M., Dong, Y., Yu, X. et al. (2016). Inhibitory effect of flavonoids on human glutaminyl cyclase. *Bioorganic & Medicinal Chemistry* 24: 2280–2286.

58 Li, Z., Gu, X., Rao, D. et al. (2021). Luteolin promotes macrophage-mediated phagocytosis by inhibiting CD47 pyroglutamation. *Translational Oncology* 14: 101129.

59 Tsai, K.C., Zhang, Y.X., Kao, H.Y. et al. (2022). Pharmacophore-driven identification of human glutaminyl cyclase inhibitors from foods, plants and herbs unveils the bioactive property and potential of Azaleatin in the treatment of Alzheimer's disease. *Food & Function* 13: 12632–12647.

60 Frost, J.L., Le, K.X., Cynis, H. et al. (2013). Pyroglutamate-3 amyloid-β deposition in the brains of humans, non-human primates, canines, and Alzheimer disease-like transgenic mouse models. *American Journal of Pathology* 183: 369–381.

61 Morawski, M., Schilling, S., Kreuzberger, M. et al. (2014). Glutaminyl cyclase in human cortex: correlation with (pGlu)-amyloid-β load and cognitive decline in Alzheimer's disease. *Journal Of Alzheimers Disease* 39: 385–400.

62 Schilling, S., Zeitschel, U., Hoffmann, T. et al. (2008). Glutaminyl cyclase inhibition attenuates pyroglutamate Abeta and Alzheimer's disease-like pathology. *Nature Medicine* 14: 1106–1111.

63 Lues, I., Weber, F., Meyer, A. et al. (2015). A phase 1 study to evaluate the safety and pharmacokinetics of PQ912, a glutaminyl cyclase inhibitor, in healthy subjects. *Alzheimers & Dementia* 1: 182–195.

64 Scheltens, P., Hallikainen, M., Grimmer, T. et al. (2018). Safety, tolerability and efficacy of the glutaminyl cyclase inhibitor PQ912 in Alzheimer's disease: results of a randomized, double-blind, placebo-controlled phase 2a study. *Alzheimers Research & Therapy* 10: 107.

65 Vijverberg, E.G.B., Axelsen, T.M., Bihlet, A.R. et al. (2021). Rationale and study design of a randomized, placebo-controlled, double-blind phase 2b trial to evaluate efficacy, safety, and tolerability of an oral glutaminyl cyclase inhibitor varoglutamstat (PQ912) in study participants with MCI and mild AD-VIVIAD. *Alzheimers Research & Therapy* 13: 142.

66 Schloesser, D., Lindenthal, L., Sauer, J. et al. (2023). Senescent cells suppress macrophage-mediated corpse removal via upregulation of the CD47-QPCT/L axis. *Journal of Cell Biology* 222: e202207097.

18

Drug Discovery Targeting Tryptophan/Indoleamine 2,3-Dioxygenase

*Xiang-Li Ning, Lin Ma, and Guo-Bo Li**

West China School of Pharmacy, Sichuan University, Department of Medicinal Chemistry, No. 17, Section 3, Renmin South Road, Chengdu 610041, P.R. China

Section I

18.1 Introduction

Tryptophan (**Trp**) is the least abundant essential amino acid that the human body can solely acquire from diet. Its uniqueness lies in the fact that only a small fraction of free **Trp** is dedicated to protein synthesis; the remaining free **Trp** is converted into bioactive metabolites via three metabolic pathways: kynurenine (**Kyn**), 5-hydroxytryptamine (**5-HT**), and indole pathways. These pathways enable **Trp** metabolism to partake in a diverse range of physiological and pathological processes such as inflammation, metabolism, immune responses, and nerve functions [1].

The kynurenine (**Kyn**) pathway (KP) accounts for approximately 95% of **Trp** degradation [2, 3]. Within this pathway, **Trp** is first transformed into N-formylkynurenine (**NFK**) by three rate-limiting enzymes: human indoleamine 2,3-dioxygenase 1 (hIDO1, EC1.13.11.52), indoleamine 2,3-dioxygenase 2 (hIDO2, EC1.13.11), and tryptophan 2,3-dioxygenase (hTDO, EC1.13.11.11) (Figure 18.1). **NFK** is then further transformed into kynurenine (**Kyn**), the first stable metabolite of the KP, by the enzyme arylformamidase (AFMID). In the primary branch of the KP, **Kyn** is metabolized to 3-hydroxykynurenine (**3-HK**) by kynurenine monooxygenase (KMO). Subsequently, kynureninase (KYNU) generates 3-hydroxyanthranilic acid (**3-HAA**) and alanine from **3-HK**, and Kyn aminotransferase (KAT) [4] catalyzes the conversion of **3-HK** to xanthurenic acid (**XA**). **3-HK**- and **3-HAA**-mediated neurotoxicity is induced by reactive oxygen species.

* X.–L.N and L.M. are co–first authors

Drug Discovery Targeting Metalloenzymes: Strategies and Applications, First Edition. Edited by Guo-Bo Li.

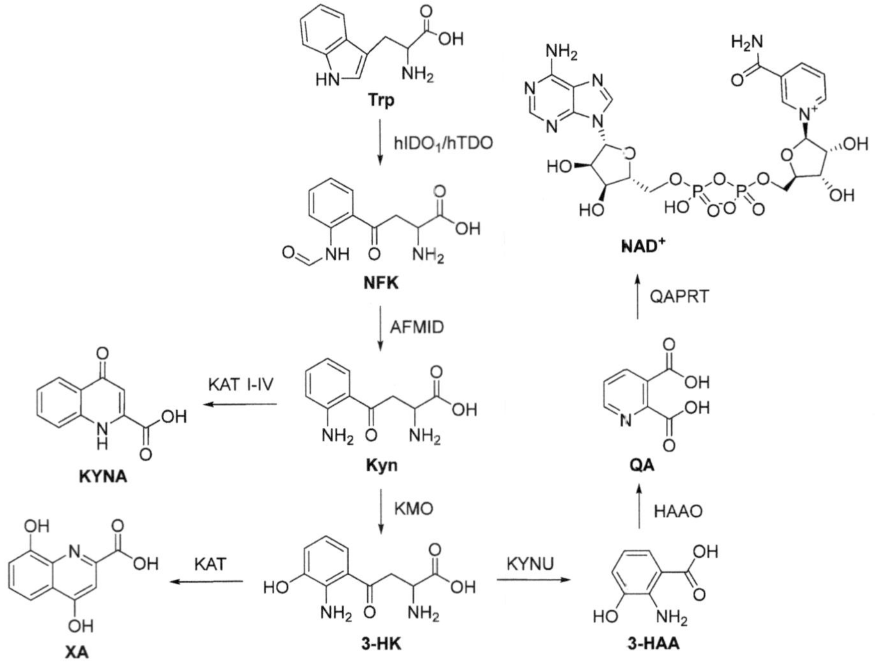

Figure 18.1 Overview of the metabolism of tryptophan through the kynurenine pathways.

The arm of **3-HAA** metabolism catalyzed by 3-hydroxyanthranilate-3,4-dioxygenase (HAAO) produces quinolinic acid (**QA**), which exerts neurotoxicity through the activation of N-methyl-D-aspartate (NMDA) receptors, inhibition of glutamatergic neurotransmission, and induction of oxidative stress [5]. Lastly, **QA** is transaminated by quinolinate phosphoribosyltransferase (QPRT) to generate NAD^+, a crucial coenzyme in energy metabolism (Figure 18.1). In an alternative branch of the KP, **Kyn** can be converted to neuroprotective kynurenic acid (**KYNA**) by KAT isoenzymes [6]. **KYNA** serves as a significant antagonist of NMDA receptors and possesses antioxidative properties to inhibit excitotoxicity and neuroinflammation [7]. Additionally, both kynurenine and **KYNA** act as endogenous activating ligands of the aryl hydrocarbon receptor (AHR), a pivotal ligand-activated transcription factor involved in a multitude of physiological functions, including immune regulation, which will be discussed in detail later.

Imbalances in tryptophan metabolism found in various disorders, such as cancer and neurodegenerative diseases, have sparked interest in targeting the KP therapeutically, especially its key rate-limiting enzymes hIDO1, hIDO2, and hTDO [8, 9]. The three evolutionarily related heme-containing enzymes mediate oxidative cleavage of the indole ring of **Trp** at the 2,3-position to generate N-formyl kynurenine (**NFK**) in the first step of the **Trp–Kyn** axis [10]. Despite performing the same biochemical reaction, these enzymes exhibit obvious differences in structure, substrate specificity, substrate conversion, tissue distribution, and expression regulation [11].

The intracellular monomeric heme enzyme hIDO1 can catalyze a broad range of physiological substrates, including L-tryptophan (L-**Trp**), D-tryptophan (D-**Trp**), serotonin, melatonin, tryptamine, and various indoleamine derivatives [12]. hTDO, as an isozyme of hIDO1, is a cytosolic tetramer with high substrate specificity for L-**Trp**, while it exhibits lower affinity for L-**Trp** ($K_m \approx 190\,\mu mol/l^{-1}$) compared to hIDO1($K_m \approx 20\,\mu mol/l^{-1}$) [13]. Despite sharing 43% sequence homology with the genes encoding hIDO1, hIDO2 exhibits a significantly lower catalytic capacity for degrading L-**Trp** ($Km \approx 6.8\,mmol/l^{-1}$) [13, 14]. The hTDO enzyme is almost exclusively present in the liver and brain, where its expression levels are regulated by systemic levels of L(L-**Trp**) and corticosteroids [15, 16]. hIDO1 is expressed at low levels in extrahepatic tissues, and its expression and activity can be tightly regulated in inflamed tissues and the immune system by cytokines such as IFN-γ [17], prostaglandin E2 (PGE2) [18], IL-6 [19], TNF-α, TGF-β, and immune checkpoint molecules (including PD-1, GITRL, CTLA-4) to establish an immunosuppressive environment [20, 21]. In contrast, the hIDO1 paralog hIDO2 mRNA expression is more restricted; it is constitutively found in the placenta, testis, liver, thyroid, and brain [22]. Notably, limited information is available on hIDO2, and its biological function is still not fully understood, largely because of its low tryptophan degradation activity and the complexity of its transcription process [14, 23, 24]. Therefore, despite all three enzymes catalyzing the same key step in the KP, current studies have focused on hIDO1 and hTDO. In the following, we outline the physiological and pathological roles of hIDO and hTDO and highlight recent progress in developing small-molecule inhibitors, with a special emphasis on emerging trends in therapies targeting hIDO/hTDO.

18.2 Catalytic and Structural Characteristics of hIDO and hTDO

18.2.1 Catalytic Mechanisms of hIDO/hTDO

The enzymatic dioxygenase reactions catalyzed by hIDO1 and hTDO are considered as unique cases compared to heme-containing monooxygenases (such as cytochrome P450, peroxygenases, and hemoglobin oxygenase) and non-heme dioxygenases (such as catechol dioxygenase and naphthalene dioxygenase). These enzymes follow an analogous two-step dioxygenase mechanism, where the activation of dioxygen reactivity is facilitated by the substrate tryptophan rather than electrons and protons [25]. Recent studies, including Resonance Raman spectroscopy, computational modeling, and structural analysis, have proposed mechanistic viewpoints that have been widely accepted, in which the primary distinction lies in the initial indole activation step through heme superoxide (Figure 18.2) [26–30]. The first proposal supports the idea that lone pairs on nitrogen triggers electrophilic addition of bound O_2 ligand [31]; in the other case, it is thought that the process commences with the radical addition of the ferric heme

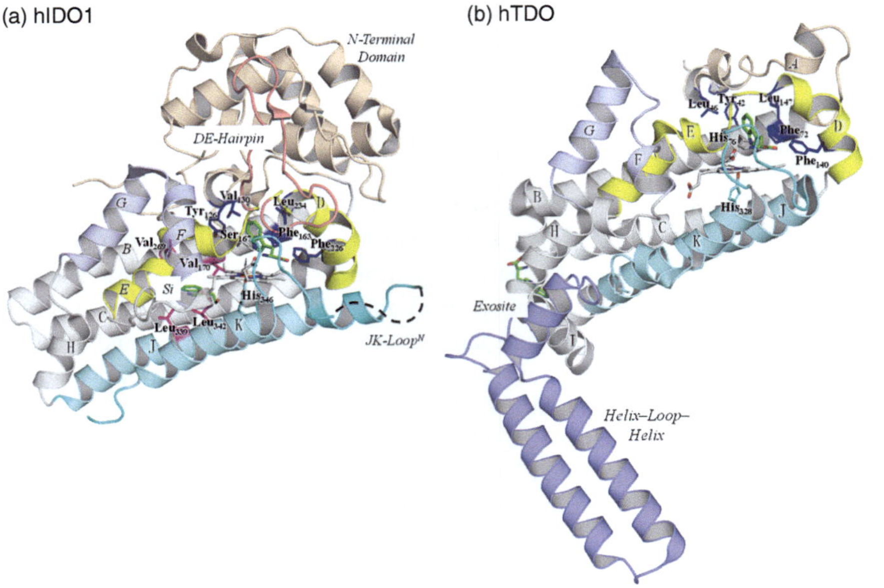

Figure 18.2 Proposed pathways for hIDO/hTDO-mediated tryptophan oxidative cleavage.

iron-bound superoxide to the C_2 of **Trp**, resulting in the formation of an alkylperoxo transition state [32]. Interestingly, both of the suggested mechanisms meet at a shared middle stage: the creation/ formation of a ferryl intermediate and the indole epoxide. Subsequently, the ammonium group of **Trp** protonates the epoxide ring in **Trp** epoxide, leading to the opening of the ring, which facilitates the addition of ferryl oxygen to C_2 of **Trp**, resulting in the formation of **NFK** [12, 33].

18.2.2 Structural Characteristics of hIDO/hTDO

hIDO1 is a monomeric α-helical protein with two main domains: a large C-terminal domain (CTD, residues 155–403) housing Sa site where the heme cofactor, **Trp**, and O_2 bind, and a small N-terminal domain (colored in wheat, residues 1–154) containing a A-Helix located on the CTD [34] (Figure 18.3a). hTDO forms a homotetramer through a dimer of dimers structure, with each monomeric unit featuring a large core (C-terminal) domain at one end, which exhibits significant structural resemblance to the CTD of hIDO1, and an additional long helix–loop–helix domain at the other end (colored in slate) (Figure 18.3b). At odds with hTDO, hIDO1 is distinguished by the presence of a N-terminal domain, a long DE-Hairpin, and a highly flexible JK-Loop ^{N} (highlighted by the black dotted line), which might at least partially contribute to its distinctive protein conformational flexibility [33].

The unique nature of the oxidation reaction catalyzed by hIDO/hTDO necessitates the precise positioning of the substrate **Trp** in a specific orientation relative to the heme iron-bound dioxygen. Consequently, the key structural components critical

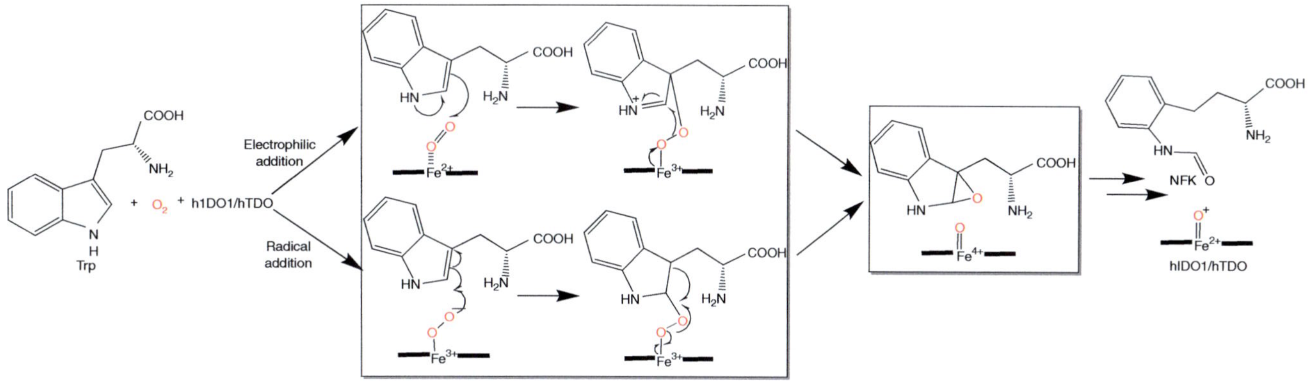

Figure 18.3 Comparison of the structure of hIDO1 with hTDO. (aA) The structures of hIDO1--CN--**Trp** complex (PDB code: 5WMU). (bB) The structures of hTDO--O_2--**Trp** complex (PDB code: 5TI9).

for substrate recognition and binding are largely conserved in these two enzymes. Recent crystallographic studies have also unsurprisingly revealed that hIDO1 and hTDO share a similar active site structure, albeit having distinct overall protein folding structures [33]. When binding to **Trp**, the C-terminal domain of a highly flexible loop (JK-loop; residues 360–382) in hIDO1 CTD undergoes a conformational rearrangement from a disordered helical structure to a β-hairpin configuration to protect the Sa site from the surrounding solvent, while the N-terminal segment of JK-loop (JK-Loop ^{N}) maintains disordered state (Figure 18.3a) [35]. The **Trp** binds in the distant heme pocket, encircled by the JK-Loop ^{C} and DE-Loop, and capped with a small helix from the hIDO1 N–terminal domain (NTD), while the roof of the pocket in hTDO is A-Helix [30] from the adjacent subunit (highlighted in blue). The **Trp** binding site is surrounded by a cluster of hydrophobic residues, including Tyr_{126}, Val_{130}, Phe_{163}, Leu_{234}, and Phe_{226} in the case of hIDO1, which is substituted by Tyr_{42}, Leu_{46}, Phe_{72}, Leu_{147}, and Phe_{140} in hTDO (colored in blue) (Figure 18.3b). The indole group of the **Trp** lies perpendicular to the heme, with its indoleamine group forming a hydrogen bond with Ser_{167} through a water molecule in hIDO1 [36]; while in hTDO, a hydrogen bond is directly formed between residue His_{76} and the substrate. The ammonium and carboxylate groups of **Trp** create an interlaced H-bonding network with the 7-propionate group of the heme and several residues in the JK-Loop ^{C} and DE-Loop; similar interactions are observed in hTDO.

Notably, recent crystallographic studies cast light on the second **Trp**-binding site, Si, in both hIDO1 and hTDO, but with different binding positions [30, 37]. In IDO1, L-**Trp** interacts with the side chains of Val_{170}, Val_{269}, Leu_{339}, and Leu_{342} (colored in magenta) to form an accessory site that is located below the heme group (Figure 18.3a); conversely, in hTDO, the second **Trp** is situated at a separate exosite approximately 42 Å away from the Sa site (Figure 18.3b). The different second tryptophan binding sites in the two enzymes were discovered to be potentially crucial for regulating their activity *in vivo*. As an inducible enzyme, the expression of hIDO1 can be significantly upregulated upon stimulation. Encouragingly, **Trp** binding to the Si negatively regulates its activity, permitting it to control the imbalance of KP to some extent, especially during the significant fluctuations in **Trp** levels during meals [34]. In contrast, **Trp** binding at exosite in hTDO does not influence enzyme catalysis, but rather impedes hTDO degradation through the ubiquitin-dependent proteasomal pathway involved in a set of ubiquitination sites in the helix–loop–helix domain. Considering hTDO's role as a constitutive liver enzyme crucial in regulating systemic tryptophan levels, it is reasonable to posit that this pathway may be vital for maintaining normal tryptophan balance [30]. Actually, a group of posttranslational phosphorylation sites has been identified in the JK-Loop ^{N} region [38], the DE-hairpin motif, and the N-terminal domain in hIDO1, which are potentially associated with the noncatalytic signaling function of the enzyme [38–41]. The small N-terminal domain featuring two functional immunoreceptor tyrosine-based inhibitory motifs (ITIMs; Tyr_{111}, Tyr_{249}), once bound by distinct molecular partners, will either facilitate degradation or trigger signaling activity and self-maintenance of the enzyme [40].

18.3 Targeting IDO/TDO for Neurological and Immune-Related Diseases

Extensive research findings have pointed out the participation of the KP in neurophysiology and immunology, which is mainly mediated by the diverse biological functions of pathway metabolites and the activity of key enzymes in the channel. As the primary rate-limiting enzyme, abnormal activity of hIDO/ hTDO will disrupt the delicate balance of **Trp** and its metabolites and impact the pathogenesis of various human diseases, including immune regulation, cell proliferation, and neurotransmission via interacting with downstream molecules or pathways. Here, the representative hIDO/hTDO-regulated immune-related diseases, such as cancer, central nervous system (CNS) disorders, are discussed.

18.3.1 Cancer

The relationship between cancer and elevated **Trp** catabolism was recognized as early as the 1950s [42]. Recently, several lines of evidence indicate that hIDO1/hTDO-mediated tryptophan metabolism exerts a nuclear function in cancer progression by suppressing antitumor immune responses and boosting the malignant characteristics of cancer cells [43, 44]. First, **Trp**-degrading enzymes are present in many malignancies, and aberrant protein expression and activity are associated with poor prognosis in diverse types of cancers, such as glioma, colorectal cancer, breast cancer, lung cancer, liver cancer, pancreatic cancer, ovarian cancer, endometrial cancers, and hematological neoplasms [45–52]. Secondly, there is evidence indicating the involvement of tryptophan degradation in the regulation of Treg cells and immune cell infiltration in cancer. hIDO1 suppresses the tumor infiltration of $CD3^+$ T, $CD8^+$ T, $CD3^+CD8^+$ T, and $CD57^+$ NK cells in patients with colorectal cancer, and a significant correlation was found between high IDO expression and reduced numbers of $CD3^+$, $CD8^+$, and $CD57^+$ cells infiltrating into both the endometrial tumor epithelium and stroma [52, 53]. Furthermore, the heightened hIDO1 expression is associated with a significant increase of $CD4^+$ $CD25^+$ $FOXP3^+$ Treg cells in metastatic pancreatic ductal adenocarcinoma and is also accountable for the infiltration of neutrophils in patients with hepatocellular carcinoma [54, 55]. In addition, research suggests that hIDO1/hTDO can strongly enhance the motility and metastasis of cancer cells. For instance, *in vitro* and *in vivo* studies have shown that knockdown or inhibition of hTDO suppressed the migration and invasion of hepatocellular carcinoma (HCC) cells, and high levels of hIDO1 expression were significantly correlated with HCC high metastasis rates [56, 57]. In a similar manner, overexpression of hIDO1 in lung cancer promotes cell migration and invasion, while inhibition decreases motility [58]. Furthermore, studies have identified that hTDO is the primary enzyme found in lung fibroblasts responsible for tryptophan metabolism, and it can inhibit dendritic cell differentiation and promote cancer proliferation and migration when activated by lung cancer cells [59, 60]. Furthermore, overexpression of hTDO drives the proliferation, migration, and invasion of glioma cells via the hTDO–**Kyn**–AHR signaling axis, and in human colon cancer cells, blockade of IDO1 can inhibit cell proliferation [61, 62]. Altogether, these observations collectively provide a mechanistic rationale for the involvement of **Trp** metabolism in immune evasion by tumor cells.

Currently, hIDO1 and hTDO are proposed to act as immunosuppressors mainly through **Trp** depletion and kynurenine metabolite production to foster an immunosuppressive tumor microenvironment [63]. Specifically, on one hand, the aberrant activation of hIDO1 causes **Trp** depletion and the accumulation of uncharged tryptophan-transporter RNA, which triggers the general control nonderepressible 2 kinase (GCN2) to suppress $CD8^+$ T-cell proliferation and function by inducing cell cycle arrest and energy and promote the differentiation of immune cells, such as NK cells, into Treg cells [64, 65]. Another relevant response to local **Trp** depletion is the suppression of the mTORC1 pathway, which can be enhanced to stabilize Treg cells through the FOXO1/3A-PTEN loop [66]. An additional metabolism involves the impact of the accumulation of IDO1-mediated kynurenine (**Kyn**) and its derivative metabolites on immune cells to induce immunoregulatory effects in the absence of **Trp** starvation [67, 68]. **Kyn** exerts immunosuppressive functions by acting as a specific activating ligand for AHR, which plays a crucial role in T cell differentiation and the induction of tolerogenic dendritic cells (DCs) [11, 67, 69, 70]. In fact, the IDO1–Kyn–AHR signaling pathway encompasses multiple stages in cancer development and metastasis [71]. Activation of AHR can promote the recruitment of macrophages to tumors and their polarization toward tumor-associated macrophages (TAMs), thereby inhibiting the antitumor function of intratumoral $CD8^+$ T cells [72]. Furthermore, **Kyn**-activated AHR involves the differentiation of regulatory T (Treg) cells through the direct upregulation of critical transcription factor Forkhead box P3 (FoxP3) in T cells or by stimulating the differentiation of tolerogenic DCs [73, 74]. The downstream metabolites of **Kyn**, such as kynurenic acid and xanthurenic acid (**XA**), can engage with AHR and potentially regulate the immune response [75, 76]. Additionally, research has indicated that **Kyn**, **3-HK**, and **3-HANA** can suppress T cell proliferation while also triggering apoptosis [77, 78].

Recent studies have shown that hIDO1 possesses nonenzymatic signaling activity through its immunoreceptor tyrosine inhibitory motifs (ITIMs), which are widely used negative regulators of signaling proteins in the immune regulatory mechanism [40]. Once phosphorylated, the ITIMs bind protein tyrosine phosphatases (SHP-1 and SHP-2) and thus trigger an immunoregulatory signaling in DCs [41]. Actually, hIDO1 was reported to be able to induce a long-term tolerogenic phenotype in DCs as well as a malignant advancement in a murine melanoma preclinical model, wherein inoculated $B16^{H350A}$ cells expressing a mutant IDO1 – lacking catalytic activity but retaining signaling function – exhibited accelerated proliferation, accompanied by a reduction in tumor-infiltrating $CD8^+$ T cells and an elevated $Foxp3^+$ regulatory T cells, independently of catalytic activity of hIDO1 [41, 79]. Interestingly, current study demonstrated that, in SKOV-3 tumor cells, epacadostat increases and continuously stabilizes hIDO1 in a catalytically inactive conformation, facilitating the formation of IDO1-SHP-2 complex, which accelerates the migratory capacity and the colony-forming ability of SKOV-3 cells [80]. To some extent, this finding bolsters the hypothesis that the noncatalytic function of IDO1 may be one of the underlying reasons for the clinical ineffectiveness of epacadostat in the Phase III ECHO-301 trial [81].

In fact, the tumorigenic function of hIDO1/hTDO is not limited to inducing immunosuppressive effects on immune cells; it may also serve as a contributing factor to tumor neovascularization, although the mechanism of its involvement in angiogenesis is still under investigation [82–86]. Some studies have demonstrated the favorable influence of IDO1 on angiogenesis in ovarian types and the formation of vasculogenic mimicry of lung cancer cells [82, 87]. Bioinformatic analyses showed a positive correlation between IDO1 expression and angiogenesis markers VEGFA and CD34 in glioma, or CD105+ endothelium in breast cancer, and with a worse prognosis [47, 84]. Besides, pharmacological hIDO1 inhibition showed anti-angiogenesis effect in glioblastoma, possibly by inducing tryptophan depletion in the tumor microenvironment [84]. Additionally, research has found that, in the presence of inhibition, TDO, catalyzing a similar reaction as IDO1, can hinder spontaneous capillary formation and efficiently counteract the proangiogenic effects triggered by VEGF-A in both human umbilical venous endothelial cells (HUVECs) and human endothelial colony-forming cells (ECFCs) [86].

Collectively, these findings underscore the multifaceted role of IDO1/TDO in tumor formation and their intricate mode of operation in relation to cancer immunotherapy, leading to the recognition of IDO1/TDO as promising targets for various cancer therapies and sparking researchers' interest in developing potent IDO1 inhibitors.

18.3.2 CNS Disorders

In recent years, there has been an increasing recognition of the complex interactions between the nervous and immune systems, characterized by shared humoral factors and receptors, forming the neuroimmune system. As **Trp** metabolites of the KP such as **QA**, **3-HK**, **3-HANA,** and **XA** exhibit distinct neuroactive properties, and aberrant activity of IDO1 and TDO results in dysregulation of this pathway, the links of the KP to inflammation, the immune system, and neurological disorders grew more evident. Below, we focus on neuroimmunology, review findings related to KP and neurodegenerative diseases, and discuss the roles of **TRP** metabolites and hIDO1 and hTDO potential as therapeutic targets.

Neurodegeneration is known to be associated with neuroinflammation, where the upregulation of IDO1 by inflammatory molecules like interferon-γ, TNF-α, and toll-like receptor 4 can activate the KP in various brain cells such as microglia, astrocytes, neurons, and infiltrating macrophages, leading to metabolic imbalance of neuroactive KP metabolites, which trigger or facilitate the pathogenesis of neurodegenerative diseases like Alzheimer's Disease (AD) and Parkinson's Disease (PD). In fact, studies have long implicated abnormal hIDO1 activity and altered levels of **Kyn** downstream metabolites in patients and animal models of these disorders. For AD, increased immunoreactivity of IDO, TDO [88], and excitotoxin **QA** is observed in the hippocampus of postmortem brains of AD patients, with Aβ aggregates showing positivity for both IDO and **QA** [89]. In addition, several metabolomics-led studies reveal positive correlations between KP metabolites, including **QA**, **KYNA,** and **3-HK,** and neurodegeneration biomarkers of AD such as amyloid β (Aβ), tau, and NFL, suggesting that KP is closely related to the core AD pathology [89–91]. This is consistent with the fact that co-incubation of **QA** and primary cultured human neurons promotes tau phosphorylation and aggregation. As one of the main pathological proteins of AD, it is reported that Aβ upregulates IDO1–Kyn–AHR signal pathway, leading to a dose-dependent increase in the expression of IDO1 and tau phosphorylation in Sprague Dawley (SD) rat primary hippocampal neurons, which could be blocked by IDO1 inhibitor [92]. Inspiringly, recent research uncovered a novel role of hIDO1 in brain glucose metabolism, showing that the activation of hIDO1 by Aβ and tau oligomers boosts **Kyn** levels, leading to the inhibition of astrocytic glycolysis; conversely, inhibiting IDO1 pharmaceutically enhances hippocampal glucose metabolism and long-term potentiation, ultimately recovering spatial memory in different mouse models of AD, demonstrating the potential of repurposing IDO1 inhibitors for neurodegenerative diseases like AD [93].

In addition to AD, management of hIDO1/hTDO may have an ameliorating effect on Parkinson's disease (PD) dementia, which is characterized by α-synuclein accumulation and progressive loss of nigrostriatal dopaminergic neurons [94]. Multiple pieces of evidence suggest increased **Kyn/TRP** ratio in the plasma and cerebrospinal fluid (CSF) of PD patients, along with abnormal levels of neurotoxic **3-HK** and **QA** in the patients' brains, while reduced concentrations of neuroprotective **KYNA** have been documented in the CSF of PD patients [95–97]. This observation is corroborated by *in vivo* studies, in which an intracerebral injection of **KYNA** can reverse motor symptoms of Parkinsonism by antagonizing NMDA receptors, and deletion of TDO has been demonstrated to promote increased neurogenesis in the hippocampus and subventricular zone, possibly mitigating neurodegeneration [98–100]. Furthermore, the administration of hIDO1 inhibitor shows efficacy in the MPTP-induced PD mouse motor coordination deficits by reducing **QA** in the mouse brain and increasing **KYNA** in the mouse blood [101].

18.4 IDO/TDO Inhibitors in Clinical Trials

As of now, a total of 8 IDO1 inhibitors and 2 IDO1/TDO dual inhibitors are undergoing clinical evaluation. Epacadostat (**1**) is a *N*-hydroxyamidine derivative developed by Incyte Corporation and has been extensively investigated in clinical trials for cancer therapy [102]. Clinical studies evaluated Epacadostat both as a monotherapy and in combination with other treatments, such as the checkpoint inhibitor pembrolizumab. While initial trials indicated good safety and tolerability, the efficacy results were mixed, with some combination studies not meeting their primary endpoints. In 2018, the ECHO-301/KEYNOTE-252 clinical trial, which evaluated the combination of Epacadostat with pembrolizumab, failed to meet its primary endpoints. This large Phase III trial aimed to assess the efficacy of this combination therapy in patients with advanced cancer but did not demonstrate a significant benefit in overall survival [103]. Consequently, despite its promising start, Epacadostat has faced significant challenges and has not progressed to broader clinical use. This experience underscores the difficulties in translating preclinical success into effective clinical outcomes in the field of immuno-oncology (Table 18.1). Indoximod (**2**) is a tryptophan analog developed by NewLink Genetics, and it has undergone extensive clinical evaluation for cancer therapy [104]. Clinical studies have explored Indoximod both as a standalone treatment and in combination with immune checkpoint inhibitors like pembrolizumab. While early trials demonstrated favorable safety and tolerability, the results in terms of efficacy were inconsistent. A key example is the Phase III trial launched in 2017, which assessed the combination of Indoximod with pembrolizumab in melanoma patients. Despite initial optimism, the trial revealed that Indoximod, due to its lack of specificity as an IDO1 inhibitor, did not produce the expected survival benefits (Table 18.1). BMS-986205 (**3**), also known as linrodostat, is a potent inhibitor targeting apo-IDO1 developed by Bristol-Myers Squibb [4]. It has been the focus of several clinical trials aimed at evaluating its efficacy in treating various cancers, often in combination with other immunotherapies, such as nivolumab. The drug was notable for its strong preclinical data, which led to its advancement into clinical trials, including Phase III studies. However, recent developments in 2023 revealed that some Phase III trials, particularly those for head and neck squamous cell carcinoma (HNSCC) and non-small cell lung cancer (NSCLC), were discontinued due to a strategic shift in business objectives (Table 18.1). A tryptophan analog developed by Pfizer, PF-06840003 (**4**) [105], was evaluated in a clinical trial (NCT02764151) for monotherapy treatment of malignant glioma, but this trial has since been terminated (Table 18.1). Navoximod (**5**) is an imidazole-derived IDO1 inhibitor developed by NewLink Genetics. Combination therapy with **5** and **4** (a prodrug of Indoximod) is used for the treatment of advanced solid tumors (NCT05469490, Table 18.1). KHK2455 (**6**) is an IDO1 inhibitor developed by Kyowa Kirin. The clinical research for KHK2455 has included trials to evaluate its safety, tolerability, and efficacy in treating various cancers (Table 18.1). The studies have focused on assessing its potential as a monotherapy and in combination with other cancer treatments. LY3381916 (**7**) is an IDO1 inhibitor developed by Eli Lilly. The current clinical trials mainly evaluate its safety (Table 18.1). Additionally, two IDO1/TDO dual inhibitors, M4112 (**9**) and SHR9146 (**10**), are also in clinical trials (Table 18.1).

Table 18.1 IDO/TDO inhibitors in clinical trials.

IDO1 inhibitors in clinical trials

Drug	Strategy	Tumor type	Phase	Identifier	Status
Epacadostat (1)	Single agent	Primary Peritoneal Carcinoma	Early Phase I	NCT02042430	Active, not recruiting
	Single agent	Stage III-IV Epithelial Ovarian, Fallopian Tube, or Primary Peritoneal Cancer	Early Phase I	NCT02042430	Active, not recruiting
	Pembrolizumab/ chemotherapy	Advanced solid tumors	Phase I	NCT02862457	Completed
	INCB001158/ Pembrolizumab	Advanced Solid Tumors	Phase I/II	NCT03361228	Terminated
	Pembrolizumab	Thymic Carcinomas	Phase II	NCT02364076	Unknown
	Cladribine/ Cytarabine	relapsed / refractory AML	Phase I	NCT03491579	Withdrawn
	Idarubicin/Cytarabine/Daunorubicin	AML	Phase I	NCT03444649	Withdrawn
	Pembrolizumab	Gastrointestinal stromal tumors	Phase II	NCT03291054	Terminated
	Sirolimus	Advanced malignancy	Phase I	NCT03217669	Active, not recruiting
	Pembrolizumab	Squamous cell carcinoma of the head and neck	Phase II	NCT03823131	Terminated
	MELITAC 12.1 Peptide Vaccine	stage III-IV melanoma	Phase II	NCT01961115	Completed
	Short-course radiation/ CAPOX chemotherapy	rectal cancer	Phase I/II	NCT03516708	Recruiting
	Pembrolizumab	Advanced Pancreatic Cancer	Phase II	NCT03432676	Withdrawn
	Pembrolizumab	Locally Advanced Sarcoma	Phase II	NCT03414229	Active, not recruiting

Pembrolizumab/Azacitidine	Metastatic Colorectal Cancer	Phase I/II	NCT03182894	Withdrawn
Pembrolizumab	Muscle-invasive bladder cancer	Phase II	NCT03832673	Withdrawn
Single agent	Myelodysplastic Syndromes	Phase II	NCT01822691	Completed
Pembrolizumab	Metastatic Renal Cell Carcinoma	Phase III	NCT03260894	Active, not recruiting
Pembrolizumab	Urothelial Carcinoma	Phase III	NCT03374488	Completed
M7824/N-803/MVA-BN-Brachyury	Solid tumor	Phase I/II	NCT03493945	Active, not recruiting
Pembrolizumab	Urothelial Carcinoma	Phase III	NCT03361865	Completed
Pembrolizumab	Recurrent/Metastatic Endometrial Carcinoma	Phase II	NCT03310567	Withdrawn
Azacitidine/Pembrolizumab	Advanced Solid Tumors	Phase I/II	NCT02959437	Terminated
Pembrolizumab	Gastric Cancer	Phase II	NCT03196232	Completed
Bevacizumab/RT/Retifanlimab	Recurrent gliomas	Phase II	NCT03532295	Active, not recruiting
Pembrolizumab	Extensive Stage Small Cell Lung Cancer	Phase II	NCT03402880	Withdrawn
Pembrolizumab	Head and neck cancer	Phase II	NCT03238638	Withdrawn
Durvalumab	Advanced Solid Tumors	Phase I/II	NCT02318277	Completed
Pembrolizumab	Head and neck cancer	Phase II	NCT03463161	Terminated
Pembrolizumab	Stage II-III Esophageal or Gastroesophageal Cancer	Phase II	NCT03592407	Withdrawn
Pembrolizumab/CRS-207	Metastatic Pancreas Cancer	Phase II	NCT03006302	Active, not recruiting
SD-101/RT	Lymphoma	Phase I/II	NCT03322384	Completed
CRS-207/Pembrolizumab	Platinum Resistant Ovarian, Fallopian, or Peritoneal Cancer	Phase I/II	NCT02575807	Terminated

(Continued)

Table 18.1 (Continued)

Drug	Strategy	Tumor type	Phase	Identifier	Status
	Pembrolizumab	Squamous Cell Carcinoma of the Head and Neck	Phase II	NCT03325465	Withdrawn
	Durvalumab	Nasopharyngeal Cancer	Phase II	NCT04231864	Withdrawn
	Pembrolizumab	Recurrent or Persistent Clear Cell Ovarian Cancer	Phase II	NCT03602586	Active, not recruiting
	ALVAC (2)-NY-ESO-1 (M)/TRICOM vaccine	Epithelial Ovarian, Fallopian Tube, or Primary Peritoneal Cancer	Phase I/II	NCT01982487	Withdrawn
	Pembrolizumab/Placebo	Metastatic Non-Small Cell Lung Cancer	Phase II	NCT03322540	Completed
	Nivolumab/Chemotherapy	Non-Small Cell Lung Cancer	Phase III	NCT03348904	Terminated
	Nivolumab/Chemotherapy	Advanced Cancers	Phase I/II	NCT02327078	Completed
	Pembrolizumab	Unresectable or Metastatic Melanoma	Phase III	NCT02752074	Completed
	Nivolumab/Ipilimumab/Lirilumab	Advanced or Metastatic Malignancies	Phase I/II	NCT03347123	Terminated
	DPX-Survivac/Cyclophosphamide	recurrent ovarian, fallopian tube, or peritoneal cancer	Phase I/II	NCT02785250	Active, not recruiting
	MK-3475	Selected Cancers	Phase I/II	NCT02178722	Completed
	Ipilimumab	Unresectable or Metastatic Melanoma	Phase I/II	NCT01604889	Terminated
	Itacitinib/INCB050465	Advanced Solid Tumors	Phase I	NCT02559492	Terminated
	Pembrolizumab/Chemotherapy	Advanced or Metastatic Solid Tumors	Phase I/II	NCT03085914	Completed
	DEC-205/NY-ESO-1 Fusion Protein CDX-1401	Ovarian, Fallopian Tube, or Primary Peritoneal Cancer in Remission	Phase I/II	NCT02166905	Completed
	Intraperitoneal Natural Killer Cells	Recurrent Ovarian, Fallopian Tube, and Primary Peritoneal Cancer	Phase I	NCT02118285	Completed
	Pembrolizumab/INCB001158	Advanced Solid Tumors	Phase I/II	NCT03361228	Terminated
	Pembrolizumab	Recurrent or Metastatic Head and Neck Squamous Cell Carcinoma	Phase III	NCT03358472	Active, not recruiting

	Nivolumab/Chemotherapy	Head and Neck Squamous Cell Carcinoma	Phase III	NCT03342352	Withdrawn
	Atezolizumab	Stage IIIB or Stage IV NMCLC/Stage IV Urothelial Carcinoma	Phase I	NCT02298153	Terminated
	Single agent	Advanced Malignancies	Phase I	NCT01195311	Completed
	Pembrolizumab/Chemotherapy	Metastatic NSCLC	Phase II	NCT03322566	Completed
Indoximod (2)	Ibrutinib/Chemotherapy	Pediatric Brain Cancer	Phase I	NCT05106296	Recruiting
	Single agent	Healthy	Early Phase I	NCT03852446	Completed
	Single agent	Relapsed or Refractory Solid Tumors	Phase I	NCT00739609	Terminated
	Single agent	Metastatic or Refractory Solid Tumors	Phase I	NCT00567931	Completed
	RT/Chemotherapy	Relapsed Brain Tumors	Phase II	NCT04049669	Recruiting
	Sipuleucel-T	Refractory Metastatic Prostate Cancer	Phase II	NCT01560923	Completed
	Temozolomide/RT	Progressive Primary Malignant Brain Tumors	Phase I	NCT02502708	Completed
	adenovirus-p53 transduced dendritic cell (DC) vaccine	Metastatic Breast Cancer	Phase I/II	NCT01042535	Completed
	Single agent	Healthy	Phase I	NCT03372239	Completed
	Docetaxel	Metastatic Solid Tumors	Phase I	NCT01191216	Completed
	Pembrolizumab/Nivolumab	Unresectable or Metastatic Melanoma	Phase II	NCT03301636	Terminated
	Chemotherapy	AML	Phase I	NCT02835729	Completed
	Chemotherapy	Metastatic Breast Cancer	Phase II	NCT01792050	Completed
	Nab-Paclitaxel/Gemcitabine	Metastatic Pancreatic Cancer	Phase I/II	NCT02077881	Completed
	Temozolomide/Bevacizumab	Primary Malignant Brain Tumors	Phase I/II	NCT02052648	Completed
	Pembrolizumab/Nivolumab	Metastatic Melanoma	Phase I/II	NCT02073123	Completed
	Docetaxel/Tergenpumatucel-L	NSCLC	Phase I	NCT02460367	Terminated

(Continued)

Table 18.1 (Continued)

Drug	Strategy	Tumor type	Phase	Identifier	Status
BMS-986205 (3)	Single agent	Healthy	Phase I	NCT03374228	Completed
	Nivolumab	Advanced Tumors	Phase I	NCT03192943	Completed
	Nivolumab/Chemotherapy	Muscle-invasive bladder cancer	Phase III	NCT03661320	Active, not recruiting
	Single agent	Healthy	Phase I	NCT03247283	Completed
	Itraconazole/Rifampin	Healthy	Phase I	NCT03346837	Completed
	Omeprazole	Healthy	Phase I	NCT03936374	Completed
	Single agent	Healthy	Phase I	NCT03378310	Completed
	Nivolumab	Advanced Malignant Solid Tumors	Phase I/II	NCT03792750	Completed
	Nivolumab	Endometrial Carcinosarcoma	Phase II	NCT04106414	Active, not recruiting
	Nivolumab/BCG	BCG Unresponsive Bladder Cancer	Phase II	NCT03519256	Terminated
	Nivolumab	Stage II-IV Squamous Cell Cancer of the Head and Neck	Phase II	NCT03854032	Active, not recruiting
	Single agent	Healthy	Phase I	NCT03312426	Completed
	Nivolumab	Advanced Melanoma	Phase III	NCT03329846	Completed
	Relatlimab/Nivolumab/Ipilimumab	Advanced Malignant Tumors	Phase I/II	NCT03459222	Active, not recruiting
	Nivolumab	Liver Cancer	Phase I/II	NCT03695250	Terminated
	Nivolumab/Ipilimumab	Advanced Malignant Tumors	Phase I/II	NCT02658890	Completed
	Nivolumab	Stage III or IV Melanoma	Phase II	NCT04007588	Withdrawn
	Nivolumab	Recurrent/Metastatic Squamous Cell Carcinoma of Head and Neck	Phase III	NCT03386838	Withdrawn
	Nivolumab/Chemotherapy	Stage IV or Recurrent NSCLC	Phase III	NCT03417037	Withdrawn

	Single agent	Healthy	Phase I	NCT03362411	Completed
	Nivolumab/RT or Chemotherapy	Newly Diagnosed Glioblastoma	Phase I	NCT04047706	Active, not recruiting
PF-06840003 (4)	Single agent	Malignant glioma	Phase I	NCT02764151	Terminated
Navoximod (5)	NLG-802/ Stereotactic Body Radiotherapy	Recurrent advanced solid tumors	Phase I	NCT05469490	Withdrawn
KHK2455 (6)	Mogamulizumab	Locally Advanced or Metastatic Solid Tumors	Phase I	NCT02867007	Completed
	Avelumab	Locally Advanced or Metastatic Urothelial Carcinoma	Phase I	NCT03915405	Terminated
LY3381916 (7)	LY3300054	Solid Tumors	Phase I	NCT03343613	Terminated
NLG802 (8)	Single agent	Advanced Solid Tumors	Phase I	NCT03164603	Completed
	Navoximod/Stereotactic Body Radiotherapy	Advanced Solid Tumors	Phase I	NCT05469490	Withdrawn
IDO1/TDO dual inhibitors in clinical trials					
M4112 (9)	MS201408-0005C or MS201408-0005B	Metastatic or Locally Advanced Unresectable Solid Tumors	Phase I	NCT03306420	Terminated
SHR9146 (10)	SHR-1210 or SHR-1210 + Apatinib	Advanced Solid Tumors	Phase I	NCT03491631	Active, not recruiting

18.5 Recently Disclosed IDO/TDO Inhibitors

Recently, numerous series of compounds have been developed as IDO/TDO inhibitors. However, the failure of the Phase III ECHO-301/KEYNOTE-252 trial has cast doubt on the viability of the IDO1-targeting approach. Despite this setback, new strategies have been proposed to bridge the gap between laboratory research and clinical application. In the following section, we will provide a review of IDO/TDO inhibitors and degraders reported up to August 2024, categorizing them based on their binding modes with IDO/TDO and their structural frameworks.

18.5.1 Inhibitors Targeting Holo IDO/TDO

18.5.1.1 Trp Analogs

Tryptophan-derived inhibitors (Figure 18.4) have generally been reported to exhibit moderate inhibitory activities. These compounds are characterized by the presence of an indole group, which is central to their structure, accompanied by a variety of side chains that contribute to their inhibitory function. Over the past few decades, numerous tryptophan analogs have been proven to act as IDO/TDO inhibitors. The racemic compound 1-methyl-DL-tryptophan (1-MT) is the most widely studied nonselective IDO inhibitor. However, the two stereoisomers of 1-MT demonstrate distinct potencies in inhibiting IDO1. Among them, D-1-MT (**2**, Indoximod) was the first IDO1 inhibitor to enter clinical trials. Additionally, its prodrug, NLG802 (**8**), has also been evaluated in a Phase I clinical trial (Table 18.1) [104]. In 2017, Pfizer developed a class of tryptophan analogs featuring a unique succinimide group, with the most optimized compound, PF-06840003 (**4**), demonstrating sub-micromolar potency (hIDO1 IC_{50} = 0.15 μM). According to the reported co-crystal structure of **4** with IDO1 (Figure 18.5, PDB code: 5WHR), the succinimide ring is positioned parallel and in close proximity to the heme group, while the indole ring is located within the lipophilic pocket. However, **4** does not exhibit any direct interaction with the heme iron. It is noteworthy that all four heteroatoms of compound **4** participate in hydrogen bonding. Specifically, the indole NH group engages in an interaction with Ser167, while the succinimide moiety establishes hydrogen bonds with Ala264, Thr379, and the carboxylate group of the heme. Unfortunately, the clinical development program (NCT02764151, Table 18.1) for **4** was terminated in 2018 [105]. In 2016, Antonio Coluccia and colleagues conducted a virtual screening of 2500 indole analogs, leading to the identification of **11**, an IDO1 inhibitor with micromolar potency (hIDO1 IC_{50} = 7 μM) [106]. Additionally, **12** (IDO1 K_d = 17.8 μM, Cellular IC_{50} = 14.4 μM), a 3-substituted indole derivative containing a thiourea group, was identified through virtual screening [107]. **13**, derived from the structural modification of anthocyanin, exhibits micromolar potency (IDO1 K_i = 11.55 μM) [108]. In 2013, Manna et al. synthesized a series of oxindole derivatives, among which **14** demonstrated the highest potency, exhibiting over 200-fold selectivity for IDO1 (IC_{50} = 0.19 μM) over TDO· (IC_{50} = 39.92 μM) [109].

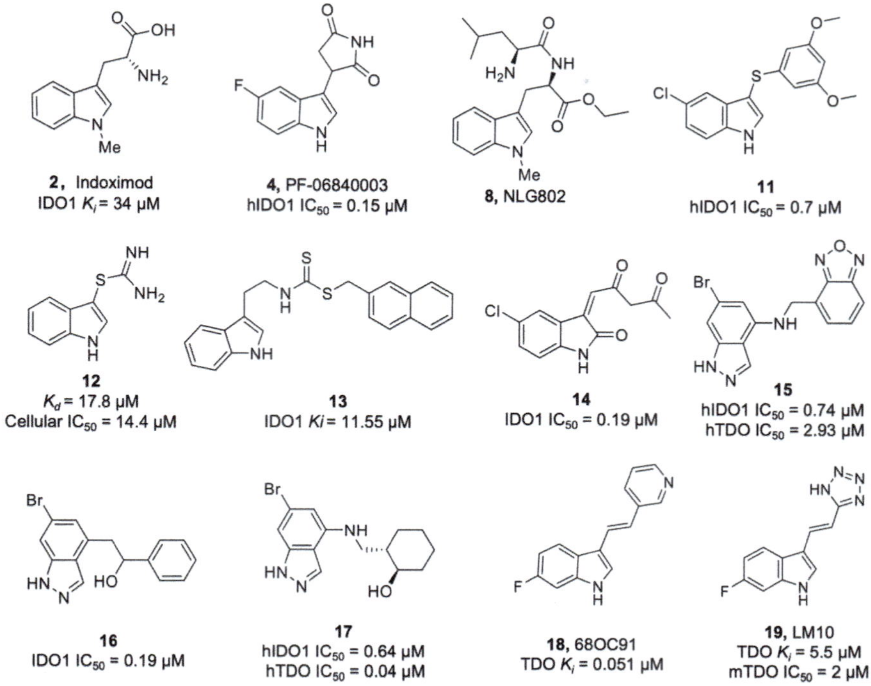

Figure 18.4 Reported tryptophan-derived IDO/TDO inhibitors.

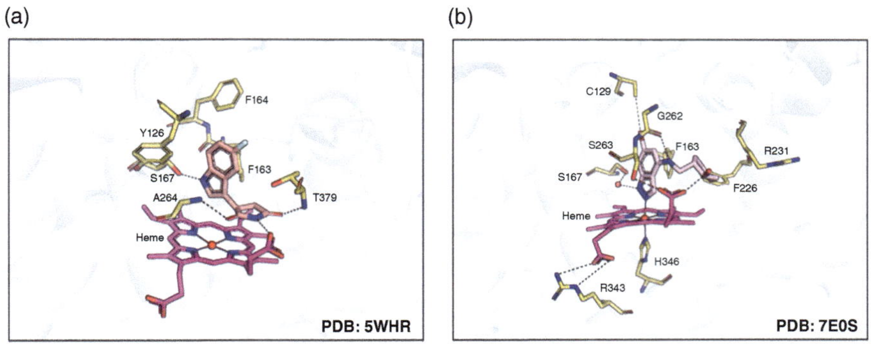

Figure 18.5 Crystallographic analysis of representative **Trp** analogs with holo IDO1. (a) IDO1 complexed with heme iron and **4** (PDB code: 5WHR); (b) IDO1 complexed with heme iron and **17** (PDB code: 7E0S).

Additionally, in 2019, Yang and colleagues reported a class of 4,6-substituted 1H-indazole derivatives. Among these, the most optimized compound, **15**, demonstrated micromolar potency against both IDO1 (IC_{50} = 0.74 μM) and TDO (IC_{50} = 2.93 μM) [110]. Similarly,**16** (IDO1 K_d = 0.14 μM) is also an effective indazole derivative [111]. In 2021, Ning et al. utilized X-ray crystallography to guide the optimization of 6-bromo-1H-indazole-4-amine derivatives, leading to the identification of **17**, a dual IDO/TDO inhibitor with nanomolar potency (hIDO1

IC_{50} = 0.64 μM, hTDO IC_{50} = 0.04 μM). According to the reported co-crystal structure of **17** with hIDO1 (Figure 18.5, PDB code: 7E0S), the compound forms a water bridge with Ser167 and a halogen bond with Cys129. The cyclohexanol moiety establishes an additional hydrogen bond with the heme carboxylate. Furthermore, pyrazole nitrogen coordinates with the heme iron, which is a key factor contributing to its superior potency compared to other tryptophan analogs. It is noteworthy that **17** exhibits favorable pharmacokinetic properties and good brain permeability in mice. In a mouse model of motor coordination impairment induced by 1-methyl-4-phenyl-1,2,3,6-tetrahydropyridine (MPTP), **17** demonstrated significant therapeutic efficacy [101].

Since the discovery of TDO, only a few indole-based compounds have been identified with TDO inhibitory activity. In 1994, Salter et al. developed a series of 3-(2-[(pyridyl)]ethenyl)indole derivatives as dual inhibitors of TDO and serotonin reuptake for the treatment of depression. Among these, 680C91 (**18**, K_i = 0.051 μM) exhibited excellent *in vitro* inhibitory activity against liver-extracted TDO. However, due to its low solubility and poor bioavailability, further research on this compound was not pursued. In 2011, Dolusic et al. synthesized over 70 analogs of **18** and identified the notable LM10 (**9**), which demonstrated significant TDO inhibitory activity at the cellular level (TDO K_i = 5.5 μM, mTDO IC_{50} = 2 μM). It is noteworthy that although **19** exhibits slightly weaker activity compared to **18**, it offers improved physicochemical properties. Specifically, **19** has lower lipophilicity, higher solubility, and greater stability, contributing to its enhanced oral bioavailability [112].

18.5.1.2 Imidazole/Triazole Derivatives

In 2006, Sugimoto et al reported the co-crystal structure of 4-PI (**20**) with IDO1 (Figure 18.7a), a compound identified as a weak IDO1 inhibitor (hIDO1 IC_{50} = 48 μM) (Figure 18.6) in 1989 [113, 114]. **20** occupies Pocket A, with the N1 atom of imidazole forming a coordination bond with the heme iron. Additionally, Pocket B is occupied by two molecules of 2-(*N*-cyclohexylamino)ethane sulfonic acid (component of the crystallization buffer) [114]. This finding holds substantial significance for the development of various imidazole/triazole-based IDO/TDO inhibitors, positioning **20** as a crucial lead compound in this area of research. In 2018, Michael G. et al. reported **21**, a potent inhibitor of hIDO1 with nanomolar potency (hIDO1 IC_{50} = 33.8 nM) (Figure 18.6), which contains a 5-fluoroindole fragment. Molecular docking studies reveal that, in addition to the coordination bond between the imidazole N1 atom and the heme iron, the phenolic hydroxyl group forms a hydrogen bond with Ser167 in Pocket A, while the 5-fluoroindole occupies Pocket B [115]. **22** is a submicromolar IDO1 inhibitor (IC_{50} = 0.16 μM, EC_{50} = 0.3 μM) (Figure 18.6) with a similar structure [116]. In contrast to the previous two inhibitors, **23** (hIDO1 IC_{50} = 0.3 μM) (Figure 18.6) does not introduce a substituent at the imidazole N3 position. Instead, it utilizes a strategy of incorporating a polar side chain into the phenyl ring to occupy Pocket B [117]. In 2011, Huang et al. reported a series of triazole compounds with weak inhibitory activity, among which **24** exhibited an IC_{50} of 86 μM against hIDO1 [118]. Discovered in 2018, **25** demonstrates nanomolar cellular activity (HeLa IDO1 IC_{50} = 23 nM,

Figure 18.6 Reported imidazole/triazole derivative IDO/TDO inhibitors.

HEK293 IDO1 IC_{50} = 67 nM) (Figure 18.6) but shows relatively weak enzymatic inhibitory activity (hIDO1 IC_{50} = 11.3 μM). Its co-crystal structure with hIDO1 (Figure 18.7b, PDB code: 6F0A) reveals that, similar to **20**, the N3 atom forms a coordination bond with the heme iron [119]. Subsequently, Manna et al. reported a series of 4,5-disubstituted 1,2,3-triazole derivatives, among which **26** exhibited submicromolar potency (hIDO1 IC_{50} = 0.11 μM) (Figure 18.6) [120]. In 2012, Zoete and colleagues successfully developed **27**, a compound exhibiting submicromolar potency (hIDO1 IC50 = 0.33 μM), through strategic modifications of the substituents on the phenyl ring of **24** [121]. In 2016, they explored the inhibitory potential of triazole compounds against IDO2, identifying **28** as a compound with micromolar potency (hIDO1 IC_{50} = 100 μM, mIDO2 IC_{50} = 51 μM) against mIDO2. Regrettably, due to the high cytotoxicity exhibited by **28,** no further studies were conducted on this compound [122]. Interestingly, in 2021, Zoete et al. synthesized 36 phenyl-azole compounds by combining various substituted benzenes with different azole derivatives, based on the existing 4-phenyl-1,2,3-triazole scaffold. **29**, containing a 1,2,4-triazole moiety, demonstrates nanomolar potency against both the enzyme and cellular assay (hIDO1 IC_{50} = 35 nM, Cellular IC_{50} = 34 nM) (Figure 18.6). Notably, the co-crystal structure of **29** with IDO1 (Figure 18.7c,

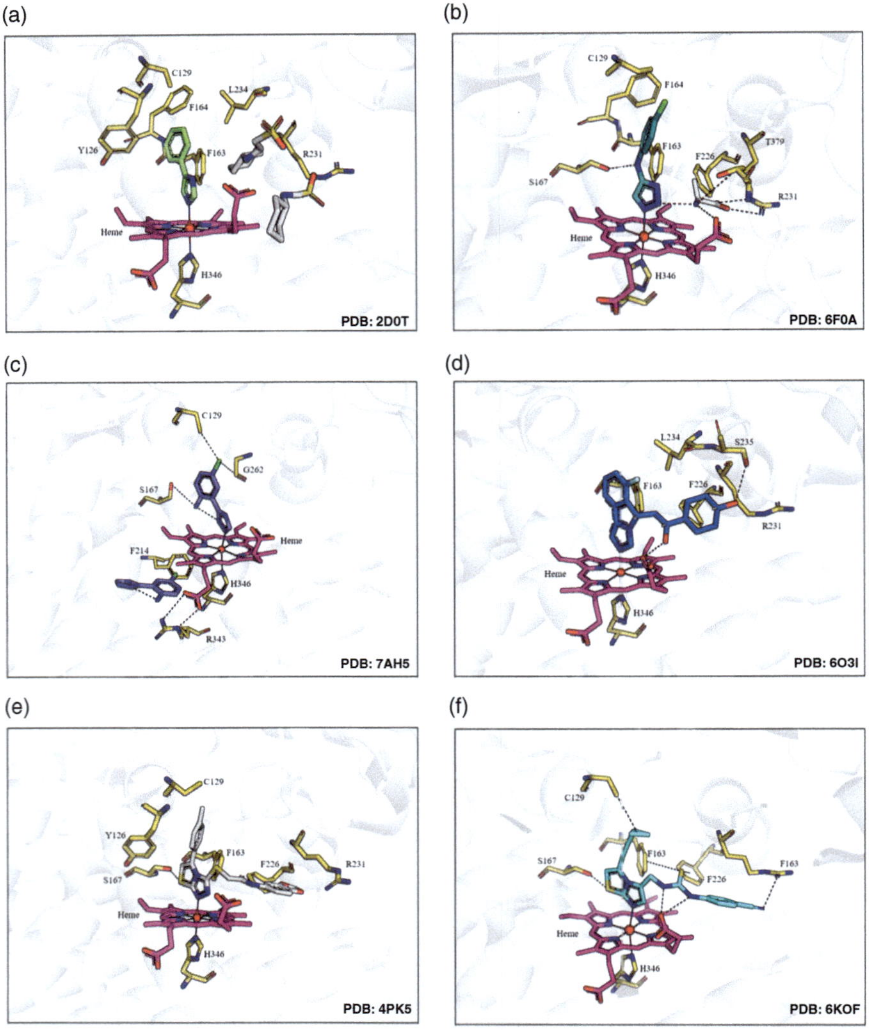

Figure 18.7 Crystallographic analysis of representative imidazole/ triazole derivatives with holo IDO1. (a) IDO1 complexed with heme iron and **20** (PDB code: 2D0T), (b) IDO1 complexed with heme iron and **25** (PDB code: 6F0A), (c) IDO1 complexed with heme iron and **29** (PDB code: 7AH5), (d) IDO1 complexed with heme iron and **5** (PDB code: 6O3I), (e) IDO1 complexed with heme iron and **33** (PDB code: 4PK5), (f) IDO1 complexed with heme iron and **37** (PDB code: 6KOF).

PDB code: 7AH5) demonstrates that **29** is present in both pocket A and pocket D. In pocket A, the binding mode of the 1,2,4-triazole is highly similar to that of the 1,2,3-triazole, with the chloro substituent positioned near Cys129 and Gly262, and the amino group oriented toward the back of pocket A, where it forms two hydrogen bonds with Ser167 and the N2 atom of the triazole ring. In pocket D, the phenyl ring is aligned toward the heme, the chloro substituent is directed toward Phe214, and the amino group points toward Arg343. In addition, it was found in the study that regardless of the oxidation state of the heme iron, the electrostatic potential created by the protein and the heme cofactor in pocket D is negative, whereas the electrostatic potential in pocket A depends on the iron's charge. This supports the earlier hypothesis that the 1,2,3-triazoles bind to ferric heme in their deprotonated form [123]. In a subsequent study conducted the following year, Zoete et al. further expanded the series of 1,2,3-triazole and 1,2,4-triazole inhibitors. Among these, **30** emerged as the most promising compound, demonstrating an IC_{50} value of 34 nM (Figure 18.6) in both enzymatic and cellular assays [124].

In 2019, NewLink Genetics Corporation leveraged a structure-based drug design strategy to develop and report a novel class of 5-substituted 5*H*-imidazo[5,1-*a*] isoindoles, demonstrating their efficacy as potent inhibitors of IDO1 [125]. Within this series, Navoximod (**5**), which demonstrates nanomolar potency (hIDO1 IC_{50} = 28 nM, 293 IDO1 EC_{50} = 75 nM), was the focus of a Phase I clinical trial (Table 18.1, NCT05469490) initiated in 2022. This study aimed to evaluate the safety of **5** in combination with NLG802 (**8**) and stereotactic body radiotherapy (SBRT) in patients with advanced solid tumors. Unfortunately, this study has since been withdrawn. In the co-crystal structure of **5** with IDO1 (Figure 18.7d, PDB code: 6O3I), as reported by NewLink, the N2 atom of the imidazoisoindole core exhibits coordination with the heme iron, thereby anchoring the compound within the active site. The phenyl ring extends into the hydrophobic pocket A, while the cyclohexanol moiety projects outward toward the solvent-accessible opening of the heme's proximal cavity. This saturated volume engages within the expanded channel, facilitating additional interactions. Furthermore, the terminal hydroxyl group forms a hydrogen bond with Ser235, which is instrumental in positioning the distal end of the ligand in a specific orientation [125]. **31** is an IDO1 inhibitor characterized by a moderate potency (hIDO1 IC_{50} = 0.84 μM) and distinguished by its imidazoisoindole core structure [126]. **32**, developed by Hengrui Co., is a potent inhibitor of both IDO1 (IC_{50} = 9.7 nM) and TDO (IC_{50} = 47 nM) (Figure 18.6), featuring a structure based on an imidazoisoindole derivative. In the MC38 xenograft tumor model, **32** shows significant oral efficacy and displays synergistic antitumor activity in combination with anti-PD1 monoclonal antibodies [127].

The first thiophene–triazole IDO1 inhibitor, Amg-1 (**33**), was reported in 2011 and exhibits micromolar-level potency (hIDO1 IC_{50} = 3 μM) against IDO1 [128]. Subsequently, Dainippon Sumitomo Pharma Co. identified a series of IDO1 inhibitors featuring imidazothiazole or thiophene–triazole scaffolds through structure-based drug design (SBDD). Among this series, **34** stands out as the most effective compound, demonstrating nanomolar potency against IDO1 (IC_{50} = 77 nM). Furthermore, this study elucidates the co-crystal structure of **33** with IDO1 (Figure 18.7e, PDB code: 4PK5), providing insights that contrast with earlier predictions [128]. The tolyl group is situated in pocket A, while the nitrogen atom of the thiazole–triazole moiety coordinates with the heme iron. Additionally, the extended amide side chain is accommodated within pocket B, where it engages in π–π interactions with residues F226 and R231. In contrast to **33**, **34** (PDB code: 4PK6) exhibits an induced fit mechanism, extending interactions with residues F226 and R231 in Pocket B [129]. This could be a contributing factor to why **34** demonstrates markedly superior inhibitory effects against IDO1 compared to **33**. Following the discovery of **33** and the reporting of its co-crystal structure with IDO1, a series of IDO1 inhibitors featuring triazolethiophene and imidazothiazole core structures have been subsequently identified. In 2018, Fallarini et al. reported **35**, an IDO1 inhibitor with moderate inhibitory activity (hIDO1 $IC_{50} = 0.2\,\mu M$) [130]. Subsequently, in 2019, they utilized click chemistry to identify **36**, which exhibited comparable inhibitory effects (hIDO1 $IC_{50} = 0.2\,\mu M$) (Figure 18.6) [131]. In 2020, Ueng et al. reported a series of imidazothiazole-based IDO1 inhibitors featuring thiourea side chains. Among these, **37** exhibits potent inhibitory activity against IDO1 ($IC_{50} = 16.4\,nM$). The co-crystal structure of **37** with IDO1 (Figure 18.7f, PDB code: 6KOF) reveals that, in addition to the imidazothiazole forming a coordination bond with the heme iron, the unique cyclopropyl group occupies pocket A. This cyclopropyl ring interacts with Cys129, displaying π-like properties. Additionally, the thiourea moiety establishes an extra network of sulfur-aromatic interactions with the adjacent residues Phe163 and Phe226 [132].

In 2022, Yang et al. employed a structure-based drug design strategy to develop a series of derivatives featuring 1,2,3-triazole linked to erlotinib. **38** (hIDO1 $IC_{50} = 0.32\,\mu M$) and **39** (hIDO1 $IC_{50} = 0.59\,\mu M$) (Figure 18.6) exhibit submicromolar potency against IDO1. Molecular docking studies indicate that the triazole group coordinates with the heme iron, while the hydrophilic ether chain of erlotinib can penetrate the hydrophilicity region of the IDO1 target [133, 134]. Additionally, in the same year, their other work reported **40**, another IDO1 inhibitor with submicromolar potency (hIDO1 $IC_{50} = 0.75\,\mu M$) (Figure 18.6) [135].

References

1 Cervenka, I., Agudelo, L.Z., and Ruas, J.L. (2017). Kynurenines: tryptophan's metabolites in exercise, inflammation, and mental health. *Science (New York, N.Y.)* 357 (6349): eaaf9794.

2 Vécsei, L., Szalárdy, L., Fülöp, F., and Toldi, J. (2013). Kynurenines in the CNS: recent advances and new questions. *Nature Reviews Drug Discovery* 12 (1): 64–82.

3 Takikawa, O. (2005). Biochemical and medical aspects of the indoleamine 2,3-dioxygenase-initiated L-tryptophan metabolism. *Biochemical and Biophysical Research Communications* 338 (1): 12–19.

4 Nelp, M.T., Kates, P.A., Hunt, J.T. et al. (2018). Immune-modulating enzyme indoleamine 2,3-dioxygenase is effectively inhibited by targeting its apo-form. *Proceedings of the National Academy of Sciences of the United States of America* 115 (13): 3249–3254.

5 Maddison, D.C. and Giorgini, F. (2015). The kynurenine pathway and neurodegenerative disease. *Seminars in Cell & Developmental Biology* 40: 134–141.

6 Lim, C.K., Fernández-Gomez, F.J., Braidy, N. et al. (2017). Involvement of the kynurenine pathway in the pathogenesis of Parkinson's disease. *Progress in Neurobiology* 155: 76–95.

7 Biernacki, T., Sandi, D., Bencsik, K., and Vécsei, L. (2020). Kynurenines in the pathogenesis of multiple sclerosis: therapeutic perspectives. *Cells* 9 (6): 1343.

8 Fatokun, A.A., Hunt, N.H., and Ball, H.J. (2013). Indoleamine 2,3-dioxygenase 2 (IDO2) and the kynurenine pathway: characteristics and potential roles in health and disease. *Amino Acids* 45 (6): 1319–1329.

9 Platten, M., von Knebel Doeberitz, N., Oezen, I. et al. (2014). Cancer immunotherapy by targeting IDO1/TDO and their downstream effectors. *Frontiers in Immunology* 5: 673.

10 Röhrig, U.F., Majjigapu, S.R., Vogel, P. et al. (2015). Challenges in the discovery of indoleamine 2,3-dioxygenase 1 (IDO1) inhibitors. *Journal of Medicinal Chemistry* 58 (24): 9421–1937.

11 Tang, K., Wu, Y.H., Song, Y., and Yu, B. (2021). Indoleamine 2,3-dioxygenase 1 (IDO1) inhibitors in clinical trials for cancer immunotherapy. *Journal of Hematology & Oncology* 14 (1): 68.

12 Mondal, P. and Wijeratne, G.B. (2020). Modeling tryptophan/indoleamine 2,3-dioxygenase with heme superoxide mimics: is ferryl the key intermediate? *Journal of the American Chemical Society* 142 (4): 1846–1856.

13 Pantouris, G. and Mowat, C.G. (2014). Antitumour agents as inhibitors of tryptophan 2,3-dioxygenase. *Biochemical and Biophysical Research ommunications* 443 (1): 28–31.

14 Pantouris, G., Serys, M., Yuasa, H.J. et al. (2014). Human indoleamine 2,3-dioxygenase-2 has substrate specificity and inhibition characteristics distinct from those of indoleamine 2,3-dioxygenase-1. *Amino Acids* 46 (9): 2155–2163.

15 Uhlén, M., Fagerberg, L., Hallström, B.M. et al. (2015). Tissue-based map of the human proteome. *Science (New York, N.Y.)* 347 (6220)): 1260419.

16 Ott, M., Litzenburger, U.M., Rauschenbach, K.J. et al. (2015). Suppression of TDO-mediated tryptophan catabolism in glioblastoma cells by a steroid-responsive FKBP52-dependent pathway. *Glia* 63 (1): 78–90.

17 Konan, K.V. and Taylor, M.W. (1996). Importance of the two interferon-stimulated response element (ISRE) sequences in the regulation of the human indoleamine 2,3-dioxygenase gene. *The Journal of Biological Chemistry* 271 (32): 19140–19145.

18 Hennequart, M., Pilotte, L., Cane, S. et al. (2017). Constitutive IDO1 expression in human tumors is driven by cyclooxygenase-2 and mediates intrinsic immune resistance. *Cancer Immunology Research* 5 (8): 695–709.

19 Wang, L.T., Chiou, S.S., Chai, C.Y. et al. (2017). Intestine-specific homeobox gene ISX integrates IL6 signaling, tryptophan catabolism, and immune suppression. *Cancer Research* 77 (15): 4065–4077.

20 Vacchelli, E., Aranda, F., Eggermont, A. et al. (2014). Trial watch: IDO inhibitors in cancer therapy. *Oncoimmunology* 3 (10): e957994.

21 Kozuma, Y., Takada, K., Toyokawa, G. et al. (1990). Indoleamine 2,3-dioxygenase 1 and programmed cell death-ligand 1 co-expression correlates with aggressive features in lung adenocarcinoma. *European Journal of Cancer (Oxford, England)* 2018 (101): 20–29.

22 Prendergast, G.C., Malachowski, W.J., Mondal, A. et al. (2018). Indoleamine 2,3-dioxygenase and its therapeutic inhibition in cancer. *International Review of Cell and Molecular Biology* 336: 175–203.

23 Metz, R., Smith, C., DuHadaway, J.B. et al. (2014). IDO2 is critical for IDO1-mediated T-cell regulation and exerts a non-redundant function in inflammation. *International Immunology* 26 (7): 357–367.

24 Mirgaux, M., Leherte, L., and Wouters, J. (2024). Human indoleamine-2,3-dioxygenase 2 cofactor lability and low substrate affinity explained by homology modeling, molecular dynamics and molecular docking. *Journal of Biomolecular Structure & Dynamics* 42 (9): 4475–4488.

25 Sono, M., Roach, M.P., Coulter, E.D., and Dawson, J.H. (1996). Heme-containing oxygenases. *Chemical Reviews* 96 (7): 2841–2888.

26 Efimov, I., Basran, J., Thackray, S.J. et al. (2011). Structure and reaction mechanism in the heme dioxygenases. *Biochemistry* 50 (14): 2717–2724.

27 Chung, L.W., Li, X., Sugimoto, H. et al. (2008). Density functional theory study on a missing piece in understanding of heme chemistry: the reaction mechanism for indoleamine 2,3-dioxygenase and tryptophan 2,3-dioxygenase. *Journal of the American Chemical Society* 130 (37): 12299–12309.

28 Basran, J., Efimov, I., Chauhan, N. et al. (2011). The mechanism of formation of N-formylkynurenine by heme dioxygenases. *Journal of the American Chemical Society* 133 (40): 16251–16257.

29 Basran, J., Booth, E.S., Lee, M. et al. (2016). Analysis of reaction intermediates in tryptophan 2,3-dioxygenase: a comparison with indoleamine 2,3-dioxygenase. *Biochemistry* 55 (49): 6743–6750.

30 Lewis-Ballester, A., Forouhar, F., Kim, S.M. et al. (2016). Molecular basis for catalysis and substrate-mediated cellular stabilization of human tryptophan 2,3-dioxygenase. *Scientific Reports* 6: 35169.

31 Chauhan, N., Thackray, S.J., Rafice, S.A. et al. (2009). Reassessment of the reaction mechanism in the heme dioxygenases. *Journal of the American Chemical Society* 131 (12): 4186–4187.

32 Lewis-Ballester, A., Batabyal, D., Egawa, T. et al. (2009). Evidence for a ferryl intermediate in a heme-based dioxygenase. *Proceedings of the National Academy of Sciences of the United States of America* 106 (41): 17371–17376.

33 Pham, K.N., Lewis-Ballester, A., and Yeh, S.R. (2021). Conformational plasticity in human heme-based dioxygenases. *Journal of the American Chemical Society* 143 (4): 1836–1845.

34 Lewis-Ballester, A., Pham, K.N., Batabyal, D. et al. (2017). Structural insights into substrate and inhibitor binding sites in human indoleamine 2,3-dioxygenase 1. *Nature Communications* 8 (1): 1693.

35 Mirgaux, M., Leherte, L., and Wouters, J. (2020). Influence of the presence of the heme cofactor on the JK-loop structure in indoleamine 2,3-dioxygenase 1. *Acta Crystallographica Section D, Structural Biology* 76 (Pt 12): 1211–1221.

36 Pham, K.N., Lewis-Ballester, A., and Yeh, S.R. (2019). Structural basis of inhibitor selectivity in human indoleamine 2,3-dioxygenase 1 and tryptophan dioxygenase. *Journal of the American Chemical Society* 141 (47): 18771–18779.

37 Luo, S., Xu, K., Xiang, S. et al. (2018). High-resolution structures of inhibitor complexes of human indoleamine 2,3-dioxygenase 1 in a new crystal form. *Acta Crystallographica Section F, Structural Biology Communications* 74 (Pt 11): 717–724.

38 Orabona, C., Pallotta, M.T., Volpi, C. et al. (2008). SOCS3 drives proteasomal degradation of indoleamine 2,3-dioxygenase (IDO) and antagonizes IDO-dependent tolerogenesis. *Proceedings of the National Academy of Sciences of the United States of America* 105 (52): 20828–20833.

39 Álvarez, L., Lewis-Ballester, A., Roitberg, A. et al. (2016). Structural study of a flexible active site loop in human indoleamine 2,3-dioxygenase and its functional implications. *Biochemistry* 55 (19): 2785–2793.

40 Orabona, C., Pallotta, M.T., and Grohmann, U. (2012). Different partners, opposite outcomes: a new perspective of the immunobiology of indoleamine 2,3-dioxygenase. *Molecular Medicine (Cambridge, Mass)* 18 (1): 834–842.

41 Pallotta, M.T., Orabona, C., Volpi, C. et al. (2011). Indoleamine 2,3-dioxygenase is a signaling protein in long-term tolerance by dendritic cells. *Nature Immunology* 12 (9): 870–878.

42 Boyland, E. and Williams, D.C. (1955). The estimation of tryptophan metabolites in the urine of patients with cancer of the bladder. *The Biochemical Journal (Annual General Meeting)* 60: v.

43 Muller, A.J., DuHadaway, J.B., Donover, P.S. et al. (2005). Inhibition of indoleamine 2,3-dioxygenase, an immunoregulatory target of the cancer suppression gene Bin1, potentiates cancer chemotherapy. *Nature Medicine* 11 (3): 312–319.

44 Uyttenhove, C., Pilotte, L., Théate, I. et al. (2003). Evidence for a tumoral immune resistance mechanism based on tryptophan degradation by indoleamine 2,3-dioxygenase. *Nature Medicine* 9 (10): 1269–1274.

45 Panitz, V., Končarević, S., Sadik, A. et al. (2021). Tryptophan metabolism is inversely regulated in the tumor and blood of patients with glioblastoma. *Theranostics* 11 (19): 9217–9233.

46 Shi, D., Wu, X., Jian, Y. et al. (2022). USP14 promotes tryptophan metabolism and immune suppression by stabilizing IDO1 in colorectal cancer. *Nature Communications* 13 (1): 5644.

47 Wei, L., Zhu, S., Li, M. et al. (2018). High indoleamine 2,3-dioxygenase is correlated with microvessel density and worse prognosis in breast cancer. *Frontiers in Immunology* 9: 724.

48 Zhang, M.L., Kem, M., Mooradian, M.J. et al. (2019). Differential expression of PD-L1 and IDO1 in association with the immune microenvironment in resected lung adenocarcinomas. *Modern Pathology : An Official Journal of The United States and Canadian Academy of Pathology, Inc* 32 (4): 511–523.

49 Wu, Z., Yan, L., Lin, J. et al. (2021). Constitutive TDO2 expression promotes liver cancer progression by an autocrine IL-6 signaling pathway. *Cancer Cell International* 21 (1): 538.

50 Zhang, T., Tan, X.L., Xu, Y. et al. (2017). Expression and prognostic value of indoleamine 2,3-dioxygenase in pancreatic cancer. *Chinese Medical Journal* 130 (6): 710–716.

51 Inaba, T., Ino, K., Kajiyama, H. et al. (2009). Role of the immunosuppressive enzyme indoleamine 2,3-dioxygenase in the progression of ovarian carcinoma. *Gynecologic Oncology* 115 (2): 185–192.

52 Ino, K., Yamamoto, E., Shibata, K. et al. (2008). Inverse correlation between tumoral indoleamine 2,3-dioxygenase expression and tumor-infiltrating lymphocytes in endometrial cancer: its association with disease progression and survival. *Clinical Cancer Research : An Official Journal of The American Association for Cancer Research* 14 (8): 2310–2317.

53 Brandacher, G., Perathoner, A., Ladurner, R. et al. (2006). Prognostic value of indoleamine 2,3-dioxygenase expression in colorectal cancer: effect on tumor-infiltrating T cells. *Clinical Cancer Research : An Official Journal of The American Association for Cancer Research* 12 (4): 1144–1151.

54 Witkiewicz, A., Williams, T.K., Cozzitorto, J. et al. (2008). Expression of indoleamine 2,3-dioxygenase in metastatic pancreatic ductal adenocarcinoma recruits regulatory T cells to avoid immune detection. *Journal of the American College of Surgeons* 206 (5): 849–854 discussion 854–6.

55 Ishio, T., Goto, S., Tahara, K. et al. (2004). Immunoactivative role of indoleamine 2,3-dioxygenase in human hepatocellular carcinoma. *Journal of Gastroenterology and Hepatology* 19 (3): 319–326.

56 Li, L., Wang, T., Li, S. et al. (2020). TDO2 promotes the EMT of hepatocellular carcinoma through Kyn-AhR pathway. *Frontiers in Oncology* 10: 562823.

57 Pan, K., Wang, H., Chen, M.S. et al. (2008). Expression and prognosis role of indoleamine 2,3-dioxygenase in hepatocellular carcinoma. *Journal of Cancer Research and Clinical Oncology* 134 (11): 1247–1253.

58 Tang, D., Yue, L., Yao, R. et al. (2017). P53 prevent tumor invasion and metastasis by down-regulating IDO in lung cancer. *Oncotarget* 8 (33): 54548–54557.

59 Hsu, Y.L., Hung, J.Y., Chiang, S.Y. et al. (2016). Lung cancer-derived galectin-1 contributes to cancer associated fibroblast-mediated cancer progression and immune suppression through TDO2/kynurenine axis. *Oncotarget* 7 (19): 27584–27598.

60 Feng, H., Cao, B., Peng, X., and Wei, Q. (2022). Cancer-associated fibroblasts strengthen cell proliferation and EGFR TKIs resistance through aryl hydrocarbon receptor dependent signals in non-small cell lung cancer. *BMC Cancer* 22 (1): 764.

61 Zhong, C., Peng, L., Tao, B. et al. (2022). TDO2 and tryptophan metabolites promote kynurenine/AhR signals to facilitate glioma progression and immunosuppression. *American Journal of Cancer Research* 12 (6): 2558–2575.

62 Thaker, A.I., Rao, M.S., Bishnupuri, K.S. et al. (2013). IDO1 metabolites activate β-catenin signaling to promote cancer cell proliferation and colon tumorigenesis in mice. *Gastroenterology* 145 (2): 416–425.e1–4.

63 Platten, M., Wick, W., and Van den Eynde, B.J. (2012). Tryptophan catabolism in cancer: beyond IDO and tryptophan depletion. *Cancer Research* 72 (21): 5435–5440.

64 Munn, D.H., Sharma, M.D., Baban, B. et al. (2005). GCN2 kinase in T cells mediates proliferative arrest and anergy induction in response to indoleamine 2,3-dioxygenase. *Immunity* 22 (5): 633–642.

65 Fallarino, F., Grohmann, U., You, S. et al. (2006). The combined effects of tryptophan starvation and tryptophan catabolites down-regulate T cell receptor zeta-chain and induce a regulatory phenotype in naive T cells. *Journal of Immunology (Baltimore, Md. : 1950)* 176 (11): 6752–6761.

66 Munn, D.H. and Mellor, A.L. (2016). IDO in the tumor microenvironment: inflammation, counter-regulation, and tolerance. *Trends in Immunology* 37 (3): 193–207.

67 Zhai, L., Ladomersky, E., Lenzen, A. et al. (2018). IDO1 in cancer: a Gemini of immune checkpoints. *Cellular & Molecular Immunology* 15 (5): 447–457.

68 Zhai, L., Bell, A., Ladomersky, E. et al. (2020). Immunosuppressive IDO in cancer: mechanisms of action, animal models, and targeting strategies. *Frontiers in Immunology* 11: 1185.

69 Bessede, A., Gargaro, M., Pallotta, M.T. et al. (2014). Aryl hydrocarbon receptor control of a disease tolerance defence pathway. *Nature* 511 (7508): 184–190.

70 Gargaro, M., Scalisi, G., Manni, G. et al. (2022). Indoleamine 2,3-dioxygenase 1 activation in mature cDC1 promotes tolerogenic education of inflammatory cDC2 via metabolic communication. *Immunity* 55 (6): 1032–1050.e14.

71 Opitz, C.A., Somarribas Patterson, L.F., Mohapatra, S.R. et al. (2020). The therapeutic potential of targeting tryptophan catabolism in cancer. *British Journal of Cancer* 122 (1): 30–44.

72 Takenaka, M.C., Gabriely, G., Rothhammer, V. et al. (2019). Control of tumor-associated macrophages and T cells in glioblastoma via AHR and CD39. *Nature Neuroscience* 22 (5): 729–740.

73 Quintana, F.J., Basso, A.S., Iglesias, A.H. et al. (2008). Control of T(reg) and T(H)17 cell differentiation by the aryl hydrocarbon receptor. *Nature* 453 (7191): 65–71.

74 Nguyen, N.T., Kimura, A., Nakahama, T. et al. (2010). Aryl hydrocarbon receptor negatively regulates dendritic cell immunogenicity via a kynurenine-dependent mechanism. *Proceedings of the National Academy of Sciences of the United States of America* 107 (46): 19961–19966.

75 DiNatale, B.C., Murray, I.A., Schroeder, J.C. et al. (2010). Kynurenic acid is a potent endogenous aryl hydrocarbon receptor ligand that synergistically induces interleukin-6 in the presence of inflammatory signaling. *Toxicological Sciences : An Official Journal of The Society of Toxicology* 115 (1): 89–97.

76 Novikov, O., Wang, Z., Stanford, E.A. et al. (2016). An aryl hydrocarbon receptor-mediated amplification loop that enforces cell migration in ER-/PR-/Her2- human breast cancer cells. *Molecular Pharmacology* 90 (5): 674–688.

77 Terness, P., Bauer, T.M., Röse, L. et al. (2002). Inhibition of allogeneic T cell proliferation by indoleamine 2,3-dioxygenase-expressing dendritic cells: mediation of suppression by tryptophan metabolites. *The Journal of Experimental Medicine* 196 (4): 447–457.

78 Fallarino, F., Grohmann, U., Vacca, C. et al. (2002). T cell apoptosis by tryptophan catabolism. *Cell Death and Differentiation* 9 (10): 1069–1077.

79 Orecchini, E., Belladonna, M.L., Pallotta, M.T. et al. (2023). The signaling function of IDO1 incites the malignant progression of mouse B16 melanoma. *Oncoimmunology* 12 (1): 2170095.

80 Rossini, S., Ambrosino, S., Volpi, C. et al. (2024). Epacadostat stabilizes the apo-form of IDO1 and signals a pro-tumorigenic pathway in human ovarian cancer cells. *Frontiers in Immunology* 15: 1346686.

81 Van den Eynde, B.J., van Baren, N., and Baurain, J.-F.J.A. (2020). Is there a clinical future for IDO1 inhibitors after the failure of epacadostat in melanoma? *Annual Review of Cancer Biology* 4 (1): 241–256.

82 Pan, J., Yuan, K., Peng, S. et al. (2017). Gene silencing of indoleamine 2,3-dioxygenase hinders tumor growth through angiogenesis inhibition. *International Journal of Oncology* 50 (6): 2136–2144.

83 Zhang, W., Mao, S., Shi, D. et al. (2019). MicroRNA-153 decreases tryptophan catabolism and inhibits angiogenesis in bladder cancer by targeting indoleamine 2,3-dioxygenase 1. *Frontiers in Oncology* 9: 619.

84 Xing, Z., Li, X., He, Z.N.T. et al. (2024). IDO1 inhibitor RY103 suppresses Trp-GCN2-mediated angiogenesis and counters immunosuppression in glioblastoma. *Pharmaceutics* 16 (7): 870.

85 Ying, X., Zheng, X., Zhang, X. et al. (2024). Kynurenine in IDO1(high) cancer cell-derived extracellular vesicles promotes angiogenesis by inducing endothelial mitophagy in ovarian cancer. *Journal of Translational Medicine* 22 (1): 267.

86 Cecchi, M., Anceschi, C., Silvano, A. et al. (2024). Unveiling the role of tryptophan 2,3-dioxygenase in the angiogenic process. *Pharmaceuticals (Basel, Switzerland)* 17 (5): 558.

87 Nonaka, H., Saga, Y., Fujiwara, H. et al. (2011). Indoleamine 2,3-dioxygenase promotes peritoneal dissemination of ovarian cancer through inhibition of natural killercell function and angiogenesis promotion. *International Journal of Oncology* 38 (1): 113–120.

88 Wu, W., Nicolazzo, J.A., Wen, L. et al. (2013). Expression of tryptophan 2,3-dioxygenase and production of kynurenine pathway metabolites in triple transgenic mice and human Alzheimer's disease brain. *PLoS One* 8 (4): e59749.

89 Guillemin, G.J., Brew, B.J., Noonan, C.E. et al. (2005). Indoleamine 2,3 dioxygenase and quinolinic acid immunoreactivity in Alzheimer's disease hippocampus. *Neuropathology and Applied Neurobiology* 31 (4): 395–404.

90 Chatterjee, P., Zetterberg, H., Goozee, K. et al. (2019). Plasma neurofilament light chain and amyloid-β are associated with the kynurenine pathway metabolites in preclinical Alzheimer's disease. *Journal of Neuroinflammation* 16 (1): 186.

91 van der Velpen, V., Teav, T., Gallart-Ayala, H. et al. (2019). Systemic and central nervous system metabolic alterations in Alzheimer's disease. *Alzheimer's Research & Therapy* 11 (1): 93.

92 Duan, Z., Zhang, S., Liang, H. et al. (2020). Amyloid β neurotoxicity is IDO1-Kyn-AhR dependent and blocked by IDO1 inhibitor. *Signal Transduction and Targeted Therapy* 5 (1): 96.

93 Minhas, P.S., Jones, J.R., Latif-Hernandez, A. et al. (2024). Restoring hippocampal glucose metabolism rescues cognition across Alzheimer's disease pathologies. *Science (New York, N.Y.)* 385 (6711): eabm6131.

94 Charvin, D., Medori, R., Hauser, R.A., and Rascol, O. (2018). Therapeutic strategies for Parkinson disease: beyond dopaminergic drugs. *Nature Reviews Drug Discovery* 17 (11): 804–822.

95 Widner, B., Leblhuber, F., and Fuchs, D. (2002). Increased neopterin production and tryptophan degradation in advanced Parkinson's disease. *Journal of Neural Transmission (Vienna, Austria : 1996)* 109 (2): 181–189.

96 Lovelace, M.D., Varney, B., Sundaram, G. et al. (2017). Recent evidence for an expanded role of the kynurenine pathway of tryptophan metabolism in neurological diseases. *Neuropharmacology* 112 (Pt B): 373–388.

97 Sorgdrager, F.J.H., Vermeiren, Y., Van Faassen, M. et al. (2019). Age- and disease-specific changes of the kynurenine pathway in Parkinson's and Alzheimer's disease. *Journal of Neurochemistry* 151 (5): 656–668.

98 Graham, W.C., Robertson, R.G., Sambrook, M.A., and Crossman, A.R. (1990). Injection of excitatory amino acid antagonists into the medial pallidal segment of a 1-methyl-4-phenyl-1,2,3,6-tetrahydropyridine (MPTP) treated primate reverses motor symptoms of parkinsonism. *Life Sciences* 47 (18): Pl91–PL97.

99 Luccini, E., Musante, V., Neri, E. et al. (2007). N-methyl-D-aspartate autoreceptors respond to low and high agonist concentrations by facilitating, respectively, exocytosis and carrier-mediated release of glutamate in rat hippocampus. *Journal of Neuroscience Research* 85 (16): 3657–3665.

100 Kanai, M., Funakoshi, H., Takahashi, H. et al. (2009). Tryptophan 2,3-dioxygenase is a key modulator of physiological neurogenesis and anxiety-related behavior in mice. *Molecular Brain* 2: 8.

101 Ning, X.L., Li, Y.Z., Huo, C. et al. (2021). X-ray structure-guided discovery of a potent, orally bioavailable, dual human indoleamine/tryptophan 2,3-dioxygenase (hIDO/hTDO) inhibitor that shows activity in a mouse model of Parkinson's disease. *Journal of Medicinal Chemistry* 64 (12): 8303–8332.

102 Yue, E.W., Sparks, R., Polam, P. et al. (2017). INCB24360 (Epacadostat), a highly potent and selective indoleamine-2,3-dioxygenase 1 (IDO1) inhibitor for immuno-oncology. *ACS Medicinal Chemistry Letters* 8 (5): 486–491.

103 Long, G.V., Dummer, R., Hamid, O. et al. (2019). Epacadostat plus pembrolizumab versus placebo plus pembrolizumab in patients with unresectable or metastatic melanoma (ECHO-301/KEYNOTE-252): a phase 3, randomised, double-blind study. *The Lancet Oncology* 20 (8): 1083–1097.

104 Kumar, S., Jaipuri, F.A., Waldo, J.P. et al. (2020). Discovery of indoximod prodrugs and characterization of clinical candidate NLG802. *European Journal of Medicinal Chemistry* 198: 112373.

105 Crosignani, S., Bingham, P., Bottemanne, P. et al. (2017). Discovery of a novel and selective indoleamine 2,3-dioxygenase (IDO-1) inhibitor 3-(5-fluoro-1H-indol-3-yl)pyrrolidine-2,5-dione (EOS200271/PF-06840003) and its characterization as a potential clinical candidate. *Journal of Medicinal Chemistry* 60 (23): 9617–9629.

106 Coluccia, A., Passacantilli, S., Famiglini, V. et al. (2016). New inhibitors of indoleamine 2,3-dioxygenase 1: molecular modeling studies, synthesis, and biological evaluation. *Journal of Medicinal Chemistry* 59 (21): 9760–9773.

107 Coletti, A., Camponeschi, F., Albini, E. et al. (2017). Fragment-based approach to identify IDO1 inhibitor building blocks. *European Journal of Medicinal Chemistry* 141: 169–177.

108 Gaspari, P., Banerjee, T., Malachowski, W.P. et al. (2006). Structure-activity study of brassinin derivatives as indoleamine 2,3-dioxygenase inhibitors. *Journal of Medicinal Chemistry* 49 (2): 684–692.

109 Paul, S., Roy, A., Deka, S.J. et al. (2017). Synthesis and evaluation of oxindoles as promising inhibitors of the immunosuppressive enzyme indoleamine 2,3-dioxygenase 1. *MedChemComm* 8 (8): 1640–1654.

110 Yang, L., Chen, Y., He, J. et al. (2019). 4,6-Substituted-1H-indazoles as potent IDO1/TDO dual inhibitors. *Bioorganic & Medicinal Chemistry* 27 (6): 1087–1098.

111 Tsujino, H., Uno, T., Yamashita, T. et al. (2019). Correlation of indoleamine-2,3-dioxigenase 1 inhibitory activity of 4,6-disubstituted indazole derivatives and their heme binding affinity. *Bioorganic & Medicinal Chemistry Letters* 29 (19): 126607.

112 Dolusić, E., Larrieu, P., Moineaux, L. et al. (2011). Tryptophan 2,3-dioxygenase (TDO) inhibitors. 3-(2-(pyridyl)ethenyl)indoles as potential anticancer immunomodulators. *Journal of Medicinal Chemistry* 54 (15): 5320–5334.

113 Tomek, P., Palmer, B.D., Flanagan, J.U. et al. (2017). Discovery and evaluation of inhibitors to the immunosuppressive enzyme indoleamine 2,3-dioxygenase 1 (IDO1): probing the active site-inhibitor interactions. *European Journal of Medicinal Chemistry* 126: 983–996.

114 Sugimoto, H., Oda, S., Otsuki, T. et al. (2006). Crystal structure of human indoleamine 2,3-dioxygenase: catalytic mechanism of O2 incorporation by a heme-containing dioxygenase. *Proceedings of the National Academy of Sciences of the United States of America* 103 (8): 2611–2616.

115 Brant, M.G., Goodwin-Tindall, J., Stover, K.R. et al. (2018). Identification of potent indoleamine 2,3-dioxygenase 1 (IDO1) inhibitors based on a phenylimidazole scaffold. *ACS Medicinal Chemistry Letters* 9 (2): 131–136.

116 Zheng, Y., Stafford, P.M., Stover, K.R. et al. (2021). A series of 2-((1-phenyl-1H-imidazol-5-yl)methyl)-1H-indoles as indoleamine 2,3-dioxygenase 1 (IDO1) inhibitors. *ChemMedChem* 16 (14): 2195–2205.

117 Wen, H., Liu, Y., Wang, S. et al. (2019). Design and synthesis of indoleamine 2,3-dioxygenase 1 inhibitors and evaluation of their use as anti-tumor agents. *Molecules (Basel, Switzerland)* 24 (11): 2124.

118 Huang, Q., Zheng, M., Yang, S. et al. (2011). Structure-activity relationship and enzyme kinetic studies on 4-aryl-1H-1,2,3-triazoles as indoleamine 2,3-dioxygenase (IDO) inhibitors. *European Journal of Medicinal Chemistry* 46 (11): 5680–5687.

119 Alexandre, J.A.C., Swan, M.K., Latchem, M.J. et al. (2018). New 4-amino-1,2,3-triazole inhibitors of indoleamine 2,3-dioxygenase form a long-lived complex with the enzyme and display exquisite cellular potency. *Chembiochem : A European Journal of Chemical Biology* 19 (6): 552–561.

120 Panda, S., Pradhan, N., Chatterjee, S. et al. (2019). 4,5-Disubstituted 1,2,3-triazoles: efective inhibition of indoleamine 2,3-dioxygenase 1 enzyme regulates T cell activity and mitigates tumor growth. *Scientific Reports* 9 (1): 18455.

121 Röhrig, U.F., Majjigapu, S.R., Grosdidier, A. et al. (2012). Rational design of 4-aryl-1,2,3-triazoles for indoleamine 2,3-dioxygenase 1 inhibition. *Journal of Medicinal Chemistry* 55 (11): 5270–5290.

122 Röhrig, U.F., Majjigapu, S.R., Caldelari, D. et al. (2016). 1,2,3-Triazoles as inhibitors of indoleamine 2,3-dioxygenase 2 (IDO2). *Bioorganic & Medicinal Chemistry Letters* 26 (17): 4330–4333.

123 Röhrig, U.F., Majjigapu, S.R., Reynaud, A. et al. (2021). Azole-based indoleamine 2,3-dioxygenase 1 (IDO1) inhibitors. *Journal of Medicinal Chemistry* 64 (4): 2205–2227.

124 Röhrig, U.F., Majjigapu, S.R., Vogel, P. et al. (2022). Structure-based optimization of type III indoleamine 2,3-dioxygenase 1 (IDO1) inhibitors. *Journal of Enzyme Inhibition and Medicinal Chemistry* 37 (1): 1773–1811.

125 Kumar, S., Waldo, J.P., Jaipuri, F.A. et al. (2019). Discovery of clinical candidate (1R,4r)-4-((R)-2-((S)-6-fluoro-5*H*-imidazo[5,1-*a*]isoindol-5-yl)-1-hydroxyethyl) cyclohexan-1-ol (Navoximod), a potent and selective inhibitor of indoleamine 2,3-dioxygenase 1. *Journal of Medicinal Chemistry* 62 (14): 6705–6733.

126 Zou, Y., Wang, F., Wang, Y. et al. (2017). Discovery of imidazoleisoindole derivatives as potent IDO1 inhibitors: design, synthesis, biological evaluation and computational studies. *European Journal of Medicinal Chemistry* 140: 293–304.

127 Tu, W., Yang, F., Xu, G. et al. (2019). Discovery of imidazoisoindole derivatives as highly potent and orally active indoleamine-2,3-dioxygenase inhibitors. *ACS Medicinal Chemistry Letters* 10 (6): 949–953.

128 Meininger, D., Zalameda, L., Liu, Y. et al. (2011). Purification and kinetic characterization of human indoleamine 2,3-dioxygenases 1 and 2 (IDO1 and IDO2) and discovery of selective IDO1 inhibitors. *Biochimica et Biophysica Acta* 1814 (12): 1947–1954.

129 Tojo, S., Kohno, T., Tanaka, T. et al. (2014). Crystal structures and structure-activity relationships of imidazothiazole derivatives as IDO1 inhibitors. *ACS Medicinal Chemistry Letters* 5 (10): 1119–1123.

130 Griglio, A., Torre, E., Serafini, M. et al. (2018). A multicomponent approach in the discovery of indoleamine 2,3-dioxygenase 1 inhibitors: Synthesis, biological investigation and docking studies. *Bioorganic & Medicinal Chemistry Letters* 28 (4): 651–657.
131 Serafini, M., Torre, E., Aprile, S. et al. (2019). Synthesis, docking and biological evaluation of a novel class of imidazothiazoles as IDO1 inhibitors. *Molecules (Basel, Switzerland)* 24 (10): 1874.
132 Peng, Y.H., Liao, F.Y., Tseng, C.T. et al. (2020). Unique sulfur-aromatic interactions contribute to the binding of potent imidazothiazole indoleamine 2,3-dioxygenase inhibitors. *Journal of Medicinal Chemistry* 63 (4): 1642–1659.
133 Xu, G.Q., Gong, X.Q., Zhu, Y.Y. et al. (2022). Novel 1,2,3-triazole erlotinib derivatives as potent IDO1 inhibitors: design, drug-target interactions prediction, synthesis, biological evaluation, molecular docking and ADME properties studies. *Frontiers in Pharmacology* 13: 854965.
134 Hou, X.X., Gong, X.Q., Mao, L.F. et al. (2022). Design, synthesis and biological evaluation of erlotinib-based IDO1 inhibitors. *Frontiers in Pharmacology* 13: 940704.
135 Hou, X., Gong, X., Mao, L. et al. (2022). Discovery of novel 1,2,3-triazole derivatives as IDO1 inhibitors. *Pharmaceuticals (Basel, Switzerland)* 15 (11): 1316.

Section II

18.5.1.3 *N*-Hydroxyamidines

In 2009, Incyte Corporation identified *N*-hydroxyamidines as a class of potent, reversible, competitive IDO1 inhibitors through high-throughput screening. The oxygen atom of the hydroxylamine moiety in these compounds was found to directly coordinate with the heme iron, contributing to their inhibitory activity. The most potent compound (**41**, INCB14943) in this series exhibited nanomolar potency (hIDO1 IC_{50} = 67 nM, HeLa IDO1 IC_{50} = 19 nM) (Figure 18.8). In mice testing, **41** reduced plasma kynurenine levels by over 50% and inhibited the growth of B16-GM-CSF tumors in a dose-dependent manner [1]. In 2017, Wu et al. reported the co-crystal structure of **41** bound to IDO1 (Figure 18.9a, PDB code: 5XE1), which aligned with initial predictions. The hydroxylamine oxygen coordinates with the heme iron, and the halogenated phenyl is deeply embedded within the A pocket, establishing hydrophobic interactions with V130, F164, and L234, along with π–π stacking interactions with Y126 and F163. Furthermore, the chlorine atom at the three-position forms a strong halogen bond with the sulfur atom of C129, while the fluorine atom at the four-position engages in hydrophobic interactions with V130 and F164 [2]. Subsequently, Incyte Corporation leveraged **41** as a lead compound, introducing polar side chains at the four-position of the furazan ring. This optimization led to the development of **1** (INCB24360, Epacadostat; hIDO1 IC_{50} = 73 nM, HeLa IDO1 IC_{50} = 7.4 nM) (Figure 18.8), which

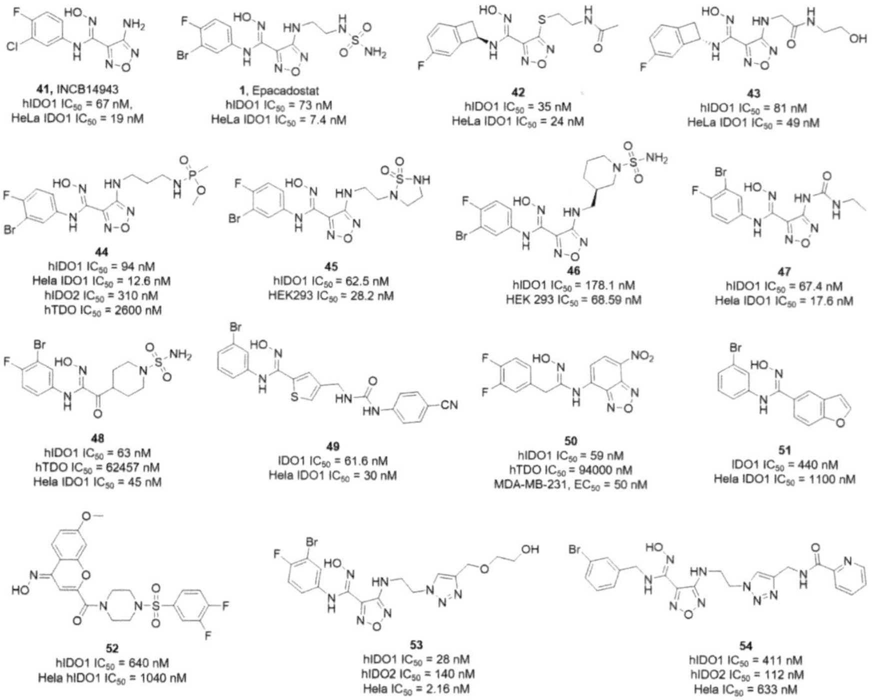

Figure 18.8 Reported *N*-hydroxyamidine IDO/TDO inhibitors.

demonstrated enhanced pharmacokinetic properties. In 2017, the crystal structure of IDO1 complexed with epacadostat was elucidated (Figure 18.9b, PDB code: 5WN8). The binding mode of compound **1** with hIDO1 is similar to that of **41**, with a coordination bond formed between the *N*-hydroxyoxime oxygen and the heme iron, and the halogenated benzene inserted into pocket A. However, the sulfonamide side chain forms a hydrogen bond with Arg231 [34]. **1** exhibited significant efficacy in rodent models of melanoma and was well-tolerated in preclinical Investigational New Drug (IND) toxicology assessments. Although the Phase III clinical trial (Table 18.1, NCT02752074) evaluating the combination of Epacadostat with the anti-PD1 monoclonal antibody pembrolizumab for the treatment of unresectable or metastatic melanoma ultimately failed, **41** has been widely utilized as a reference compound in the development of *N*-hydroxyamidine-based IDO/TDO inhibitors. In 2019, Zhang et al. identified a series of unique *N*-hydroxyamidine-based IDO1 selective inhibitors featuring an amino-cyclobutene motif through SBDD, and obtained the co-crystal structure of **42** with IDO1. Among them, **43** demonstrated a highly favorable overall profile, characterized by strong potency (hIDO1 IC_{50} = 81 nM, HeLa IDO1 IC_{50} = 49 nM) (Figure 18.8), selectivity, favorable pharmacokinetics, and predicted human dosing. Furthermore, **43** showed significant synergistic effects when combined with anti-PD-1 monoclonal antibody in a murine EMT6 tumor syngeneic model. In the co-crystal structure of **42** with IDO1 (Figure 18.9c, PDB code: 6PU7), a binding mode similar to that of **1** can be observed. The 5-fluoro-substituted

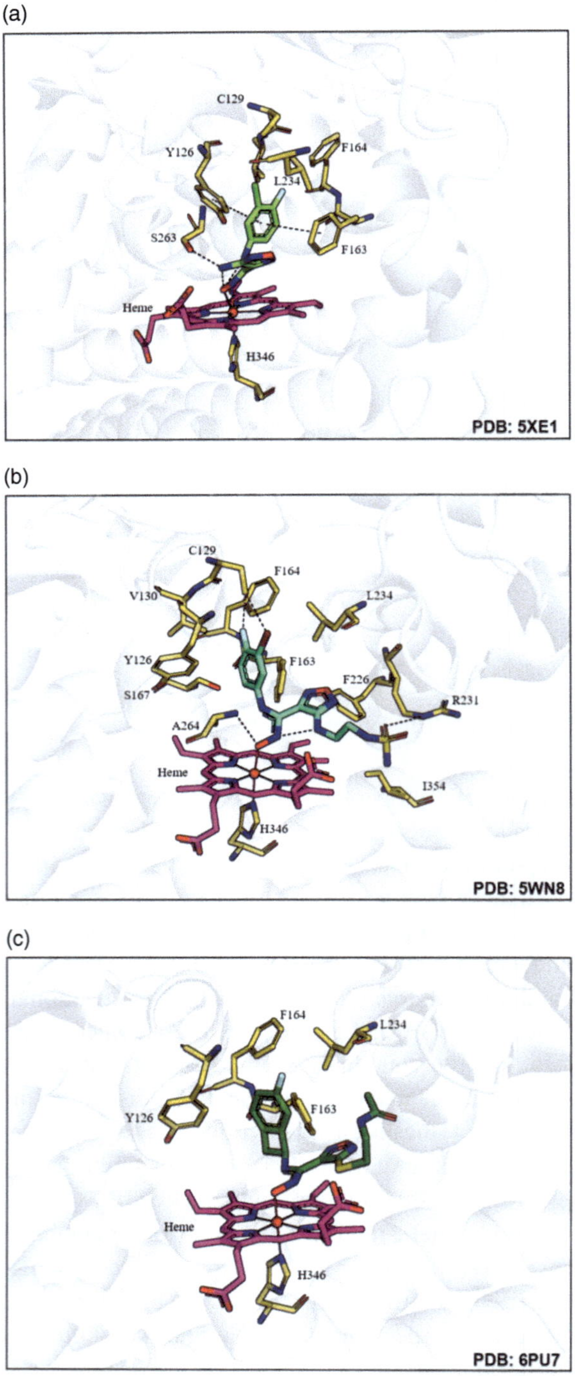

Figure 18.9 Crystallographic analysis of representative *N*-hydroxyamidines with holo IDO1. (a) IDO1 complexed with heme Iron and **41** (PDB code: 5XE1), (b) IDO1 complexed with heme Iron and **1** (PDB code: 5WN8), (c) IDO1 complexed with heme Iron and **42** (PDB code: 6PU7).

cyclobutene ring is deeply embedded within the A pocket, while the oxygen atom of the hydroxylamine moiety coordinates with the heme iron [3].

Recently, the development of several nanomolar potency compounds has been achieved by retaining the critical *N*-hydroxyamidine moiety and the halogenated phenyl group that extends into the A pocket of compound **1**, while introducing structural modifications to the side chain extending into the solvent region. Bian et al. reported a series of phosphonamidite-based derivatives of **1**. Interestingly, **44** exhibited significant inhibitory activity against hIDO1, hIDO2, and hTDO (hIDO1 IC_{50} = 94 nM, HeLa hIDO1 IC_{50} = 12.6 nM, hIDO2 IC_{50} = 310 nM, hTDO IC_{50} = 2600 nM) (Figure 18.8). Additionally, **44** exhibits a significant ability to reduce kynurenine levels in both plasma and the tumor microenvironment [4, 5]. By cyclizing the aminosulfonamide moiety of **1**, **45** was obtained, which exhibits activity (hIDO1 IC_{50} = 62.5 nM, HEK293 IC_{50} = 28.2 nM) similar to that of **1** [6]. Similarly, **46** (hIDO1 IC_{50} = 104 nM, HeLa IDO1 IC_{50} = 10.1 nM, hTDO = IC_{50} = 3900 nM) (Figure 18.8), which demonstrates comparable activity to **1**, incorporates a rigid heterocycle into the side chain of **1**. This structural modification increases steric hindrance and enhances the compound's lipophilicity [7]. Incorporating functional group urea into the side chain resulted in the development of **47**, which demonstrates significant potency (hIDO1 IC_{50} = 67.4 nM, HeLa IDO1 IC_{50} = 17.6 nM) [8]. Jin et al. identified **48** by employing bioisosteric replacement of the furazan moiety and substituting alternative groups for the sulfonamide side chain. **48** also exhibits activity (hIDO1 IC_{50} = 63 nM, hTDO IC_{50} = 62 457 nM, HeLa IDO1 IC_{50} = 45 nM) (Figure 18.8) similar to that of **1** [9]. **49** replaces the furazan of compound **1** with a thiophene group, and its side chain with a phenylcarbamoyl moiety is inserted into pocket B [10]. **50**, which incorporates a nitrobenzofurazan moiety, displays robust inhibitory activity against IDO1 both in enzymatic assays (hIDO1 IC_{50} = 59 nM, hTDO IC_{50} = 94,000 nM) and cellular models (MDA-MB-231, EC_{50} = 50 nM) (Figure 18.8). Notably, **50** exhibits approximately 1593-fold greater selectivity for IDO1 compared to TDO [11]. **51**, which bears a structural resemblance to **50**, exhibits significant IDO1 inhibitory activity in enzymatic assays (IDO1 IC_{50} = 440 nM). However, its efficacy is somewhat diminished in cellular assays (HeLa IDO1 IC_{50} = 1100 nM) [12]. In 2023, Wang et al. described a series of chromone-oxime derivatives containing piperazine sulfonamide moieties. Notably, **52** demonstrated moderate IDO1 inhibitory activity, with an IC_{50} value in the low micromolar range (hIDO1 IC_{50} = 640 nM, HeLa hIDO1 IC_{50} = 1040 nM) (Figure 18.8) [13].

The structure of the active site of hIDO2 differs from that of hIDO1 in two key areas: the "site A" and the "solvent-accessible (SA) region." Specifically, the heme group in hIDO2 is surrounded by three distinct amino acid residues, resulting in a slightly larger volume of site A compared to that in hIDO1. In the SA region, hIDO2 contains three polar residues that are absent in hIDO1, which enhances the polarity of this site in hIDO2 relative to hIDO1. Based on this, in 2021, He et al. proposed the hypothesis that extending the side chain of Epacadostat could enable interactions with the polar residues in the SA region of hIDO2. Following extensive structural optimization, compound **53** was developed, demonstrating nanomolar potency against both hIDO1 and hIDO2 in enzymatic assays (hIDO1 IC_{50} = 28 nM, hIDO2 IC_{50} = 140 nM) (Figure 18.8). Molecular docking studies indicate that **53** exhibits a binding mode similar to that of compound **1** in both proteins. However, **53** additionally forms hydrogen bonds with Tyr244 and Lys366 in the SA region of hIDO2, which enhances its inhibitory activity against IDO2. Moreover, **53** (TGI = 69.7%) exhibited superior efficacy compared to compound **1** (TGI = 49.4%) in the CT26 xenograft mouse model. **53** represents the first highly potent dual inhibitor targeting both IDO1 and IDO2 [14]. In 2022, the team modified the structure of **53** to create **54**, which demonstrates enhanced selectivity for hIDO2 (IC_{50} = 112 nM) compared to hIDO1 (IC_{50} = 633 nM) (Figure 18.8) [15].

18.5.2 Naturally Derived Inhibitors

18.5.2.1 Quinone Derivatives

Natural products are characterized by their novel and diverse structural scaffolds, as well as a wide range of biological activities, including antitumor and antibacterial properties. Consequently, the structural optimization and modification of natural products have been a cornerstone in drug discovery. Natural products are also a vital source for the discovery of novel scaffolds that can serve as potential lead compounds for IDO/TDO inhibitors. To date, several scaffolds, including quinones and naphthotriazinediones, have been identified as IDO/TDO inhibitors (Figure 18.10) [16].

In 2006, Annulin B (**55**), which exhibits submicromolar potency (IDO1 IC_{50} = 120 nM), was isolated from marine hydroids in the northeastern Pacific [17]. Interestingly, in 2008, Trauner et al. achieved the total synthesis of the alkaloid **56**, which also exhibits submicromolar potency (IDO1 IC_{50} = 200 nM) against IDO1. **57**, which has a structure similar to **56**, also exhibits nanomolar potency (hIDO1 IC_{50} = 65.3 nM) against IDO1 [18]. They discovered that the presence of a quaternary ammonium ion is crucial for its activity [19]. In 2018, Meng and colleagues reported **58**, which exhibited nanomolar potency (hIDO1 IC_{50} = 23 nM, hTDO IC_{50} = 1200 nM). But **58** did not show activity in cellular assays [20]. Subsequently,

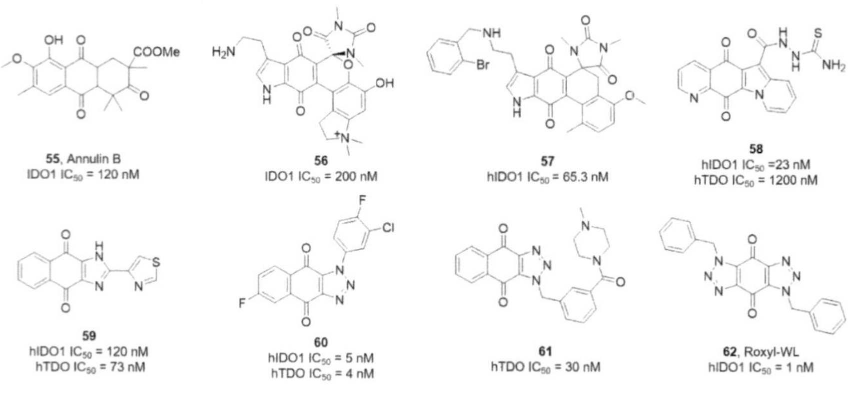

Figure 18.10 Reported quinone derivative IDO/TDO inhibitors.

in another study by Meng et al. **59** was identified as a compound with nanomolar inhibitory activity against both hIDO1 (IC_{50} = 120 nM) and hTDO (IC_{50} = 73 nM) [21]. Additionally, **60**, developed by Yang et al., is also a potent dual inhibitor of IDO1 and TDO (hIDO1 IC_{50} = 5 nM, hTDO IC_{50} = 4 nM) [22]. In 2015, Wu et al. identified **61** (hTDO IC_{50} = 30 nM) as a potent TDO inhibitor through virtual screening [23]. It is noteworthy that Xiang et al. developed a potent IDO1 inhibitor (hIDO1 IC_{50} = 1 nM), Roxyl-WL (**62**), featuring a symmetric structure. In a B16F10 melanoma xenograft mouse model, **62** significantly inhibited tumor growth and induced an immune response [24].

18.5.2.2 Tryptanthrin Derivatives

In 2013, Yang et al. identified the natural product tryptanthrin as a new and effective IDO-1 inhibitor through screening of indole-based structures. Through structure–activity relationship (SAR) studies, it was found that the 8-F substituted tryptanthrin **63** is an effective dual-target inhibitor of IDO1 and TDO (hIDO1 IC_{50} = 534 nM, HEK 293 IDO1 IC_{50} = 23 nM, HEK 293 IDO1 IC_{50} = 68 nM) (Figure 18.11) [25]. Additionally, 8-nitro substituted tryptanthrin (**64**) appears to exhibit high selectivity for IDO2 (hIDO1 IC_{50} = 1800 nM, hIDO2 IC_{50} = 112 nM) (Figure 18.11) [26]. **65** and **66**, which are also potent dual inhibitors of IDO1/TDO, were reported in another study by the same research group [27].

18.5.2.3 Tanshinone Derivatives

Additionally, a class of natural products containing ortho-naphthoquinone has been reported to exhibit moderate inhibitory activity against IDO1/TDO. In 2018, Xu et al. used virtual screening to identify a tanshinone-derived natural product **67** with micromolar inhibitory potency (hIDO1 IC_{50} = 1.3 μM) (Figure 18.12) against IDO1 [28]. **68** and **69** are two modified tanshinone derivatives that exhibit notable inhibitory activity against IDO1/TDO [29, 30].

18.5.3 Other Scaffolds

In addition to the aforementioned inhibitors, various structurally diverse small molecules have been reported to inhibit IDO1/TDO activity to varying extents. Virtual screening has been a key approach in identifying these compounds. In 2019, Lai et al. identified **70** as a nanomolar IDO1 inhibitor (HeLa IDO1 IC_{50} = 59.8 nM) (Figure 18.13) through virtual screening. This compound was shown to effectively

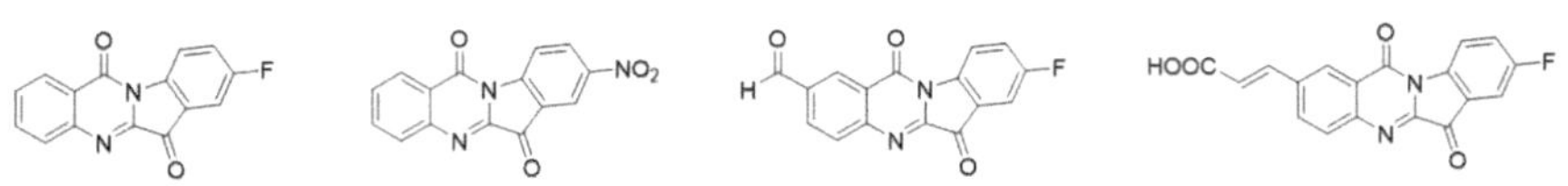

63
hIDO1 IC_{50} = 534 nM
HEK 293 IDO1 IC_{50} = 23 nM

64
hIDO1 IC_{50} = 1800 nM
hIDO2 IC_{50} = 112 nM

65
hIDO1 IC_{50} = 460 nM
hTDO IC_{50} = 60 nM
Hela IDO1 IC_{50} = 160 nM

66
hIDO1 IC_{50} = 120 nM
hTDO IC_{50} = 30 nM
Hela IDO1 IC_{50} = 60 nM

Figure 18.11 Reported tryptanthrin derivative IDO/TDO inhibitors.

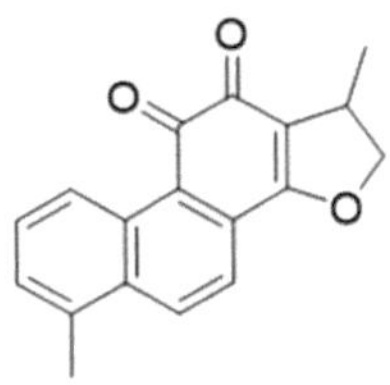

67
hIDO1 IC_{50} = 1.3 μM

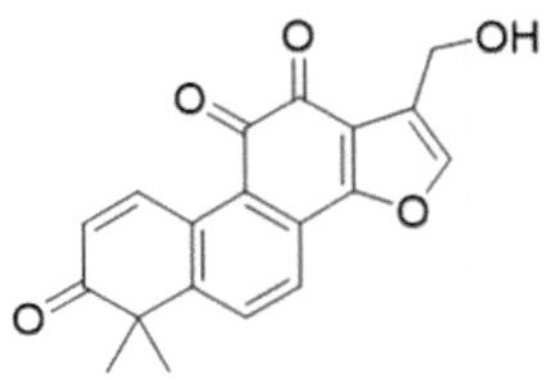

68
hIDO1 IC_{50} = 0.37 μM

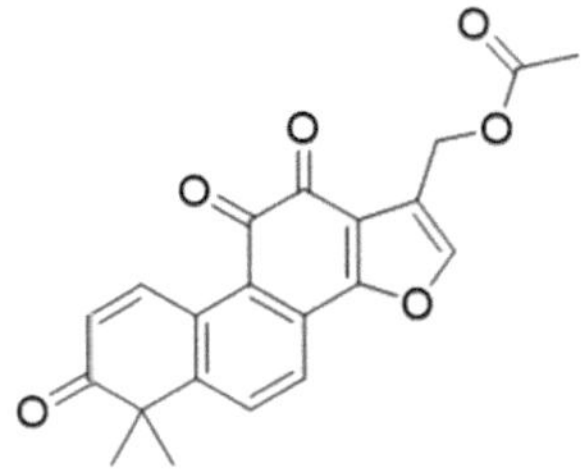

69
hIDO1 IC_{50} = 0.07 μM
hTDO IC_{50} = 0.16 μM

Figure 18.12 Reported tanshinone derivative IDO/TDO inhibitcrs.

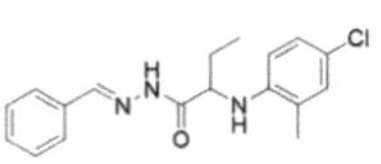

70
hIDO1 IC_{50} = 59.8 nM

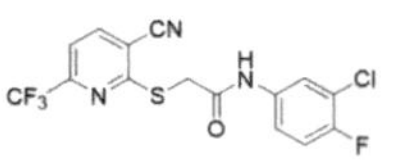

71
hIDO1 IC_{50} = 840 μM

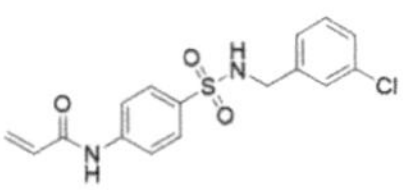

72
Hela IDO1 IC_{50} = 6.26 μM

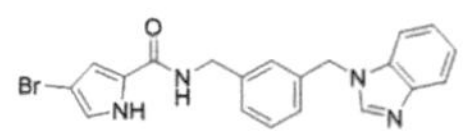

73
K_d = 0.55 μM
A375 IDO1 IC_{50} = 16 nM

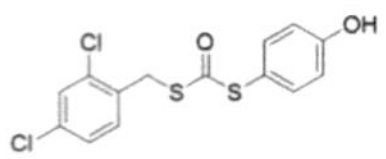

74
hIDO1 IC_{50} = 100 nM
Cellular EC_{50} = 400 nM

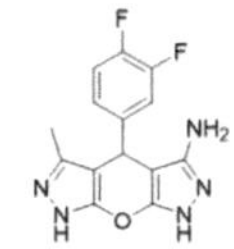

75
hIDO1 IC_{50} = 151 nM
MDA-MB-231 EC_{50} = 48 nM

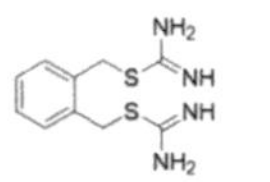

76
hIDO1 IC_{50} = 1.71 μM
hTDO IC_{50} = 0.62 μM

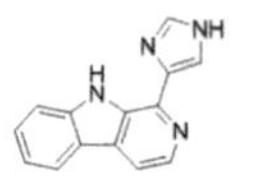

77
hIDO1 IC_{50} = 3.53 μM
hTDO IC_{50} = 1.15 μM

Figure 18.13 Reported other scaffold IDO/TDO inhibitors.

inhibit tumor growth in the CT26 xenograft mouse model [31]. **71** is an IDO1 inhibitor (hIDO1 IC_{50} = 0.84 μM) identified through virtual screening, featuring a cyanopyridine scaffold [32]. Additionally, in 2020, they identified another compound, **72**, which possesses a sulfonamide structure and exhibits moderate inhibitory efficacy (HeLa IDO1 IC_{50} = 6.26 μM) (Figure 18.13) [33]. In the same year, Fallarini et al. reported the identification of a novel class of IDO1 inhibitors based on a benzimidazole substructure. Among them, the most effective compound, **73**, does not share structural similarity with previously reported IDO1 inhibitors and exhibits a distinct predicted binding mode at the active site. The benzimidazole moiety is positioned within pocket A, where its nitrogen coordinates with the heme group. The extended side chain of **73** extends into pocket C. This arrangement facilitates a dense packing within the enzyme, resulting in an extensive network of interactions, including one halogen bond and three hydrogen bonds, which contribute to a strong binding affinity (K_d = 0.55 μM) and significant inhibition potency (A375 IC_{50} = 16 nM) [34]. **74**, which features a carbonodithioate scaffold, exhibits submicromolar efficacy (hIDO1 IC_{50} = 100 nM, Cellular EC_{50} = 400 nM) (Figure 18.13) against IDO1. Molecular docking studies reveal that its binding mode resembles that of **1**, with the formation of a coordination bond with the heme iron. Additionally, the halogenated benzene moiety within the deep A-pocket establishes a halogen bond with Cys129 [35]. In 2016, Manna et al. utilized a fused heterocycle strategy to synthesize a series of pyranopyrimidine, pyrazolopyranopyrimidine, and dipyrazolopyran derivatives. Among these, **75** was identified as exhibiting potent IDO1 inhibitory activity (hIDO1 IC_{50} = 151 nM, MDA-MB-231 EC_{50} = 48 nM) [36]. **76** is a bisisothiourea derivative that demonstrates moderate inhibitory activity against both IDO1 (hIDO1 IC_{50} = 1.71 μM) and TDO (hTDO IC_{50} = 0.62 μM) [37]. Similarly, the 1-(Hetero)aryl-β-carboline derivative **77** is another IDO1/TDO inhibitor with moderate potency (hIDO1 IC_{50} = 3.53 μM, hTDO IC_{50} = 1.15 μM) (Figure 18.13). Experimental results indicate that it can alleviate lipopolysaccharide-induced depressive-like behavior in mice [38].

18.5.4 Inhibitors Targeting apo-IDO1

In recent years, numerous pharmaceutical companies and research institutions, including Bristol-Myers Squibb, Merck, and GlaxoSmithKline, have advanced the development of inhibitors specifically targeting apo-IDO1. Most of these compounds were identified through high throughput screening (HTS), and the inhibition mechanisms of some of these compounds remain undetermined. However, it is noteworthy that these inhibitors exhibit very high potency in cellular assays, with some demonstrating efficacy in the picomolar range.

18.5.4.1 Heme Displacers

It is noteworthy that BMS-986205 (**3**), a compound developed by Bristol-Myers Squibb with nanomolar potency (HeLa IDO1 IC_{50} = 2 nM, M109 IDO1 IC_{50} = 5 nM), is currently being evaluated in a Phase III clinical trial (**Table 1**, NCT03661320). This trial is investigating the efficacy of **3** in combination with nivolumab for the treatment of muscle-invasive bladder cancer [39]. According to the co-crystal structure of **3** with IDO1 (Figure 18.15a, PDB code: 6MQ6), **3** replaces the heme-coordinated residue A264 and forms a stacking interaction with another heme-coordinated residue, H346. Furthermore, the halogenated phenyl group engages in π–π interactions with Cys129 and Tyr126 [40]. In 2021, Bristol-Myers Squibb performed more extensive structural modifications on **3** to enhance its pharmacokinetic properties, resulting in the development of **78**. It demonstrated strong cellular (HeLa IDO1 IC_{50} = 2 nM, M109 IDO1 IC_{50} = 3 nM) (Figure 18.14) and human whole blood (hWB) activity (hWB IDO1 IC_{50} = 21 nM) (Figure 18.14), along with enhanced metabolic stability ($T_{1/2}$). Furthermore, it exhibited an appropriate permeability profile [41]. Interestingly, in 2021, Hamilton et al. reported a novel class of IDO1 inhibitors featuring a conformationally constrained bicyclo [3.1.0] hexane core. These compounds (**79, 80, 81, 82**) (Figure 18.14) demonstrated potent inhibition of IDO1 in a cellular context by binding to the apoenzyme, as confirmed through biochemical characterization and X-ray crystallography. Specifically, the bicyclo [3.1.0] hexane scaffold fits into a hydrophobic cavity created by the displaced heme cofactor, positioned between Ala264 and Tyr126 on one side and Phe214 on the other. The equatorial hydrogen on the 3-carbon of the scaffold, adopting a boat conformation, aligns with the center of the Phe214 phenyl ring, establishing an arene–proton interaction with the protein. The amide linker

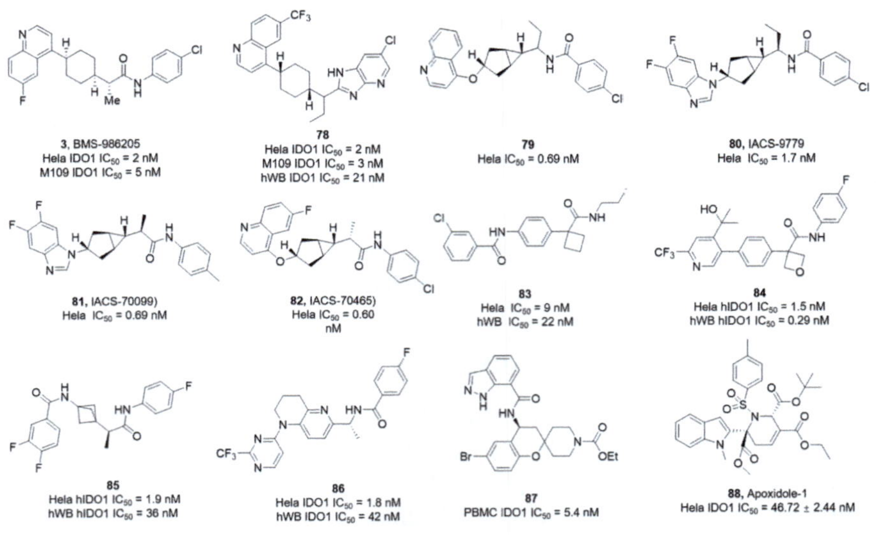

Figure 18.14 Reported heme displacer IDO/TDO inhibitors.

extends deep into the enzyme's substrate pocket, with the chlorobenzene group specifically occupying pocket A. The quinoline N forms a hydrogen bond with Arg343, while Ser167 establishes a second direct hydrogen bond with the amide N. Moreover, **80** (Figure 18.14) exhibited an acceptable safety margin in both rodent toxicology studies and canine cardiovascular evaluations [42]. This study is of great significance for the exploration of stereochemically constrained IDO/TDO inhibitors.

In 2021, Merck & Co., Inc. reported a class of IDO1 inhibitors featuring 3,3-disubstituted oxetanes. To facilitate subsequent structure-based drug design, this study first developed a co-crystal structure of the lead compound **83** with IDO1 (Figure 18.15b, PDB code: 6V52). The co-crystal structure of **83** with IDO1 confirmed that it acts as a heme displacer. Interactions in the pocket A involved two

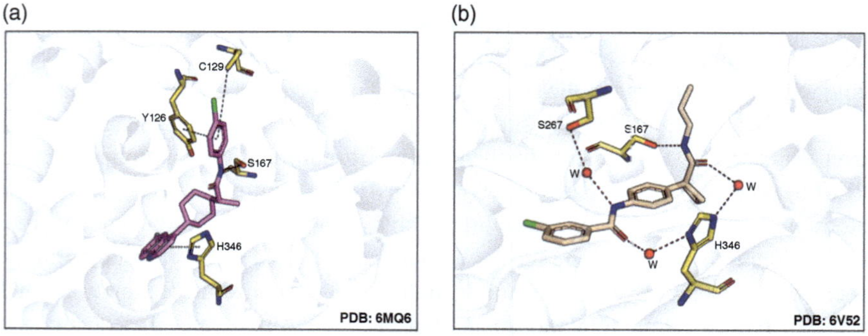

Figure 18.15 Crystallographic analysis of representative heme displacers with apo-IDO1. (a) apo-IDO1 complexed with **3** (PDB code: 6MQ6); (b) apo-IDO1 complexed with **83** (PDB code: 6V52).

crucial hydrogen bonds with Ser167 and a water-mediated interaction with His346. The rest of the molecule traversed the plane previously occupied by the heme cofactor and extended into a newly formed hydrophobic pocket, referred to as the pocket C. Within the pocket C, the amide group established two additional significant hydrogen bonds, including a water-mediated interaction with His346 and Ser267. Structural optimization revealed that the introduction of the oxabicyclobutane moiety, replacing the cyclobutane ring, significantly enhanced the potency in cellular assays. Structural optimization revealed that replacing the cyclobutane ring with an oxabicyclobutane moiety significantly increased potency in cellular assays. However, the compound's pharmacokinetic properties remained suboptimal. Fortunately, the introduction of trifluoromethyl and tert-butyl substituents on the pyridine ring, replacing the chlorobenzene group, achieved a balance between inhibitory activity and pharmacokinetic properties, resulting in the development of **84** (HeLa hIDO1 IC_{50} = 1.5 nM, hWB hIDO1 IC_{50} = 0.29 nM) (Figure 18.14) [43]. In a subsequent study, they introduced a bicyclo [1.1.1] pentane moiety as a bioisostere for the benzene ring. This modification significantly improved metabolic stability by reducing the amide hydrolysis potential of the pocket D arylamide portion, resulting in the development of **85** (HeLa IDO1 IC_{50} = 1.9 nM, hWB IDO1 IC_{50} = 36 nM) (Figure 18.14). It exhibits excellent pharmacokinetic properties: Rat hepatic clearance (CLint) is 195 ml/min/kg, *in vivo* clearance (Clu) is 37 ml/min/kg, and the logarithm of the octanol–water partition coefficient (AlogP) is 3.3 [44]. Additionally, **86**, developed by Merck & Co., Inc., is a potent apo-IDO1 inhibitor with excellent pharmacokinetic properties (rat PK CL_p,=7 ml/min/kg) [45]. GlaxoSmithKline identified a novel class of IDO1 inhibitors featuring a spiro[piperidine-4,4′-chroman] core through screening a unique indole-based DNA-encoded library. **87** demonstrated the most effective low nanomolar activity in PBMCs (IDO1 IC_{50} = 5.4 nM) and HeLa cells (IDO1 IC_{50} = 7.9 nM). Additionally, spectroscopic studies revealed that **87** is a competitive IDO1 inhibitor with respect to heme [46]. Interestingly, Waldmann et al. reported in 2022 a class of pseudo-natural products as inhibitors targeting apo-IDO1. Apoxidole-1 (**88**) demonstrated nanomolar potency in cellular assays and effectively (HeLa IDO1 IC_{50} = 46.72 nM) (Figure 18.14) reduced cellular Kyn levels [47].

18.5.4.2 Biaryl Urea Derivatives

BMS978587 (**89**) was reported in a Bristol-Myers Squibb patent in 2015, and its co-crystal structure with IDO1 (Figure 18.17a, PDB code: 6AZV) was subsequently disclosed in 2018 [4]. Similarly, **90** (HeLa IDO1 IC_{50} = 20 nM) and **91** (HeLa IDO1 IC_{50} = 0.5 nM) (Figure 18.16) were also developed by Bristol-Myers Squibb [48]. It is noteworthy that in 2022, Guo et al. reported a compound (**92**) with picomolar potency (HeLa IDO1 IC_{50} = 22 pM) in cellular assays. According to the disclosed co-crystal structure of **92** with IDO1 (Figure 18.17b, PDB code: 8I7L), **92** replaces the heme-coordinated residue A264 and stacks with another heme-coordinated residue, H346. Compared to **3**, **92** demonstrates a more extensive range of non-covalent interactions. It forms two halogen bonds with residues S167 and C129 and establishes a hydrogen bond with residue H346. Furthermore,

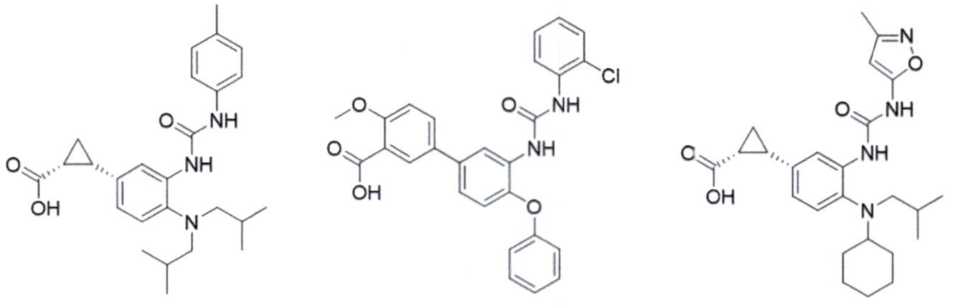

89, BMS978587
Hela IDO1 IC_{50} = 4.2 nM

90
Hela IDO1 IC_{50} = 20 nM

91
Hela IDO1 IC_{50} = 0.5 nM

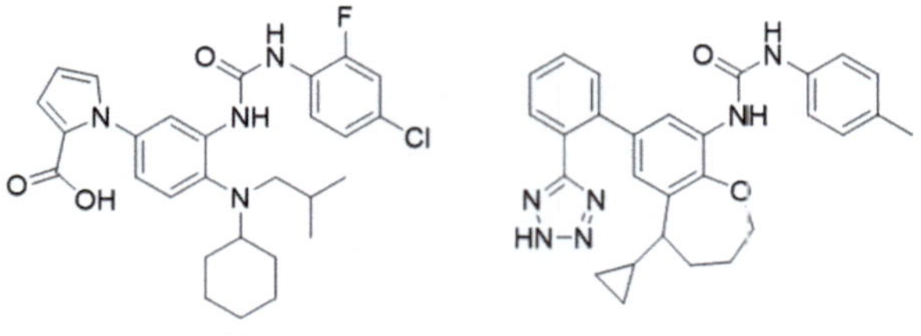

92
Hela IDO1 IC_{50} = 22 pM

93
Hela hIDO1 IC_{50} = 3.6 nM

Figure 18.16 Reported biaryl urea derivative IDO/TDO inhibitors.

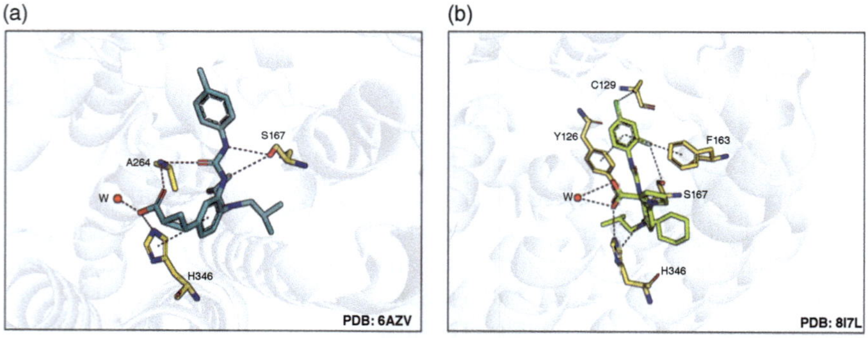

Figure 18.17 Crystallographic analysis of representative biaryl urea derivatives with apo-IDO1. (a) apo-IDO1 complexed with **89** (PDB code: 6AZV), (b) apo-IDO1 complexed with **92** (PDB code: 8I7L).

the cyclohexane and isobutyl moieties of **92** engage in significant hydrophobic interactions with surrounding residues V166, I217, V350, and I354. In contrast, **3** exhibits weaker hydrophobic interactions with apo-IDO1. In comparison, although **89** and **92** occupy similar binding positions, **92**'s chlorine atom forms a halogen bond with Cys129. This halogen bond may contribute to an increased potency of **92** relative to **89** (Figure 18.16) [49].

In 2023, Bristol-Myers Squibb identified a new class of compounds with tetrazole moieties substituting aromatic acids. Notably, **93** managed to maintain high potency (HeLa hIDO1 IC_{50} = 3.6 nM) (Figure 18.16) while effectively addressing several critical issues, including lipophilicity, inhibition of cytochrome P450 (CYP), hERG (human potassium channel Kv11.1) inhibition, antagonism of the pregnane X receptor (PXR), and oxidative metabolic stability [50].

18.5.5 IDO1 Degrader

Proteolysis targeting chimera (PROTAC) is a novel technology that utilizes bifunctional small molecules to target and degrade specific proteins within cells. These molecules consist of two functional components: one that binds to the target protein and another that recruits an E3 ubiquitin ligase [51]. By bringing the target protein into proximity with the ubiquitin–proteasome system, PROTACs induce the ubiquitination and subsequent degradation of the target protein, thereby offering a powerful strategy for selectively modulating protein levels and activity in drug development.

In 2020, Xie et al. designed a series of bispecific molecules with varying lengths of PEG linkers, using **1** as the IDO1-targeting warhead and pomalidomide as the E3 ligase ligand. It is noteworthy that the co-crystal structure of Epacadostat with IDO1 reveals that the sulfonamide moiety extends into the solvent region, making it an appropriate site for linking with a suitable linker. Among the series, the most effective degrader, **94**, exhibits moderate IDO1 degradation capability (DC_{50} = 2.84 μM, D_{max} = 93%) (Figure 18.18) in HeLa cells. As the first IDO1 degrader, **94**, although exhibiting somewhat weaker degradation capability, offers a novel approach for designing targeted degraders for IDO/TDO therapeutic applications [52]. In 2022, Wainwright et al. reported another IDO1 degrader (**95**), using **3**, an apo-IDO1 inhibitor, as the lead compound. **95** exhibited submicromolar degradation capability in both U87 (DC_{50} = 0.3290 μM) and PDX43 (DC_{50} = 0.5483 μM)

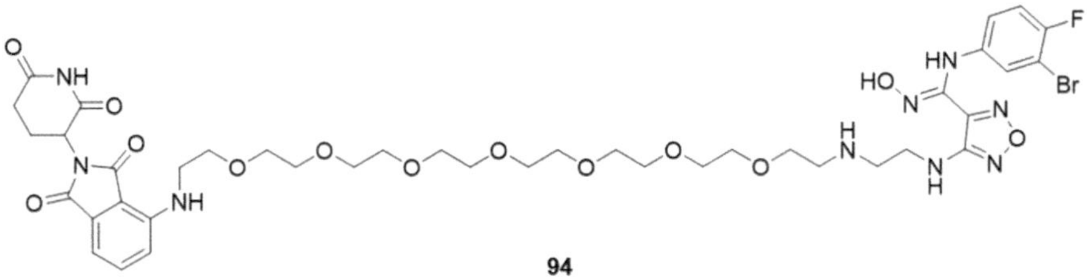

94
Hela IDO1 DC_{50} = 2.84 μM

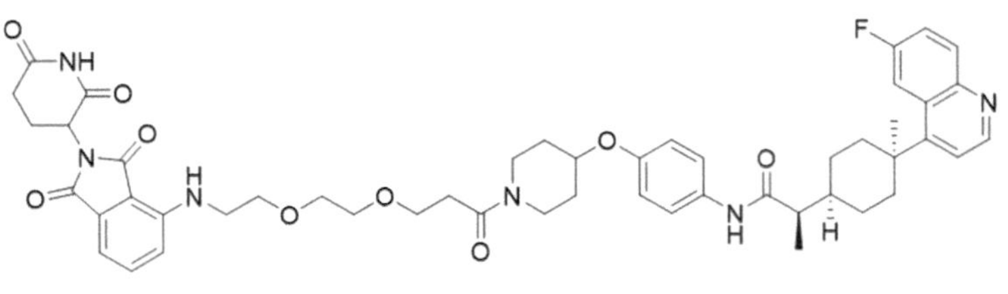

95
U87 DC_{50} = 0.3290 μM
PDX43 DC_{50} = 0.5483 μM

Figure 18.18 Reported IDO1 degraders.

cells (Figure 18.18). Due to the large molecular weight and high polar surface area of PROTACs, which result in poor physicochemical properties, there are virtually no reports of PROTACs achieving sufficient brain exposure to produce pharmacological effects. Notably, **95** is capable of penetrating the blood–brain barrier, reaching a concentration of 2 μM in brain tissue and inducing IDO1 degradation in brain tumors [53]. These advancements underscore the potential of PROTACs in targeted protein degradation, with **95** paving the way for future development of brain-penetrant IDO1 degraders that could address therapeutic challenges in brain tumors.

18.6 Concluding Remarks and Future Perspectives

In conclusion, this chapter provides an overview of the latest research on the Trp metabolic pathway and its key rate-limiting enzymes, hIDO and hTDO, which are promising targets for treating immune-related diseases, including cancer. To unlock the clinical potential of hIDO/hTDO inhibitors, it is critical to investigate the downstream immunosuppressive effects of **Trp** metabolites, as well as the role of additional enzymes in the KP. Understanding these regulatory mechanisms is essential for enhancing the therapeutic efficacy of hIDO/hTDO inhibitors.

The intricate compartmentalization of the KP and its sensitivity to various environmental factors present significant challenges. Thus, further research is needed to assess whether systemic targeting of hIDO/hTDO is effective and safe without causing unintended toxicity. While hIDO1/hTDO inhibitors have shown promise in immuno-oncology, clinical success has been limited. Factors such as enzyme compensation and drug dosages may explain the lack of breakthroughs.

On a positive note, new inhibitors, including dual or pan inhibitors targeting hIDO1, TDO, or IDO2, as well as apo-IDO1 inhibitors and IDO1 PROTACs, are being explored, though these advancements are still in the early stages. Further studies are necessary to refine these compounds and investigate optimal immunotherapeutic combinations with other immune-modulating agents. In addition to cancer, recent studies suggest that targeting hIDO/hTDO may offer therapeutic potential for neurodegenerative diseases. However, further research is needed to understand the interactions between hIDO/hTDO and the brain to explore their potential in treating neurodegenerative disorders.

Glossary

hIDO human indoleamine 2,3-dioxygenase
hTDO human tryptophan 2,3-dioxygenase
Trp tryptophan
Kyn kynurenine
5-HT 5-hydroxytryptamine
KP kynurenine pathway

NFK N-formyl-kynurenine
AFMID arylformamidase
3-HK 3-hydroxykynurenine
KMO kynurenine monooxygenase
KYNU kynureninase
3-HAA 3-hydroxyanthranilic acid
KAT kynurenine aminotransferase
XA xanthurenic acid
HAAO 3-hydroxyanthranilate-3,4-dioxygenase
QA quinolinic acid
NMDA N-methyl-D-aspartate
QPRT quinolinate phosphoribosyltransferase
NAD$^+$ nicotinamide adenosine dinucleotide
KYNA kynurenic acid
AHR aryl hydrocarbon receptor
IFN-γ interferon-γ
PGE2 prostaglandin E2
IL-6 Interleukin 6
TNF-α tumor necrosis factor alpha
TGF-β transforming growth factor-β
PD-1 programmed death-1
CTLA-4 cytotoxic T-lymphocyte-associated protein 4
CTD C-terminal domain
CNS central nervous system
HCC hepatocellular carcinoma
GCN2 general control nonderepressible 2 kinase
mTORC1 mechanistic target of rapamycin complex 1
FOXO1 forkhead box transcription factor O1
DCs dendritic cells
TAMs tumor-associated macrophages
Treg cell regulatory T cell
FoxP3 forkhead box P3
ITIMs immunoreceptor tyrosine inhibitory motifs
VEGFA vascular endothelial growth factor A
HUVECs human umbilical venous endothelial cells
ECFCs human endothelial colony-forming cells
AD Alzheimer's Disease
PD Parkinson's Disease
Aβ β-amyloid peptide
NFL neurofilament light chain
SD rat Sprague Dawley rat
CSF cerebrospinal fluid
Hwb human whole blood
HNSCC neck squamous cell carcinoma
MPTP 1-methyl-4-phenyl-1,2,3,6-tetrahydropyridine

NSCLC non-small cell lung cancer
PK pharmacokinetic properties
PROTAC proteolysis targeting chimera
SA solvent-accessible
SAR structure–activity relationship
SBDD scaffolds through structure-based drug design
TGI tumor growth inhibition value
1-MT 1-methyl-DL-tryptophan

References

1 Yue, E.W., Douty, B., Wayland, B. et al. (2009). Discovery of potent competitive inhibitors of indoleamine 2,3-dioxygenase with *in vivo* pharmacodynamic activity and efficacy in a mouse melanoma model. *Journal of Medicinal Chemistry* 52 (23): 7364–7367.

2 Wu, Y., Xu, T., Liu, J. et al. (2017). Structural insights into the binding mechanism of IDO1 with hydroxylamidine based inhibitor INCB14943. *Biochemical and Biophysical Research Communications* 487 (2): 339–343.

3 Zhang, H., Liu, K., Pu, Q. et al. (2019). Discovery of amino-cyclobutarene-derived indoleamine-2,3-dioxygenase 1 (IDO1) inhibitors for cancer immunotherapy. *ACS Medicinal Chemistry Letters* 10 (11): 1530–1536.

4 Du, Q., Feng, X., Wang, Y. et al. (2019). Discovery of phosphonamidate IDO1 inhibitors for the treatment of non-small cell lung cancer. *European Journal of Medicinal Chemistry* 182: 111629.

5 Feng, X., Shen, P., Wang, Y. et al. (2019). Synthesis and *in vivo* antitumor evaluation of an orally active potent phosphonamidate derivative targeting IDO1/IDO2/TDO. *Biochemical Pharmacology* 168: 214–223.

6 Chen, S., Guo, W., Liu, X. et al. (2019). Design, synthesis and antitumor study of a series of N-Cyclic sulfamoylaminoethyl substituted 1,2,5-oxadiazol-3-amines as new indoleamine 2, 3-dioxygenase 1 (IDO1) inhibitors. *European Journal of Medicinal Chemistry* 179: 38–55.

7 Song, X., Sun, P., Wang, J. et al. (2020). Design, synthesis, and biological evaluation of 1,2,5-oxadiazole-3-carboximidamide derivatives as novel indoleamine-2,3-dioxygenase 1 inhibitors. *European Journal of Medicinal Chemistry* 189: 112059.

8 Xie, Y., Chen, C., Lin, S. et al. (2023). Design, synthesis and anti-AD effects of dual inhibitor targeting glutaminyl cyclase/GSK-3β. *European Journal of Medicinal Chemistry* 248: 115089.

9 Jin, F., Hu, Q., Fei, H. et al. (2021). Discovery of hydroxyamidine derivatives as highly potent, selective indoleamine-2,3-dioxygenase 1 inhibitors. *ACS Medicinal Chemistry Letters* 12 (2): 195–201.

10 Yeh, T.K., Song, J.S., Chang, P.W. et al. (2022). Discovery and development of a novel N-(3-bromophenyl)-{[(phenylcarbamoyl)amino]methyl}-N-hydroxythiophene-2-carboximidamide indoleamine 2,3-dioxygenase inhibitor using

knowledge-based drug design. *European Journal of Medicinal Chemistry* 229: 114043.

11 Paul, S., Roy, A., Deka, S.J. et al. (2016). Nitrobenzofurazan derivatives of N′-hydroxyamidines as potent inhibitors of indoleamine-2,3-dioxygenase 1. *European Journal of Medicinal Chemistry* 121: 364–375.

12 Jung, J., Yoon, H., Sohn, T.I. et al. (2021). Discovery of 5-(N-hydroxy-carbamimidoyl) benzofuran derivatives as novel indoleamine 2,3-dioxygenase 1 (IDO1) inhibitors. *Bioorganic & Medicinal Chemistry Letters* 40: 127963.

13 Wang, K., Song, L.H., Liang, Q.L. et al. (2023). Discovery of novel sulfonamide chromone-oxime derivatives as potent indoleamine 2,3-dioxygenase 1 inhibitors. *European Journal of Medicinal Chemistry* 254: 115349.

14 He, X., He, G., Chu, Z. et al. (2021). Discovery of the first potent IDO1/IDO2 dual inhibitors: a promising strategy for cancer immunotherapy. *Journal of Medicinal Chemistry* 64 (24): 17950–17968.

15 He, G., Wan, S., Wu, Y. et al. (2022). Discovery of the first selective IDO2 inhibitor as novel immunotherapeutic avenues for rheumatoid arthritis. *Journal of Medicinal Chemistry* 65 (21): 14348–14365.

16 Tang, K., Wang, B., Yu, B., and Liu, H.M. (2022). Indoleamine 2,3-dioxygenase 1 (IDO1) inhibitors and PROTAC-based degraders for cancer therapy. *European Journal of Medicinal Chemistry* 227: 113967.

17 Pereira, A., Vottero, E., Roberge, M. et al. (2006). Indoleamine 2,3-dioxygenase inhibitors from the northeastern pacific marine hydroid Garveia annulata. *Journal of Natural Products* 69 (10): 1496–1499.

18 Dong, J., Pan, X., Yang, Y. et al. (2021). Design, synthesis and biological evaluation of exiguamine A analogues as IDO1 inhibitors. *European Journal of Medicinal Chemistry* 223: 113631.

19 Volgraf, M., Lumb, J.P., Brastianos, H.C. et al. (2008). Biomimetic synthesis of the IDO inhibitors exiguamine A and B. *Nature Chemical Biology* 4 (9): 535–537.

20 Yang, R., Chen, Y., Pan, L. et al. (2018). Design, synthesis and structure-activity relationship study of novel naphthoindolizine and indolizinoquinoline-5,12-dione derivatives as IDO1 inhibitors. *Bioorganic & Medicinal Chemistry* 26 (17): 4886–4897.

21 Pan, L., Zheng, Q., Chen, Y. et al. (2018). Design, synthesis and biological evaluation of novel naphthoquinone derivatives as IDO1 inhibitors. *European Journal of Medicinal Chemistry* 157: 423–436.

22 Pan, S., Zhou, Y., Wang, Q. et al. (2020). Discovery and structure-activity relationship studies of 1-aryl-1H-naphtho[2,3-d][1,2,3]triazole-4,9-dione derivatives as potent dual inhibitors of indoleamine 2,3-dioxygenase 1 (IDO1) and trytophan 2,3-dioxygenase (TDO). *European Journal of Medicinal Chemistry* 207: 112703.

23 Wu, J.S., Lin, S.Y., Liao, F.Y. et al. (2015). Identification of substituted naphthotriazolediones as novel tryptophan 2,3-dioxygenase (TDO) inhibitors through structure-based virtual screening. *Journal of Medicinal Chemistry* 58 (19): 7807–7819.

24 Xu, G., Wang, T., Li, Y. et al. (2018). A highly potent and selective inhibitor Roxyl-WL targeting IDO1 promotes immune response against melanoma. *Journal of Enzyme Inhibition and Medicinal Chemistry* 33 (1): 1089–1094.

25 Yang, S., Li, X., Hu, F. et al. (2013). Discovery of tryptanthrin derivatives as potent inhibitors of indoleamine 2,3-dioxygenase with therapeutic activity in Lewis lung cancer (LLC) tumor-bearing mice. *Journal of Medicinal Chemistry* 56 (21): 8321–8331.

26 Li, J., Li, Y., Yang, D. et al. (2016). Establishment of a human indoleamine 2, 3-dioxygenase 2 (hIDO2) bioassay system and discovery of tryptanthrin derivatives as potent hIDO2 inhibitors. *European Journal of Medicinal Chemistry* 123: 171–179.

27 Li, Y., Zhang, S., Wang, R. et al. (2020). Synthesis of novel tryptanthrin derivatives as dual inhibitors of indoleamine 2,3-dioxygenase 1 and tryptophan 2,3-dioxygenase. *Bioorganic & Medicinal Chemistry Letters* 30 (11): 127159.

28 Zhang, H., Liu, W., Liu, Z. et al. (2018). Discovery of indoleamine 2,3-dioxygenase inhibitors using machine learning based virtual screening. *MedChemComm* 9 (6): 937–945.

29 Zhao, H., Sun, P., Guo, W. et al. (2019). Discovery of indoleamine 2,3-dioxygenase 1 (IDO-1) inhibitors based on ortho-naphthaquinone-containing natural product. *Molecules (Basel, Switzerland)* 24 (6): 1059.

30 Liu, J., Ren, J., Yang, K. et al. (2022). Discovery and biological evaluation of tanshinone derivatives as potent dual inhibitors of indoleamine 2, 3-dioxygenase 1 and tryptophan 2, 3-dioxygenase. *European Journal of Medicinal Chemistry* 235: 114294.

31 Zou, Y., Hu, Y., Ge, S. et al. (2019). Effective virtual screening strategy toward heme-containing proteins: identification of novel IDO1 inhibitors. *European Journal of Medicinal Chemistry* 184: 111750.

32 Xu, X., Ren, J., Ma, Y. et al. (2019). Discovery of cyanopyridine scaffold as novel indoleamine-2,3-dioxygenase 1 (IDO1) inhibitors through virtual screening and preliminary hit optimisation. *Journal of Enzyme Inhibition and Medicinal Chemistry* 34 (1): 250–263.

33 Ge, S., Zhong, H., Ma, X. et al. (2020). Discovery of secondary sulphonamides as IDO1 inhibitors with potent antitumour effects *in vivo*. *Journal of Enzyme Inhibition and Medicinal Chemistry* 35 (1): 1240–1257.

34 Serafini, M., Torre, E., Aprile, S. et al. (2020). Discovery of highly potent benzimidazole derivatives as indoleamine 2,3-dioxygenase-1 (IDO1) inhibitors: from structure-based virtual screening to *in vivo* pharmacodynamic activity. *Journal of Medicinal Chemistry* 63 (6): 3047–3065.

35 Kumazawa, M., Tejima, M., Fukuda, M. et al. (2021). Discovery of carbono(di)thioates as indoleamine 2,3-dioxygenase 1 inhibitors. *ACS Medicinal Chemistry Letters* 12 (2): 211–216.

36 Panda, S., Roy, A., Deka, S.J. et al. (2016). Fused heterocyclic compounds as potent indoleamine-2,3-dioxygenase 1 inhibitors. *ACS Medicinal Chemistry Letters* 7 (12): 1167–1172.

37 Yoshioka, S., Ikeda, T., Fukuchi, S. et al. (2022). Identification and characterization of a novel dual inhibitor of indoleamine 2,3-dioxygenase 1 and tryptophan 2,3-dioxygenase. *International Journal of Tryptophan Research* 15: 11786469221138456.

38 Zhang, Y., Li, Y., Chen, X. et al. (2022). Discovery of 1-(Hetero)aryl-β-carboline derivatives as IDO1/TDO dual inhibitors with antidepressant activity. *Journal of Medicinal Chemistry* 65 (16): 11214–11228.

39 Sonpavde, G., Necchi, A., Gupta, S. et al. (2020). ENERGIZE: a Phase III study of neoadjuvant chemotherapy alone or with nivolumab with/without linrodostat mesylate for muscle-invasive bladder cancer. *Future Oncology (London, England)* 16 (2): 4359–4368.

40 Pham, K.N. and Yeh, S.R. (2018). Mapping the binding trajectory of a suicide inhibitor in human indoleamine 2,3-dioxygenase 1. *Journal of the American Chemical Society* 140 (44): 14538–14541.

41 Zhang, L., Cherney, E.C., Zhu, X. et al. (2021). Discovery of imidazopyridines as potent inhibitors of indoleamine 2,3-dioxygenase 1 for cancer immunotherapy. *ACS Medicinal Chemistry Letters* 12 (3): 494–501.

42 Hamilton, M.M., Mseeh, F., McAfoos, T.J. et al. (2021). Discovery of IACS-9779 and IACS-70465 as potent inhibitors targeting indoleamine 2,3-dioxygenase 1 (IDO1) apoenzyme. *Journal of Medicinal Chemistry* 64 (15): 11302–11329.

43 Li, D., Sloman, D.L., Achab, A. et al. (2022). Oxetane promise delivered: discovery of long-acting IDO1 inhibitors suitable for Q3W oral or parenteral dosing. *Journal of Medicinal Chemistry* 65 (8): 6001–6016.

44 Pu, Q., Zhang, H., Guo, L. et al. (2020). Discovery of potent and orally available bicyclo[1.1.1]pentane-derived indoleamine-2,3-dioxygenase 1 (IDO1) inhibitors. *ACS Medicinal Chemistry Letters* 11 (8): 1548–1554.

45 Li, D., Deng, Y., Achab, A. et al. (2021). Carbamate and N-pyrimidine mitigate amide hydrolysis: structure-based drug design of tetrahydroquinoline IDO1 inhibitors. *ACS Medicinal Chemistry Letters* 12 (3): 389–396.

46 Kazmierski, W.M., Xia, B., Miller, J. et al. (2020). -encoded library technology-based discovery, lead optimization, and prodrug strategy toward structurally unique indoleamine 2,3-dioxygenase-1 (IDO1) inhibitors. *Journal of Medicinal Chemistry* 63 (7): 3552–3562.

47 Davies, C., Dötsch, L., Ciulla, M.G. et al. (2022). Identification of a novel pseudo-natural product type IV IDO1 inhibitor chemotype. *Angewandte Chemie (International Ed. in English)* 61 (40): e202209374.

48 Markwalder, J.A., Seitz, S.P., Blat, Y. et al. (2017). Identification and optimization of a novel series of indoleamine 2,3-dioxygenase inhibitors. *Bioorganic & Medicinal Chemistry Letters* 27 (3): 582–585.

49 Liu, W., Zou, Y., Li, K. et al. (2022). Apo-form selective inhibition of IDO for tumor immunotherapy. *Journal of Immunology (Baltimore, Md. : 1950)* 209 (1): 180–191.

50 Markwalder, J.A., Balog, A.J., Williams, D.K. et al. (2023). Synthesis and biological evaluation of biaryl alkyl ethers as inhibitors of IDO1. *Bioorganic & Medicinal Chemistry Letters* 88: 129280.

51 Burslem, G.M. and Crews, C.M. (2020). Proteolysis-targeting chimeras as therapeutics and tools for biological discovery. *Cell* 181 (1): 102–114.

52 Hu, M., Zhou, W., Wang, Y. et al. (2020). Discovery of the first potent proteolysis targeting chimera (PROTAC) degrader of indoleamine 2,3-dioxygenase 1. *Acta Pharmaceutica Sinica B* 10 (10): 1943–1953.

53 Bollu, L.R., Bommi, P.V., Monsen, P.J. et al. (2022). Identification and characterization of a novel indoleamine 2,3-dioxygenase 1 protein degrader for glioblastoma. *Journal of Medicinal Chemistry* 65 (23): 15642–15662.

Index

Drug Discovery Targeting Metalloenzymes: Strategies and Applications, First Edition. Edited by Guo-Bo Li.

C

i

n

q

t